D1417828

THE BIOCHEMISTRY
OF ANIMAL
DEVELOPMENT

Volume I

THE BIOCHEMISTRY OF ANIMAL DEVELOPMENT

Volume I   Descriptive Biochemistry of Animal Development

Volume II Biochemical Control Mechanisms and
Adaptations in Development

THE BIOCHEMISTRY
OF ANIMAL
DEVELOPMENT

Edited by RUDOLF WEBER

ZOOLOGISCHES INSTITUT
BERN, SWITZERLAND

Volume I

Descriptive Biochemistry of Animal Development

1965

ACADEMIC PRESS   New York and London

ACADEMIC PRESS INC.
111 Fifth Avenue, New York, New York 10003

United Kingdom Edition published by
ACADEMIC PRESS INC. (LONDON) LTD.
Berkeley Square House, London W.1

LIBRARY OF CONGRESS CATALOG CARD NUMBER: 65-23841

PRINTED IN THE UNITED STATES OF AMERICA

CONTRIBUTORS TO VOLUME I

Numbers in parentheses indicate the pages on which the authors' contributions begin.

JEAN BRACHET, Laboratoire de Morphologie animale, Faculté des Sciences, Université libre de Bruxelles, Brussells, Belgium (1)

J. R. COLLIER, Department of Biology, Rensselaer Polytechnic Institute, Troy, New York, and The Marine Biological Laboratory, Woods Hole, Massachusetts (203)

ELIZABETH M. DEUCHAR, Department of Anatomy, University College, London, England (245)

PHILIP GRANT, National Science Foundation, Washington, D. C. (483)

TRYGGVE GUSTAFSON, Department of Developmental Physiology, The Wenner-Gren Institute, University of Stockholm, Stockholm, Sweden (139)

ALBERTO MONROY, Laboratory of Comparative Anatomy, University of Palermo, Palermo, Italy (73)

FLORENCE MOOG, Department of Zoology, Washington University, St. Louis, Missouri (307)

J. B. SOLOMON, Chester Beatty Research Institute, London, England (367)

MATTHYS STAEHELIN, Research Laboratories, Pharmaceutical Department, CIBA Limited, Basel, Switzerland (441)

J. WILLIAMS, Medical Research Council, Laboratory of Molecular Biology, Cambridge, England (13)

PREFACE

In recent years the development of revolutionary new methods in biological research has led to impressive advances in our ability to assign cell functions to the activity of specific molecular components. By applying biochemical tools to the study of living cells, much new information has been obtained about the molecular organization of cells and the role of macromolecules in the regulation of cellular activities. In addition, the advent of electron microscopy has led to new discoveries on the ultrastructural architecture of cells, thus establishing direct contact between the morphological and the physiological areas of inquiry. At the conceptual level, the progressive comminution of cell functions to finer levels of organization has brought into proper focus the importance of molecular interactions in cellular activities.

In view of the increasing amount of information on molecular aspects of development, an evaluation of current trends in the biochemical study of animal development seems to be highly appropriate. The present treatise is, therefore, intended to introduce advanced students already familiar with elementary embryology and biochemistry to various areas of biochemical embryology. On considering the diversity of approaches and methods employed, it was thought important to rely on the competence of active investigators in order to obtain authoritative reviews on the subject. In selecting the material, emphasis has been placed on those problems in which research is currently most active and in which a promising contact between experimental embryology and biochemical inquiry has been established. Since our task consists of defining the selectivity of structural-chemical interactions a strictly biochemical view would have been too narrow. An attempt has, therefore, been made to include, whenever possible, relevant findings on ultrastructure and topochemistry in order to obtain an integrated picture of developmental phenomena.

The treatise will comprise two volumes—the first one covering the descriptive biochemistry of animal development and the second the more dynamic aspect achieved by emphasizing biochemical factors involved in the control of development.

Aside from a historical introduction, in which J. Brachet presents an authoritative picture of the achievements and illusions of biochemical embryology, Volume I is divided into three parts in which the following topics are discussed: biochemistry of the ovum and fertilization, the role of biochemical patterns in embryogenesis, and selective aspects of the ontogeny of proteins with enzymatic and nonenzymatic properties, including the problem of information transfer in developing systems.

Since the chapters have been arranged in a logical sequence, the treatise may be read in continuity if a survey of the current trends in biochemical embryology is desired. On the other hand, each chapter is complete in itself and thus may be of value to readers who seek specific information in selected areas of biochemical embryology.

There is no need to emphasize that in approaching the molecular level the study of development has been confronted with a diversity of new problems. The fact that our knowledge is still fragmentary and even controversial precludes a unified and consistent presentation. Yet it is hoped that the present treatise by emphasizing the recent advances in biochemical embryology may serve as a source of inspiration and thus promote further research in this exciting field.

I am most grateful to the contributors for their patience and positive cooperation and to the publishers for their continuous assistance. I am also greatly indebted to the members of my department for their kind and efficient help.

Berne, Switzerland   R. WEBER
August, 1965

CONTENTS

INTRODUCTION

The History of Chemical Embryology

J. BRACHET

PART I

Biochemistry of Germ Cells and Fertilization

CHAPTER 1

Chemical Constitution and Metabolic Activities of Animal Eggs

J. WILLIAMS

CHAPTER 2

Biochemical Aspects of Fertilization

ALBERTO MONROY

PART II

Biochemical Patterns in Embryos

CHAPTER 3

Morphogenetic Significance of Biochemical Patterns in Sea Urchin Embryos

TRYGGVE GUSTAFSON

CHAPTER 4

Morphogenetic Significance of Biochemical Patterns in Mosaic Embryos

J. R. COLLIER

CHAPTER 5

Biochemical Patterns in Early Developmental Stages of Vertebrates

E. M. DEUCHAR

PART III

General Biochemistry of Development

CHAPTER 6

Enzyme Development in Relation to Functional Differentiation

FLORENCE MOOG

CHAPTER 7

Development of Nonenzymatic Proteins in Relation to Functional Differentiation

J. B. SOLOMON

CHAPTER 8

Biochemical Mechanism of Information Transfer

MATTHYS STAEHELIN

CHAPTER 9

Informational Molecules and Embryonic Development

PHILIP GRANT

TENTATIVE CONTENTS OF VOLUME II

Introduction

THE HISTORY OF CHEMICAL EMBRYOLOGY

J. Brachet

Laboratoire de Morphologie animale
Faculté des Sciences
Université libre de Bruxelles
Brussels, Belgium

Embryology, the science of development, has, like all other sciences, its own embryology—how and when it was conceived remains unknown; its first steps were as hesitant as those of a baby. Those very early days have been well described by the founder of chemical embryology, Joseph Needham, a gifted historian as well as an embryologist. After man discovered artificial incubation which was used even in the oldest civilizations for very practical purposes, he must have had sufficient curiosity to break the shell immediately and look at the developing chick embryo. Without knowing it, he thus became a "descriptive embryologist." When he made the same kind of observation on a duck embryo also, he became a "comparative embryologist." Descriptive and comparative embryology remain at the root of modern embryology. These two branches of embryology, which grew so successfully in the eighteenth and nineteenth centuries, may now look old; but they are by no means dead, especially in view of the continuous progress made in the optical means of observation. First, only the naked eye was used, then the primitive lens, and then the compound microscope; today the electron microscope is used in many laboratories. Numerous and valuable indeed are the papers which today describe the ultrafine structure of normal sea urchin, frog, or chicken embryos. This is the modern form of descriptive and comparative embryology.

However, after man had a good look at the developmental steps which lead to the formation of the adult, he became more curious than ever—"how" does this thing develop? After discussing at length—as we still do—"preformation" and "epigenesis," he decided to play with embryos, as a child does with watches. So, eggs were partially destroyed

1

by pricking; blastomeres were killed; embryos were centrifuged. Thus, "experimental embryology" was born, culminating in discoveries, such as the organizer by Spemann. New theoretical concepts, such as potentialities, determination, regulation, morphogenetic fields, and gradients, progressively emerged. Since these concepts remain as obscure today as ever, experimental embryology, even though it is showing signs of senescence, is still fruitful.

Since chemical embryology is nothing more than the biochemical analysis of embryonic development, it naturally followed the same trends as embryology itself and its development has been necessarily linked to that of embryology. As we shall see, chemical embryology began as a descriptive and comparative science and was deeply influenced by the progress of experimental embryology. It is now being exposed to the impact of bacterial genetics and molecular biology, which will long prevent it from senescence. In fact, it is shifting more and more toward "molecular embryology."

The first important landmark in the history of chemical embryology was Joseph Needham's "Chemical Embryology" (1931). Not only did Needham coin the name of the new science, but he assembled in three large volumes everything that was known at the time about the chemical composition of embryos at all stages of their development. This was the *opus magnum* of a great modern humanist and a bible for the small group of chemical embryologists just beginning research at that time. In hundreds of tables data concerning the protein, glycogen, lipid, and water content of all sorts of embryos were summarized from multitudinous papers. This compilation, which was so valuable at the time of its publication, has lost most of its usefulness now, since both problems and methods have undergone considerable changes; but "Chemical Embryology" remains a monument of the early days (antiquity and the middle ages, perhaps), when descriptive and comparative embryology were the only guides for the biochemist interested in embryonic development.

Yet, many papers published in those days still deserve mention and remain as models of good scientific analysis—for instance, Fauré-Fremiet's important monographs on the biochemistry of *Ascaris* and *Sabellaria* eggs or Needham's own contributions to comparative embryology. Needham was interested in the "succession of energy sources" during development (carbohydrates being utilized before fats and proteins) in various animal forms, in nitrogen excretion in "cleidoic" and "acleidoic" eggs, in the possible dissociation, by experimental means, of growth and differentiation, in Child's axial gradients, and in many other problems. Some of these questions are of interest to this day. For example, the decrease in arginase activity in chick embryo when it shifts from a "ureo-telic" to a "uricotelic" metabolism remains puzzling; but this problem is now attacked from a very different angle. Is there inhibition of the enzyme, disappearance of an activator, repression by reaction end products, negative feedback control, or loss of inducibility? Today papers are being published on these problems which have great theo-retical importance and are well integrated in the realm of molecular biology.

Recent progress made in biochemistry and in physical chemistry, of course, had as much influence on the orientation of the more modern work in 1930, as these subjects do now. While reinvestigating Warburg's former observations on the increase of oxygen consumption during ferti-lization in sea urchin eggs, Runnström introduced for the first time in these studies some really important factors: cytochrome oxidase (pre-viously considered the *Atmungsferment*), cytochromes, dehydrogenases, and adenosine triphosphate. Interesting work, such as that in Monroy's laboratory, is still going on in exactly the same field. It was in the 1930s too that Needham, Chambers, Rapkine, Ephrussi and Wurmser, and Reiss tried to measure the pH and the redox potential of these eggs. Since the ultrastructure of eggs is now known to be so complicated that we can hardly consider them (even as a first approximation) as a water solution surrounded by a lipid membrane, this type of research is no longer being performed. However, it was shown by Chambers that the germinal vesicle of ovocytes neither reduces nor oxidizes injected dyes, and more recent studies have shown that the cell nucleus is remarkably inadequate in oxidizing and reducing enzymes.

So much for the "pre-Needhamian" era. We now come to the "rinas-cimento" and the "modern ages" of chemical embryology. In 1932, a revolution occurred, namely the discovery by Bautzmann *et al.* that a killed organizer is still capable of inducing a neural system. Biochemists discovered the existence of experimental embryology, and the whole course of chemical embryology changed. This shift in interests is obvious when one compares Needham's "Chemical Embryology" (1931) with his "Biochemistry and Morphogenesis" (1942) or the author's own "Em-bryologie chimique" (Brachet, 1944). Because of wartime conditions, there was no possible contact between the two authors; nevertheless, the general spirit of the two books is remarkably the same.

As soon as Holtfreter (1935) and Wehmeier (1934) found that the "inducing substance" (or "evocating substance" as the Cambridge group, following Waddington's suggestion, preferred to call it) was of very widespread distribution in Nature, the quest for its identification began. Since an alcohol-treated fragment of horse or ox liver, as a killed organizer, also "induces" the formation of neural structures in competent ectoblasts, why not take the whole liver and fractionate it, following the biochemical methods which led to the isolation and purification of vitamins and hormones? This was done in several laboratories and the field was almost as "hot" as the field of molecular genetics is right now. Preliminary notes, with stern remarks about priority, were shooting from all sides. The contest became worse when it clearly appeared that every leading laboratory had its own "active substance," different from those found in the others—Glycogen is the active substance! No, it is a sterol, and your glycogen is contaminated with sterols! No, all acids are inductors, and your sterols must contain fatty acids! No, the substance must be specific in order to explain why an embryo possesses a head and a tail: it must be a protein!

Suddenly, the setback came and the excitement ceased. In Cambridge we (Waddington, Needham, and the author) were studying the respiratory metabolism of the organizer as compared to other parts of the gastrula (a warm field too, but not really hot). Since methylene blue was known to increase the respiratory rate of many cells, it was decided to implant pieces of agar containing methylene blue in gastrulae. Neural inductions were obtained using an "inductor" of nonbiological origin, which could not have been contaminated with sterols, fatty acids, or glycogen. Still worse, neutral red, which has no effect on oxygen consumption, was also active. So, all these theories were both right and wrong—all the substances tested were more or less active; but is was impossible to decide which was the right one, since the ectoblast (like the unfertilized egg treated with parthenogenetic agents) could react in the same way (neural induction) to a large variety of chemical substances. This led Waddington *et al.* (1936) to suggest that the neuralizing factor was already present in the ectoblast, but in a bound form; any agent which could "unmask" the inducing substance would induce the transformation of ectoderm into neural tissue. Later work by Barth and Graff (1938) led Waddington to the sad conclusion that both heterogeneous inductors and chemical substances easily produce cytolysis of part of the very fragile ectoderm cells. The "true" active substance would be liberated by the dying cells, and the hope of isolating and identifying it became still more remote. The final blow came when Holtfreter (1947) demonstrated that even sublethal cytolysis is sufficient to induce the neuralization of ectodermal explants; a short acid or alkaline shock, which is insufficient to kill the cells, is sufficient to obtain a high percentage of nervous structures in such explants. Now, one could and did despair.

However, things are never as bad as they look. Discussions about the mechanisms of cephalic (neural) and caudal (mesodermal) inductions led to a resumption of work in a field which looked most unpromising from the time of Holtfreter's observations. Were these differences due to quantitative or qualitative factors? Were there distinct neuralizing and mesodermalizing substances? It has been to the credit of men like Toivonen, Yamada, and Tiedemann to resume the quest for specific cephalic and caudal inducing substances this time (see Volume II, Chapter 1). Refined methods of protein chemistry (ultracentrifugation, electrophoresis, column chromatography) were used which led to the isolation from various tissues (liver, bone marrow, chick embryos) of purified active neural and mesodermal inducing substances. Cephalic induction can be obtained with ribonucleoproteins (the protein part apparently being the active one), whereas pure proteins from bone marrow and chick embryos act as caudal (mesodermal) inductors. Many problems, of course, remain to be solved. Are the mesodermal inducing proteins of bone marrow and chick embryo identical, similar, or entirely different? Have they common antigenic sites? Have they some enzymatic activity? There are other, perhaps still more important, questions to answer. Is it certain that these specific substances act directly (and not by a relay mechanism, the former unmasking of the true inducing substance)? The doubts we had 25 years ago are not yet completely dissipated. Are the isolated proteins present in a normal gastrula or neurula? If so, where is their localization? These important questions can and will be solved. Yamada, in particular, is using a whole array of modern techniques, such as electron microscopy, autoradiography, and detection of the protein with labeled antibodies, according to the method of Coons. Immunological techniques, in particular, should be powerful tools for the solution of these basic problems.

But the topic of this introduction is the history of chemical embryology, not its present state. We have moved, in the case of inducing substances, from the 1930–1945 problems to the present ones almost without noticing a transition. Is there a fundamental difference between the "modern history" of chemical embryology and its "contemporary history"? The author should know the answer, since he wrote books on this same subject both in 1944 and in 1960. The main change between the modern and the contemporary history of chemical embryology is that we have undergone during the past 15 years an equivalent of the industrial revolution in the nineteenth century. It has been a revolution in the "techniques," rather than in the ideas, of chemical embryologists. We have now much more powerful weapons at hand, but the great problems to be solved remain the same.

Yet, there is another revolution occurring at this moment, a revolution in our theoretical approaches stemming from the tremendous development of molecular genetics. It is often said that molecular biologists, after having solved the riddles of heredity, will then enter the field of embryology and solve the problems of cell differentiation. We hope that this will really happen; a massive injection of first-class brains in our field would undoubtedly lead to spectacular progress. However, until these welcome reinforcements arrive, chemical embryologists will carry the fight alone, using the concepts and methods which have been so successfully employed in genetics.

This new trend can be exemplified in a field which has been the main battleground for molecular biologists, the control of specific protein synthesis by nucleic acids. In the pre-Needhamian period, around 1930, there were no such things as deoxyribonucleic acid (DNA) and ribonucleic acid (RNA). Thanks to the Feulgen reaction, it was known, however, that "thymonucleic acid" (our DNA) is present in the nuclei of all cells, hence, no longer deserving its name of "animal" nucleic acid. Pentose nucleic acids (RNA) were supposed to be "plant" nucleic acids, although one of these acids had already been isolated from the pancreas. No reliable method for the estimation of the two nucleic acids was available, since it was still believed that they could not coexist in the same cell, one being specific for animal cells, the other for plant cells.

In the case of ovocytes, the very presence of thymonucleic acid in lampbrush chromosomes was still hotly disputed; discussions between the holders of the "migration" theory and those of the "net synthesis" theory were intense. According to the former, the germinal vesicle contained a reserve of nucleic acid which moved into the cytoplasm at maturation and migrated back into the nuclei during cleavage. Their opponents, of course, denied the existence of such a reserve and claimed that thymonucleic acid was formed *de novo* in the nuclei after fertilization. The fact that the very unreliable biochemical methods available for nucleic acid determination indicated that there was no change during development confused the situation even more. This constancy of the nucleic acid content during development was, of course, the main argument in favor of the migration theory; but the fact that the Feulgen reaction was negative in the ovocyte and strongly positive in the nuclei of blastulae and gastrulae apparently demonstrated the correctness of the net synthesis hypothesis.

As usual, it was the development of a new and more specific technique (the diphenylamine method for DNA estimation of Dische) and of new hypotheses which clarified the situation. In 1933, it could be demonstrated that the unfertilized eggs contained only traces of DNA as compared to the high DNA content of gastrulae or neurulae. The reality of a net synthesis of DNA during development thus became an established fact. It was also proven at the same time that eggs contain large amounts of RNA; therefore, the latter is not a plant nucleic acid at all, but is present in all cells. It was concluded on the basis of pentose estimations made with still very crude methods that there is a conversion of RNA (possibly after its degradation to the nucleotide level) into DNA. That such a conversion occurs on a large scale was disproven when about 15 years later radioactive phosphate became a new tool for the study of nucleic acid synthesis.

A new question arose—what is the intracellular localization of RNA? In 1940 studies with the UV-microscope by Caspersson and the utilization of a simple staining procedure (combined with a digestion of the tissue sections with ribonuclease in order to ensure greater specificity) brought the desired answer: RNA is an ubiquitous constituent of all cells; it is localized in the nucleolus and the cytoplasm; there is a close correlation between the RNA content of a given cell and its ability to synthesize proteins.

In the eggs of the vertebrates (those of the amphibians, in particular) RNA is distributed along a primary polarity (animal–vegetal) gradient already present in the ovocyte and the unfertilized egg. At gastrulation a new gradient, which is more dynamic and results from synthesis of fresh RNA, spreads from the dorsal to the ventral side. As a result of mutual interaction, dorsoventral and cephalocaudal RNA gradients become apparent in the late gastrula and the early neurula stages. These gradients are parallel to or identical with the morphogenetic gradients of the experimental embryologists. Disorganization of the gradients by chemical or physical means and abnormalities in development go hand in hand.

This was the situation in 1940 during "rinascimento" and the "modern ages" of chemical embryology. How much has it changed during the "contemporary period" of this science? Once again, new and powerful methods (autoradiography, for example) have been put into operation; but still, the problems have remained the same, and many observations are still disputed vigorously.

For instance, the migration versus net synthesis controversy is not yet extinct. New, even more sensitive and specific methods for DNA estimation have been developed; they have confirmed that the cytoplasm of unfertilized eggs contains some kind of DNA. But, at the same time, autoradiography has shown that a net synthesis of DNA at the expense of simple precursors, such as thymidine and uridine, also occurs during cleavage. The fact that uridine, a ribonucleoside, can be utilized for DNA synthesis in the cleaving egg shows that, after all, conversion of ribose derivatives into DNA actually occurs, even if only on a small scale. Again it looks as if both theories are correct. It is very likely now (but it has not yet been proved) that during cleavage DNA partly originates from migration of a cytoplasmic DNA reserve and partly from a net synthesis at the expense of simple deoxyribose and ribose precursors. The recent finding of Agrell and Bergqvist (1963) that during cleavage in frog eggs nuclei contain two different types of DNA, unequally resistant to acid hydrolysis, speaks strongly in favor of such a conclusion.

The significance of the RNA gradients in amphibian eggs is also becoming somewhat clearer. Autoradiography has now shown that RNA synthesis, which leads to the formation of the dorsoventral gradient at the gastrula stage, begins in the nucleus. On the other hand, electron microscopy has shown that the primary (polarity) gradient is essentially a ribosomal gradient. Combining these two findings, we can arrive at the following explanation: The inert polarity gradient of ribosomes becomes activated toward gastrulation by messenger RNAs formed in the nuclei along the dorsoventral gradient. The result would be that protein synthesis will be more active in the anterior (cephalic) part of the embryo than in its posterior (ventral) part; protein synthesis would also decrease progressively from dorsal to ventral. Very recent experiments with specific inhibitors of messenger RNA synthesis (actinomycin D) and of protein synthesis (puromycin) entirely confirm these deductions.

This is certainly progress; but the real problem, that of morphogenesis, remains unsolved. To understand how production of specific messenger RNAs, controlled by localized gene activation leading to the synthesis of presumably specific proteins, ultimately leads to the differentiation of nervous system, chorda, or muscle cells is a task for the *future*; it is a task for "molecular embryology," whose birth we are now watching. It is hoped that this new science, based on solid theoretical foundations, will not be groping in darkness, as chemical embryology did initially. Hypotheses which "predict" (it is very exceptional now that the predictions are not fulfilled by the experiments designed to test them) will replace our present "guesses" and "hunches." One guess (almost a prediction) is that electron microscopes with still higher and higher resolution will be built and will show in the developing egg the most important macromolecules changing their shapes or accumulating at strategic spots. On that day "molecular embryology" and "descriptive embryology" will be synonymous.

Let us step back from the future for a final remark about the present,

Joseph Needham's *opus magnum* was a one-man work; the present treatise is the result of the cooperation of many scientists. This difference shows what great progress has been made during the last 30 years. Those who took part in this battle against ignorance can be justifiably proud of what their generation has achieved in the field of chemical embryology. We hope that the present treatise will be, as Needham's book was, a new milestone on the road and a new source of inspiration for the next generation of chemical embryologists. If so, it will have fulfilled a great purpose.

REFERENCES

Agrell, I., and Bergqvist, H.–Å. (1963). *J. Cell Biol.* **15**, 604.
Barth, D. G., and Graff, S. (1938). *Cold Spring Harbor Symp. Quant. Biol.* **6**, 385.
Bautzmann, H., Holtfreter, J., Spemann, H., and Mangold, O. (1932). *Naturwissenschaften* **20**, 971.
Brachet, J. (1933). *Arch. Biol. (Liege)* **44**, 519.
Brachet, J. (1944). "Embryologie chimique." Desoer, Liège (Masson, Paris, 1945).
Brachet, J. (1960). "The Biochemistry of Development." Pergamon, New York.
Holtfreter, J. (1935). *Wilhelm Roux' Arch. Entwicklungsmech. Organ.* **133**, 367.
Holtfreter, J. (1947). *J. Exptl. Zool.* **106**, 197.
Needham, J. (1931). "Chemical Embryology." Cambridge Univ. Press, London and New York.
Needham, J. (1942). "Biochemistry and Morphogenesis." Cambridge Univ. Press, London and New York.
Waddington, C. H., Needham, J., and Brachet, J. (1936). *Proc. Roy. Soc.* **B120**, 173.
Wehmeier, E. (1934). *Wilhelm Roux' Arch. Entwicklungsmech. Organ.* **132**, 384.

Part I

BIOCHEMISTRY OF GERM CELLS AND FERTILIZATION

Chapter 1

CHEMICAL CONSTITUTION AND METABOLIC ACTIVITIES OF ANIMAL EGGS

J. WILLIAMS

Medical Research Council
Laboratory of Molecular Biology
Cambridge, England

In this chapter on the biochemistry of eggs and oogenesis we should observe at the outset that while the egg cell possesses the structural and functional properties of cells in general, it is highly differentiated in relation to its developmental tasks, e.g., in the accumulation of yolk during oogenesis. Recent work has yielded much information on the structure and metabolism of the egg, but practically nothing is known about the biochemical basis of its specific developmental properties. Some deeply entrenched ideas on egg structure were derived many years ago from embryological data and their study by physical or chemical methods is still lacking. In this category are the oriented liquid crystal which may be responsible for polarity and bilateral symmetry (Wilson, 1928; Needham, 1942; Harrison, 1945; Costello, 1948) and the differentiated cortex or surface layer which has been invested with many important embryological properties (Dalcq and Pasteels, 1937; Raven, 1958, 1961, 1963). The greatest problem, however, is the physical basis of determination which is presumed to cause different gene activities in the various regions of the embryo and, in those cases where determination occurs before cleavage, it is likely to be connected with the localization of certain egg constituents.

I. Structure of the Egg

Electron microscopy has made important contributions to the study of egg structure and it may throw some light on the nature of regional determination (Waddington, 1962) or, at least, on the early structural effects of determination. These studies will be discussed in some detail in this section because of the close connection between structure and biochemical activities. The application of electron microscopy to the localization of antigens and enzymes has been discussed recently (Symposium of the Royal Microscopical Society, 1962). With few exceptions, appearances have been accepted as representing the natural condition and the critical accounts of fixation by Sjöstrand (1962) and Afzelius (1962) are valuable. Gross *et al.* (1960) have attempted to relate electron microscope images to the physical properties of the egg cytoplasm and they have considered some possible sources of artifacts.

A. *Accessory Cells*

In some species the oocytes are more or less independent cells, but more often they are surrounded by nutritive cells (Korschelt and Heider, 1936; Tyler, 1955) which are very active in supplying the oocyte with materials. The prominent endoplasmic reticulum of some follicle cells may be connected with this activity (Anderson and Beams, 1960; Wartenberg and Stegner, 1960; Kessel and Kemp, 1962). Fine branching processes from the follicle cells pass through an amorphous zona pellucida and end in contact with the oocyte. The surface membrane of the oocyte is studded with short microvilli which effectively increase its area (Kemp, 1956a, b). This arrangement exists in the follicles of mammals (Duryee, 1954; Sotelo and Porter, 1959; Trujillo-Cenóz and Sotelo,

1959; Anderson and Beams, 1960; Wartenberg and Stegner, 1960; Franchi, 1960; Blanchette, 1961), birds (Press, 1959), amphibians (Kemp, 1956a, b), ascidians (Kessel and Kemp, 1962), and mollusks (Humphreys, 1962a; Rebhun, 1962). In these cases there is no cytoplasmic continuity between the follicle cells and the oocyte, but in *Drosophila* the nurse cells are connected to the oocyte by special apertures (fusomes) which may be open, allowing even mitochondria to enter the oocyte, or may be closed off (Hsu, 1952; Meyer, 1961). These arrangements are evidently connected with the transport of materials into the oocyte, and Lanzavecchia (1962) has observed vesicles under the surface membrane of the oocyte which suggests that the oocyte absorbs materials by pinocytosis.

Follicle cells may also play a role in morphogenesis by causing localized changes in the oocyte membrane which becomes the seat of a cortical field, as Raven (1961, 1963) has proposed for *Limnaea*. No direct confirmation of this hypothesis has yet been devised.

B. *Egg Membranes*

Egg coverings are classified as primary when secreted by the oocyte itself, secondary if laid down by the follicle cells, and tertiary if produced by the oviduct. The distinction is not always simple. In human eggs the zona pellucida arises mainly from the follicle cells together with some material produced by the oocyte (Wartenberg and Stegner, 1960). The presence in the zona pellucida of polysaccharide is deduced from staining reactions (Tandler, 1957; Franchi, 1960; Wartenberg and Stegner, 1960) and that of protein from the action of proteases upon the membrane (Chang and Hunt, 1956; Mintz, 1962). The chorion of teleost eggs arises solely from the oocyte and contains protein and polysaccharide (Arndt, 1960). The vitelline membrane of avian eggs was tackled chemically by Liebermann (1888), but since then its proposed collagenous or keratinous nature has been discussed on the basis of histochemical tests (Moran and Hale, 1936; McNally, 1943). Bellairs *et al.* (1963) have now studied its ultrastructure and composition; it is neither keratin nor collagen, but a glycoprotein containing hexoses, hexosamines, and sialic acid. Possible chemical differences between the layers of the membrane are still not clear.

The best known egg covering is the white of the avian egg; the chemistry was reviewed by Fevold (1951) and Warner (1953). Recent developments include the finding of genetically determined variations in egg-white proteins (Lush, 1961; Williams, 1962b; Baker and Manwell, 1962) and the use of electrophoretic patterns of egg white in taxonomy (McCabe and Deutsch, 1952; Sibley, 1960).

C. Cortical Structures

The most prominent cortical structures are the granules of unfertilized sea urchin (Monné and Harde, 1951; Afzelius, 1956a; Gross et al., 1960; Mercer and Wolpert, 1962), mollusk (Humphreys, 1962a), and amphibian eggs (Kemp, 1956a, b). Austin (1956, 1961) described cortical granules in hamster eggs. In sea urchin oocytes the granules first appear near the nucleus and move to the periphery in the mature egg. They are spiral or concentric lamellar bodies enclosed in an outer membrane and are composed, in part, of polysaccharides (Monné and Harde, 1951; Afzelius, 1956a). The granules from different species of sea urchins show morphological and histochemical differences (Afzelius, 1956a; Immers, 1960). Acidic polysaccharides exist in the cortical granules of some species; Immers (1961) found that radioactive sulfate injected into the female entered the granules and he confirmed the migration of bound sulfate from the interior of the oocyte to the periphery in mature oocytes. Aketa's claim (1963) that inorganic sulfate is released from fertilized eggs when the cortical granules break down is interesting in this connection. Very little is known about the detailed chemical structure of the granules or their origin, and the isolation of intact granules has apparently not yet been achieved (Allen, 1958). Some fish eggs contain cortical alveoli composed of polysaccharide and enclosed in a lipid membrane (Aketa, 1954), although the lipid component is absent in other species. Kusa (1956) has discussed the structure and functions of the cortical alveoli. The disappearance of the cortical granules at fertilization and their contribution to the fertilization membrane is discussed by Allen (1958) and by Monroy in this volume (Chapter 2).

An important role has often been attributed to a gel layer under the cell membrane. It is, however, a largely hypothetical entity whose existence is postulated on the basis of the mechanical properties of the egg (Mitchison, 1956), micromanipulation studies (Hiramoto, 1957), and centrifugation studies in which the stationary cortical granules are supposed to be fixed in a viscous gel. The oriented protein structure deduced from birefringence studies is now doubtful in view of the microvillous structure of the egg surface (Mitchison, 1956). Mercer and Wolpert (1962) could find no differentiated cortical region in *Psammechinus* eggs by means of electron microscopy and suggested that the immobility of cortical granules upon centrifugation depends on continuity of the membrane of the granules with the surface membrane of the egg. Although a cortical region appears to exist in other eggs, it presumably lacks the universal character frequently ascribed to it, and Mercer and Wolpert (1962) suggest that its role as the seat of animal–

vegetal polarity is probably fulfilled by the surface membrane itself or by the ground substance of the endoplasm.

D. *Endoplasmic Membranous Structures*

Electron microscopy has revealed a wide range of membranous structures in eggs—the yolk nuclei of invertebrate eggs, annulate lamellae, nuclear membrane, and Golgi apparatus may be regarded as parts of the endoplasmic reticulum. The membranes enclose flattened cisternae or expanded vesicles of various sizes and may be arranged randomly or in regular formations. The outer surfaces of the vesicles may be smooth or studded with dense ribosomes (Palade, 1958), large numbers of which are also found free in the cytoplasmic matrix (Fig. 1). The interrelationships of the different structures are discussed by Siekevitz (1959).

1. ENDOPLASMIC RETICULUM

In mammalian (Anderson and Beams, 1960; Sotelo and Porter, 1959; Wartenberg and Stegner, 1960) and invertebrate (Gross *et al.*, 1960; Humphreys, 1962a) eggs the endoplasmic reticulum consists of sparse granule-studded vesicles, and Gross *et al.* (1960) relate the scarcity of membranes in *Arbacia* eggs to the well-known absence of non-Newtonian viscosity (Heilbrunn, 1952, p. 84). It is often stated that the endoplasmic reticulum of eggs and of early stages of development is characteristically rudimentary, but Rebhun (1961) points out that extensive membranous formations are present in several types of eggs. Abundant endoplasmic reticulum is found in the eggs of crayfish (Beams and Kessel, 1962) and the ascidian *Molgula* (Kessel and Kemp, 1962). In the crayfish egg there are regions of oriented, dilated cisternae which contain granules possibly representing early stages in the formation of yolk.

2. GOLGI APPARATUS

In mammalian oocytes stacks of smooth Golgi cisternae occur near the nucleus in young stages and are found later near the periphery. The cisternae are continuous at places with those of the endoplasmic reticulum (Anderson and Beams, 1960; Sotelo and Porter, 1959; Wartenberg and Stegner, 1960; Blanchette, 1961). Similar structures occur in sea urchin eggs (Fig. 2) and some of them contain granules which may be yolk granules (Afzelius, 1956b), although it may be remarked that no chemical or morphological definition of yolk exists and almost any granule could be called a yolk granule.

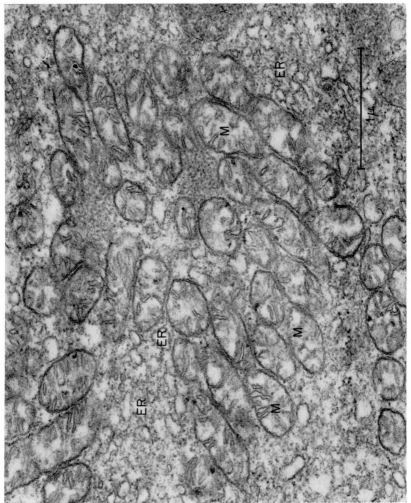

Fig. 1.   Electron micrograph of the endoplasm in the mature sea urchin egg, showing the abundant mitochondria (M), the vesicular endoplasmic reticulum (ER), and the numerous free ribosomes. Courtesy of Dr. B. Afzelius.

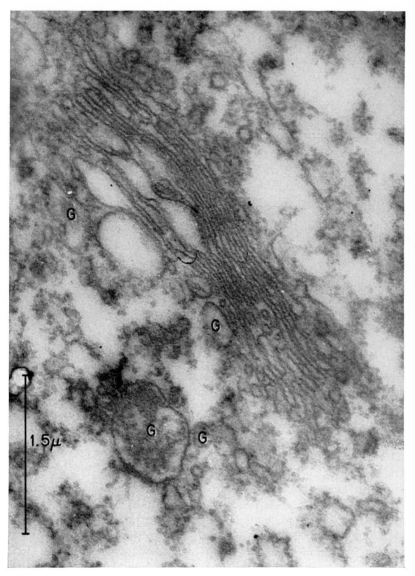

FIG. 2. Electron micrograph of a section through the Golgi apparatus of a *Strongylocentrotus droebachiensis* oocyte. There are flattened vesicles and some expanded vacuoles. A few of the vacuoles (G) contain granules and they may be stages in the formation of yolk bodies. From Afzelius (1956b).

3. Yolk Nuclei

The so-called yolk nuclei of vertebrate eggs will be excluded from this section since they appear to consist of clusters of mitochondria surrounding the centrosomes (Wittek, 1952; Kemp, 1956b; van der Stricht, 1923) or of Golgi vesicles (Anderson and Beams, 1960). In invertebrate oocytes yolk nuclei are found before and in the early stages of yolk formation as deeply basophilic bodies composed of straight or whorled arrays of cisternae. Palade granules, mitochondria, lipid droplets, and yolk granules are found between the cisternae (Rebhun, 1956a, b, 1961), and there is no evidence that the yolk nucleus plays any part in yolk formation in the species studied by Rebhun (the mollusk *Spisula*). In the mollusk *Planorbis* similar lamellar formations enclose mitochondria in which some of the crystalline yolk granules appear to arise; other yolk granules arise within ordinary mitochondria (Favard and Carasso, 1958). Some spiders have no yolk nuclei, whereas others have large complex arrays of granule-studded endoplasmic vesicles surrounding a central area of vesicles, granules, and capsulated bodies (Sotelo and Trujillo-Cenóz, 1957; André and Rouiller, 1957). The abundant ribosomes of sea urchin eggs are free except for those bound to the concentric membranes of the yolk nuclei (Afzelius, 1957). There is no obvious functional justification for the term yolk nucleus as applied to these structures.

4. Nuclear Membrane

In amphibian oocytes the nucleus is bounded by two membranes separated by a narrow space and interrupted by numerous annulated pores which form a hexagonal pattern in surface view (Callan and Tomlin, 1950; Gall, 1954; Wischnitzer, 1958); the annuli are composed of granules or microcylinders and they project a short distance into the nucleoplasm on one side and into the cytoplasm on the other. The membrane is dissolved by trypsin but not by ribonuclease (Merriam, 1961). Similar structures are present in mammalian (Wartenberg and Stegner, 1960), sea urchin (Afzelius, 1955), and mollusk eggs (Rebhun, 1956a). The passage of materials through the nuclear membrane must certainly occur, but direct proof of the permeability of the nuclear membrane to albumin could not be obtained by Battin (1959) using isolated amphibian oocyte nuclei. Poly(vinylpyrrolidone) of molecular weight 40,000 was not admitted to the nucleus after being injected into the cytoplasm of young oocytes (Harding and Feldherr, 1958). On the other hand, Feldherr (1962) found that in *Amoeba* particles of colloidal gold in the cytoplasm entered the nucleus apparently by passing through the center of the annulate pores. Whether more than free diffusion is involved in transfers across the membrane is not known, but both Marshak (1957) and Battin (1959) have shown that isolated nuclei behave differently from intracellular nuclei and suggest that cytoplasmic factors are involved in transport. Miller (1962) has obtained electron micrographs which suggest the passage of nucleolar material through the annulated pores.

5. ANNULATE LAMELLAE

These structures are basophilic stacks of double membranes which are interrupted by annulated pores. The membranes are very similar to the nuclear membrane and they have been found near to or in contact with the nuclear membrane in some adult cells as well as in the oocytes of echinoderms (Merriam, 1959; Afzelius, 1957; Gross et al., 1960), mollusks (Swift, 1956; Rebhun, 1956a, 1961), and man (Wartenberg and Stegner, 1960). The membranes comprising the stack lie with their annulated pores in line, and it seems likely that the lamellae are derived from the nuclear membrane, although precisely how is not known (Swift, 1956; Merriam, 1959) (Figs. 3 and 4). The function of these intriguing structures is unknown. Afzelius (1957) discovered "heavy bodies" in sea urchin eggs; they consist of a mass of 150-Å granules enclosed in annulate lamellae, and there is presumably some functional relationship between the lamellae and the granules (Fig. 5).

6. FUNCTIONAL ASPECTS OF THE MEMBRANOUS STRUCTURES

There is very little information on the chemistry of the various membranous formations of eggs. Edström (1960) found that the nucleotide composition of ribonucleic acid (RNA) of yolk nuclei in spider oocytes is very variable. In adult liver cells the endoplasmic membranes are associated with some oxidative enzymes, glucose-6-phosphatase and nucleoside triphosphatases (Siekevitz, 1959; Ernster et al., 1962; Novikoff, 1960), although in homogenates of sea urchin eggs glucose-6-phosphatase sediments with the "yolk fraction" (Cousineau and Gross, 1960). Dalcq and Pasteels (1963) have found that the nucleoside triphosphatase activities of formalin-fixed invertebrate eggs are very low and apparently associated with the yolk fraction after centrifugation. In fixed material, however, the pattern of the remaining enzyme activities may be different from that in the living cell, and in the experiments of Dalcq and Pasteels (1963) mitochondria did not react. Novikoff et al. (1961) found that mitochondrial adenosinetriphosphatase (ATPase) is inhibited by fixation with formol-calcium. The isolated Golgi apparatus of adult cells has no RNA, which agrees with the absence of Palade granules, but contains high levels of acid phosphatase and phospholipid (Dalton,

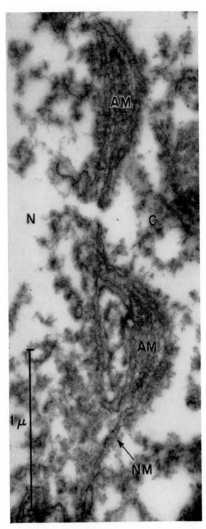

Fig. 3. Part of the nucleocytoplasmic border of a *Psammechinus* oocyte. The nucleus (N) is to the left and the cytoplasm (C) to the right. The picture shows the possible origin of heavy bodies and annulate lamellae (AM) at the nuclear membrane (NM). From Afzelius (1957).

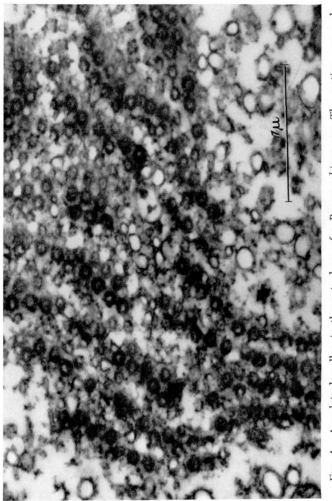

FIG. 4. Annulate lamellae in the cytoplasm of a *Psammechinus* egg. The section passes obliquely through the structure and shows the annuli. Some annuli appear to contain a central granule. From Afzelius (1957).

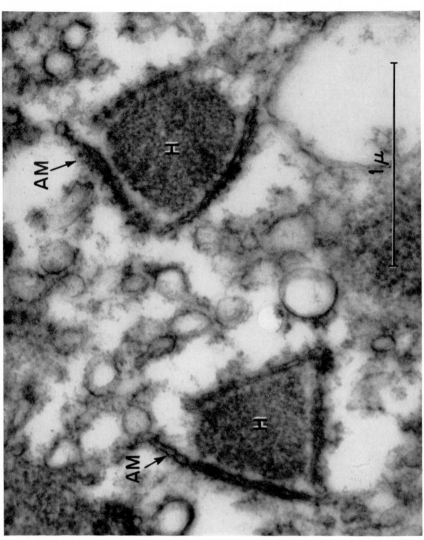

Fig. 5. Two heavy bodies (H) in the cytoplasm of a *Strongylocentrotus* oocyte. They are surrounded by annulate membranes (AM). From Afzelius (1957).

1961); phospholipid is probably a major component of all these membranes (Porter, 1961).

Morphological studies do not reveal the functions of the endoplasmic membranes although along with mitochondria, nucleoli, and the ground substance they have been supposed to play some part in yolk formation. Since the term yolk includes a wide range of lipid and protein-inclusion bodies, uniformity of origin is perhaps not to be expected.

E. Ribosomes and Cytoplasmic Basophilia

Abundant 150-Å granules have been observed in egg cytoplasm, mostly lying free. Allison and Clarke (1960) have isolated 70S ribosomes from homogenates of sea urchin eggs and have shown that they differ from the ribosomes of bacterial and mammalian cells in their Mg^{++} requirements. The ribosomes of amphibian eggs are difficult to isolate because of adsorption by yolk platelets (Brown and Caston, 1962a), which may, at the same time, explain the earlier reports that yolk platelets contain RNA. Brown and Caston (1962a), using an isotope dilution method, found 1.5 µg ribosomal RNA per egg.

Cytoplasmic basophilia when checked by the use of ribonuclease is generally thought to reveal ribosomal RNA (Palade, 1958; Sotelo and Porter, 1959), although some data are difficult to reconcile to this idea (Deane and Porter, 1960). In amphibia, basophilia is greatest in young oocytes and diminishes during yolk formation. It is also more marked at the animal pole than at the vegetal pole; the reverse of the yolk gradient (Brachet, 1950, 1957, 1960; Wittek, 1952; Pasteels, 1958a). In centrifuged eggs the basophilia is mostly displaced to the centripetal pole leaving a stationary peripheral layer of basophilia which, however, disappears when yolk formation is over; this is sometimes held to show that it plays some role in yolk formation. In centrifuged *Tubifex* eggs basophilia is found in a centripetal zone which contains Palade granules and endoplasmic vesicles (Weber, 1958); in centrifuged *Paracentrotus* eggs there is a similar basophilic hyaline zone but the strongest basophilia is at the centrifugal end of the egg, where it is apparently not associated with visible particles (Pasteels, 1958b; Pasteels *et al.*, 1958a, b). The nature of this "heavy" RNA is not known. In the case of the rat egg Jones-Seaton (1950), Dalcq (1957), and Pasteels (1958a) report that basophilia is linked to "cortical mitochondria," whose unequal distribution with respect to the polar axis confers bilateral symmetry upon the egg. The reality of this pattern seems doubtful in view of the possibility of fixation artifacts, and the ultraviolet absorption studies by Austin (1961) showed a uniform distribution of nucleic acid in the cytoplasm.

It does not seem likely that the distribution of basophilia plays any specific part in development; although it is probably related to the total capacity of a region to carry out protein synthesis, it is probably not related to the nature of the protein produced. In the experiments of Pasteels (1953) the positions of so many types of inclusions were altered by inversion or centrifugation that the effects on development cannot be attributed to any given type of particle or substance. Thus, the modifications of development were not obviously caused by the displacement of the gradient of basophilic substances.

F. *Mitochondria*

According to Blanchette (1961) the mitochondria of the young oocyte in mammals are devoid of cristae, and the typical adult arrangement arises gradually during oogenesis. These morphological changes do not appear to have been observed by other workers, although Weber (1958) found that the mitochondria of the polar plasm of *Tubifex* eggs are characterized by a mainly longitudinal arrangement of cristae. A close contact between mitochondria and lipid drops has been noted in both normal and centrifuged eggs (Lansing *et al.*, 1952; Pasteels *et al.*, 1958a, b; Gross *et al.*, 1960) and this contact leads to the displacement of some mitochondria to the centripetal pole of centrifuged eggs, which is important in connection with the developmental capacities of the "light" halves of sea urchin eggs (cf. Harvey, 1953). It is unlikely that any cell activities could occur for long in the absence of mitochondria. Weber (1958) found that in *Tubifex* eggs some mitochondria are apparently attached to a fibrillar cortical layer and are not displaced by centrifugation, but in *Psammechinus* eggs all mitochondria are free to move (Mercer and Wolpert, 1962) and can be driven to within 0.1 µ of the surface membrane at the centrifugal pole which argues against the presence of a gelatinous cortex.

1. Mitochondrial Enzymes

The biochemical properties of mitochondria from eggs appear to be similar to those from other tissues. Thus, all the cytochrome oxidase is present in mitochondria and a complete cytochrome system is present (Recknagel, 1950; Boell and Weber, 1955; Weber and Boell, 1955; Maggio and Ghiretti-Magaldi, 1958; Strittmatter *et al.*, 1960). Petrucci (1960) found that the cytochrome oxidase level of toad oocytes is highest at the time of yolk formation. The cytochrome oxidase of unfertilized sea urchin eggs is slightly less active than that from fertilized eggs when the isolated mitochondria are compared (Maggio, 1959), but a potent competitive inhibitor of cytochrome oxidase is present in the supernatant fraction from unfertilized eggs (Maggio and Monroy, 1959; Maggio *et al.*, 1960). The inhibitor disappears or becomes inactive shortly after fertilization and it may be connected with the well-known respiratory decline of unfertilized sea urchin eggs which is promptly corrected by fertilization (Brachet, 1950). Monroy (1957c) has demonstrated Mg^{++}-activated adenosinetriphosphatase activity in the mitochondria of sea urchin eggs. The effect of fertilization upon the metabolism of the egg is discussed further by Monroy in this volume (Chapter 2).

2. Mitochondria and Yolk Formation

It seems likely that mitochondria play a part in yolk formation in some amphibians and mollusks. In amphibia mitochondria begin to collect in the peripheral part of the oocyte during yolk formation (Kemp, 1956b; Ward, 1962a, b), and in *Rana pipiens* hexagonal protein crystals appear and grow between the membranes of cristae which are progressively expanded by the growing crystal (Ward, 1962a, b) (Fig. 6). According to Lanzavecchia (1961) some of the yolk platelets arise inside sacs budded off by mitochondria and others by the transformation of bodies composed of aggregates of vesicles (multivesicular bodies) near the nucleus. Possibly the mitochondrial formation corresponds to the primary vitellogenesis of Wittek (1952) and the juxtanuclear formation to the delayed vitellogenesis of that author. Intramitochondrial yolk platelets in embryonic stages have been observed by Lanzavecchia and Le Coultre (1958) and by Sung (1962). The former suggested that the platelets were undergoing transformation into mitochondria, the latter suggested that the yolk platelets were taken up by the mitochondria and utilized for metabolic reactions. The pictorial evidence for the intramitochondrial origin of yolk platelets is very striking, and it is surprising that neither Karasaki (1959) nor Kemp (1956b) observed any relation between yolk and mitochondria in their amphibian material. It is not yet clear, therefore, that the association is a general one.

In the mollusk *Planorbis* some mitochondria lose their internal membranes and granules, either single or in crystalline arrays, appear within them. Other mitochondria are themselves enclosed in flattened endoplasmic vesicles and crystalline yolk granules appear within the mitochondria (Favard and Carasso, 1958).

Electron microscopy cannot show the precise role of mitochondria in yolk formation in these cases. Ward (1962b) suggests that the mitochondria synthesize the yolk proteins and it might be possible to test this with an *in vitro* system, since there is now evidence that mitochondria can carry out protein synthesis (Truman and Korner, 1962) and Giudice (1960) has demonstrated the incorporation of S^{35}-methionine

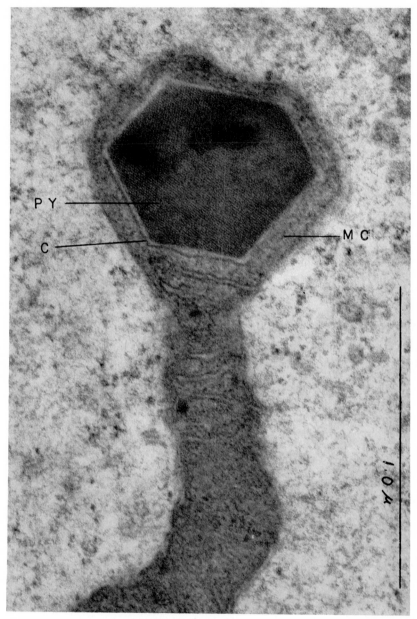

Fig. 6. Electron micrograph of a section of a hexagonal crystal of protein yolk (PY) inside a mitochondrion in a young oocyte of *Rana pipiens*. The membrane (C) surrounding the crystal probably represents an expanded mitochondrial crista; (MC) the surrounding mitochondrial cortex. From Ward (1962b).

into mitochondrial proteins of sea urchin eggs. Other evidence, however, suggests that yolk proteins are synthesized in the liver and transported to the oocyte in the blood stream (Flickinger, 1961), and the role of the mitochondria might be to concentrate the proteins and bring about their crystallization. It is very suggestive that Ringle and Gross (1962a) have found that yolk protein can be made to precipitate from a salt solution as a semicrystalline mass.

Ward (1962a, b) has also presented electron microscopic evidence for the participation of mitochondria in the secretion of fatty droplets (lipo-chondria) by amphibian oocytes. Kemp (1956b), who also noted the peripheral site of origin of lipochondria, did not mention an association with mitochondria.

G. Yolk Inclusions

The yolk inclusions form an ill-defined class of structures which appear in the growing oocyte and disappear during embryonic development, as they are utilized as sources of energy and raw materials. As Wilson (1928) pointed out long ago, no morphological or chemical criteria, such as are available in defining mitochondria for instance, have been discovered so far. Only the yolk platelets of amphibian eggs and the yolk spheres of avian eggs have received any detailed chemical study. The use of the term yolk in connection with mammalian eggs seems to be particularly arbitrary (Wartenberg and Stegner, 1960; Austin, 1961), and Dalcq's (1957) statement that the growth of the mammalian egg ceases just before yolk deposition, with a resultant diversion of the yolk material to other sites, is biochemically meaningless.

1. AMPHIBIAN YOLK PLATELETS

Two distinct classes of yolk platelets may be defined by size and chemical composition (Morgenthaler, 1951; Panijel, 1950), and the familiar yolk gradient arises from the unequal distribution of the two classes throughout the cytoplasm. Holtfreter (1946a,b,c) has contributed a great deal of information on the morphology and properties of the platelets. Birefringence (Holtfreter, 1946c; Gallera and Baud, 1954) and electron diffraction (Karasaki, 1959) indicate a highly oriented internal structure which is confirmed by electron microscopy. The main part of the platelet is a hexagonal plate composed of closely packed granules (possibly laminae) and is surrounded by an external layer of granules and a membrane, smoothing the outline into an ellipsoid (Wischnitzer, 1957; Karasaki and Komoda, 1958; Karasaki, 1959, 1962; Ward, 1959, 1962a,b; Sung, 1962; Ringle and Gross, 1962a). The chemical composition of the platelets will be discussed later, but it may be noted here that their structure changes in postgastrular stages with disappearance of the outer granular layer and the development of laminated membranes. The chemical composition of these platelets may not be valid for the platelets of oocytes (Deuchar, 1958).

Yolk platelets first appear in the basophilic peripheral part of the oocyte (Wittek, 1952; Kemp, 1956b), and C^{14}-glycine injected into the female also appears in this region (Kemp, 1955, 1956c). This does not prove that yolk proteins are synthesized in the basophilic cortex, as Kemp (1956c) proposes, and the relationship between the basophilia and the formation of the platelets is not clear. The platelets move inwards from the periphery, continuing to enlarge either by continuing synthesis or crystallization. It would be interesting to know whether the yolk platelet constituents are also present in the cytoplasmic matrix, i.e., prior to their inclusion in the platelets.

2.   FATTY YOLK IN AMPHIBIAN EGGS

The electron microscope data of Ward (1962b) show that the lipochondria of Holtfreter consist of dense droplets which have no limiting membrane. Apparently similar bodies are present in most types of eggs, and it is presumed that they possess nonlipid coats, because on displacement to the centripetal pole of the egg they do not coalesce.

3.   YOLK BODIES IN INVERTEBRATE EGGS

In *Limnaea* and *Planorbis* the yolk bodies contain crystalline regions composed of 60-Å granules, each of which is probably composed of subunits. The crystalline regions appear to be embedded more or less at random in a ground substance (Elbers, 1957; Favard and Carasso, 1958; Waddington *et al.*, 1961). Histochemical tests for protein and iron suggest a comparison with ferritin (Favard and Carasso, 1958), although direct chemical data are clearly needed on this point. The yolk bodies of snails (Yasuzumi and Tanaka, 1957), *Mytilus* (Humphreys, 1962a), sea urchins (Pasteels *et al.*, 1958a,b; Gross *et al.*, 1960), ascidians (Kessel and Kemp, 1962), and annelids (Weber, 1958) are granular or lamellar, but not obviously crystalline. Worley and Moriber (1961) have described crystalline yolk in the gastropod *Crepidula*. There is no information on the homogeneity, or otherwise, of this group of inclusions. Their response to centrifugation is variable; they are usually found in the centrifugal half of the egg, either above or below the mitochondria, but in other cases they are found in the centripetal half (Mercer and Wolpert, 1962). In sea urchin eggs the yolk contains PAS-reactive (periodic acid-Schiff) materials and probably sialic acid (Perlmann *et al.*, 1959).

In *Ostraea* the yolk bodies contain RNA and proteolytic enzymes (Cleland, 1951), although these are absent from the yolk of *Ilyanassa* (Collier, 1957, 1960).

4. AVIAN YOLK

The white yolk of the latebra is the first part of the mature egg to be formed in the early period of slow growth. It contains 86 % water as compared with the 45 % water of the yellow yolk which is laid down in the final period of rapid growth (Romanoff, 1931). The yolk solids consist mainly of protein and lipid. Carbohydrate is not a major reserve in avian eggs and is mainly present as the glycoproteins, lipovitellenin and α_2-glycoprotein.

The histological studies of Grodzinski (1938, 1946, 1951) showed that avian yolk is an oil-in-water emulsion in which lipid drops are distributed in a protein phase. The yellow and white yolk spheres are protein inclusions containing further lipid subdroplets. Electron microscope studies by Bellairs (1961) confirm this general picture, although they do not support the suggestion that the yolk spheres have membranous boundaries, which was proposed by Grodzinski (1951) to explain the swelling and shrinking of the spheres when placed in various salt solutions. Prolonged centrifugation of yolk gives a packed sediment of granules which are chemically similar to the yolk platelets of amphibian eggs (Fuji, 1960; Burley and Cook, 1961; Wallace, 1963), although no crystalline structure has been reported. Yolk constituents are thus distributed between a granular phase (phosphoprotein and high-density lipoprotein) and a fluid phase (water-soluble proteins and low-density lipoproteins). Unfortunately, there appears to be no information on the mechanisms by which the yolk spheres are formed from the materials delivered to the oocyte by the follicle cells.

H. *Nucleus*

Oocyte nuclei are often characterized by their large size, specialized chromosomes, and numerous or large nucleoli. These features have been studied most thoroughly in amphibian and starfish eggs, and the situation is not necessarily the same in other types of eggs.

1. LAMPBRUSH CHROMOSOMES

In many species the diplotene chromosomes of the oocyte produce numerous lateral loops during the period of rapid growth. Afterward the loops retract and a compact structure is restored by the metaphase of the first maturation division. The structure and function of lampbrush chromosomes is reviewed by Gall (1958); each chromatid consists of a pair of deoxyribonucleic acid (DNA) strands which are tightly coiled to form the Feulgen-positive chromomeres and which unwind to form the loops. The axis of the loop is surrounded by a granular material which is more abundant around one of the limbs of the loop than around the other (Fig. 7). The DNA component of the loop is inferred from

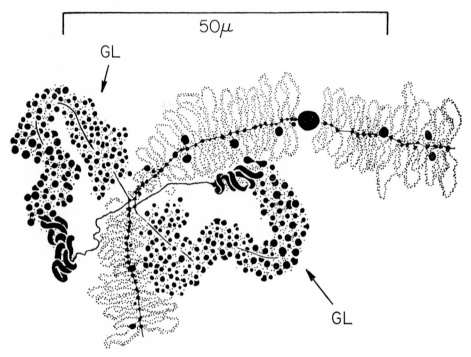

Fig. 7. A drawing of the left end of chromosome XII from an oocyte of the newt *Triturus cristatus*. There are many normal loop pairs and a single pair of giant granular loops (GL). In the giant loops the thin insertion consists of a fine thread leading to a dense, contorted region. From Gall and Callan (1962).

the fact that deoxyribonuclease specifically digests the loop axis, whereas ribonuclease and proteolytic enzymes only remove the surrounding matrix (Callan and Macgregor, 1958). In urodeles many of the loops have characteristic length and granularity, as shown by Callan and Lloyd (1960) in their memoir on the morphology of the lampbrush chromosomes. The function of the loops will be discussed in connection with RNA synthesis, and it will be seen that there are some differences between the giant granular loops and the smaller normal loops in their metabolic activities.

2. NUCLEOLI

Frequently, a single large nucleolus or a small number of nucleoli are present, attached to specific chromosomal loci. In amphibia, on the other hand, the number of nucleoli rises to about one thousand during early yolk formation and they lie close to the nuclear membrane, not physically joined to the chromosomes. The origin of these bodies from the lampbrush chromosomes is discussed by Callan (1952) and Gall (1958). Brown and Ris (1959) have shown that these nucleoli are similar to the normal attached nucleoli of somatic cells (general review by Sirlin, 1962); they are rich in protein and the RNA content, which has been estimated by interference microscopy before and after treatment with ribonuclease, is about 15 %. Direct analysis of isolated amphibian nucleoli (Finamore, 1961) confirms the results of Brown and Ris (1959). Isolated nucleoli from starfish oocytes contain about 5% RNA (Vincent, 1957). Nucleoli do not contain DNA except for the shell of DNA which surrounds the nucleolus in mammalian eggs (Austin, 1961). Nucleoli appear to be composed of granules (Brown and Ris, 1959), and Miller (1962) observed an inner fibrous zone and an outer granular one in which the RNA is concentrated. There is no boundary membrane and the passage of nucleolar material through the pores in the nuclear membrane is described by Miller (1962). This process has been mentioned frequently in light microscope studies as playing some role in yolk formation (e.g., Bonhag, 1958).

I. *Metachromatic Granules*

Recently, Pasteels and Mulnard (1957), Mulnard (1958), Kojima (1959a, b) and Filosa (1960) have described metachromatic granules in the eggs of several invertebrates. Brief immersion of the unfertilized egg in dilute toluidine blue revealed small metachromatic granules referred to as α-granules. After fertilization the dye was transferred to so-called β-granules. Centrifugation sediments the α-granules to the heavy end of the yolk zone, whereas the β-granules move to the centripetal zone of the yolk where the electron microscope reveals Golgi vesicles. Dalcq (1960) similarly suggests that the metachromatic granules of the egg of *Ascidiella* may be Golgi vesicles. Staining reactions with alcian blue, PAS reagent, and metachromatic dyes suggest that the α- and β-granules contain acidic polysaccharides (Hale, 1957; Pasteels, 1958b), and the β-granules appear also to be rich in acid phosphatase. Under anaerobic conditions the dye is released from the granules and stains the cytoplasmic background.

The origin of some of these obscure granules from yolk bodies has been proposed. Fautrez and Fautrez-Firlefyn (1961) suggest that the metachromatic granules of the *Artemia* egg arise from yolk granules, and the same idea is proposed by Dalcq and Pasteels (1963) for the ATPase-rich granules of several invertebrate eggs.

Sotelo and Porter (1959) showed by electron microscopy that rat eggs contain multivesicular bodies, consisting of an aggregate of small vesicles bounded by a membrane. A dense central "nucleoid" is also present. Their significance is still not clear; but Wartenberg and Stegner (1960) suggest that they may be precursors of mitochondria in the human egg, and Lanzavecchia (1961) suggests that they may be involved in yolk formation in amphibian eggs. Humphreys (1962a) has suggested that in *Mytilus* eggs the multivesicular bodies may correspond to the metachromatic granules of Pasteels and Mulnard (1957), but a means of isolating them should greatly assist the study of their nature and significance.

II. Morphogenetic Aspects of Egg Structure

It is a truism that the fertilized, uncleaved egg contains all the specific factors necessary for the complete development of the organism. With equal clarity, regional differentiation depends on the localized distribution of agents which control the development of the areas in which they occur. This may occur at a relatively early stage by the sorting-out of agents which already exist in the egg or at a relatively late stage by means of processes which involve interactions between layers of cells. Frequently, it has been pointed out that the distinction between the preformational or mosaic and the epigenetic or regulative varieties of embryonic determination is not absolute because even in predominantly mosaic embryos development still depends to some extent upon interactions between groups of cells (Dalcq, 1938; Weber, 1961). Nevertheless, the distinction is broadly valid, and it has been hoped that a study of the structure of the organism at the time of determination would indicate the nature of the controlling agents. Changes in determined areas may, however, be effects of determination and not the cause, unless similar experimentally produced changes also cause the same kind of determination.

A. *Polarity and Ooplasmic Segregation*

Many oocytes and eggs show axial polarity because of the eccentric position of the nucleus and the collection of cell particles at one side of the cell. In amphibia the polarity of the egg corresponds to the cephalo-caudal polarity of the embryo and, according to Pasteel's study (1953) of the results of displacement of particles by inversion with or without centrifugation, the polarity of the embryo is caused by the gradient distribution of cell particles along the axis of the egg. Ancel and Vintemberger (1948) have shown that the plane of bilateral symmetry is not predetermined in the unfertilized amphibian egg, but arises from external factors at the time of fertilization. The subsequent determination of the major regions of the amphibian egg is of the delayed type.

In many mosaic-type eggs a more or less uniform distribution of visible components is present until, at the time of the maturation divisions or fertilization, a drastic shifting of materials into discrete areas or zones takes place (see Wilson, 1928; Lehmann, 1956; Watterson, 1955). This may produce stratification along an axis, and in spirally cleaving eggs one or two distinct polar areas become visible. In most cases the localizations are stable and different blastomeres receive different quotas of the egg cytoplasm. A relatively transient ooplasmic segregation occurs in the mollusk *Limnaea* (Raven, 1958, 1963): azan staining reveals evenly distributed red and blue granules in the unovulated egg; shortly after ovulation and during passage of the egg down the oviduct the red granules segregate to the animal two-thirds area and the blue granules to the vegetal one-third area of the egg. The zones begin to disperse after about 1 hour, when the blue granules flow back toward the animal pole.

Nothing is known about the mechanism of ooplasmic segregation. Costello (1948) proposed an explanation in terms of potential differences created by diffusion of ions through membranes inside the egg, although it has been argued that such potential differences would not be large enough to cause the observed movements of cell particles. Raven (1963) suggests that a differentiated cortex or surface layer exerts attractive forces upon the internal components, so that separation of these components occurs.

B. *Significance of Ooplasmic Segregation*

The localizations of cell particles, enzymes, materials yielding colored products with indicator dyes, etc., appear to correspond to determined regions (Needham, 1942; Pasteels, 1958a), but it is still not known whether these materials cause the regional determination (i.e., whether they are inducers) or are merely visible effects of it (Watterson, 1955; Costello, 1955). Probably the only method which has been used is the observation of the effects of centrifuging upon development. If displacement of mitochondria, yolk granules, lipid drops, etc., does not affect development, it is concluded that the visible segregation has no causal role; if, on the other hand, a given type of differentiation can be associated with the localization of a certain type of granule or substance, then this may be a specific inducer. Unfortunately, it is difficult to know precisely the effects of centrifuging upon cells, and a variety of conclusions have been reached. In most cases it is not known whether the centrifuging has displaced only visible inclusions or also some invisible or soluble components. Most frequently, it has been found that displacement of visible particles does not disturb development and that the causes of regional determination are invisible and unmoved by relatively light centrifuging. A cortex and/or viscous "ground substance" composed of asymmetric molecules have been proposed as the required structural elements, but current ideas on this seem to be much the same as those which, according to Wilson (1928), were held by Driesch, Boveri, Conklin, and Lillie at the beginning of the century.

In ascidians, on the other hand, there is some evidence that certain aggregations of mitochondria may play a causal role in the differentiation of trunk musculature. In *Styela* a yellow area of the egg cytoplasm (myoplasm) is distributed to the muscle cells. The yellow material is of lipid nature, and Conklin (1931) found that its displacement by centrifuging did not disturb muscle development. He found, however, that with longer and stronger centrifuging development was disturbed and he concluded that the varying potencies of the visibly different areas of the ascidian egg "are not due to mitochondria, yolk, pigment or free water but rather to physical and chemical differences in the cytoplasm or 'ground-substance' of these areas." Ries (1937), however, found that the myoplasm in *Ciona* contains abundant mitochondrial oxidative enzymes as shown by the Nadi reaction and that displacement of the Nadi-positive material leads to a corresponding displacement of the trunk muscles. Biochemical and ultrastructural differences between the anterior blastomeres and the posterior ones (which receive the myoplasm at the four-cell stage) have been studied by Berg (1956, 1957) and Berg and Humphreys (1960). The mitochondria of the posterior blastomeres are three times as numerous as those of the anterior ones, and lipid droplets are eight times as numerous in the posterior cells. Correspondingly, mitochondrial enzymes are more abundant in the posterior blastomeres. The Nadi reaction is clearly of low sensitivity because only the posterior blastomeres reacted positively and the differentiation is by no means as sharp as Ries believed. The electron microscope data show that some mitochondria are attached to the yellow lipid droplets and are displaced with them to the centripetal pole of the egg. Thus, the situation is still confused. It seems that neither the lipid drops nor the mitochondria attached to them are important, but the aggregate of mitochondria which forms either as a result of natural ooplasmic segregation or centrifuging can direct differentiation toward the production of muscle. This is, however, difficult to understand because none of the known biochemical properties of mitochondria suggest that they might control protein synthesis, and it seems reasonable to suppose that muscle differentiation depends upon the synthesis of muscle proteins. It is likely that the mitochondria and the yolk are general rather than specific factors in development, as Conklin (1931) stated.

Weber (1958, 1961, 1962) has discussed the relation between cell structure and determination in the spirally cleaving *Tubifex* egg. The polar plasms pass into the ectodermal somatoblast (2d) and the mesodermal somatoblast (4d), and they and the polar plasms are distinguished from the rest of the egg by abundant mitochondria and endoplasmic vesicles. The cytochrome oxidase activity of the somatoblasts is three times that of the endoblasts, although their catheptic activities are about the same. As with the ascidian myoplasm the differentiation of the polar plasm and its derivatives is quantitative and not qualitative. The different potencies of the ectodermal and mesodermal somatoblasts is not reflected in their ultrastructures. Similarly, the polar lobe of *Dentalium* is particularly rich in mitochondria (Reverberi, 1958), but that of *Mytilus*, which also shows early determination, is not different from the rest of the egg in its ultrastructure (Humphreys, 1962b). The oxygen consumption of the CD blastomere, which contains the polar plasm, is 13 % less than that of the AB blastomere in *Mytilus* (Berg and Kutsky, 1951), but the alanylglycine dipeptidase activity is equally distributed (Berg, 1954). In the *Mytilus* egg mosaic development is not associated with any particular localization of the visible inclusions (Humphreys, 1962b).

Thus, in some cases regional determination is accompanied by changes in the relative proportions of some cell components and the accompanying biochemical functions (Dalcq, 1960; Weber, 1962), but the cause of determination is still obscure. Perhaps, as Weber (1961) suggests, sharper differences between determined regions might be revealed by immunological methods. The control of gene activity may be brought about by means of localized substances capable of acting as repressors or inducers (Jacob and Monod, 1961), and histones might play such a part as inhibitors of gene activity (Huang and Bonner, 1962; Hindley, 1963). However, even when the nature and action of gene-controlling agents is understood, it remains necessary to discover how their correct localization is brought about, i.e., how ooplasmic segregation is controlled.

III. Biochemical Studies on Nucleic Acids and Proteins in Oogenesis

A. *Deoxyribonucleic Acid*

1. NUCLEAR DNA

The prematuration oocyte nucleus should contain four times as much DNA as a sperm and twice as much as a diploid nucleus. Accordingly, Pasteels and Lison (1951) found by a spectrophotometric Feulgen method that the DNA contents of the first metaphase plate, second metaphase plate, and the pronucleus of sea urchin eggs were in the ratio 4:2:1. Alfert's photometric study (1950) of mouse oocytes also gave predicted values, but the chemical study by England and Mayer (1957) gave twice as much DNA in amphibian oocyte nuclei and diploid cells as in the sperm. This work has been criticized by Finamore *et al.* (1960) who think that the objects studied by England and Mayer (1957) were not nuclei at all but clumps of TCA-precipitated (trichloroacetic acid) yolk. The value obtained by Finamore *et al.* (1960) also seems suspect, however; they isolated nuclei from papain-treated oocytes and measured DNA phosphorus. Their value of 6 × 10^{-3} µg DNA per nucleus is some eight hundred times the value for the nuclei of liver cells, and possible contamination by oocyte cytoplasm and follicle cells does not seem to have been convincingly excluded. The suggestion that the lampbrush chromosomes and the numerous nucleoli of amphibian oocytes are responsible for this high DNA value does not seem likely, since autoradiographic studies suggest that the lampbrush chromosomes do not synthesize DNA and we have already seen that nucleoli do not contain DNA (Finamore, 1961).

Nuclear DNA synthesis does not occur in the later stages of oocyte growth. Thus, thymidine is not incorporated into the lampbrush chromosomes of newt oocytes (Ficq, 1961a; Izawa *et al.*, 1963). In the nucleus of sand dollar eggs, thymidine incorporation commences in the male and female pronuclei 15 minutes after fertilization (Simmel and Karnofsky, 1961). Lack of incorporation into the nucleus of the growing oocyte has also been observed in *Gryllus* (Durand, 1961; Favard-Séréno and Durand, 1963a, b), *Drosophila* (Nigon and Nonnenmacher, 1960b), and sea urchins (Nigon and Nonnenmacher, 1960a; Esper, 1962; Ficq *et al.*, 1963). The use of radioactive phosphorus has given contradictory results in amphibia. Grant (1958) observed no labeling of DNA phosphorus until 16 hours after fertilization following the injection of P^{32} into the female. Finamore and Volkin (1958), on the other hand, reported incorporation of the phosphorus into nuclear DNA under similar conditions and suggested that DNA synthesized in the nucleus was stored in the cytoplasm. This result seems difficult to reconcile with the other evidence for DNA stability during oogenesis. The question of "metabolic DNA" is discussed by Lima-da-Faria (1962).

2. CYTOPLASMIC DNA

This subject has attracted a good deal of discussion in recent years as is seen from the extensive reviews by Brachet (1960, 1962), Løvtrup (1959), and Durand (1961). Many workers, using a variety of methods, have found that the DNA content of the eggs of invertebrates, amphibians, and birds exceeds the expected chromosomal DNA by a factor which may be as low as ten or as high as many thousands. Some of these results are given in Table I. There are two main difficulties: (a) Specificity. The DNA or DNA-like material is present in very low concentration, and the estimation of DNA phosphorus gives much higher values than chemical estimation of deoxyribose or microbiological estimation of deoxyribonucleosides and deoxyribonucleotides using Thermobacterium acidophilus R 26 (Hoff-Jørgensen, 1952). The microbiological method appears to be the most satisfactory for the determination of the total amount of DNA-like material; supplemented media should be used because the addition of growth factors to the standard medium increases growth in the presence of deoxyribonucleosides (Siedler et al., 1957). (b) Contamination. Contamination by polar bodies and follicle cells was said by Marshak and Marshak (1955a,b) to account for all the DNA of mature sea urchin eggs.

Egg cytoplasm is generally said to be Feulgen-negative, but Sze (1953) points out that this is caused by the low concentration of DNA. No direct analyses have been carried out on mammalian eggs, and it is quite possible that they contain as much as other types of eggs despite Austin's view (1961) that on the basis of histochemistry mammalian eggs do not contain large amounts of DNA.

Apparently, a purified DNA has not yet been isolated from egg cytoplasm, so that very little is known about its physical and chemical properties. It is, however, certain that a variety of molecules is included in the category of cytoplasmic DNA. Much of it appears to be of lower molecular weight than normal DNA. According to Hoff-Jørgensen and Zeuthen (1952) one-third of the DNA of amphibian eggs passes through dialysis membrane, and Grant (1958) found that one-half is extracted by cold perchloric acid. Only 15 % of the deoxyribose-containing material of amphibian eggs is precipitated by ethanol (Bieber et al., 1959). Free deoxyribonucleosides, however, are probably not present because the egg homogenates do not support growth of Thermobacterium acidophilus without prior digestion (Gregg and Løvtrup, 1955), and Fina-

TABLE I
DNA Contents of Eggs

Egg	Total DNA content of egg (μg/egg)	Equivalent number of diploid cells	Method	Reference
Echinoderm	$700–4000 \times 10^{-6}$	—	UV absorption of Schmidt-Thannhauser DNA fraction	Agrell and Persson (1956)
	600×10^{-6}	—	DNA phosphorus	Schmidt et al. (1948)
	220×10^{-6}	157	Diphenylamine	Vendrely and Vendrely (1949)
	28×10^{-6}	14	Microbiological assay of thymine	Elson and Chargaff (1952)
	$20–30 \times 10^{-6}$	10–15	Microbiological assay of thymine	Elson et al. (1954)
	16.6×10^{-6}	12	Microbiological assay of deoxyribosides	Hoff-Jørgensen (1954)
Parascaris	290×10^{-6}	116	Indole reaction	Nigon and Bovet (1955)
Insects	5×10^{-3}	250–2500	Diphenylamine reaction	Nigon and Daillie (1958)
	83×10^{-3}	7400	Indole reaction	Durand (1961)
	1000×10^{-3}	100,000	DNA phosphorus	
Mollusk	4.28×10^{-4}	64	Diphenylamine	Collier and McCann-Collier (1962)
	1.0	—	Diphenylamine	Brown and Caston (1962a)
	0.95	95,000	DNA phosphorus	Sze (1953)
	6.9×10^{-10} moles	25,000	Indole reaction	Bieber et al. (1959)
	0.26	—	Indole reaction	Brachet (1954)
	0.073	4250	Microbiological assay of deoxyribosides	Hoff-Jørgensen (1954)
Amphibians	0.069	—	Fluorescent method	Baltus and Brachet (1962)
	0.063	—	Microbiological assay of deoxyribosides	Gregg and Løvtrup (1955)

TABLE I (*Continued*)

Egg	Total DNA content of egg (μg/egg)	Equivalent number of diploid cells	Method	Reference
Amphibians (*Cont.*)	0.032 0.027	— —	Microbiological assay of deoxyribosides	Kuriki and Okasaki (1959)
	0.023	—	Microbiological assay of deoxyribosides	Grant (1958)
Hen	118	5×10^7	Microbiological assay of deoxyribosides	Hoff-Jørgensen (1954)
	52	2.6×10^7	Isotope dilution assay of thymine	Solomon (1957a,b)

more and Crouse (1958) found no deoxyribonucleotides in the perchloric acid extracts. Kuriki and Okasaki (1959) especially have emphasized the contribution of low molecular weight compounds to the "DNA" and demonstrated a large number of deoxyribonucleoside di- and triphosphates together with traces of free deoxyribonucleosides. The acid-soluble deoxyribonucleoside derivatives were about three times as abundant as the acid-insoluble DNA.

The base composition of the DNA of the ovary of *Gryllus*, including nuclear and cytoplasmic material from the oocytes and follicle cells, shows a very high thymine content with the ratio adenine/thymine = 0.57 which is not compatible with the normal double-stranded DNA structure (Durand, 1961). Finamore and Volkin (1958), on the other hand, found that the labeled DNA of the ovary of a frog which had been injected with P^{32} had the same base composition as the labeled liver DNA.

Several authors have suggested that the cytoplasmic DNA is bound to the yolk platelets in amphibian eggs (Brachet, 1954; Baltus and Brachet, 1962; Brown and Caston, 1962a), although the amount found by Brown and Caston (1 μg per egg) is considerably higher than the value usually accepted (0.06 μg per egg). Ringle and Gross (1962a,b) state that platelets are weakly Feulgen-positive *in situ* but become Feulgen-negative after isolation and washing. Suzuki (quoted by Karasaki, 1959) found the platelets to be Feulgen-negative. Chemical analyses of platelets have suggested values of 0.1 % DNA (Ringle and Gross, 1962a, b), less than 0.05 % (Wallace, 1962, 1963), or none at all (Gross and Gilbert, 1956). It seems unlikely, on the whole, that DNA is a genuine constituent of the platelet, and the possibility of a falsely positive Feulgen reaction in the presence of lipid was pointed out long ago by Brachet (1950). Also, in connection with interference by lipids, see the dispute between Burgos (1955) and Marshak and Marshak (1955b).

It should be mentioned that according to Chèvremont (1963) mitochondria of chick embryo fibroblasts synthesize DNA which is then transferred to the nucleus. Zeigler and Schmidt (1957) observed the appearance of DNA-containing granules in the cytoplasm of cells treated with acridine orange.

3. Cytoplasmic DNA as a Reserve Material

The theory that cytoplasmic DNA serves as a reserve rests on the claim that the total DNA content of the embryo remains constant during cleavage stages, when the amount of nuclear DNA must be increasing rapidly. It would be expected that net DNA synthesis should be detected when all the cytoplasmic DNA has been converted into nuclear DNA and the total DNA corresponds to the number of diploid nuclei. The DNA content of sea urchin eggs is roughly equivalent to 16 diploid nuclei and increase in the DNA content appears to begin at about the 16-cell stage (Hoff-Jørgensen, 1954). Agrell and Persson (1956) found that *Echinus*, which contained a large amount of DNA ($\sim 4 \times 10^{-3}$ µg per egg), begins to show a net increase in DNA at the 500-cell stage, whereas *Paracentrotus*, which contains only 0.7 $\times$ 10^{-3} µg DNA per egg, showed a net increase at the 32-cell stage. Unfortunately, for any simple assumptions about the relation between the DNA content of the egg and the time when DNA increases, Agrell and Persson (1956) also noted that individual batches of eggs might contain only 10% of the average DNA content for the species, although net synthesis of DNA in these batches began at the normal time. The values obtained by these workers were exceptionally high, however, and the alleged species differences are doubtful. In amphibian eggs the reserve is equivalent to 5000–10,000 cells and DNA begins to increase at mid- to late blastula stages, when approximately this number of cells is present (Hoff-Jørgensen, 1954; Gregg and Løvtrup, 1955; Baltus and Brachet, 1962). The data for the gastropod *Ilyanassa* do not fit the prediction so well (Collier and McCann-Collier, 1962); the DNA of the egg is equivalent to 64 diploid nuclei, but at the 25-cell stage total DNA has already increased by an amount which corresponds to 66 diploid nuclei. Thus, the increase is too soon and too much. Grant (1958) found a slow rate of increase in total DNA in *Rana* up to the time when the excess DNA had been utilized; after this the increase in DNA paralleled the increasing number of cells. Kuriki and Okasaki (1959) also found a rise in the DNA content of the amphibian embryo during cleavage stages; this correctly refers to acid-insoluble DNA and not to the total of soluble and insoluble materials.

Moore (1962) suggests that cytoplasmic DNA is utilized in the formation of new chromosomal material with retention of its genetic specificity. It is clear, however, that some incorporation of low molecular weight precursors into nuclear DNA can occur during cleavage and even before fusion of the pronuclei (Simmel and Karnofsky, 1961; Ficq et al., 1963) and the deoxyribonucleoside derivatives studied by Kuriki and Okasaki (1959) could serve as DNA precursors. In *Arbacia* the incorporation of thymidine into nuclear DNA commences 30 minutes after fertilization according to Nigon and Nonnenmacher (1960a) who conclude that any high molecular weight reserves are probably degraded to small compounds before utilization in DNA synthesis.

4. THE ORIGIN OF CYTOPLASMIC DNA

The basic requirements for DNA synthesis appear to be the four deoxyribonucleoside triphosphates, Mg^{++}, deoxyribonucleic nucleotidyltransferase, and a DNA primer (Kornberg, 1961), and it is likely that DNA is not synthesized in the cytoplasm because of the absence of a suitable primer (Prescott et al., 1962). Cytoplasmic DNA may, therefore, originate in the nuclei of the oocyte or the follicle cells. The oocyte nucleus does not appear to synthesize DNA during the period of rapid growth of the oocyte, but DNA synthesis in nondividing follicle cells has been reported for amphibia (Ficq, 1961a) and especially for insects (Schrader and Leuchtenberger, 1952; Bonhag, 1955a,b, 1958; Durand, 1958, 1961; Nigon and Nonnenmacher, 1961; Favard-Séréno and Durand, 1963a). In insects the follicle cell nuclei become highly polyploid during yolk formation (Yao, 1949), and intense incorporation of thymidine into the nuclei occurs. Labeled DNA then enters the cytoplasm where it becomes Feulgen-negative and, perhaps, depolymerized (loss of methyl green stainability) before entering the cytoplasm of the oocyte. The labeled material is assumed to be DNA, although Ficq (1961a) found that it was extracted by perchloric acid. It is still too early to state definitely that the cytoplasmic DNA of the oocyte is derived from the follicle cells in other species, although this seems a reasonable hypothesis (see Lima-da-Faria, 1962, on thymidine incorporation into the cytoplasm of other cells).

Thymidine incorporation as an indicator of DNA synthesis is open to some criticism because it is not a natural precursor of DNA and has first to be converted to thymidine phosphate which normally arises from deoxyuridine phosphate. Bianchi (1962) has shown that in some tissues thymidine kinase is present in rate-limiting amounts, whereas the nucleotide kinases and deoxyribonucleic nucleotidyltransferase are generally found in much larger amounts. Absence of thymidine incorporation may reflect lack of thymidine kinase rather than absence of normal DNA synthesis.

An enzyme which catalyzes the deamination of pyrimidine deoxyribonucleotides has been studied by Scarano and his collaborators. It appears to be particularly abundant in unfertilized sea urchin and amphibian eggs and it rapidly diminishes after fertilization. It is also present in a variety of cells from bacteria to mammals (Scarano, 1958, 1960, 1961; Scarano and Maggio, 1959; Scarano et al., 1960, 1962). The enzyme converts deoxycytidine phosphate to deoxyuridine phosphate and methyl deoxycytidine phosphate to thymidine phosphate. Its function is not clear, but it may play a part in DNA synthesis by controlling the production of thymidylate.[1]

$$\text{dCMP} \xrightarrow{-\text{NH}_2} \text{dUMP} \xrightarrow{+\text{CH}_3} \text{dTMP}$$

or

$$\text{CH}_3\text{-dCMP} \xrightarrow{-\text{NH}_2} \text{dTMP}$$

and regulating the deoxyribonucleotide pool (Scarano et al., 1962). Scarano (1960) points out, however, that pyrimidine deoxyribonucleotides may have special functions since conjugated compounds, such as deoxycytidine diphosphate choline, have been isolated from sea urchin eggs (Sugino et al., 1957; Sugino, 1957) as well as from other tissues. Sugino and Potter (1960), however, have found evidence that in rat thymus the deaminase is important in producing the thymidylate required for DNA synthesis.

B. Ribonucleic Acid

Histochemical tests suggest that the cytoplasm of the oocyte is rich in RNA during cytoplasmic growth and the early part of yolk formation (Brachet, 1950). Figure 8 shows that as yolk accumulates the RNA concentration falls because its absolute rate of increase is less than that of the mass of cytoplasm (Osawa and Hayashi, 1953; Edström et al., 1961). Cowden (1962) suggests that the prolonged increase in RNA in Arbacia and Lytechinus oocytes is associated with a relatively late onset of yolk formation. The main sites of RNA in the cell are the chromosomes, nucleoli, ribosomes, and membranous structures, such as the an-

---

[1] dCMP: 2-deoxyribosylcytosine 5′-phosphate; dUMP: 2-deoxyribosyluracil 5′-phosphate; CH$_3$-dCMP: 5-methyl-2-deoxyribosylcytosine 5′-phosphate; dTMP: 2-deoxyribosylthymine 5′-phosphate.

nulate lamellae (Swift, 1958). At one time amphibian yolk platelets were thought to contain RNA (Panijel, 1950; Grant, 1953; Gross and Gilbert, 1956; Rounds and Flickinger, 1958), but the later work by Ringle and Gross (1962b) and Wallace (1962, 1963) makes it unlikely that RNA is a genuine constituent of the platelets. Histochemical studies by Takata and Ono (quoted by Yamada, 1961) also failed to reveal RNA in the platelets. The question of the adsorption of ribosomes by platelets during isolation procedures is discussed by Brown and Caston (1962a). Yolk granules of invertebrate eggs may (Cleland, 1951) or may not (Collier, 1960) contain RNA.

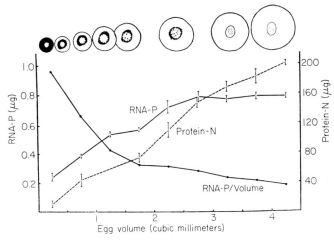

FIG. 8. A diagram of the relation between total RNA phosphorus, total protein nitrogen, RNA phosphorus per unit volume, and the intensity of basophilia during the growth of the oocyte of the newt *Triturus pyrrhogaster*. From Osawa and Hayashi (1953).

The main chemical categories are high molecular weight ribosomal RNA, high molecular weight unstable RNA (messenger), and low molecular weight soluble or transfer RNA. Recent reviews on the functions of these compounds in protein synthesis are given by McQuillen (1962), Sirlin (1962), and Franklin and Baltimore (1962). Brown and Caston (1962b) have isolated a high molecular weight (16 S) RNA from amphibian eggs and embryos and shown that in its base composition it resembles ribosomal RNA from other tissues. The base composition of the RNA from isolated nucleoli of starfish (Vincent, 1952; Edström *et al.*, 1961) and spider (Edström, 1960) oocytes is similar to that of the bulk cytoplasmic RNA. Similarly, Finamore (1961) and Finamore and Volkin (1961) showed by P[32]-labeling that the nucleotide composition of nucleolar RNA is similar to cytoplasmic RNA in amphibian oocytes. Nuclear RNA, on the other hand, differed in having a high ratio of adenine to cytidine. There is not complete identity of composition between nucleolar and cytoplasmic RNA (Vincent, 1952), however; and the differences increase in magnitude during oogenesis (Edström et al., 1961). Nevertheless, it is likely that ribosomal RNA is present in nucleoli, and it would be interesting to have information on the question of ribosomal proteins in the nucleoli. It seems unwise to place too much emphasis on the composition of structures which contain several different categories of RNA.

It has long been known that much of the RNA of the amphibian oocyte is readily soluble (Brachet and Jeener, 1944), and Ficq (1961b) has shown that the intense cytoplasmic radioactivity following the administration of tritiated cytidine is almost completely removed by extraction with cold perchloric acid after trichloroacetic acid treatment. About half the RNA of the amphibian egg is soluble in 0.5 M perchloric acid and has a different base composition from the acid-insoluble RNA according to Finamore and Volkin (1961). These workers also found an unexpectedly high proportion of the RNA to be resistant to digestion by alkali and ribonuclease. The acid extract has been shown to contain the four ribonucleotides, as well as ADP, ATP, GTP, and UTP (Finamore and Crouse, 1958).

1. CHROMOSOMAL SYNTHESIS OF RNA

The germinal vesicle of amphibian oocytes contains a large amount of RNA; Finamore et al. (1960) found 3000 times as much as in the nucleus of liver cells. Gall and Callan (1962) found that, after short periods of administration of tritiated uridine to the newt, labeled nuclear RNA was confined to short segments of the large, coarsely granular loops of the lampbrush chromosomes at the point where the DNA strand leaves the compact chrommomere and where the surrounding matrix is thinnest. With increasing periods of labeling the isotopic RNA was located on longer stretches of the loop until, after 10 days, it covered its whole length. With the smaller loops which make up the bulk of the lampbrush chromosomes RNA synthesis occurred simultaneously at all points along the loop and was not confined to the thin end.

The role of the DNA strand in priming the synthesis of RNA by lampbrush chromosomes was shown by the inhibition of the labeling of the RNA by actinomycin D and arginine-rich histones which combine with the DNA (Izawa et al., 1963). These inhibitors also cause rapid disappearance of the loops, whereas actinomycin C_3 and lysine-rich histone, which probably combine with the DNA without inhibiting

RNA synthesis, have no effect on the morphology of the chromosomes. This suggests that RNA synthesis is somehow necessary for the maintenance of the loops, and unwinding of the coiled DNA thread may, in turn, be necessary for RNA synthesis to occur (Izawa et al., 1963).

Administration of radioactive phenylalanine did not give sequential labeling of either the giant granular loops or the normal loops, but gave simultaneous labeling along the whole length (Gall and Callan, 1962). Puromycin, which inhibited this incorporation, had no effect on the structure of the loops (Izawa et al., 1963). It may be tentatively concluded, therefore, that protein synthesis occurs in close association with the matrix of the loops.

Gall and Callan (1962) have proposed a "conveyor-belt" model according to which the DNA strand is continually unwinding from the chromomere at one side of the loop and rewinding at the other. RNA is synthesized at the site of unwinding and is then carried round as a passenger by the moving loop. This seems to imply that qualitatively different DNA sequences are used to produce the RNA during the lifetime of the loop, and the RNA will also change. An alternative hypothesis, that the axis of the loop remains stationary and only the matrix moves, would allow the output of each loop to remain qualitatively constant. Since the labeled material appears to be stable for at least 10 days, it may possibly represent ribosomal RNA. Because the normal loops incorporate RNA precursors along their whole length, there is, at present, no evidence that the "conveyor-belt" model is valid for the majority of the loops.

In contrast to this situation, the oocyte nucleus in insects does not appear to synthesize RNA (Bier, 1963), perhaps because the intense RNA synthesis by the follicle cells and nurse cells supplies the oocyte with all its RNA. The studies of Schultz (1956), Levenbook et al. (1958), and Travaglini et al. (1958) on Drosophila eggs have shown that there is a close relation between genetic constitution and RNA metabolism. RNA from eggs laid by females with an added Y chromosome (sex chromosome type $\overline{XXY}$) was compared with that from eggs laid by normal females of chromosome type XX. The total amount of RNA was equal in the two cases, but the $\overline{XXY}$ type contained more adenine than the normal type. Acid extracts of the eggs also contained more adenine derivatives in the case of the $\overline{XXY}$ eggs. The precise nature and function of the aberrant RNA have not been studied, but the effects of the extra heterochromatin are evidently complex, because the nurse cells of the $\overline{XXY}$ females also produce 36 % more DNA during oogenesis than do normal nurse cells (Schultz, 1956).

2. Nucleolar RNA Metabolism

There is now evidence that the nucleolus plays a role in nucleic acid and protein metabolism, and precursors of nucleic acids and proteins are actively incorporated into the nucleoli of oocytes. The incorporation of radioactive adenine into oocyte nucleoli has been studied by Ficq (1955a, b), Ficq et al. (1963), and van den Broek and Tates (1961). Some of the newly synthesized material appears to be transferred rapidly to the nucleolus after being synthesized in close contact with the chromosomes, as in the case of the follicle cells of Gryllus (Favard-Séréno and Durand, 1963a). According to Ficq (1961b) the nucleolar label represents acid-insoluble RNA, in contrast to the evenly distributed labeled RNA of the cytoplasm which was soluble in acid. On the whole, these experiments indicate active RNA synthesis either in the nucleolus itself or in the chromosome and its rapid transfer to the nucleolus, but the experiments give little information on the nature of the RNA, which is likely to be heterogeneous.

Isolated nucleoli from starfish oocytes labeled with P^{32} yield two independent RNA fractions (Vincent, 1957; Vincent and Baltus, 1960a, b). The acid-insoluble fraction incorporates the isotope slowly but reaches a high, final specific activity and may represent ribosomal RNA. The second fraction has the properties of amino acid transfer RNA; it is acid-soluble, shows terminal turnover of two residues of cytidylic acid and one residue of adenylic acid, and binds leucine. This fraction rapidly acquires label, but the specific activity reached is not so high as that finally attained by the first fraction; it cannot, therefore, be a precursor of the first fraction. The synthesis of transfer RNA in the nucleolus would be expected to lead to a rapid uptake of amino acids by that organelle and this has been observed in autoradiographic studies (Ficq, 1955a,b; Immers, 1961). That this uptake represents amino acyl RNA does not appear to have been proved, however, and according to Sirlin (1962) nucleolar uptake of amino acids occurs only in oocytes and other growing cells and represents actual protein synthesis. The nucleoli of differentiated cells may be engaged only in nucleic acid synthesis. Recently, Brandt and Finamore (1963) have provided evidence that isolated nucleoli of amphibian eggs are complete protein-synthesizing units. Amino acid-activating enzymes were demonstrated, and added amino acids were shown to be incorporated into nucleolar protein. The insensitivity of nucleolar protein synthesis to treatment with ribonuclease, as reported by Brandt and Finamore (1963), seems surprising, although Finamore (1961) claims that amphibian oocyte RNA as a whole is characterized by this resistance to ribonuclease digestion.

Although it is now generally thought that all normal RNA is synthesized in the nucleus with the participation of DNA, it was claimed by Malkin (1954) that enucleated sea urchin eggs incorporated C^{14}-glycine into RNA. This result could be caused by bacterial contamination, but it should be pointed out that some forms of RNA synthesis appear to be RNA-primed, since they are insensitive to actinomycin D (Barry *et al.*, 1962; Paul and Struthers, 1963).

C. Egg Proteins

1. AVIAN YOLK PROTEINS

Since the last main reviews on the chemistry of yolk proteins (Fevold, 1951; Warner, 1953) much work on the physical properties of the yolk lipoproteins has been carried out, especially by Sugano (1957, 1958a,b, 1959a,b) and by Cook and his collaborators; see Cook (1961) and Cook and Martin (1962) for summaries and earlier literature. Complete agreement on the precise nature of the yolk protein has not been reached, and the nomenclature is unsettled (Schjeide and Urist, 1960).

Centrifugation of yolk yields granules which probably correspond to the yolk spheres observed by microscopy. They consist mainly of a water-insoluble complex of lipovitellin and phosvitin as well as large amounts of metal, possibly complexed with the phosphoprotein, and a small amount of low-density lipoprotein (Schmidt *et al.*, 1956; Burley and Cook, 1961). The granules contain nearly all the protein-bound phosphorus of the yolk, 70 % of the calcium, 95 % of the iron, but only about 10 % of the yolk phospholipid (Schmidt *et al.*, 1956; Schjeide and Urist, 1959, 1960; Burley and Cook, 1961). Lipovitellin contains 20 % lipid and has been fractionated into α-lipovitellin (0.5 % protein phosphorus) and β-lipovitellin (0.27 % protein phosphorus) by Bernardi and Cook (1960). The possible effects of adsorption of phosvitin to the lipoprotein have not been settled, and the α- and β-lipoproteins appear to be very similar (Cook *et al.*, 1962). The lipid moiety has been studied by Hawke and Lea (1953). It appears likely that the so-called β-lipovitellin of Sugano (1959a, b) corresponds to the lipovitellenin reported by other workers. The report of Enselme *et al.* (1951) on a soluble preparation of lipid-free vitellin has never been confirmed, although such material would be very useful in the study of the protein chemistry of these difficult molecules. Phosvitin is a much smaller protein (molecular weight of 36,000) and contains 10 % phosphorus. Its isolation and physicochemical properties have been studied by Mecham and Olcott (1949), Joubert and Cook (1958), Allgen and Norberg (1959), Williams and Sanger (1959), Mok *et al.* (1961), Connelly and Taborsky (1961), and Taborsky and Allende (1962).

The fluid phase of the yolk contains the bulk of the yolk lipid, in the form of the low-density lipoprotein lipovitellenin which contains 89 % lipid and 2.5 % carbohydrate (Nichols *et al.*, 1954; Turner and Cook, 1958; Abraham *et al.*, 1960). Unlike lipovitellin it is apparently not a phosphoprotein. The water-soluble proteins which constitute the livetin fraction (Plimmer, 1908) occur in the fluid phase.

All the yolk proteins appear to be present at some time in the blood. The lipophosphoproteins are found there only in connection with egg laying (Mok *et al.*, 1961; Heald and McLachlan, 1963; Schjeide and Urist, 1960; Roepke and Bushnell, 1936; Laskowski, 1935; McIndoe, 1959; Abraham *et al.*, 1960). The conditions used to isolate phosvitin from the serum of laying hens suggest that it is present in different complexes from those present in yolk (Heald and McLachlan, 1963). The water-soluble proteins, on the other hand, appear to be normal serum proteins among which albumin, 3 S α_2-glycoproteins, transferrin, and γ-globulin are the most abundant in the egg yolk (Jukes and Kay, 1932; Nace, 1953; Knight and Schechtman, 1954; Shepard and Hottle, 1949; Williams, 1962a,b).

2. Fish Egg Proteins

Young and Phinney (1951) have described an electrophoretically homogeneous lipovitellin from salmon eggs. In both teleosts and elasmobranchs the lipovitellin is broadly similar to the lipovitellin of avian egg yolk (Fuji, 1960), and a heterogeneous water-soluble livetin fraction is also present. Ohi (1962) has employed paper electrophoresis to show the presence of phosphoproteins, lipoproteins, and some enzymes in aqueous extracts of three teleost species. Some of the bands also contained carbohydrate.

3. Amphibian Egg Proteins

The dense yolk platelets account for 25 % of the weight of the egg (Fauré-Fremiet and de Streel, 1921) and contain 87 % protein, 5 % lipid, and 1.5 % phosphorus on a dry-weight basis (Gross and Gilbert, 1956). Panijel (1950) found some difference in the distribution of the phosphorus compounds in the large and small platelets, and the large platelets also contain more total phosphorus per milligram nitrogen. The significance of these differences is not clear, and the proteins of the two classes of platelets have apparently never been compared. Changes of at least a quantitative nature may occur in the composition of the platelets during their growth. The large platelets have been compared to the extraembryonic yolk of avian eggs (Denis, 1961), although there is as yet no chemical basis for this comparison.

Platelet proteins are similar to those of the granules of avian yolk in that they contain a high molecular weight lipoprotein and a much smaller phosphoprotein which appears to be chemically similar to phosvitin (Barth and Barth, 1954; Schjeide et al., 1955; Gross and Gilbert, 1956; Flickinger and Schjeide, 1957; Fuji, 1960; Ringle and Gross, 1962b; Wallace, 1963). The ability of the phosphoprotein to bind calcium is indicated by Flickinger and Schjeide (1957). The presence of carbohydrate in the outer granular part of the platelet is suggested by the PAS reagent (Yamada, 1961; Ringle and Gross, 1962a), but no chemical studies on platelet carbohydrates appear to exist.

The existence of water-soluble proteins as normal constituents of the platelet is still an unsettled question. It has been claimed that precipitation of the lipovitellin component from a saline extract of platelets upon dilution leaves a water-soluble fraction which resembles lipovitellin in immunological properties, lipid content, and sedimentation behavior (Schjeide et al., 1955; Flickinger and Rounds, 1956; Flickinger and Schjeide, 1957). Schjeide et al. (1955) found three livetin fractions by means of ultracentrifugation and observed that their relative proportions were variable. It would seem desirable to isolate the components and attempt their characterization by more rigorous methods. On the other hand, Nass (1956, 1962), Gross and Gilbert (1956), and Ringle and Gross (1962b) found no water-soluble material in fresh preparations. Dephosphorylation of the lipovitellin–phosvitin complex, by enzymatic or nonenzymatic means, is said to yield only water-soluble proteins (Flickinger, 1956; Nass, 1956, 1962) and the so-called livetin fraction may arise secondarily in this way by the adsorption of phosphoprotein phosphatase-rich granules to the yolk platelets during isolation procedures (Nass, 1962). Changes in the protein composition of the platelets owing to instability of the dissolved proteins and phosphatase activity may account for the contradictory accounts given by different authors (Nass, 1962), and possible proteolytic artifacts should be considered as well. In any case, it is clear that the livetin fraction of avian yolk is present in the fluid phase and is not comparable to the soluble proteins derived from the amphibian yolk platelets.

Alkaline-fast green, which is believed to indicate basic substances, stains the platelets of amphibian oocytes and blastomeres, but not their nuclei. After gastrulation the nuclei are stained, whereas the yolk platelets in the neural plate and later in the muscles are unstained. Horn (1962) has isolated a mixture of histone-like proteins from platelets, and Nace (1963) claims that platelets contain lysozyme and that Horn's preparation possesses lysozyme activity. Earlier, Taleporos (1959) found basic proteins in echinoderm eggs by means of alkaline-fast green staining and by acid extraction; evidence was given that in the egg the basic protein is cytoplasmic, later disappearing from the cytoplasm until in plutei the total "histone" content approximates to the nuclear histones. The situation bears an obvious resemblance to the distribution of DNA in early developmental stages, although no physical relationship has been proved so far. Further work on the purification of these proteins is needed, and it is not yet clear that the yolk platelet "histones" have any role in controlling the activity of genes, as Horn (1962) suggests.

The possible presence of enzymes in yolk platelets has attracted attention. Harris (1946) found that the phosphoprotein phosphatase activity of homogenates of amphibian eggs was distributed between the supernatant and yolk fractions, and Panijel (1950) reported a much higher activity in the small platelets than in the large ones. Barth and Barth (1954) found the enzyme activity in the pigment granules, whereas according to Flickinger (1956) it is water-soluble. Most recently, Nass (1962) considers the enzyme to be present in the pigment granule fraction and that "endogenous" platelet activity is caused by adsorption of pigment. Cathepsin and lysozyme have also been attributed to yolk platelets (Deuchar, 1958; Nace, 1962, 1963), but here, too, the possibility of contamination remains to be excluded.

Brown and Caston (1962c) found that centrifugation of a homogenate of the egg of R. pipiens yielded a pellet of ferritin which was immunologically and chemically similar to the ferritin of horse spleen. The quantity of ferritin was 0.4–1.0 μg per egg and decreased during development, disappearing by Shumway stage 25. The site of the origin of this iron reserve is not known. Very little has been done so far on the characterization of individual water-soluble proteins from amphibian eggs. Electrophoresis on paper and cellulose acetate membrane suggests a high level of complexity (Spiegel, 1960; Denis, 1961), and the immunological studies by Cooper (1946, 1948, 1950) show that there are at least five antigens common to the egg and to adult frog serum.

4. INVERTEBRATE EGG PROTEINS

Fuji (1960) showed that cuttlefish eggs contain a lipoprotein of very high molecular weight (19 % lipid, 0.7 % P) which is distinguished from the lipovitellins of vertebrates because it is soluble in water. The protein of the mitotic apparatus of dividing sea urchin eggs forms a large part (12 %) of the total protein of the cell, and the immunological studies by Went (1959a, b) and Went and Mazia (1959) show that this protein is not synthesized by the dividing cell but is present in the unfertilized egg in the form of a soluble precursor which appears to be related to the fibrous water-soluble protein which Kane and Hersh (1959) found in large amounts in unfertilized sea urchin eggs. This protein has a molecular weight of 350,000 and forms a gel in the presence of calcium. Nothing appears to be known about the formation and chemistry of this material at present.

Monroy (1950, 1957a, b) and D'Amelio (1955) found by electrophoresis that the proteins of sea urchin eggs undergo some changes at the time of fertilization, but their significance, and even their nature, is unknown. Possible quantitative changes in the glycoprotein fraction are indicated by Monroy (1960). Perlmann has made preliminary analyses of the antigens present in sea urchin eggs (Perlmann, 1957; Perlmann and Perlmann, 1957a,b; Perlmann and Kaltenbach, 1957; Perlmann et al., 1960; Kaltenbach and Perlmann, 1961). In the case of insect oocytes Telfer (1961) has isolated yolk spheres and demonstrated the presence of serum proteins within them.

5. Enzymes

In addition to the bulk of the storage proteins the egg contains enzymes which reflect its metabolic activities. They are for the most part concerned with general metabolism and are not characteristic of oocytes or eggs.

a. Energy Metabolism. Oocytes appear to contain normal pathways for glycolysis, the citric acid cycle, and respiration (Boell, 1955; Gonse, 1957). The utilization of glycogen appears to begin very early in amphibian eggs; Fitch and Merrick (1958) found that the glycogen content of ovarian eggs was 2.07 gm/100 gm, in agreement with earlier workers, but the content had fallen to 1.48 gm/100 gm in body cavity and uterine eggs.

Multiple forms of enzymes have recently been demonstrated in eggs. In sea urchin eggs Moore and Villee (1962) found at least ten different malic acid dehydrogenases: five oxidized L-malic acid and five oxidized D-malic acid. Goldberg and Cather (1963) demonstrated five lactic acid dehydrogenases (LDH) in the uncleaved egg of the snail *Argobuccinum*. Nace et al. (1961) combined immunoelectrophoresis with histochemical staining for lactic acid dehydrogenase and revealed four serologically distinct enzymes in amphibian oocytes. They also described an ingenious method for localization of the enzymes in the cell. Fluorescent antibody was recovered from the individual precipitin lines and allowed to react with tissue sections. One isozyme was found only in the cytoplasmic ground substance, whereas another was also bound to yolk platelets. It is, however, probably too soon to assume that this enzyme is a constituent of yolk platelets. A study of the distribution of the isozymes between isolated cell fractions should be used to confirm the histochemical localizations.

b. *Proteolytic Enzymes.* Protease and peptidase activity in eggs has been measured by many workers, although the question of substrate specificity has not received much attention (Duspiva, 1942; Berg, 1954; Emanuelsson, 1955; Ito, 1957; Collier, 1957; Deuchar, 1958; Lundblad and Runnström, 1962). The task of isolating and characterizing the individual enzymes has hardly begun. Their most likely roles are the liberation of amino acids from yolk proteins and later the removal of tissue in metamorphosing organisms.

c. *Phosphatases.* Many phosphatase activities have been demonstrated in eggs, e.g., glucose-6-phosphatase, acid and alkaline phosphatases in sea urchin eggs (Cousineau and Gross, 1960). Dalcq and Pasteels (1963) have surveyed the distribution of nucleoside triphosphatases in several invertebrate eggs. Osawa (1951) showed that the apparently intense localization of alkaline phosphatase in the nucleoli of amphibian oocytes (Krugelis, 1947) is a diffusion artifact. Only the follicle cells had genuinely high levels of activity and this may be connected with the absorption of materials by the follicle cells for subsequent transfer to the oocyte.

Phosphoprotein phosphatase has only been found in amphibian eggs so far, although its widespread distribution in mammalian tissues suggests that other eggs also will be found to contain it. Nass (1962) found that the phosphoprotein phosphatase activity of homogenates of amphibian eggs was principally associated with the pigmented residue which is insoluble in 0.5 M NaCl. A dramatic fall in the activity of this material occurred after fertilization. Nass (1962) used the apparent localization of the enzyme in the pigmented residue to revive the cortical field/yolk gradient concept of Dalcq and Pasteels (1937) with a more chemical slant. According to this picture phosphoprotein phosphatase activity is located in the cortex and attacks the yolk platelets causing release of materials which are necessary for neural induction; the interaction is supposed to occur first at the dorsal lip of the blastopore. It can be pointed out, however, that the evidence does not show that the enzyme is a component of pigment granules or that it is localized in the cortical or peripheral part of the egg.

6. Protein Synthesis

It may be noted first that the existence of abundant yolk protein is not in itself evidence of intense protein synthesis by those oocytes which have access to proteins synthesized by follicle cells or other tissues. In insects, in particular, the studies of Telfer (1960), Zalokar

(1960), and Bier (1962) suggest that the growth of the oocyte owes little to its own capacity for protein synthesis. There is still very little information on individual egg proteins and their synthesis during oogenesis. The occurrence of protein synthesis in oocytes is shown by amino acid-incorporation studies, and most of the materials thought to be involved in protein synthesis have been demonstrated in oocytes (for general reviews on protein synthesis see Campbell, 1960; McQuillen, 1962; Simpson, 1962; Watson, 1963): (a) *Ribosomes* have been observed by electron microscopy and have been isolated from homogenates of eggs. (b) *Transfer RNA* has been identified in isolated nucleoli of oocytes and is indicated in the cytoplasm by the autoradiographic studies of Ficq (1961b). (c) *Amino acid-activating enzymes* have been found in nucleoli (Brandt and Finamore, 1963) and in the mitochondria-free supernatant of eggs (Scarano and Maggio, 1957; Burr and Finamore, 1963). (d) *Messenger RNA* has not been demonstrated, although the data of Edström (1960) suggest the existence of a DNA-like RNA in oocyte nuclei. (e) The raw materials are represented by the pool of *free amino acids* (Deuchar, 1962 for a general review; Evans *et al.*, 1962).

In sea urchin oocytes protein synthesis appears to occur only in the growing, medium-sized oocytes and is slight or absent in very young or mature unfertilized eggs (Nakano and Monroy, 1958; Immers, 1959; Esper, 1962; Monroy and Vitorelli, 1962). Burr and Finamore (1963) have shown incorporation of amino acids into protein by a supernatant fraction of ovarian eggs in amphibia, but the oocytes were probably at various stages of growth. The incorporation of amino acids into protein is renewed shortly after fertilization (Nakano and Monroy, 1958; Monroy and Vitorelli, 1962). Hultin and Bergstrand (1960) and Hultin (1961) showed that amino acid incorporation into the ribosomes of unfertilized sea urchin eggs proceeds very slowly; after fertilization the rate is much higher. If messenger RNA, in the form of polyuridylic acid, is added to the egg homogenates the incorporation of amino acid (phenylalanine) into the ribosomes of both unfertilized and fertilized eggs is increased to the same final value (Wilt and Hultin, 1962). The renewed synthesis of protein which follows fertilization is not accompanied by a synthesis of ribosomes since, according to the data of Brown and Caston (1962b) on amphibia, ribosomes do not begin to increase until a relatively late stage of development. The data of Nemer and Bard (1963) also indicate the production of messenger RNA shortly after fertilization.

A possible role of mitochondria in protein synthesis is suggested by the finding that isolated mitochondria from sea urchin eggs and embryos can incorporate amino acids into protein (Giudice, 1960). Incorporation of S^{35}-methionine into mitochondrial proteins does not occur *in vivo* until about 4 hours after fertilization (Nakano and Monroy, 1958), which perhaps suggests that an extramitochondrial substance which inhibits protein synthesis by mitochondria is gradually destroyed after fertilization (Monroy, 1961).

Autoradiographic studies on protein synthesis by amphibian oocytes have been carried out by Ficq (1955a, 1961b), Brachet and Ficq (1956), Pantelouris (1958), and Kemp (1956c). Even in the very prolonged experiments of Kemp (1955, 1956c) in which incorporation of radioactive glycine was allowed to proceed for periods of 1 to 5 days, labeling was confined to the cytoplasmic matrix and was not apparently concentrated on the yolk platelets. Nucleolar labeling occurred at a later stage of growth than that of the cytoplasm but the suggestion by Pantelouris (1958) that protein travels from the cytoplasm to the nucleus during previtellogenesis and back to the cytoplasm during vitellogenesis has little to support it. It is difficult to draw precise conclusions from autoradiographic studies unless very short periods of labeling are used. With the very long periods used by Kemp (1956c) it is not even certain that the peripheral localization of label represented *in situ* synthesis despite the peripheral basophilia of the oocyte. Materials deposited in the oocyte from the blood stream will also be found in a peripheral position, as has been demonstrated on many occasions with avian oocytes [e.g., Halkett *et al.* (1958), on the uptake of iron].

IV. Growth of the Oocyte

A large amount of histological and histochemical data on the accumulation of protein, lipid, and carbohydrate reserves by oocytes is reviewed by Raven (1961). It is sometimes possible to distinguish a period of slow oocyte growth during which lipid and carbohydrate accumulate, followed by a period of rapid growth in which mainly protein is deposited. Grant (1953) has shown that the amphibian oocyte has an early growth phase in which lipid formation is rapid and a second period, coinciding with the onset of yolk formation, when phosphoprotein increases rapidly. On the other hand, Ando (1960) has shown that in the teleost *Oryzias* growth in volume of the oocyte begins 48 hours before spawning and that protein and glycogen contents rise in a parallel manner. The rate of increase falls off some hours before ovulation. The mechanisms of nucleic acid and protein synthesis by the oocyte itself have already been discussed, and in the present section we will outline the contributions of the maternal organism to the oocyte growth.

A. *Follicle Cell Activity in Oogenesis*

Histochemical and autoradiographic studies suggest that in arthropods follicle cells and trophocytes play a major part in supplying materials which they have synthesized to the oocyte. Hsu (1952) observed the passage of mitochondria into the oocyte in *Drosophila*. Bonhag (1955a,b, 1956, 1958) found that in insects lipid is transferred to the oocyte from follicle cells and trophocytes, and in *Anisolabis* glycogen appeared to be derived partly from trophocytes and partly from *in situ* synthesis. The protein-polysaccharide yolk spheres of *Anisolabis* and *Oncopeltus* arise in the periphery of the oocyte and the studies of Telfer (1954, 1958, 1961) show that in saturniid moths they consist entirely of proteins absorbed from the hemocoel.

The transfer of nucleic acids from accessory cells to oocyte is particularly striking in insects. The passage of DNA has already been described. In the ovary of the house fly and *Drosophila* the nuclei of the nurse cells show intense RNA synthesis (Sirlin and Jacob, 1960; Zalokar, 1960; Bier, 1963). The newly formed RNA enters the cytoplasm of the nurse cells and then crosses the fusomes into the oocyte. Radioactivity present in this RNA does not accumulate in the oocyte and it may, therefore, represent an unstable RNA. Later, when the nurse cells begin to degenerate, large amounts of RNA enter the oocyte which becomes increasingly basophilic (Bier, 1963). The oocyte nucleus in insects appears to be inactive, in marked contrast to the active synthesis of RNA by amphibian oocyte nuclei. Protein synthesis by accessory cells in insect ovaries is indicated by the rapid incorporation of leucine and histidine into cytoplasmic proteins (Zalokar, 1960; Bier, 1962). The autoradiographic study by Bier (1962) suggests that yolk proteins in *Calliphora* oocytes are synthesized in the follicle cells and transferred to the oocyte.

Histochemical evidence for follicle cell activity in crustaceans is much less clear and both glycogen and the protein-polysaccharide yolk appear to arise in the oocyte (Linder, 1959), although it must be said that staining reactions only show where substances are present above a certain minimum concentration and not where they are synthesized.

Much less has been done on the synthetic activities of follicle cells in other groups. Autoradiography indicates the occurrence of DNA synthesis and protein synthesis by follicle cells in amphibia (Ficq, 1961a), and Nace *et al.* (1961) have given immunological evidence of the synthesis of oocyte proteins by the follicle cells. In birds the follicle cells can synthesize fatty acids and cholesterol from added acetate, although the yolk itself has no detectable activity (Popják and Tietz, 1953). There is no evidence that these lipids enter the oocyte, and the isotopic studies of Hahn and Hevesy (1937) suggest that the phospholipids of the egg are taken up from the serum. Popják and Tietz (1953) also found that the follicle membranes have a large reserve of oxidizable substrates and continue to respire for many hours. During the period of rapid oocyte growth in birds a large number of substances can enter the oocyte from the blood (reviews by Schechtman, 1956; Clavert, 1953, 1958). Thus, trypan blue injected into the blood stream is absorbed by those follicle cells which are in contact with an oocyte in the phase of rapid growth, and is then transmitted to the oocyte. Clavert (1958) suggests that this localized follicle cell activity is the result of an increased local capillary permeability caused by hormones secreted by the follicle cells. It seems possible that the growth of the oocyte is regulated by follicle cell activity rather than by factors inside the oocyte itself. In many cases it seems to be quite artificial to separate the activities of the oocyte from those of the follicle cells and both are integrated into the whole of the maternal organism.

B. Transfer of Proteins from Serum to the Oocyte

1. INSECTS

Telfer (1954, 1960, 1961) has used immunological methods to show the transference of hemocoel proteins to the oocyte, passing between the follicle cells and being taken up by the brush-border of the oocyte. The large nurse cells play no part in the process. It was shown that all antigens present in the blood are also present in the yolk spheres but not in the cytoplasmic matrix of the oocyte. Some oocyte antigens, on the other hand, were not present in blood. Several foreign proteins also entered the oocyte from the hemocoel; only hen lipovitellenin out of seven proteins tried failed to do so. The concentration factors were widely different, suggesting the existence of a selective permeability mechanism. An antigen which occurred only in female blood ("female" protein) and a carotenoid–protein complex were concentrated the most, and Telfer (1960) suggests that the selective mechanism is designed mainly for these proteins, the others being accidental contaminants. The selectivity may involve a temporary combination between the surface of the oocyte and the protein (Telfer, 1960). It would be of great interest if this could be demonstrated in vitro. After forming beneath the microvillous surface of the oocyte the yolk spheres move deeper into the oocyte and increase in size. The mechanisms of this secondary growth have not been studied, although fusion of yolk spheres or the continued uptake of proteins from the cytoplasm (not necessarily serum proteins) have been suggested (Telfer, 1961).

2. Birds

The chemical similarity of egg yolk proteins and serum proteins might, in theory, be due to the synthesis of serum proteins by the oocyte, but the rate of growth of the oocyte during the 7 days which precede ovulation makes this an unlikely explanation of the accumulation of yolk proteins. Systemic changes in association with egg formation are discussed by Clavert (1958); the liver becomes heavier and blood levels of calcium, phosphorus, and lipid rise. The protein concentration of the blood rises and this particularly affects the phosphoproteins. These systemic changes can be induced in immature female birds and male birds by injections of gonadotropin or estrogen.

The ability of the growing oocyte to incorporate proteins from the blood is well known in the case of antibodies, and it has also been demonstrated for foreign proteins (Knight and Schechtman, 1954; Schechtman, 1956) and for labeled homologous serum proteins (Patterson, 1961). The absorption of serum proteins appears to be selective, since the relative proportions of the serum proteins in the yolk is different from those in serum; the livetin fraction contains relatively little albumin and more α_2-glycoprotein and γ-globulin (Shepard and Hottle, 1949; Williams, 1962a). Patterson (1961) found that γ-globulin of the hen is concentrated more than albumin by the oocyte. As was suggested in the case of insects, it may be considered that the mechanism of transfer is designed for the specific egg proteins (lipovitellin, phosvitin, and lipovitellenin) but is relatively inefficient in discarding the other serum proteins. Although it is generally assumed that the proteins are not changed in any major respects during their transfer to the oocyte, the data of Heald and McLachlan (1963) suggest some change in the physical state of the proteins (see also Schjeide and Urist, 1960).

3. Amphibia

Several authors have shown that some proteins present in the oocyte are also present in the blood stream. So far, only immunological methods have been used and not direct chemical comparisons (Cooper, 1946, 1948, 1950; Clayton, 1953; Flickinger and Rounds, 1956). Glass (1959) has used fluorescent antisera to locate adult serum proteins. Oocyte cytoplasm stained strongly in the period before yolk formation, and with the onset of yolk formation staining became restricted to peripheral clumps of material. Yolk platelets themselves were not stained until late stages, and it is not clear whether they ever actually contained serum-like antigens. Progressively increased staining of the follicle cells was observed throughout the period of yolk formation. A number of unanswered questions remain in connection with these studies: (a) Since antisera against whole adult serum was used, the presence or absence of any given protein cannot be inferred. It is, for instance, not clear whether antibodies to lipovitellin and phosvitin were present in the antisera. (b) It is surprising that fluorescent staining was most intense in the very early stages since it might be expected that transfer of serum proteins would be greatest during the deposition of yolk. (c) The fate of the serum proteins is not clear; since the intensity of staining does not increase throughout oogenesis, the protein must be presumed to either leak out of the oocyte or to be degraded in some way with loss of immunological identity.

4. MAMMALS

Using fluorescent antibodies Glass (1961) found homologous serum proteins in mouse oocytes at all stages of oogenesis, whereas bovine serum albumin injected into the female was found only in tertiary oocytes, follicle cells, and the follicular fluid. Rabbit globulin was not taken up at all by mouse oocytes. Similar results were obtained for the rat by Mancini et al. (1963) who used fluorescent serum proteins as well as fluorescent antibodies. Only growing oocytes took up proteins from the blood stream and the route lay between the follicle cells rather than through them. Maximum concentration of labeled protein in the oocyte was found 8 hours after administration and was followed by a decrease. Labeled protein was not released into the blood stream, which suggests that it was degraded inside the oocyte with loss of the fluorescent label. Serum proteins may thus contribute amino acids to the oocyte to be used in protein synthesis. The physiological significance of the process still has to be investigated.

V. Conclusion

From this brief account of some of the more recent work on the biochemistry of the egg, a number of general conclusions may be drawn. Although much more is known about the physiology of the egg than about the specific causes of morphogenesis and differentiation, it is clear that relatively little is known about the constitution of the egg in molecular terms. Thus, even for such regular formations as the yolk platelets of amphibian oocytes the precise arrangement of the constituent proteins and lipids is not known. It is clear, however, that the egg is structurally and metabolically complex. As Boell (1958) has already stressed, the metabolic apparatus of embryonic cells is at least as complex as that of mature cells, and Weber (1962) points out that such structures as mitochondria and endoplasmic reticulum are present in the egg and are not formed in the course of differentiation. Thus, cytodifferentiation is seen as involving the control and direction of pre-existing mechanisms to produce specific populations of molecules rather than the creation of the mechanisms themselves.

The nature of the control mechanisms remains unknown, however. Nothing is known about "organ-forming substances," and the "organ-forming areas" of mosaic eggs appear to be differentiated structurally only in the relative proportions of such common structures as mitochondria and endoplasmic reticulum. The effects of such variations on the synthesis of specific molecules is not known.

REFERENCES

Abraham, S., Hillyard, L. A., and Chaikoff, I. L. (1960). *Arch. Biochem. Biophys.* **89**, 74.

Afzelius, B. A. (1955). *Exptl. Cell Res.* **8**, 147.

Afzelius, B. A. (1956a). *Exptl. Cell Res.* **10**, 257.

Afzelius, B. A. (1956b). *Exptl. Cell Res.* **11**, 67.

Afzelius, B. A. (1957). *Z. Zellforsch. Mikroskop. Anat.* **45**, 660.

Afzelius, B. A. (1962). *In* "The Interpretation of Ultrastructure," I.S.C.B. Symp., Vol. 1 (R. J. C. Harris, ed.), p. 1. Academic Press, New York.

Agrell, I., and Persson, H. (1956). *Nature* **178**, 1398.

Aketa, K. (1954). *Embryologia* (*Nagoya*) **2**, 63.

Aketa, K. (1963). *Exptl. Cell Res.* **30**, 93.

Alfert, M. (1950). *J. Cellular Comp. Physiol.* **36**, 381.

Allen, R. D. (1958). *In* "The Chemical Basis of Development" (W. D. McElroy and B. Glass, eds.), p. 17. Johns Hopkins Press, Baltimore, Maryland.

Allgen, L. G., and Norberg, B. (1959). *Biochim. Biophys. Acta* **32**, 514.

Allison, W. D., and Clarke, E. E. (1960). *Biol. Bull.* **119**, 302.

Ancel, P., and Vintemberger, P. (1948). *Bull. Biol. Suppl.* **31**, 1.

Anderson, E., and Beams, H. W. (1960). *J. Ultrastruct. Res.* **3**, 432.

Ando, S. (1960). *Embryologia* (*Nagoya*) **5**, 239.

André, J., and Rouiller, C. (1957). *J. Biophys. Biochem. Cytol.* **3**, 977.

Arndt, E. A. (1960). *Z. Zellforsch. Mikroskop. Anat.* **52**, 315.

Austin, C. R. (1956). *Exptl. Cell Res.* **10**, 533.

Austin, C. R. (1961). "The Mammalian Egg." Blackwell, Oxford, England.

Baker, C. M. A., and Manwell, C. (1962). *Brit. Poultry Sci.* **3**, 161.

Baltus, E., and Brachet, J. (1962). *Biochim. Biophys. Acta* **61**, 157.

Barry, R. D., Ives, D. R., and Cruickshank, J. G. (1962). *Nature* **194**, 1139.

Barth, L. G., and Barth, L. J. (1954). "The Energetics of Development." Columbia Univ. Press, New York.

Battin, W. T. (1959). *Exptl. Cell Res.* **17**, 59.

Beams, H. W., and Kessel, R. (1962). *J. Cell Biol.* **13**, 158.

Bellairs, R. (1961). *J. Biophys. Biochem. Cytol.* **11**, 207.

Bellairs, R., Harkness, M., and Harkness, R. D. (1963). *J. Ultrastruct. Res.* **8**, 339.

Berg, W. E. (1954). *Proc. Soc. Exptl. Biol. Med.* **85**, 606.

Berg, W. E. (1956). *Biol. Bull.* **110**, 1.

Berg, W. E. (1957). *Biol. Bull.* **113**, 365.
Berg, W. E., and Humphreys, W. J. (1960). *Develop. Biol.* **2**, 42.
Berg, W. E., and Kutsky, P. B. (1951). *Biol. Bull.* **101**, 47.
Bernardi, G., and Cook, W. H. (1960). *Biochim. Biophys. Acta* **44**, 96.
Bianchi, P. A. (1962). *Biochim. Biophys. Acta* **55**, 547.
Bieber, S., Spence, J. A., and Hitchings, G. H. (1959). *Exptl. Cell Res.* **16**, 202.
Bier, K. (1962). *Naturwissenschaften* **49**, 332.
Bier, K. (1963). *J. Cell Biol.* **16**, 436.
Blanchette, E. J. (1961). *J. Ultrastruct. Res.* **5**, 349.
Boell, E. J. (1955). In "Analysis of Development" (B. H. Willier, P. A. Weiss, and V. Hamburger, eds.), p. 520. Saunders, Philadelphia, Pennsylvania.
Boell, E. J. (1958). In "Embryonic Nutrition" (D. Rudnick, ed.), p. 1. Univ. Chicago Press, Chicago, Illinois.
Boell, E. J., and Weber, R. (1955). *Exptl. Cell Res.* **9**, 559.
Bonhag, P. F. (1955a). *J. Morphol.* **96**, 381.
Bonhag, P. F. (1955b). *J. Morphol.* **97**, 283.
Bonhag, P. F. (1956). *J. Morphol.* **99**, 433.
Bonhag, P. F. (1958). *Ann. Rev. Entomol.* **3**, 137.
Brachet, J. (1950). "Chemical Embryology." Wiley (Interscience), New York.
Brachet, J. (1954). *Arch. Biol. (Liege)* **65**, 1.
Brachet, J. (1957). "Biochemical Cytology." Academic Press, New York.
Brachet, J. (1960). "The Biochemistry of Development." Pergamon, New York.
Brachet, J. (1962). *J. Cellular Comp. Physiol.* **60** (Suppl. 1), 1.
Brachet, J., and Ficq, A. (1956). *Arch. Biol. (Liege)* **67**, 431.
Brachet, J., and Jeener, R. (1944). *Enzymologia* **11**, 196.
Brandt, E. E., and Finamore, F. J. (1963). *Biochim. Biophys. Acta* **68**, 618.
Brown, C. A., and Ris, H. (1959). *J. Morphol.* **104**, 377.
Brown, D. D., and Caston, J. D. (1962a). *Develop. Biol.* **5**, 412.
Brown, D. D., and Caston, J. D. (1962b). *Develop. Biol.* **5**, 435.
Brown, D. D., and Caston, J. D. (1962c). *Develop. Biol.* **5**, 445.
Burgos, M. H. (1955). *Exptl. Cell Res.* **9**, 360.
Burley, R. W., and Cook, W. H. (1961). *Can. J. Biochem. Physiol.* **39**, 1295.
Burr, M. J., and Finamore, F. J. (1963). *Biochim. Biophys. Acta* **68**, 608.
Callan, H. G. (1952). *Symp. Soc. Exptl. Biol.* **6**, 243.
Callan, H. G., and Lloyd, L. (1960). *Phil. Trans. Roy. Soc. London* **B243**, 135.
Callan, H. G., and Macgregor, H. C. (1958). *Nature* **181**, 1479.
Callan, H. G., and Tomlin, S. G. (1950). *Proc. Roy. Soc.* **B137**, 367.
Campbell, P. N. (1960). *Biol. Rev. Cambridge Phil. Soc.* **35**, 413.
Chang, M. C., and Hunt, D. M. (1956). *Exptl. Cell Res.* **11**, 497.
Chèvremont, M. (1963). In "Cell Growth and Cell Division," I.S.C.B. Symp., Vol. 2 (R. J. C. Harris, ed.), p. 323. Academic Press, New York.
Clavert, J. (1953). *Arch. Neerl. Zool.* **10** (Suppl. 1), 1.
Clavert, J. (1958). *Arch. Anat. Microscop. Morphol. Exptl.* **47**, 653.
Clayton, R. M. (1953). *J. Embryol. Exptl. Morphol.* **1**, 25.
Cleland, K. W. (1951). *Australian J. Exptl. Biol. Med. Sci.* **29**, 35.
Collier, J. R. (1957). *Exptl. Cell Res.* **13**, 122.
Collier, J. R. (1960). *Exptl. Cell Res.* **21**, 126.
Collier, J. R., and McCann-Collier, M. (1962). *Exptl. Cell Res.* **27**, 553.

Conklin, E. G. (1931). *J. Exptl. Zool.* **60**, 1.
Connelly, C., and Taborsky, G. (1961). *J. Biol. Chem.* **236**, 1364.
Cook, W. H. (1961). *Nature* **190**, 1173.
Cook, W. H., and Martin, W. G. (1962). *Can. J. Biochem. Physiol.* **40**, 1273.
Cook, W. H., Burley, R. W., Martin, W. G., and Hopkins, J. W. (1962). *Biochim. Biophys. Acta* **60**, 98.
Cooper, R. S. (1946). *J. Exptl. Zool.* **101**, 143.
Cooper, R. S. (1948). *J. Exptl. Zool.* **107**, 397.
Cooper, R. S. (1950). *J. Exptl. Zool.* **114**, 403.
Costello, D. P. (1948). *Ann. N. Y. Acad. Sci.* **49**, 663.
Costello, D. P. (1955). *In* "Analysis of Development" (B. H. Willier, P. A. Weiss, and V. Hamburger, eds.), p. 213. Saunders, Philadelphia, Pennsylvania.
Cousineau, G., and Gross, P. R. (1960). *Biol. Bull.* **119**, 292.
Cowden, R. R. (1962). *Exptl. Cell Res.* **28**, 600.
Dalcq, A. M. (1938). "Form and Causality in Early Development." Cambridge Univ. Press, London and New York.
Dalcq, A. M. (1957). "Introduction to General Embryology." Oxford Univ. Press, London and New York.
Dalcq, A. M. (1960). *Arch. Biol. (Liege)* **71**, 93.
Dalcq, A. M., and Pasteels, J. (1937). *Arch. Biol. (Liege)* **48**, 669.
Dalcq, A. M., and Pasteels, J. (1963). *Develop. Biol.* **7**, 457.
Dalton, A. J. (1961). *In* "The Cell" (J. Brachet and A. E. Mirsky, eds.), Vol. II, p. 603. Academic Press, New York.
D'Amelio, V. (1955). *Experientia* **11**, 443.
Deane, H. W., and Porter, K. R. (1960). *Z. Zellforsch. Mikroskop. Anat.* **52**, 697.
Denis, H. (1961). *J. Embryol. Exptl. Morphol.* **9**, 422.
Deuchar, E. M. (1958). *J. Embryol. Exptl. Morphol.* **6**, 223.
Deuchar, E. M. (1962). *Biol. Rev. Cambridge Phil. Soc.* **37**, 378.
Durand, M. (1958). *Exptl. Cell Res.* **15**, 257.
Durand, M. (1961). *Bull. Biol.* **95**, 28.
Duryee, W. R. (1954). *Trans. N. Y. Acad. Sci.* [2] **17**, 103.
Duspiva, F. (1942). *Biol. Zentr.* **62**, 403.
Edström, J. E. (1960). *J. Biophys. Biochem. Cytol.* **8**, 47.
Edström, J. E., Grampp, W., and Schor, N. (1961). *J. Biophys. Biochem. Cytol.* **11**, 549.
Elbers, P. F. (1957). *Koninkl. Ned. Akad. Wetenschap. Proc. Ser. C.* **60**, 96.
Elson, D., and Chargaff, E. (1952). *Experientia* **8**, 143.
Elson, D., Gustafson, T., and Chargaff, E. (1954). *J. Biol. Chem.* **209**, 285.
Emanuelsson, H. (1955). *Acta Physiol. Scand.* **34**, 124.
England, M. C., and Mayer, D. T. (1957). *Exptl. Cell Res.* **12**, 249.
Enselme, J., Creyssel, R., and Parraud, S. (1951). *Bull. Soc. Chim. Biol.* **33**, 1016.
Ernster, L., Siekevitz, P., and Palade, G. E. (1962). *J. Cell Biol.* **15**, 541.
Esper, H. (1962). *Biol. Bull.* **123**, 475, 476.
Evans, T., Monroy, A., and Senft, A. (1962). *Biol. Bull.* **123**, 476.
Fauré-Fremiet, E., and de Streel, V. du V. (1921). *Bull. Soc. Chim. Biol.* **3**, 476.
Fautrez, J., and Fautrez-Firlefyn, N. (1961). *J. Embryol. Exptl. Morphol.* **9**, 60.
Favard, P., and Carasso, N. (1958). *Arch. Anat. Microscop. Morphol. Exptl.* **47**, 211.
Favard-Séréno, C., and Durand, M. (1963a). *Develop. Biol.* **6**, 184.

Favard-Séréno, C., and Durand, M. (1963b). *Develop. Biol.* **6**, 206.
Feldherr, C. M. (1962). *J. Cell Biol.* **14**, 65.
Fevold, H. L. (1951). *Advan. Protein Chem.* **6**, 187.
Ficq, A. (1955a). *Exptl. Cell Res.* **9**, 286.
Ficq, A. (1955b). *Arch. Biol.* (*Liege*) **66**, 509.
Ficq, A. (1961a). *In* "Symposium on Germ Cells and Earliest Stages of Development," p. 121. Ist. Lombardo, Fondazione A. Baselli, Milan.
Ficq, A. (1961b). *Exptl. Cell Res.* **23**, 427.
Ficq, A., Ajello, F., and Scarano, E. (1963). *Exptl. Cell Res.* **29**, 128.
Filosa, M. (1960). *Biol. Bull.* **119**, 313.
Finamore, F. J. (1961). *Quart. Rev. Biol.* **36**, 117.
Finamore, F. J., and Crouse, G. T. (1958). *Exptl. Cell Res.* **14**, 160.
Finamore, F. J., and Volkin, E. (1958). *Exptl. Cell Res.* **15**, 405.
Finamore, F. J., and Volkin, E. (1961). *J. Biol. Chem.* **238**, 443.
Finamore, F. J., Thomas, D. J., Crouse, G. T., and Lloyd, B. (1960). *Arch. Biochem. Biophys.* **88**, 10.
Fitch, K. L., and Merrick, A. W. (1958). *Exptl. Cell Res.* **14**, 644.
Flickinger, R. A. (1956). *J. Exptl. Zool.* **131**, 307.
Flickinger, R. A. (1961). *In* "Symposium on Germ Cells and Earliest Stages of Development," p. 29. Ist. Lombardo, Fondazione A. Baselli, Milan.
Flickinger, R. A., and Rounds, D. E. (1956). *Biochim. Biophys. Acta* **22**, 38.
Flickinger, R. A., and Schjeide, O. A. (1957). *Exptl. Cell Res.* **13**, 312.
Franchi, L. L. (1960). *J. Biophys. Biochem. Cytol.* **7**, 397.
Franklin, R. M., and Baltimore, D. (1962). *Cold Spring Harbor Symp. Quant. Biol.* **27**, 175.
Fuji, T. (1960). *Acta Embryol. Morphol. Exptl.* **3**, 260.
Gall, J. G. (1954). *Exptl. Cell Res.* **7**, 197.
Gall, J. G. (1958). *In* "The Chemical Basis of Development" (W. D. McElroy and B. Glass, eds.), p. 103. Johns Hopkins Press, Baltimore, Maryland.
Gall, J. G., and Callan, H. G. (1962). *Proc. Natl. Acad. Sci. U. S.* **48**, 562.
Gallera, J., and Baud, C. A. (1954). *J. Embryol. Exptl. Morphol.* **2**, 106.
Giudice, G. (1960). *Exptl. Cell Res.* **21**, 222.
Glass, L. E. (1959). *J. Exptl. Zool.* **141**, 257.
Glass, L. E. (1961). *Develop. Biol.* **3**, 787.
Goldberg, E., and Cather, J. N. (1963). *J. Cellular Comp. Physiol.* **61**, 31.
Gonse, P. (1957). *Biochim. Biophys. Acta* **24**, 267.
Grant, P. (1953). *J. Exptl. Zool.* **124**, 513.
Grant, P. (1958). *J. Cellular Comp. Physiol.* **52**, 229.
Gregg, J. R., and Løvtrup, S. (1955). *Biol. Bull.* **108**, 29.
Grodzinski, Z. (1938). *Bull. Acad. Polon. Sci. Classe II*, p. 317.
Grodzinski, Z. (1946). *Bull. Acad. Polon. Sci. Classe II*, p. 169.
Grodzinski, Z. (1951). *Biol. Rev. Cambridge Phil. Soc.* **26**, 253.
Gross, P. R., and Gilbert, L. I. (1956). *Trans. N.Y. Acad. Sci.* [2] **19**, 108.
Gross, P. R., Philpott, D. E., and Nass, S. (1960). *J. Biophys. Biochem. Cytol.* **7**, 135.
Hahn, L., and Hevesy, G. (1937). *Nature* **140**, 1059.
Hale, A. J. (1957). *Intern. Rev. Cytol.* **6**, 193.
Halkett, J. A. E., Peters, T., and Ross, J. F. (1958). *J. Biol. Chem.* **231**, 187.

Harding, C. V., and Feldherr, C. (1958). *Nature* **182**, 676.

Harris, D. L. (1946). *J. Biol. Chem.* **165**, 541.

Harrison, R. G. (1945). *Trans. Conn. Acad. Arts Sci.* **36**, 277.

Harvey, E. B. (1953). *J. Histochem. Cytochem.* **1**, 265.

Hawke, J. C., and Lea, C. H. (1953). *Biochem. J.* **54**, 479.

Heald, P. J., and McLachlan, P. M. (1933). *Biochem. J.* **87**, 571.

Heilbrunn, L. V. (1952). "An Outline of General Physiology," 3rd ed. Saunders, Philadelphia, Pennsylvania.

Hindley, J. (1963). *Biochem. Biophys. Res. Commun.* **12**, 175.

Hiramoto, Y. (1957). *Embryologia (Nagoya)* **3**, 361.

Hoff-Jørgensen, E. (1952). *Biochem. J.* **50**, 400.

Hoff-Jørgensen, E. (1954). *In* "Recent Developments in Cell Physiology" (J. A. Kitching, ed.), p. 79. Academic Press, New York.

Hoff-Jørgensen, E., and Zeuthen, E. (1952). *Nature* **169**, 245.

Holtfreter, J. (1946a). *J. Exptl. Zool.* **101**, 355.

Holtfreter, J. (1946b). *J. Exptl. Zool.* **102**, 51.

Holtfreter, J. (1946c). *J. Exptl. Zool.* **103**, 81.

Horn, E. C. (1962). *Proc. Natl. Acad. Sci. U. S.* **48**, 257.

Hsu, W. S. (1952). *Quart. J. Microscop. Sci.* **93**, 191.

Huang, R. C., and Bonner, J. (1962). *Proc. Natl. Acad. Sci. U. S.* **48**, 1216.

Hultin, T. (1961). *Exptl. Cell Res.* **25**, 405.

Hultin, T., and Bergstrand, A. (1960). *Develop. Biol.* **2**, 61.

Humphreys, W. J. (1962a). *J. Ultrastruct. Res.* **7**, 467.

Humphreys, W. J. (1962b). *In* "Proceedings of the Fifth International Congress for Electron Microscopy" (S. S. Breese, ed.), Vol. 2, NN-10. Academic Press, New York.

Immers, J. (1959). *Exptl. Cell Res.* **18**, 585.

Immers, J. (1960). *Exptl. Cell Res.* **19**, 499.

Immers, J. (1961). *Exptl. Cell Res.* **24**, 356.

Ito, Y. (1957). *Acta Embryol. Morphol. Exptl.* **1**, 118.

Izawa, M., Allfrey, V. G., and Mirsky, A. E. (1963). *Proc. Natl. Acad. Sci. U. S.* **49**, 544.

Jacob, F., and Monod, J. (1961). *J. Mol. Biol.* **3**, 318.

Jones-Seaton, A. (1950). *Arch. Biol. (Liege)* **61**, 291.

Joubert, F. J., and Cook, W. H. (1958). *Can. J. Biochem. Physiol.* **36**, 399.

Jukes, T. H., and Kay, H. D. (1932). *J. Exptl. Med.* **56**, 469.

Kaltenbach, J. C., and Perlmann, P. (1961). *J. Biophys. Biochem. Cytol.* **9**, 93.

Kane, R. E., and Hersh, R. T. (1959). *Exptl. Cell Res.* **16**, 59.

Karasaki, S. (1959). *Embryologia (Nagoya)* **4**, 247.

Karasaki, S. (1962). *In* "Proceedings of the Fifth International Congress for Electron Microscopy" (S. S. Breese, ed.), Vol. 2, T-7. Academic Press, New York.

Karasaki, S., and Komoda, T. (1958). *Nature* **181**, 407.

Kemp, N. E. (1955). *Science* **121**, 471.

Kemp, N. E. (1956a). *J. Biophys. Biochem. Cytol.* **2** (Suppl.), 187.

Kemp, N. E. (1956b). *J. Biophys. Biochem. Cytol.* **2**, 281.

Kemp, N. E. (1956c). *J. Exptl. Zool.* **133**, 227.

Kessel, R. G., and Kemp, N. E. (1962). *J. Ultrastruct. Res.* **6**, 57.

Knight, P. F., and Schechtman, A. M. (1954). *J. Exptl. Zool.* **127**, 271.

Kojima, M. K. (1959a). *Embryologia* (*Nagoya*) **4**, 191.

Kojima, M. K. (1959b). *Embryologia* (*Nagoya*) **4**, 211.

Kornberg, A. (1961). "Enzymatic Synthesis of DNA." Wiley, New York.

Korschelt, E., and Heider, K. (1936). "Vergleichende Entwicklungsgeschichte der Tiere." Fischer, Jena.

Krugelis, E. J. (1947). *Biol. Bull.* **93**, 215.

Kuriki, Y., and Okasaki, R. (1959). *Embryologia* (*Nagoya*) **4**, 337.

Kusa, M. (1956). *Embryologia* (*Nagoya*) **3**, 105.

Lansing, A. I., Hillier, J., and Rosenthal, T. B. (1952). *Biol. Bull.* **103**, 294.

Lanzavecchia, G. (1961). *In* "Symposium on Germ Cells and Earliest Stages of Development," p. 61. Ist. Lombardo, Fondazione A. Baselli, Milan.

Lanzavecchia, G. (1962). *In* "Proceedings of the Fifth International Congress for Electron Microscopy" (S. S. Breese, ed.), Vol. 2, WW-13. Academic Press, New York.

Lanzavecchia, G., and Le Coultre, A. (1958). *Arch. Ital. Anat. Embriol.* **63**, 445.

Laskowski, M. (1935). *Biochem. Z.* **278**, 345.

Lehmann, F. E. (1956). *Naturwissenschaften* **43**, 289.

Levenbook, L., Travaglini, E. C., and Schultz, J. (1958). *Exptl. Cell Res.* **15**, 43.

Liebermann, L. (1888). *Arch. Pflüger's Ges. Physiol.* **43**, 17.

Lima-da-Faria, A. (1962). *Progr. Biophys. Biophys. Chem.* **12**, 281.

Linder, H. (1959). *J. Morphol.* **104**, 1.

Løvtrup, S. (1959). *J. Exptl. Zool.* **141**, 545.

Lundblad, G., and Runnström, J. (1962). *Exptl. Cell Res.* **27**, 328.

Lush, I. (1961). *Nature* **189**, 981.

McCabe, R. A., and Deutsch, H. F. (1952). *Auk* **69**, 1.

McIndoe, W. M. (1959). *Biochem. J.* **72**, 153.

McNally, E. H. (1943). *Poultry Sci.* **22**, 40.

McQuillen, K. (1962). *Progr. Biophys. Biophys. Chem.* **12**, 67.

Maggio, R. (1959). *Exptl. Cell Res.* **16**, 272.

Maggio, R., and Ghiretti-Magaldi, A. (1958). *Exptl. Cell Res.* **15**, 95.

Maggio, R., and Monroy, A. (1959). *Nature* **184**, 68.

Maggio, R., Aiello, F., and Monroy, A. (1960). *Nature* **188**, 1195.

Malkin, H. M. (1954). *J. Cellular Comp. Physiol.* **44**, 105.

Mancini, R. E., Vilar, O., Heinrich, J. J., Davidson, O. W., and Alvarez, B. (1963). *J. Histochem. Cytochem.* **11**, 80.

Marshak, A. (1957). *Exptl. Cell Res.* **12**, 599.

Marshak, A., and Marshak, C. (1955a). *Exptl. Cell Res.* **8**, 126.

Marshak, A., and Marshak, C. (1955b). *Exptl. Cell Res.* **10**, 246.

Mecham, D. K., and Olcott, H. S. (1949). *J. Am. Chem. Soc.* **71**, 3670.

Mercer, E. H., and Wolpert, L. (1962). *Exptl. Cell Res.* **27**, 1.

Merriam, R. W. (1959). *J. Biophys. Biochem. Cytol.* **5**, 117.

Merriam, R. W. (1961). *J. Biophys. Biochem. Cytol.* **11**, 559.

Meyer, G. (1961). *Z. Zellforsch. Mikroskop. Anat.* **54**, 238.

Miller, O. L. (1962). *In* "Proceedings of the Fifth International Congress for Electron Microscopy" (S. S. Breese, ed.), Vol. 2, NN-8. Academic Press, New York.

Mintz, B. (1962). *Science* **138**, 594.

Mitchison, J. M. (1956). *Quart. J. Microscop. Sci.* **97**, 109.

Mok, C-C., Martin, W. G., and Common, R. H. (1961). *Can. J. Biochem. Biophys.* **39**, 109.

Monné, L., and Harde, S. (1951). *Arkiv Zool.* [2] **1**, 487.

Monroy, A. (1950). *Exptl. Cell Res.* **1**, 92.

Monroy, A. (1957a). *In* "The Beginnings of Embryonic Development" (A. Tyler, R. C. von Borstel, and C. B. Metz, eds.), p. 169. Am. Assoc. Advan. Sci., Washington, D. C.

Monroy, A. (1957b). *Intern. Rev. Cytol.* **6**, 107.

Monroy, A. (1957c). *J. Cellular Comp. Physiol.* **50**, 73.

Monroy, A. (1960). *Experientia* **16**, 56.

Monroy, A. (1961). *In* "Symposium on Germ Cells and Earliest Stages of Development," p. 202. Ist. Lombardo, Fondazione A. Baselli, Milan.

Monroy, A., and Vittorelli, M. L. (1962). *J. Cellular Comp. Physiol.* **60**, 285.

Moore, J. A. (1962). *J. Cellular Comp. Physiol.* **60** (Suppl. 1), 19.

Moore, R. O., and Villee, C. A. (1962). *Science* **138**, 508.

Moran, T., and Hale, H. P. (1936). *J. Exptl. Biol.* **13**, 35.

Morgenthaler, H. U. (1951). *Rev. Suisse Zool.* **58**, 571.

Mulnard, J. (1958). *Arch. Biol. (Liege)* **69**, 645.

Nace, G. W. (1953). *J. Exptl. Zool.* **122**, 423.

Nace, G. W. (1962). *J. Cellular Comp. Physiol.* **60** (Suppl. 1), 61.

Nace, G. W. (1963). *Develop. Biol.* **7**, 280.

Nace, G. W., Suyama, T., and Smith, N. (1961). *In* "Symposium on Germ Cells and Earliest Stages of Development," p. 564. Ist. Lombardo, Fondazione A. Baselli, Milan.

Nakano, E., and Monroy, A. (1958). *Exptl. Cell Res.* **14**, 236.

Nass, S. (1956). *Trans. N. Y. Acad. Sci.* [2] **19**, 118.

Nass, S. (1962). *Biol. Bull.* **122**, 232.

Needham, J. (1942). "Biochemistry and Morphogenesis." Cambridge Univ. Press, London and New York.

Nemer, M., and Bard, S. G. (1963). *Science* **140**, 664.

Nichols, A. V., Rubin, L., and Lindgren, F. T. (1954). *Proc. Soc. Exptl. Biol. Med.* **85**, 352.

Nigon, V., and Bovet, P. (1955). *Compt. Rend. Soc. Biol.* **149**, 129.

Nigon, V., and Daillie, J. (1958). *Biochim. Biophys. Acta* **29**, 247.

Nigon, V., and Nonnenmacher, J. (1960a). *Compt. Rend.* **251**, 1427.

Nigon, V., and Nonnenmacher, J. (1960b). *Compt. Rend.* **251**, 1583.

Nigon, V., and Nonnenmacher, J. (1961). *Develop. Biol.* **3**, 210.

Novikoff, A. B. (1960). *In* "Developing Cell Systems and their Control" (D. Rudnick, ed.), p. 167. Ronald, New York.

Novikoff, A. B., Drucker, J., Shin, W.-Y., and Goldfischer, S. (1961). *J. Histochem. Cytochem.* **9**, 434.

Ohi, Y. (1962). *Embryologia (Nagoya)* **7**, 208.

Osawa, S. (1951). *Embryologia (Nagoya)* **2**, 1.

Osawa, S., and Hayashi, Y. (1953). *Science* **118**, 94.

Palade, G. E. (1958). *In* "Microsomal Particles and Protein Synthesis" (R. B. Roberts, ed.), p. 36. Pergamon, New York.

Panijel, J. (1950). *Biochim. Biophys. Acta* **5**, 343.

Pantelouris, E. M. (1958). *Exptl. Cell Res.* **14**, 584.

Pasteels, J. (1953). *Bull. Soc. Zool. France* **76**, 231.

Pasteels, J. (1958a). *In* "The Chemical Basis of Development" (W. D. McElroy and B. Glass, eds.), p. 381. Johns Hopkins Press, Baltimore, Maryland.

Pasteels, J. (1958b). *Arch. Biol.* (*Liege*) **69**, 591.

Pasteels, J., and Lison, L. (1951). *Nature* **167**, 948.

Pasteels, J., and Mulnard, J. (1957). *Arch. Biol.* (*Liege*) **68**, 115.

Pasteels, J., Castiaux, P., and Vandermeersche, G. (1958a). *J. Biophys. Biochem. Cytol.* **4**, 575.

Pasteels, J., Castiaux, P., and Vandermeersche, G. (1958b). *Arch. Biol.* (*Liege*) **69**, 627.

Patterson, R. (1961). *Federation Proc.* **20**, 379.

Paul, J., and Struthers, M. G. (1963). *Biochem. Biophys. Res. Commun.* **11**, 135.

Perlmann, P. (1957). *Exptl. Cell Res.* **13**, 365.

Perlmann, P., and Kaltenbach, J. C. (1957). *Exptl. Cell Res.* **12**, 185.

Perlmann, P., and Perlmann, H. (1957a). *Exptl. Cell Res.* **13**, 454.

Perlmann, P., and Perlmann, H. (1957b). *Exptl. Cell Res.* **13**, 475.

Perlmann, P., Boström, H., and Vestermark, A. (1959). *Exptl. Cell Res.* **17**, 439.

Perlmann, P., Kaltenbach, J. C., and Perlmann, H. (1960). *J. Immunol.* **85**, 284.

Petrucci, D. (1960). *Acta Embryol. Morphol. Exptl.* **3**, 237.

Plimmer, R. H. A. (1908). *J. Chem. Soc.* **93**, 1500.

Popják, G., and Tietz, A. (1953). *Biochem. J.* **54**, xxxv.

Porter, K. R. (1961). *In* "The Cell" (J. Brachet and A. E. Mirsky, eds.), Vol. II, p. 621. Academic Press, New York.

Prescott, D. M., Bollum, F. J., and Kluss, B. C. (1962). *J. Cell Biol.* **13**, 172.

Press, N. (1959). *Exptl. Cell Res.* **18**, 194.

Raven, C. P. (1958). "Morphogenesis: The Analysis of Molluscan Development." Pergamon, New York.

Raven, C. P. (1961). "Oogenesis: The Storage of Developmental Information." Pergamon, New York.

Raven, C. P. (1963). *Develop. Biol.* **7**, 130.

Rebhun, L. I. (1956a). *J. Biophys. Biochem. Cytol.* **2**, 93.

Rebhun, L. I. (1956b). *J. Biophys. Biochem. Cytol.* **2**, 159.

Rebhun, L. I. (1961). *J. Ultrastruct. Res.* **5**, 208.

Rebhun, L. I. (1962). *J. Ultrastruct. Res.* **6**, 107.

Recknagel, J. O. (1950). *J. Cellular Comp. Physiol.* **35**, 111.

Reverberi, G. (1958). *Acta Embryol. Morphol. Exptl.* **2**, 79.

Ries, E. (1937). *Pubbl. Staz. Zool. Napoli* **16**, 363.

Ringle, D. A., and Gross, P. R. (1962a). *Biol. Bull.* **122**, 263.

Ringle, D. A., and Gross, P. R. (1962b). *Biol. Bull.* **122**, 281.

Roepke, R. R., and Bushnell, L. D. (1936). *J. Immunol.* **30**, 109.

Romanoff, A. L. (1931). *Biochem. J.* **25**, 994.

Rounds, D. E., and Flickinger, R. A. (1958). *J. Exptl. Zool.* **137**, 479.

Scarano, E. (1958). *Biochim. Biophys. Acta* **29**, 459.

Scarano, E. (1960). *J. Biol. Chem.* **235**, 706.

Scarano, E. (1961). *In* "Symposium on Germ Cells and Earliest Stages of Development," p. 402. Ist. Lombardo, Fondazione A. Baselli, Milan.

Scarano, E., and Maggio, R. (1957). *Exptl. Cell Res.* **12**, 403.

Scarano, E., and Maggio, R. (1959). *Exptl. Cell Res.* **18**, 333.

Scarano, E., Bonaduce, L., and de Petrocellis, B. (1960). *J. Biol. Chem.* **235**, 3556.
Scarano, E., Bonaduce, L., and de Petrocellis, B. (1962). *J. Biol. Chem.* **237**, 3742.
Schechtman, A. M. (1956). *Intern. Rev. Cytol.* **5**, 303.
Schjeide, O. A., and Urist, M. R. (1959). *Exptl. Cell Res.* **17**, 84.
Schjeide, O. A., and Urist, M. R. (1960). *Nature* **188**, 291.
Schjeide, O. A., Levi, E., and Flickinger, R. A. (1955). *Growth* **19**, 297.
Schmidt, G., Hecht, L., and Thannhauser, S. J. (1948). *J. Gen. Physiol.* **31**, 203.
Schmidt, G., Bessman, M. J., Hickey, M., and Thannhauser, S. J. (1956). *J. Biol. Chem.* **223**, 1027.
Schrader, F., and Leuchtenberger, C. (1952). *Exptl. Cell Res.* **3**, 136.
Schultz, J. (1956). *Cold Spring Harbor Symp. Quant. Biol.* **21**, 307.
Shepard, C. C., and Hottle, G. A. (1949). *J. Biol. Chem.* **179**, 349.
Sibley, C. G. (1960). *Ibis* **102**, 215.
Siedler, A. J., Nayder, F. A., and Schweigert, B. S. (1957). *J. Bacteriol.* **73**, 670.
Siekevitz, P. (1959). *Ciba Found. Symp. Regulation Cell Metab. 1959* p. 17.
Simmel, E. B., and Karnofsky, D. A. (1961). *J. Biophys. Biochem. Cytol.* **10**, 59.
Simpson, M. V. (1962). *Ann. Rev. Biochem.* **31**, 333.
Sirlin, J. L. (1962). *Progr. Biophys. Biophys. Chem.* **12**, 25.
Sirlin, J. L., and Jacob, J. (1960). *Exptl. Cell Res.* **20**, 283.
Sjöstand, F. S. (1962). *In* "The Interpretation of Ultrastructure," I.S.C.B. Symp., Vol. 1 (R. J. C. Harris, ed.), p. 47. Academic Press, New York.
Solomon, J. B. (1957a). *Biochim. Biophys. Acta* **23**, 211.
Solomon, J. B. (1957b). *Biochim. Biophys. Acta* **24**, 584.
Sotelo, J. R., and Porter, K. R. (1959). *J. Biophys. Biochem. Cytol.* **5**, 327.
Sotelo, J. R., and Trujillo-Cenóz, O. (1957). *J. Biophys. Biochem. Cytol.* **3**, 301.
Spiegel, M. (1960). *Biol. Bull.* **118**, 451.
Strittmatter, C. F., Strittmatter, P., and Burdick, C. (1960). *Biol. Bull.* **119**, 341.
Sugano, H. (1957). *J. Biochem. (Tokyo)* **44**, 205.
Sugano, H. (1958a). *J. Biochem. (Tokyo)* **45**, 393.
Sugano, H. (1958b). *J. Biochem. (Tokyo)* **45**, 667.
Sugano, H. (1959a). *J. Biochem. (Tokyo)* **46**, 417.
Sugano, H. (1959b). *J. Biochem. (Tokyo)* **46**, 549.
Sugino, Y. (1957). *J. Am. Chem. Soc.* **79**, 5074.
Sugino, Y., and Potter, R. L. (1960). *Radiation Res.* **12**, 477.
Sugino, Y., Sugino, N., Okasaki, R., and Okasaki, T. (1957). *Biochim. Biophys. Acta* **26**, 453.
Sung, H. S. (1962). *Embryologia (Nagoya)* **7**, 185.
Swift, H. (1956). *J. Biophys. Biochem. Cytol.* **2** (Suppl.), 415.
Swift, H. (1958). *In* "The Chemical Basis of Development" (W. D. McElroy and B. Glass, eds.), p. 174. Johns Hopkins Press, Baltimore, Maryland.
Symposium of the Royal Microscopical Society (1962). *J. Roy. Microscop. Soc.* [3] **80**, parts 2, 3.
Sze, L. C. (1953). *J. Exptl. Zool.* **122**, 577.
Taborsky, G., and Allende, C. C. (1962). *Biochemistry* **1**, 406.
Taleporos, P. (1959). *J. Histochem. Cytochem.* **7**, 322.
Tandler, C. J. (1957). *Exptl. Cell Res.* **14**, 408.
Telfer, W. H. (1954). *J. Gen. Physiol.* **37**, 539.
Telfer, W. H. (1958). *Anat. Record* **131**, 603.

Telfer, W. H. (1960). *Biol. Bull.* **118**, 338.

Telfer, W. H. (1961). *J. Biophys. Biochem. Cytol.* **9**, 747.

Travaglini, E. C., Levenbook, L., and Schultz, J. (1958). *Exptl. Cell Res.* **15**, 62.

Trujillo-Cenóz, O., and Sotelo, J. R. (1959). *J. Biophys. Biochem. Cytol.* **5**, 347.

Truman, D. E. S., and Korner, A. (1962). *Biochem. J.* **83**, 588.

Turner, K. J., and Cook, W. H. (1958). *Can. J. Biochem. Physiol.* **36**, 937.

Tyler, A. (1955). *In* "Analysis of Development" (B. H. Willier, P. A. Weiss, and V. Hamburger, eds.), p. 170. Saunders, Philadelphia, Pennsylvania.

van den Broek, C. J. H., and Tates, A. D. (1961). *Exptl. Cell Res.* **24**, 201.

van der Stricht, O. (1923). *Arch. Biol.* (*Liege*) **33**, 229.

Vendrely, C., and Vendrely, R. (1949). *Compt. Rend. Soc. Biol.* **143**, 1386.

Vincent, W. S. (1952). *Proc. Natl. Acad. Sci. U. S.* **38**, 139.

Vincent, W. S. (1957). *In* "The Beginnings of Embryonic Development" (A. Tyler, R. C. von Borstel, and C. B. Metz, eds.), p. 1. Am. Assoc. Advan. Sci., Washington, D. C.

Vincent, W. S., and Baltus, E. (1960a). *In* "The Cell Nucleus" (J. S. Mitchell, ed.), p. 18. Butterworths, London.

Vincent, W. S., and Baltus, E. (1960b). *Biol. Bull.* **119**, 299.

Waddington, C. H. (1962). *J. Cellular Comp. Physiol.* **60** (Suppl. 1), 93.

Waddington, C. H., Perry, M. M., and Okada, E. (1961). *Exptl. Cell Res.* **23**, 631.

Wallace, R. A. (1962). *J. Cellular Comp. Physiol.* **60** (Suppl. 1), 16.

Wallace, R. A. (1963). *Biochim. Biophys. Acta* **74**, 495.

Ward, R. T. (1959). *J. Appl. Phys.* **30**, 2040.

Ward, R. T. (1962a). *J. Cell Biol.* **14**, 303.

Ward, R. T. (1962b). *J. Cell Biol.* **14**, 309.

Warner, R. C. (1953). *In* "The Proteins" (H. Neurath and K. Bailey, eds.), Vol. 1, p. 435. Academic Press, New York.

Wartenberg, H., and Stegner, H. E. (1960). *Z. Zellforsch. Mikroskop. Anat.* **52**, 450.

Watson, J. D. (1963). *Science* **140**, 17.

Watterson, R. L. (1955). *In* "Analysis of Development" (B. H. Willier, P. A. Weiss, and V. Hamburger, eds.), p. 315. Saunders, Philadelphia, Pennsylvania.

Weber, R. (1958). *Arch. Entwicklungsmech. Organ.* **150**, 542.

Weber, R. (1961). *In* "Symposium on Germ Cells and Earliest Stages of Development," p. 225. Ist. Lombardo, Fondazione A. Baselli, Milan.

Weber, R. (1962). *In* "The Interpretation of Ultrastructure," I.S.C.B. Symp., Vol. 1 (R. J. C. Harris, ed.), p. 393. Academic Press, New York.

Weber, R., and Boell, E. J. (1955). *Rev. Suisse Zool.* **62**, 260.

Went, H. A. (1959a). *J. Biophys. Biochem. Cytol.* **5**, 353.

Went, H. A. (1959b). *J. Biophys. Biochem. Cytol.* **6**, 447.

Went, H. A., and Mazia, D. (1959). *In* "Macromolecular Complexes" (M. V. Edds, ed.), p. 161. Ronald, New York.

Williams, J. (1962a). *Biochem. J.* **83**, 346.

Williams, J. (1962b). *Biochem. J.* **83**, 355.

Williams, J., and Sanger, F. (1959). *Biochim. Biophys. Acta* **33**, 294.

Wilson, E. B. (1928). "The Cell in Development and Heredity." Macmillan, New York.

Wilt, F. H., and Hultin, T. (1962). *Biochem. Biophys. Res. Commun.* **9**, 313.

Wischnitzer, S. (1957). *J. Biophys. Biochem. Cytol.* **3**, 1040.

Wischnitzer, S. (1958). *J. Ultrastruct. Res.* **1**, 201.
Wittek, M. (1952). *Arch. Biol.* (*Liege*) **63**, 133.
Worley, L. G., and Moriber, L. G. (1961). *Trans. N. Y. Acad. Sci.* **23**, 352.
Yamada, T. (1961). *Advan. Morphogenesis* **1**, 1.
Yasuzumi, G., and Tanaka, H. (1957). *Exptl. Cell Res.* **12**, 681.
Yao, T. (1949). *Quart. J. Microscop. Sci.* **90**, 401.
Young, E. G., and Phinney, J. I. (1951). *J. Biol. Chem.* **193**, 73.
Zalokar, M. (1960). *Exptl. Cell Res.* **19**, 184.
Zeigler, K., and Schmidt, W. (1957). *Z. Zellforsch. Mikroskop. Anat.* **45**, 578.

Chapter 2

BIOCHEMICAL ASPECTS OF FERTILIZATION

Alberto Monroy

Laboratory of Comparative Anatomy
University of Palermo, Italy

I. Introduction

The fundamental steps in fertilization involve first an interaction between spermatozoa and eggs which results in the meeting of two gametes. Once contact has been established, the crucial step in fertilization, namely the penetration of the spermatozoon into the egg, occurs. This penetration produces the most dramatic structural and metabolic changes in the egg and constitutes what is called the activation of the egg. The main point of the activation is the fusion of the male and

female pronuclei resulting in the formation of the zygote nucleus. This
may be considered the final event of fertilization proper.

The discussion which follows will be based mainly on the results
obtained on the sea urchin egg, which is the most favorable material
for the study of the biochemistry of fertilization. This is certainly a
limitation. Whereas some of the results may no doubt have general
validity, this validity cannot be taken for granted; and unless extensive
comparative studies are made, any generalization must be considered
critically.

II. The Interaction between Egg and Spermatozoa and the Role of the Egg Coats in Fertilization

A. Fertilizin

Research in fertilization studies was prompted by the pioneering work
of F. R. Lillie (1914). His theory of "fertilizin" (best summarized in
1919) has, in fact, been one of the most important contributions to the
physiology of fertilization above all for the wealth of work it has stimulated.

Lillie observed that sea water in which unfertilized sea urchin eggs
had been standing (so-called egg water) had the properties of *agglutinating* the homologous spermatozoa and *activating* their motility.
The active factor responsible for these effects he named "fertilizin" and
considered it not only as a mediator of the egg-sperm interactions but
also as a key factor in fertilization. Lillie realized that the substance of
the egg's jelly coat was somehow involved in the activity of fertilizin,
after observing that the sperm-agglutinating factor was contained in
high concentration in the jelly coat. However, he erroneously suggested
that fertilizin was actively and continuously secreted by the egg, until
fertilization occurred. Further work has shown (1) that fertilizin can
be identified with the jelly-coat material which slowly goes into solution in sea water; (2) that there is no active, continuous secretion or
production of fertilizin by the unfertilized egg, the jelly coat being
manufactured in the ovary during the course of maturation of the egg
(see Tyler, 1948, for an extensive review).

B. Chemical Composition of the Jelly Coat of the Echinoderm Egg

The isolation of the jelly-coat substance in what appears to be a
pure and undenatured form can best be obtained by the simple method
developed by Tyler and Fox (1940) and Tyler (1949). This material
proves to be homogeneous from electrophoretic and ultracentrifugal
evidence (Runnström *et al.*, 1942; Tyler, 1949, 1956; Tyler *et al.*, 1954a,b).

Its electrophoretic mobility indicates a strongly acidic character (— 18 × 10⁻⁵ cm²/volt/sec). Lowering the pH from 8.6 to 2.0 has very little effect on its mobility. The best estimate of its molecular weight is about 300,000 with an axial ratio of 20:1 for the jelly-coat substance of *Arbacia*. From these data, the number of effective negatively charged groups per molecule can be calculated as 14.25 at pH 7 and 11.25 at pH 4.85 (Tyler, 1956). The strongly acidic character of the jelly substance depends on its high content of sulfate groups; indeed, according to Vasseur (1947, 1952, 1954), each monosaccharide residue is esterified with a sulfate group.

The interesting point is that the monosaccharide constituents are relatively specific for the different sea urchin genera thus far examined (Table I), which has prompted the suggestion that this may be the basis for the species specificity of fertilization. This, however, seems to be a rather unnecessary assumption. In fact, the jelly coat has been shown (Tyler, 1948; Vasseur, 1949, 1952) to contain 20% of its dry weight in amino acids; but it is entirely unknown how the amino acids are distributed in the molecules, i.e., whether they are scattered among the monosaccharide residues or clustered as peptides at certain strategic sites. There is, however, some circumstantial evidence which favors the latter assumption. In fact, the jelly coat, either *in vivo* or *in vitro*, is split into small fragments by trypsin and chymotrypsin which are known to have specific peptide bond requirements in order to be active. This favors the presence of amino acid sequences. Evidently, the relative distribution and grouping of amino acid sequences and of monosaccharide residues may give rise to a tremendous variety of structures upon which very subtle specific differences may depend.

C. *The Sperm-Agglutinating Reaction*

As mentioned previously, fertilizin was first characterized by its ability to cause a species-specific agglutination of the spermatozoa.

The agglutinating effect of solutions of the gelatinous coat of the eggs has been described in a number of invertebrates and vertebrates (for a review see Rothschild, 1956b). It consists in the formation of clusters of spermatozoa in the presence of a solution of the egg coat (Fig. 1). Evidently, for the agglutinating reaction to take place it is essential that each agglutinating unit should bear *at least* two combining groups which can react with and bind to receptor groups at the surface of different spermatozoa. Tyler (1948) has emphasized the similarity of this reaction to the antigen–antibody reactions.

In most of the sea urchin species agglutination is reversible, i.e., the clumps of agglutinated spermatozoa disperse after a short time.

TABLE I

CHEMICAL COMPOSITION OF THE JELLY COAT OF EGGS OF ECHINODERMS[a]

Organism	Composition as % of dry weight[b]								References
	G	Gl	M	F	X	Fr	N	SO$_4$	
Arbacia lixula	+[c]	+	+	+					Minganti (1958)
Echinus esculentus		+							Vasseur (1950) Vasseur and Immers (1949)
Paracentrotus lividus	4.6		3.8	24.3	0.8		4.7	20.9	Minganti and Vasseur (1959); Vasseur and Immers (1949)
Strongylocentrotus droebachiensis		+		+				25.0	Vasseur (1947); Vasseur and Immers (1949)
Strongylocentrotus purpuratus		25					5.7	23	Tyler (1948, 1949); Tyler and Fox (1940)
Sphaerechinus granularis		+	+	+					Minganti (1958)
Heliocidaris crassispina				+					Nakano and Ohashi (1954)
Echinarchnius parma						+			Bishop (1951); Bishop and Metz (1952)
Hemicentrotus pulcherrimus				+					Nakano and Ohashi (1954)
Pseudocentrotus depressus				+					Nakano and Ohashi (1954)
Echinocardium cordatum				32.7			4.1	20.5	Vasseur (1952); Vasseur and Immers (1949)
Brissopsis lyrifera								8.1	Vasseur (1952)

[a] From Minganti (1958).
[b] G = glucose; Gl = galactose; M = mannose; F = fucose; X = xylose; Fr = fructose; and N = total nitrogen.
[c] + = Qualitative estimation only.

Now, however, the spermatozoa have lost their ability to be reagglutinated by the addition of a fresh jelly-coat solution. Probably the jelly-coat micelles are somehow split into smaller units, each of them having just one combining group that remains attached to the surface of the spermatozoa; this is the so-called "univalent" fertilizin (Tyler, 1941). Support for this view comes from the demonstration that univalent fer-

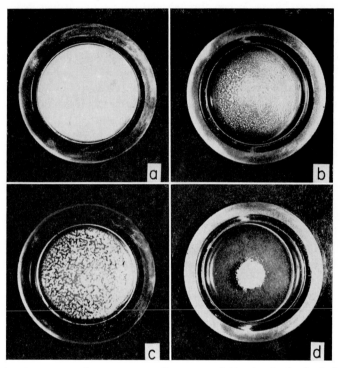

FIG. 1. A macroscopic appearance of sperm agglutination in the keyhole limpet, *Megathura crenulata*, following addition of egg water. (*a*) Untreated sperm suspension; (*b*) 15 seconds after addition of egg water; (*c*) 30 seconds later; and (*d*) 10 minutes later. From Tyler (1940).

tilizin can be obtained artificially by treating the jelly-coat solutions with ultraviolet or X-ray radiations, with trypsin or chymotrypsin, or with heat. When spermatozoa are treated with such nonagglutinating preparations, they can no longer be agglutinated by untreated jelly-coat solutions. Evidently, in both cases the only combining group of each univalent fragment has reacted with one sperm receptor group, thus making it unavailable for reaction with other jelly-coat micelles.

The attachment of jelly particles to the surface of the spermatozoa in the agglutination reaction is shown by the decrease in fucose, the main carbohydrate component of the jelly of *Arbacia* (Minganti, 1958) following addition of spermatozoa to a jelly-coat solution (Monroy *et al.*, 1954). More impressive are the results of experiments using S^{35}-labeled jelly substance which was obtained by injecting $Na_2 S^{35} O_4$ into females of *Arbacia punctulata* during the maturation of the eggs (Tyler and Hathaway, 1958). When this labeled jelly solution was reacted with spermatozoa, more than 70 % of the radioactivity was removed from the solution by the spermatozoa. Upon reversal of the agglutination, about one-half of the absorbed radioactivity was released from the spermatozoa, and it has been suggested that the reversal may be due to the activity of a sulfatase located at the surface of the spermatozoa (Hathaway, 1959; Tyler and Hathaway, 1958; Hathaway and Metz, 1961).

In spite of the electrophoretic and ultracentrifugal evidence, there are some indications that the jelly-coat substance of the sea urchin egg is nonhomogeneous (Messina and Monroy, 1956). As mentioned previously, fucose is the main carbohydrate component of the *Arbacia* jelly coat, but galactose and traces of mannose are also present. By treatment with a weakly anionic resin (Amberlite 1R-4B), a solution of *Arbacia* jelly coat can be resolved into two fractions: the larger one, which is retained on the resin, carries the entire fucose content and part of the galactose content. When eluted from the resin, this fraction is strongly agglutinating. The smaller fraction, which is not retained by the resin, contains only galactose and is very weakly agglutinating. The same fractionation is obtained with protamine, and in this case the non-precipitated fraction is entirely devoid of agglutinating ability. The amino acids, on the other hand, appear to be evenly distributed between the two fractions. Further data suggesting nonhomogeneity of the jelly-coat substance will be presented later.

D. *The Sperm-Activating Reaction*

As mentioned previously, another property of the jelly substance is the activation of the spermatozoa. The orginal meaning of the word *activation* was that addition of a jelly-coat solution to a suspension of spermatozoa causes them to move faster. The phenomenon is clearer when spermatozoa which have already exhausted their motility are used (aged spermatozoa). Furthermore, spermatozoa which have been treated with jelly solution stay motile considerably longer than un-treated ones, i.e., the life span of the spermatozoa is prolonged. This effect may be caused by a chelating action of the jelly substance anal-ogous to that of Versene or glycine (Tyler, 1950, 1953; Rothschild and Tyler, 1954). These materials remove substances from sea water that are detrimental to the spermatozoa. The increase in oxygen consumption of jelly-treated sperm was first described by Gray (1928) and alternately confirmed and denied. Sometimes, even a decreased oxygen consumption has been observed (see Rothschild, 1952). The question has been re-examined by Vasseur (1952) who has found that, whereas fresh spermatozoa are only slightly, if at all, responsive to the stimulating action of jelly substance, aged spermatozoa do respond with a remarkable increase in their oxygen consumption. The stimulation observed by Bielig and Dohrn (1950) on fresh *Arbacia* spermatozoa may be caused by their use of washed and centrifuged, i.e., most likely damaged, cells. The question is further complicated by the striking pH effects on the respiration of spermatozoa described by Rothschild (1956a).

Whether the activating principle is carried out by the same or different molecules of the jelly is not known. However, Cornman (1941) has shown that the sperm-activating ability of the jelly coat can be removed by dialysis, whereas the agglutinating principle is not affected. Furthermore, heating a jelly solution results in the destruction of the agglutinating but not the sperm-activating principle (Lillie, 1914; Tyler, 1941; Vasseur, 1952).

E. *The Question of the Chemotactic Effect*

Another point to be discussed is whether or not the egg exerts any chemotactic action on the spermatozoa. As defined by Rothschild (1956b) (the interested reader is referred to this book for an extensive discussion of the subject), "Chemotaxis means that spermatozoa are attracted towards eggs through the medium of some substance produced by the eggs or cells near them." It was Pfeffer's famous experiment (1884) which gave the first evidence of a chemotactic reaction in the fern spermatozoa. This experiment was particularly interesting because it defined a chemical substance, malic acid, as being responsible for the effect. It is now generally accepted that chemotactic reactions of a similar kind do exist among plants, whereas in the case of animal gametes the available evidence is definitely the opposite. At this point the case of the medusan, *Spyrocodon saltatrix*, is worth mentioning. In mature eggs the pronucleus lies just below the cortex at one pole of the egg. Here a depression is present where the polar bodies have been extruded. The spermatozoa are observed to accumulate only around this zone, where the penetration of the fertilizing spermatozoon also occurs. This observation suggests that some sort of sperm-attracting substance is diffusing from the surface of the egg close to the pronucleus (Dan, 1950).

The problem of chemotaxis in the sea urchin was revived when

Hartmann and his co-workers (Hartmann *et al.*, 1939, 1940; Hartmann and Schartau, 1939) indicated in the echinochrome (the pigment responsible for the deep color of the ovaries and eggs of the genus *Arbacia*) one of the chemical factors of fertilization and called it gynogamone I (GI). According to the authors, GI was endowed with three properties: (1) to activate the movement of spermatozoa; (2) to act chemotactically upon them; and (3) to remove the paralyzing effect of androgamon I, the substance responsible for the immotility of the spermatozoa in the gonad. The results of Hartmann and his co-workers, however, have not been generally accepted. Indeed, there seems to be no evidence that echinochrome is a "Befruchtungstoff" (fertilization substance). In particular, Tyler (1939b) and Cornman (1941) showed that crystalline echinochrome is devoid of any sperm-activating or chemotactic effect. More recently, extensive experiments of Bielig and Dohrn (1950) have ruled out such activity caused by GI. When studying the fertilization of eggs having gelatinous capsules, such as those of the sea urchin, the trapping action of the highly viscous jelly may give rise to the erroneous impression that the spermatozoa are being attracted by the egg. If eggs are introduced into a suspension of randomly moving spermatozoa, a somewhat dense halo of spermatozoa will stick to the capsule because each spermatozoon colliding with the jelly coat will be trapped by it. Bielig and Dohrn (1950) have carefully followed the behavior of spermatozoa moving in a fairly dense suspension of sea urchin eggs. Although the eggs were quite close to each other, often spermatozoa could be seen moving freely between the eggs. Only those spermatozoa which came into direct contact with the jelly coat exhibited first a short acceleration of their movement and then adhered to the jelly coat.

F. *The Acrosome Reaction*

More important for the physiology of fertilization is the effect of the jelly substance on the so-called acrosome reaction. Popa (1927) had observed that the egg water causes some kind of alteration in the acrosome of the sea urchin sperm resulting in the elimination "of a substance." The importance of this observation, however, was not understood until recently when the use of more powerful technical tools has permitted the analysis of this phenomenon in greater detail. Dan (1952) must be acknowledged for the pioneering work in this field. Essentially, the acrosome reaction consists in the opening up of the acrosome under certain conditions. In the spermatozoa of some animals this reaction is accompanied by the release of a filament, the acrosomal filament (Fig. 2). In the spermatozoon of *Hydroides* a bundle of tubules is formed instead (A. L. and H. L. Colwin, 1961). The length of the filament varies in different animal species and may be almost as long as the entire spermatozoon (about 25 μ in the starfish), although it may be extremely thin. In the normal, unreacted spermatozoa, the acrosome has the well-known shape of a small, rounded body at the tip of the head. The main conditions which cause the explosion of the acrosome are contact with the egg capsule or the presence in the sea water of capsular material in solution. Indeed, the most potent artificial procedure for

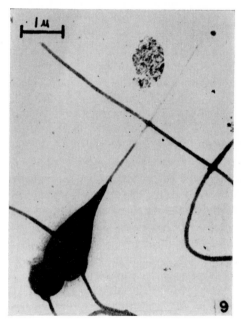

Fig. 2.   Electron micrograph of "reacted" spermatozoon of *Echinocardium corda-tum* showing acrosomal filament. From Rothschild and Tyler (1955).

inducing the acrosome reaction is the exposure of the spermatozoa to egg water or the contact with egg coats or membranes (for the details of the physiology and morphology of the acrosome reaction, see Dan, 1956, 1960; Metz, 1957). The gastropod spermatozoa do not react in the presence of egg water; however, when they reach the jelly layer surrounding the egg, they immediately eject the filament through the jelly (Dan, 1956). The importance of the acrosome reaction will be discussed further in connection with the problem of sperm penetration.

The leading role in fertilization assigned to fertilizin by Lillie and Tyler has been questioned by Runnström and his students (for a review see Runnström *et al.*, 1959), who have adopted the view that in the sea

urchin egg the jelly coat acts as a barrier to heterologous and polyspermic insemination and that it may indeed act as an inhibitor to
fertilization. However, the increase in the fertilization rate following
partial removal of the jelly coat (Hagström, 1956a,b,c) is not surprising;
under these conditions the egg surface will be much more accessible
to the spermatozoa. Similarly, that the rate of fertilization be decreased in the presence of high concentrations of jelly coat in solution
(Hagström, 1956d) is actually what one would expect. In fact, under
such conditions the reaction between spermatozoa and jelly substance
occurs prematurely causing what may be called a "false fertilization"
(Bishop and Tyler, 1956). This false fertilization consists either in the
saturation of a number of receptor sites on the sperm surface or in a premature acrosome reaction. As was aptly pointed out by Bishop and Tyler
(1956), "In order to function in the fertilization process, the agglutination reaction must occur while the substances are still an integral part
of the surface of the respective gametes."

G. *The Egg Coats in Animals Other Than the Echinoderms*

In no animals, other than the echinoderms, have the chemical and
physiological properties of the substance of the egg capsule and of the
egg secretion been studied equally thoroughly. A detailed review of
our present knowledge of the chemical composition of the egg envelopes
has been presented by Minganti (1958). There are now numerous reports on the presence of agglutinins in eggs belonging to various animal
groups as well as reports of lack of agglutinating power in the egg
secretions of some organisms. In connection with the latter, it must be
mentioned that Metz (1945) was able to make the normally nonagglutinating egg water of the starfish *Patiria miniata* become agglutinating by the addition of hen's egg white which acts as an adjuvant. In
this case, the jelly substance in solution is most likely present in an
univalent form (it is not known whether the fragmentation occurs in
solution or whether the univalent form is present also in the intact coat).
This is confirmed by the fact that a reaction with the spermatozoa does
take place and, in fact, following treatment with homologous egg water
the spermatozoa of *Patiria miniata* (Tyler, 1941) and *Spisula solidissima* (Metz and Donovan, 1949) undergo a reduction of their fertilizing
capacity. Here again either the acrosome reaction has taken place before
the spermatozoa reached the egg or a number of the receptor sites at the
surface have been saturated.

In the ascidians Minganti (1951) has observed that egg water prepared from eggs surrounded by their membranes exhibits a definite
activating effect on sperm motility, whereas the agglutinating capacity

is slight, if at all present. However, in *Ciona* this becomes evident when the egg water is prepared from denuded eggs and indicates that the agglutinating factor is located between the egg surface and the membrane, or even *at* the egg surface. This question deserves further attention. In vertebrates the problem of egg-sperm interacting substances is rather confused. Activation and agglutination of homologous spermatozoa in the presence of egg water of *Lampetra fluviatilis* has been reported (Schartau and Montalenti, 1941; Montalenti and Schartau, 1942); but a later publication of Montalenti (1949) indicated that tap water is just as effective in bringing about sperm agglutination. Also Yanagimachi (1957) has observed agglutination of herring spermatozoa in ordinary sea water and in Ringer solution. However, the present writer feels that in these experiments not enough care was taken to ensure that the spermatozoa were not damaged during the preparation, and therefore, the whole question should be reinvestigated. In the herring *Clupea pollasii* (Yanagimachi and Kanoh, 1953; Yanagimachi, 1957), in three species of bitterlings, *Acheilognathus lanceolata*, *Acheilognathus taliva*, and *Rhodeus ocellatus*, and in the fat minnow *Sarcocheilichys variegatus* (Suzuki, 1958, 1959a,b, 1960), activation of spermatozoa has been described at the micropylar area, where the spermatozoa densely aggregate: hence, the activating (and trapping) factor seems to be strictly localized in the micropyle. Eggs deprived of their membrane do not exert any activating effect. The surprising fact, however, is that the activating factor lacks any species specificity. Both Yanagimachi (1957) and Suzuki (1961) maintain that the activating factor is either a protein or a low molecular substance, which is only active when in association with a protein.

The chemical composition of the jelly coat surrounding the eggs of a number of amphibians is fairly well known, thanks to the recent work of Minganti and his collaborators (Minganti, 1954, 1955; Minganti and D'Anna, 1957, 1958). The chemical composition given in Table II indicates that this jelly is a glycoprotein in which carbohydrate residues do not seem to be esterified with sulfate groups. The protein component also appears to have an important role in the architecture and stability of the jelly since it can be dissolved by proteolytic enzymes (Spiegel, 1951). Furthermore, the protein components may possibly confer species specificity to the jelly; this is suggested by the species specificity of the hatching enzymes in dissolving the jellies (Minganti and Azzolina, 1956). The detailed knowledge of the chemistry of the amphibian jelly coat contrasts with the paucity of information regarding its physiological role. There is only a brief note by Bernstein (1952) describing the presence of agglutinin in the egg water of mature eggs of *Rana clamitans,* whereas no sperm agglutination was observed with egg water of *Rana pipiens* (contrary to an earlier report by Glaser, 1921). This is caused by the difficulty in handling amphibian spermatozoa properly. In mammals activation and agglutination of bull sper-

TABLE II

CHEMICAL COMPOSITION OF THE JELLY COAT OF AMPHIBIAN EGGS[a]

Organism	Composition as % of dry weight[b]								References
	G	Gl	M	F	X	Ga	Gla	N	
Rana temporaria	?[c]	12.7	3.5	7.1	?	8.9	9.5	8.1	Folkes *et al.* (1950)
Rana esculenta		+[d]		+		+	?	9.3	Giacosa (1882); Minganti (1955); Schulz and Becker (1935)
Rana japonica		28.0		?			14.0	8.8	Hiyama (1949a, c)
Rana clamitans	?	?	?	+			+		Bernstein (quoted by Minganti, 1958)
Discoglossus pictus	+	+	+	1.7			16.5	10.0	Minganti and D'Anna (1958)
Bufo bufo		+	+	10.4			20–40	7.6	Minganti (1955); Minganti and Azzolina (1956)
Bufo vulgaris formosus		30.0		?			20.0	8.4	Hiyama (1949a, b)
Axolotl			+	+			+	8.3	Banta and Gartner (1914); Minganti (1955)
Triturus cristatus		12.2	1.3	6.2			20.3	10.0	Minganti and D'Anna (1957)

[a] From Minganti (1958).
[b] G = glucose; Gl = galactose; M = mannose; F = fucose; X = xylose; Ga = glucosamine; Gla = galactosamine; and N = total nitrogen.
[c] ? = Result uncertain.
[d] + = Qualitative estimation only.

matozoa by the *liquor folliculi* was described for the first time by Corrias and Novarini (1950). A detailed analysis of some of the egg-sperm interacting factors has been made by Bishop and Tyler (1956) in rabbits, cows, and mice. They were able to show agglutination of spermatozoa all around the eggs and succeeded in extracting an agglutinating factor from the eggs by acidifying the water. The agglutination reaction proved to be predominantly species-specific. The reaction also occurs with eggs which have lost the cells of the cumulus and the corona and, hence, the most likely candidate as a source of the agglutinating factor is the zona pellucida which, according to Braden (1952), is a mucoprotein. This agrees with the observed inhibition of agglutination following treatment of the eggs with periodate (Bishop and Tyler, 1956).

III. The Attachment and Penetration of the Spermatozoon

A. *The Question of the Sperm Lysins*

The existence of lytic factors enabling the spermatozoon to penetrate the coats of the egg has been established in some cases, whereas in others it remains doubtful. There are indeed rather few cases in which such lysins have been ascertained beyond any doubt. Evidently, the problem is different in eggs surrounded by a gelatinous coat than in those surrounded by a real, discrete, and sometimes tough membrane. In some of the eggs of the latter category, however, a micropyle is present, for example, in the majority of fishes. Here the problem of sperm penetration appears to have been solved by nature in the easiest possible way.

A typical example of an egg surrounded by a gelatinous coat is that of the echinoderms. The presence in sperm extracts of a jelly coat-splitting enzyme was first indicated by Monroy and Ruffo (1947) and Lundblad and Monroy (1950); this, however, was questioned by Krauss (1950). The problem was reinvestigated by Monroy and Tosi (1952) and by Monroy *et al.* (1954). They were able to show that in the *in vitro* reaction between jelly-coat solutions and spermatozoa the viscosity-lowering effect was caused by the removal of the jelly-coat micelles from the solution rather than to their enzymatic depolymerization. In fact these micelles become attached to the surface of the spermatozoa. However, Messina (1954) later showed that depolymerization also occurs. The presence of a sulfatase at the surface of sea urchin spermatozoa has already been mentioned, but its role in the process of the penetration of the spermatozoon through the jelly coat has not yet been considered.

In *Holothuria atra* (A. L. and L. H. Colwin, 1955), *Thyone briareus* (L. H. and A. L. Colwin, 1956), and in three species of *Asterias* (A. L. and L. H. Colwin, 1955; L. H. and A. L. Colwin, 1956) whose eggs are also surrounded by a jelly coat, the spermatozoon produces a long acrosomal filament which goes straight through the jelly to the surface of the egg. In these cases Dan (1960) has suggested that the penetration of the acrosomal filament through the jelly layer may not require a lysin and that the filament "is able to pierce this layer with the push derived from the chemical change which causes its formation." However, further work will be necessary to find out whether the possibility of intervention of a lysin may actually be eliminated.

The problem of the membrane lysin is more acute in the case of eggs covered by a distinct and often thick membrane. Tyler (1939a) extracted a powerful membrane lysin by freezing and thawing the spermatozoa of the mollusk, *Megathura crenulata*, whose eggs have a thick and quite tough membrane. The egg-membrane lysin can also be extracted by milder procedures, for example, by weak alkali; and in this case examination of the spermatozoa with the electron microscope shows a breakdown of the acrosome. This suggests an acrosomal localization of the lysin (Tyler, 1949).

Substantial evidence concerning the existence of a lysin has also been obtained in work on fertilization of the *Mytilus* egg, which is surrounded by a thin but discrete membrane. This membrane is rapidly dissolved by extracts of homologous sperm (Berg, 1950). Wada *et al.* (1956) found that the egg membrane lysin could be obtained from the sea water in which *Mytilus* spermatozoa had been standing, only if these spermatozoa were in the reacted condition. Conversely, the lysin could be extracted only from unreacted spermatozoa. This observation also indicates that the lysin is contained in the acrosome (or in the acrosomal region) and is only released when the acrosomal reaction takes place. It will be important to carry out similar experiments with the spermatozoa of other animals. There is indeed a possibility that a number of conflicting results may depend on the fact that most of these experiments were made at a time when the acrosome reaction was not known, so that no attention was given to the condition of the spermatozoa.

Also, the eggs of the annelids *Pomatoceros* and *Hydroides* are covered by a tough membrane. If the eggs of *Pomatoceros* are transferred to dilute sea water shortly after insemination, an outflow of cytoplasm is observed from several points in the membrane. It is as if each attached spermatozoon had made a tiny hole in the membrane (Monroy, 1948b). Similar observations have been made in *Hydroides* (L. H. and A. L. Colwin, 1960). In these animals the spermatozoa do make a hole in the membrane as indicated by the electron micrographs of Colwin *et al.* (1957) (Fig. 3). Their photographs show unequivocally that the tip of the acrosome at first breaches the outer, thickened layer of the vitelline membrane and at the same time the acrosome reaction occurs.

Then, while the large acrosomal granule disappears, a clear area appears around the everted acrosome in the middle layer of the membrane, which fills the space between the outer layer and the plasma membrane. This change gives the impression that the membrane is being liquefied all around the reacted acrosome (Fig. 3). The liquefaction of the middle

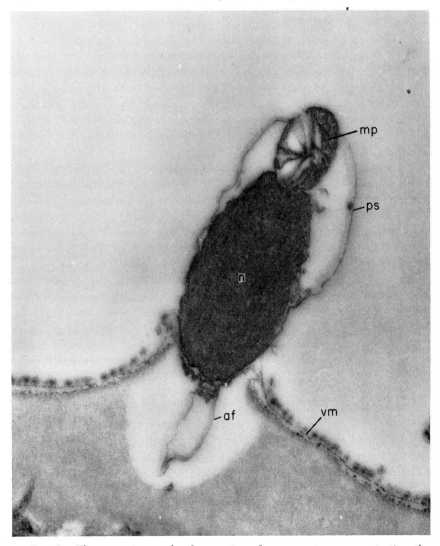

Fig. 3. Electron micrograph of a section of a spermatozoon penetrating the vitelline membrane (vm) of an egg of *Hydroides hexagonus*. Note the clear space around the acrosome filament (af). (n) sperm nucleus; (ps) sperm plasma membrane; (mp) mid piece. From Colwin *et al.* (1957).

layer of the membrane can be duplicated by treating the egg with extracts of spermatozoa, whereas the outer layer is not affected by this
treatment (A. L. and L. H. Colwin, 1960), thus suggesting that different mechanisms are instrumental in the breaching of the outer layer
and the liquefaction of the middle layer.

An interesting situation prevails in mammalian eggs. This egg is
surrounded by a thick membrane called the zona pellucida, which is
covered on the outside by the cells of the cumulus oophorus. Hence, to
reach the egg surface the spermatozoon has to pass through the cumulus
first and then the zona pellucida. It is now generally accepted that in
most mammals the penetration of the spermatozoon through the cumulus is governed by the action of the enzyme hyaluronidase. The cells
of the cumulus are held together by a mucopolysaccharide rich in hya-
luronic acid, which is acted upon and depolymerized by this specific
enzyme (Swyer, 1947). There is some evidence (Tyler, 1949) that the
enzyme may be located in the acrosome, hence, it seems reasonable to
suppose that the acrosome is directly responsible for the passage of
the spermatozoon through the cumulus. It has been observed by Austin
and Bishop (1958) that after passing through the cumulus and reaching the zona, the spermatozoa lack their acrosome and the perforatorium
(analogous to the acrosomal filament?) is exposed. In the rabbit there
is an enlargement of the apical body (Hadek, 1963). This may indeed
be analogous to the acrosome reaction described in the lower forms
and is thought to be important for the penetration of the zona pellucida.
Narrow slits have been observed in the zona following passage of the
spermatozoon, as well as zones of light contrast in front of a sperm
head embedded in the zona. This suggests that a "zona lysin" might
be secreted by or diffused from the perforatorium (Austin and Bishop,
1958).

B. *The Mechanism of Sperm Penetration into the Egg*

Once the acrosome filament has established contact with the egg
plasma membrane, how does the spermatozoon progressively approach
the egg? According to the Colwins (1955) in certain echinoderms the
fully extended filament remains visible for some time within the egg.
Although small differences in length would be difficult to evaluate,
this observation discourages the interpretation that the spermatozoon
is pulled by the contracting acrosome filament. The so-called fertilization cone may play an important role in this process. It has been known
since the pioneering work of Fol (1878-1879) that while the spermatozoon moves through the jelly layer toward the egg, a conelike protrusion of egg cytoplasm, the fertilization cone, forms which moves toward

the spermatozoon. Formerly, it was thought that the cone engulfed the spermatozoon and eventually retracted slowly. Careful observation of the process of sperm attachment in *Thyone, Holothuria,* and *Asterias* (A. L. and L. H. Colwin, 1955) indicates that actually the cytoplasm that forms the fertilization cone moves up the acrosomal filament first and then around the head of the spermatozoon. At least in this case, the cone arises as a response of the egg to contact with the filament, and in its progress toward the spermatozoon the cone is guided by the filament itself. Actually, Fol had considered the possibility that the spermatozoon might eject such a filament uniting its tip with the egg surface, but he discarded the idea because he was unable to see any such filament with the optical means available at that time.

The electron micrographic studies of L. H. and A. L. Colwin have provided evidence that in *Hydroides hexagonus* (1961) and in *Saccoglossus kowalevskii* (1963) a fusion is established between the egg plasma membrane and the plasma membrane of the head of the spermatozoon (Figs. 4–6). Upon fusing, the plasma membrane of the spermatozoon is progressively peeled off the head, while the egg cytoplasm intrudes between the latter and the elements of the sperm head. Indeed, according to Tyler (1959), the primary event in the penetration of the spermatozoon is a specific interaction between complementary groups of the two plasma membranes (viz., of the egg and of the spermatozoon). The importance of such an interaction is clearly demonstrated by the inhibition of fertilization caused by treatment of spermatozoa with antisperm serum (Tyler, 1946; Metz, 1962). This interaction is followed by the opening up of the acrosome probably caused by the stresses imposed by this interaction (Tyler, 1959, 1962) and the release of the acrosomal filament or the equivalent kind of process in those species which do not possess such a filament (as in mammals or *Hydroides*). The progressive fusion of the two plasma membranes is suggested by Tyler (1962) as a mechanism whereby the denuded sperm head is admitted within the egg. Essentially similar phenomena have been described in the sperm penetration in the rat egg (Szollosi and Ris, 1961). In the rabbit it has been observed (Hadek, 1963) that while the spermatozoon goes through the zona pellucida, the cell membrane of the spermatozoon disappears. The process of denudation then continues and when the spermatozoa reach the vicinity of the vitelline membrane, they are always observed without their head cap and cytoplasmic layer. In *Barnea* an interesting observation has been made (Pasteels, 1963); once inside the egg cytoplasm the naked sperm nucleus is covered by a new membrane derived from the endoplasmic reticulum of the egg.

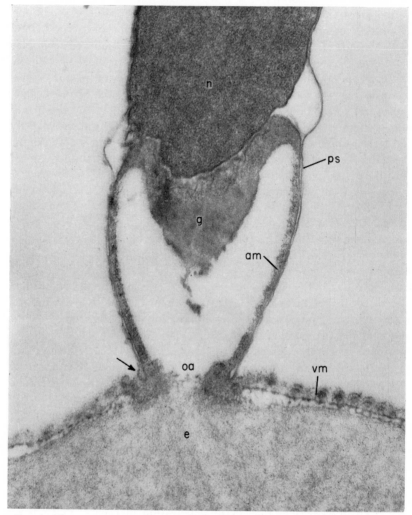

FIG. 4. Electron micrograph of an early stage in the penetration of the spermatozoon through the vitelline membrane in *Hydroides hexagonus*. Note: the opening
(oa) of the tip of the acrosomal region; the acrosomal granulus (g) has lost its
contact with acrosomal membrane (am); and at the acrosomal orifice the acrosomal
membrane fuses with the sperm plasma membrane (ps) (lower left arrow). At the
point of contact between the acrosome and the vitelline membrane (vm) the outer
border layer of the vitelline membrane is breached; compare with the unaffected
region at the right. (n) Sperm nucleus; (e) middle layer of vitelline membrane.
From L. H. Colwin and A. L. Colwin (1961).

The fact that the sperm nucleus enters the egg without its plasma membrane may be the reason why spermatozoa injected into unfertilized sea urchin eggs with a micropipette fail to activate the egg and do not show any of the changes the spermatozoon normally undergoes inside the egg (Hiramoto, 1962).

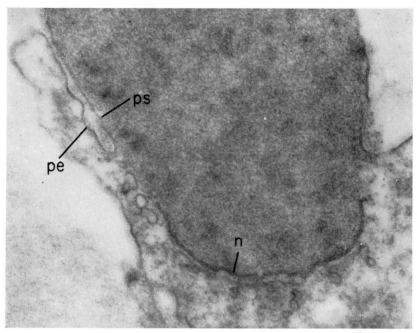

FIG. 5. Electron micrograph of a spermatozoon of *Hydroides hexagonus* in the process of entering the egg cytoplasm. Note the continuity of the egg plasma membrane (pe) with the plasma membrane of the spermatozoon (ps) and the intact nuclear envelope (n) at the apical region of the sperm nucleus. From A. L. Colwin and L. H. Colwin (1961).

Except for hyaluronidase, little or nothing is known of the chemistry of the other sperm lysins. The main difficulty obviously is that they are recovered in such minute amounts that any analysis is exceedingly difficult. The properties of the egg membrane lysins of *Megathura* (Tyler, 1939a), of *Mytilus* (Berg, 1950), and of *Hydroides* (A. L. and L. H. Colwin, 1958) suggest that they are proteins which accounts for their enzymatic nature. The activity of the sperm lysin of *Pomatoceros* is inhibited by oxidized glutathione, and the suggestion has been made that this lysin may be a proteolytic enzyme (Monroy, 1948b). Proteolytic activity has also been described in sea urchin spermatozoa (Lundblad, 1950, 1954a,b), but its significance in fertilization is not clear.

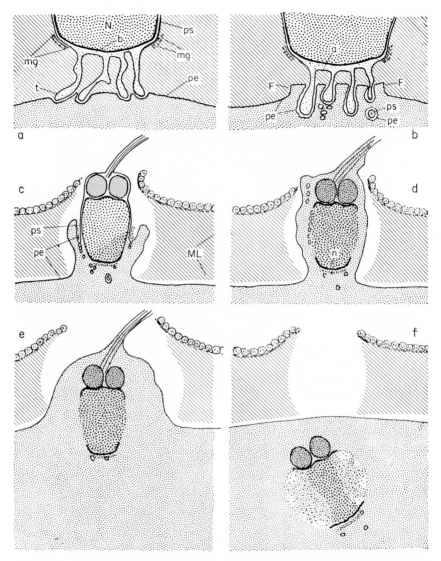

Fig. 6.   Diagrammatic representation of the stages in fusion and incorporation of the spermatozoon and egg of *Hydroides hexagonus*. (*a, b*): Acrosomal tubules of sperm head (t) have reached the egg and indent the egg plasma membrane (pe) which is, however, still intact; fertilization cone (F) begins to form. (*c*) Fusion of sperm plasma membrane (ps) and egg plasma membrane (pe) and vesiculation near presumed site of fusion occurs; acrosomal tubules are no longer visible, as such; egg cytoplasm is now in direct contact with apical part of sperm nucleus. (*d*) Sperm structures are now entirely surrounded by egg cytoplasm. Note the intact nuclear envelope (n) at the apical region of the sperm nucleus. (*e, f*): Sperm structures

The results discussed so far throw a new light on the role of the egg coats and membranes in fertilization. Indeed, these can no longer be considered merely as a protection for the egg but as being directly involved in some of the most important phenomena regulating and conditioning the penetration of the spermatozoon into the egg.

IV. The Reaction of the Egg to Sperm Penetration

A. *The Cortical Reaction and Its Role in the Activation of the Egg*

1. THE CORTEX OF THE SEA URCHIN EGG AND ITS CHANGES FOLLOWING FERTILIZATION

The contact established between the spermatozoon and the egg surface initiates the fertilization reaction. The formation of the fertilization cone might indeed be taken as an indication of a localized reaction of the egg to the stimulus of the contact with the acrosome filament. How long this reaction remains localized at the region of the cone is at present unknown—certainly not very long, since quite soon thereafter the morphological and physiological signs of its spreading all over the egg surface become apparent. It may be assumed that the fertilization cone is the site of origin of the cortical reaction and hence the place where the concentration of the factors responsible for the reaction itself attains its maximum. We will come back to this question during the course of the present discussion.

Evidence that the contact of the spermatozoon with and its penetration through the cortex brings about some kind of change in the cortex at the molecular level was first given by Runnström (1928), working with the sea urchin egg. Runnström observed that the interference color, which can be seen at the surface of the sea urchin egg when observed with dark field illumination, changes to a lower order upon fertilization, starting from the site of the entrance of the fertilizing spermatozoon. Runnström suggested that the change was due to the alteration of the dispersity of the lipids which he assumed to be the major component of the egg cortex. More compelling evidence that the molecular texture of the cortex undergoes a change at fertilization was provided by the demonstration that the cortical birefringence of

move deeply into the egg cytoplasm; the nucleus begins to become diffuse and the fertilization cone recedes. (N) Sperm nucleus; (mg) remnant of material of intermediate zone of the acrosome; (a) that part of sperm plasma membrane which was formerly acrosomal membrane; (b) ill-defined material which in earlier stages lies between nuclear envelope and acrosomal membrane at base of acrosome; (ML) middle layer of vitelline membrane. From A. L. and L. H. Colwin (1961).

the unfertilized egg transiently disappears at fertilization (Monroy, 1945, 1947; Monroy and Montalenti, 1947). The interpretation of this phenomenon is not too easy because, when it was originally discovered, it was considered as an indication of a disarrangement of the lipoprotein structure of the surface caused by some agent introduced by the sperm (Monroy, 1947, 1957b). Although this interpretation may be fundamentally correct, the electron microscope has brought to light new data which must be taken into consideration. The first concerns the thickness and structure of the cortex. Estimates derived from the examination of the cortex in polarized light had given thickness values between 1.5 and 1.8 μ (Monroy and Monroy-Oddo, 1946; Mitchison, 1952). Following the Harvey and Danielli (1936) model it was suggested that the cortex might consist of alternating protein and lipid leaflets (Runnström et al., 1943; Monroy, 1947) or of looped protein molecules with one single lipid layer at its outside (Mitchison, 1952). On the other hand, the electron micrographs (Endo, 1961) showed beyond any doubt that the cortex of the unfertilized sea urchin egg is bounded by two membranes; the outer one (about 30 Å thick) is the vitelline membrane (later part of the fertilization membrane) and the inner one (about 60 Å thick) is the egg plasma membrane. It seems doubtful that such a thin layer may give rise to the optical effects. Immediately underneath the plasma membrane and in close contact with it there is an array of globules (each 0.5–0.8 μ in diameter), which have a fairly complicated structure (Afzelius, 1956; Endo, 1961) (Fig. 7). However, they are too far apart from each other to contribute in any way to the birefringence of the cortex. Hence, there appears to be a discrepancy between the observations with the optical and with the electron microscope which it would be important to settle.

The study with the electron microscope of ultrathin sections has now shown (Endo, 1961; Mercer and Wolpert, 1962) that upon fertilization two important phenomena occur (Fig. 9).

(1) The outer membrane, i.e., the vitelline membrane, is separated from the plasma membrane; it undergoes an expansion and gives rise to the outer layer of the fertilization membrane (Fig. 8).

(2) The cortical granules explode and release three of their components. (a) The "dark bodies" which are the major component of the granules and in some electron micrographs appear as folded laminar bodies (Fig. 7). Upon release, they unfold and then join to and fuse with the inner side of the outer layer of the fertilization membrane (Fig. 9b, c); (b) the "homogeneous hemispheric globules" which slowly fuse together and build up a new covering at the surface of the egg, the hyaline layer (Fig. 9c). (c) Most probably, a "liquid" is ejected which

forms, or contributes to the formation of, the perivitelline fluid between the new egg surface and the fertilization membrane. The explosion of the cortical granules is brought about by a rupture at the outer surface which is in contact with the plasma membrane; at the point of rupture the membrane of the granule and the plasma membrane fuse together. Once the process is completed, i.e., the vitelline membrane has detached and formed the fertilization membrane, the new egg plasma membrane will be entirely different from that of the unfertilized egg.

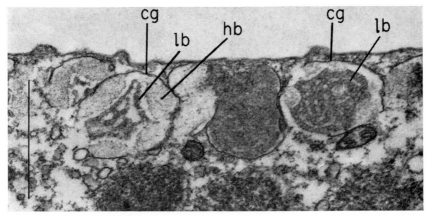

FIG. 7. Electron micrograph of the surface layer of an unfertilized egg of *Paracentrotus lividus* showing the structure of the cortical granules (cg) with the electron-opaque laminar bodies (lb) and the hemispheric bodies (hb). Courtesy of Dr. G. Millonig.

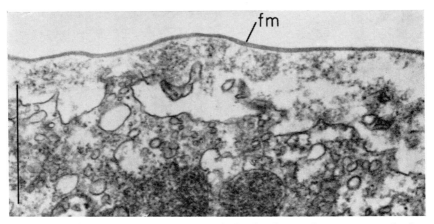

FIG. 8. Electron micrograph of a newly fertilized egg of *Paracentrotus lividus*. Fertilization membrane (fm) is just being formed; the cortical granules have emptied into the perivitelline space. Courtesy of Dr. G. Millonig.

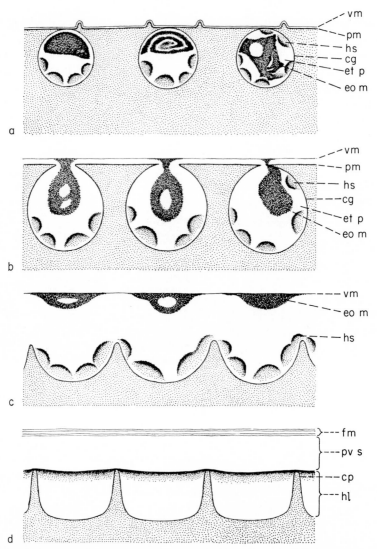

FIG. 9. Diagram showing the changes of the cortex of the egg of the sea urchin *Clypeaster japonicus* following fertilization. (*a*) Unfertilized egg; (*b*) the explosion of the cortical granules; (*c*) adhesion of electron-opaque material to the vitelline membrane now lifted up; complete fusion of this material with the membrane will give rise to the fertilization membrane. Meanwhile, the hemispheric bodies remain at the surface of the egg and give rise to the hyaline layer. (*d*) The egg surface upon completion of these changes. (cg) Cortical granules; (cp) cytoplasmic projection; (eo m) electron-opaque material; (et p) electron-transparent portion; (fm) fertilization membrane; (hl) hyaline layer; (hs) hemispheres; (pm) plasma membrane; (pv s) perivitelline space; (vm) vitelline membrane. From Endo (1961).

Indeed, apart from the newly built hyaline layer, the actual cell surface will consist of a mosaic of areas derived from the membrane of the granules and from the original plasma membrane of the unfertilized egg (Fig. 9d). These changes are considerably more complex than originally supposed and they imply a complete rearrangement in the molecular organization of the cortical layer, which may well account for the disappearance of the cortical birefringence and for the permeability changes of the egg.

2. THE CORTICAL CHANGES IN EGGS OTHER THAN ECHINODERMS

The presence of cortical granules has been recognized in the eggs of several invertebrates and vertebrates. For example, at the surface of the mature egg of the amphibians (Osanai, 1960a) there are granules whose content gives the reaction of the sulfated acid mucopolysaccharides. Following fertilization, these granules break up; and at the same time the perivitelline fluid, which also appears to contain sulfated acid mucopolysaccharides, is formed. At the same time a thin layer giving a positive periodic acid–Schiff (PAS) reaction forms at the surface of the egg. Also, in the mammalian egg, at least in the hamster (Austin, 1956), cortical granules have been described; they seem to disappear following fertilization. The cortical vacuoles of fishes may also be considered homologous to the cortical granules. The disintegration of these vacuoles begins at the animal pole, where the spermatozoon enters the egg through the micropylar canal, and proceeds toward the vegetal pole. This disintegration is accompanied by the extrusion of the vacuolar fluid content, which may be responsible for the hardening of the chorion (Nakano, 1956). There is, however, some suggestion that the hardening of the chorion may be caused by an enzyme secreted by the egg and not contained in the vacuoles (Zotin, 1958). On the other hand, there are eggs in which cortical changes, if they exist (the discussion which follows suggests that they do exist), are so subtle that they escape observation.

In the eggs of the annelids, *Pomatoceros* and *Chaetopterus*, no structural changes in the cortical layer at fertilization have been indicated by light microscopy (Monroy, 1948b, 1954). Evidence of some change has been given in *Hydroides* (L. H. and A. L. Colwin, 1961). Nevertheless, the eggs of *Hydroides norvegica* undergo a transient period of great sensitivity to taurocholate during the first 5 minutes following fertilization, whereas the eggs of *Chaetopterus* become more resistant to it (Monroy, 1954). Although difficult to interpret, these observations do suggest that some kind of a change takes place in the surface layer of these eggs. On the other hand, Pasteels and de Harven (1962) have reported that in the egg of *Barnea candida* the explosion of the cortical granules is independent of fertilization and, indeed, occurs with the same frequency before and after fertilization. Furthermore, the content of the granules appears to empty *inside* the egg cytoplasm (Fig. 10).

Therefore, the only tentative conclusion one can suggest at present is that, although in some eggs the cortical granules and vacuoles participate in an important step of fertilization, they do not seem to be directly involved in the main process of the activation itself. The ex-

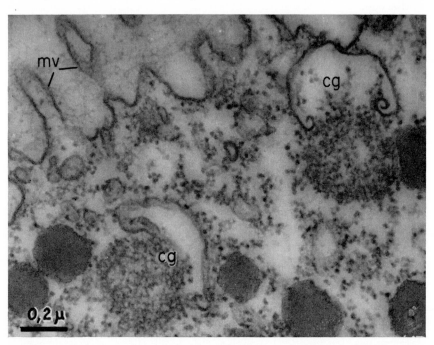

FIG. 10. Electron micrograph of an unfertilized egg of *Barnea candida,* showing two cortical granules (cg) emptying their contents toward the inside of the egg. (mv) Microvilli. From Pasteels and de Harven (1962).

periments by Sugiyama (1953a, b, 1956) are particularly relevant to this problem. Sugiyama has found that some egg activators, such as the wasp venom and various detergents, when acting on a limited area of the egg surface, initiate a kind of localized activation, i.e., the cortical granules explode and a membrane forms only in the activated area. This observation seems to eliminate the possibility that the breakdown of a cortical granule may be the cause of the breakdown of its neighbors. On the other hand, there are agents, and the spermatozoon among them, which, when acting on a point of the egg surface, give rise to a "propagating response." In this case, the breakdown of the granules starting from the point which was activated rapidly propagates over the entire egg surface. Evidently, the propagating response for the breakdown of the granules must be secondary to some other reaction— probably the activating reaction proper. Such a propagating response has also been observed in the breakdown of the cortical alveoli of fish eggs and has been described by Yamamoto (see summary, 1961) as a "fertilization wave." A mathematical analysis of the propagation of the cortical change in the sea urchin egg suggests an autocatalytic process (Kacser, 1955).

3. CORTICAL CHANGES AND ACTIVATION OF THE EGG

A problem of considerable importance is to what extent the cortical changes are a necessary prerequisite for the activation of the egg. Only a few data are available to answer this question and all of them are of an indirect character. Motomura (1954) has found that potassium permanganate causes nuclear activation in the sea urchin egg but the fertilization membrane does not form. Although Motomura's paper does not state whether cortical changes other than membrane formation were inhibited, this experiment would seem to suggest that nuclear activation may take place independently of those cortical changes which are related to membrane formation.

If eggs are drawn into glass capillaries (Allen, 1954), the cortical reaction does not spread over the entire egg surface and the egg cytoplasm lying beneath the unchanged cortex does not show any of the morphological changes usually observed at fertilization. Nevertheless, the female pronucleus, even when surrounded by unchanged cytoplasm, responds to the presence of the male pronucleus with swelling and membrane breakdown. Migration and fusion of the pronuclei are, however, inhibited. Also, the experiments by Osanai (1960b) show that nuclear activation is possible in the absence of cortical changes. These data, although scanty, suggest that upon activation either two groups of substances are released in the cortex, one acting on the cytoplasm and the other on the nucleus, or one single substance is formed, but the threshold of reaction of the cytoplasm to this substance is higher than that of the nucleus. It also seems that the activating reaction or its products diffuse *from* the cortex *to* the cytoplasm.

Another point of interest is that upon fertilization a transient or permanent shrinkage of the egg takes place. In the sea urchin egg what one usually sees is a transient wrinkling of the egg surface which becomes particularly evident when the eggs are observed with incident light. However, from time to time, batches of eggs are encountered which have undergone a marked change of shape upon fertilization (especially in *Sphaerechinus granularis*). In about 5 minutes the eggs again become perfectly spherical. In *Chaetopterus* and in *Hydroides*, on the other hand, a permanent decrease in volume follows fertilization (Monroy, 1954).

In fish eggs (*Oryzias*) a 7–13 % decrease in volume has been observed; it may be accounted for by the emptying of the cortical alveoli (Yamamoto, 1961). In the other eggs previously mentioned, where there are neither cortical granules nor alveoli, a "squeezing" of fluid from the whole cytoplasm of the egg may be suggested. The nature of this squeezing process will be discussed later.

4. THE POLYSPERMY—PREVENTING REACTION

Before entering into the discussion of the biochemical events underlying the structural change of the egg cortex upon fertilization it seems appropriate to mention briefly one of the most important physiological expressions of such changes, i.e., the polyspermy-preventing reaction. This reaction consists in a change sweeping rather rapidly over the egg surface which makes the egg impermeable to further spermatozoa after the first one has established successful contact with the egg. In the framework of his fertilizin theory, Lillie (1914) maintained that a layer of reactive fertilization molecules is present in the cortex of the unfertilized egg, each molecule bearing a spermophyle and an ovophyle group. Fertilization consists in the reaction of the sperm receptor(s) with one or more spermophyle group(s) of fertilizin. This reaction "activates" the fertilizin molecules which have reacted with the spermatozoon and the activation spreads rapidly to all the fertilizin molecules at the surface of the egg. The ovophyle group of each activated fertilizin molecule reacts with and binds an egg receptor; this is the egg-activating reaction. The spermophyle group binds an antifertilizin molecule, thus making the fertilizin molecules unreactive, i.e., the egg becomes inaccessible to further spermatozoa. The block against polyspermy results from a fertilizin-antifertilizin reaction. Rothschild and Swann (1949, 1951, 1952) have tried to calculate the rate of propagation of the polyspermy-preventing reaction and correlate it with visible surface changes. They have reached the conclusion that, as soon as contact between the spermatozoon and the egg surface is established, a rapid change occurs which covers the whole egg surface in about 2 seconds and causes a relative "refractoriness" of the egg to other spermatozoa. A slower change follows which in about 1 minute makes the egg *fully* refractory to the entrance of a second spermatozoon. Taking into consideration the structural changes of the egg surface following fertilization it is not surprising that the egg may become impermeable to spermatozoa. In some sea urchin species (*Lytechinus pictus* and *Lytechinus variegatus*) the removal of the fertilization membrane leaves the egg fully open to sperm entry (i.e., the egg may now be entered by numerous spermatozoa), whereas in others, such as *Dendraster excentricus*, the demembraned egg remains unresponsive (Tyler *et al.*, 1956a). In the latter case, however, in a Ca^{++}-free medium, the egg can be refertilized and becomes polyspermic (Ishida and Nakano, 1947, 1950; Sugiyama, 1951; Nakano, 1954). The question now is whether in such cases sperm receptors are present at the new surface of the fertilized egg and whether the kind of reaction that takes place between the spermatozoon and the egg surface is identical with or similar to the one that occurs with the unfertilized egg. Experimental evidence indicates that the surface of the fertilized egg is incapable of developing a polyspermy-preventing reaction and in this respect the surface of the fertilized egg appears somewhat like that of the oocyte. In fact it is known that oocytes are unable to develop a polyspermy-preventing reaction; when inseminated they become largely polyspermic, and from each point of sperm attachment a fertilization cone develops. It is also worthwhile mentioning that the oocyte, like the newly fertilized egg, lacks cortical birefringence which is progressively established during the course of maturation (Monroy, 1948a). Also, the cortical granules reach the surface upon maturation (Runnström and Monné, 1945; Monné and Hårde, 1951). This indicates that a certain specific molecular arrangement is necessary for the defense mechanism to become operative. Circumstantial evidence in support of this view is derived from the results of a number of experiments on the effect of proteolytic enzymes on the living egg. Trypsin treatment of the unfertilized egg prevents the elevation of the fertilization membrane and renders the egg highly susceptible to polyspermy (Hagström and Hagström, 1954; Tyler and Metz, 1955). Probably, this occurs not through the removal of the vitelline membrane but only through the breaking of some bonds both in the vitelline membrane and in the plasma membrane; thus, the latter becomes unable to propagate the defense response. Indeed, unless very high concentrations of trypsin are used, no change in the surface of the egg can be detected with the electron microscope (Wolpert and Mercer, 1961).

In some animals the defense mechanisms against polyspermy are not located in the egg cortex. In the ascidians, for example, the defense mechanism against self-fertilization and heterologous fertilization resides in the chorion (Morgan, 1923; Reverberi, 1935; Minganti, 1948). Whether the polyspermy-preventing mechanisms reside in the membranes or in the cortex remains to be ascertained. In the eggs of the Mediterranean *Ciona*, Ortolani (personal communication, 1963) did not find any polyspermy following removal of the membranes even in the presence of excess spermatozoa. On the other hand, the denuded eggs of *Ciona* of the Pacific coast were found to be more susceptible to polyspermic fertilization (Tyler, personal communication, 1963).

In some mammals (e.g., hamster, dog) the defense against polyspermy resides in the zona pellucida which upon penetration of one spermatozoon becomes inaccessible to further penetrations. In other mammals, on the other hand, this zona reaction (Braden *et al.*, 1954) is less efficient (as in rat and mouse) or is entirely lacking (as in rabbit). Since these eggs, however, are normally monospermic, some other mechanism, probably a surface change, must be operative (for further details, see Austin, 1961).

5. CHANGES IN PERMEABILITY FOLLOWING FERTILIZATION

One of the typical changes occurring in the egg as a result of fertilization has often been considered an increase in permeability. It must be stressed that the word "permeability" will be used here only operationally, i.e., merely to indicate the rate of traffic across the egg surface. Experiments show that when unfertilized sea urchin eggs are exposed to labeled inorganic or organic molecules saturation is rapidly attained (see, e.g., Bolst and Whiteley, 1957; Tyler and Monroy, 1959; Monroy *et al.*, 1961; Monroy and Vittorelli, 1962). Immediately following fertilization, the rate of transfer of these molecules across the membrane is considerably increased. Whiteley and Chambers (1960) have shown that in the case of phosphate this increase is probably due to the differentiation, within the first few minutes following fertilization, of a phosphate transport mechanism in the egg surface. This correlates with the extensive structural changes that take place in the egg cortex at fertilization and further extends their significance in the metabolism of the egg. Indeed, if the breakdown of the cortical granules in the sea urchin egg is inhibited, the permeability changes do not take place (Ishikawa, 1954). It may also be pertinent to mention here that in the transformation of normal plant cells into crown-gall tumors a change in the membrane permeability (or in the ion-transport systems) takes place. This is considered of fundamental importance for the activation by ions of a number of metabolic processes specifically concerned with cell growth and division (Braun and Wood, 1962). Indeed, if it were shown that the increased ionic exchange following fertilization does play an important role in the activation of some of the fundamental metabolic events that follow fertilization, the cortical reaction would acquire a key position in the whole process of the activation of the egg.

6. CHANGES IN THE ELECTRICAL PROPERTIES AS A RESULT OF
   FERTILIZATION

The observation of an increased permeability to water of the sea urchin egg immediately following fertilization had led R. S. Lillie (1916) to suggest the interesting hypothesis of the fundamental similarity between the phenomena of the response of the egg to fertilization and the response of the nerve fiber to stimulation. However, the situation in eggs of various animals is variable; for example, the unfertilized fish egg is freely permeable to water but becomes impermeable following fertilization (Yamamoto, 1961; Ito, 1960). A similar decrease occurs in *Rana* (Picken and Rothschild, 1948), whereas no change has been observed in the urodele *Hynobius* (Kusa, 1951).

Lillie's suggestion prompted a number of investigations aimed at finding out whether fertilization was accompanied by electrical changes similar to those observed in the stimulated nerve fiber. At first, however, conflicting results were obtained owing primarily to the difficulty in pushing microelectrodes through the highly extensible egg surface (Tyler and Monroy, 1955). Recently, a number of measurements have been made on eggs of echinoderms, fishes, and amphibians; the results are generally consistent in showing a change in the electrical properties of the egg membrane fundamentally similar to that observed in the stimulated nerve fiber. In the starfish *Asterias forbesii*, for example, a membrane potential of 30–60 mV, inside negative, has been found and this potential undergoes a decrease of about 10 mV at fertilization. The change, which lasts about 1 minute, is very slow compared with the very fast one occurring upon stimulation of the nerve fiber. It begins approximately when the first signs of egg reaction to sperm penetration become visible and terminates when the fertilization membrane is elevated (Fig. 11) (Tyler *et al.*, 1956b). Similar changes have been detected in *Peronella lesseuri* (Hiramoto, 1959a, b), where a simultaneous drop in the membrane resistance (from 3940 to 2380 ohm/cm^2) has also been recorded; this is in accord with the increased permeability to water. Also, in the egg of the teleostean fish *Oryzias latipes* as well as in the egg of *Bufo* (Maeno, 1959), a drop in membrane potential has been found to occur in conjunction with activation (Maeno *et al.*, 1956; Ito and Maeno, 1960). In general, it seems fairly safe to state that fertilization can be considered as a process of cell stimulation and, hence, that the membrane phenomena that occur in the egg at fertilization may, broadly speaking, be treated in the same way as those of the nerve. The similarity between the two is further emphasized by the results of experiments showing that in the echinoderm egg the distribution of K$^+$ and Na$^+$ between the inside and the outside medium is the same as in nerve or muscle. In fact, whereas the concentration of K+ in the egg is about seventeen times higher than in sea water, the concentration of Na+ is negligible (Rothschild and Barnes, 1953; Tyler *et al.*, 1956b). Following fertilization a transient release of K+ is observed, which coincides with the electrical changes (Tyler and Monroy, 1959).

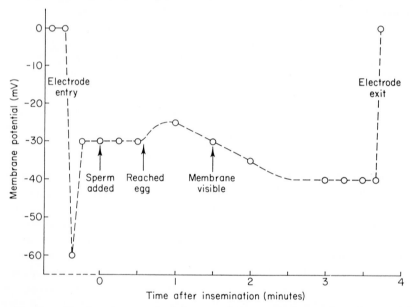

FIG. 11.   Membrane potential of the egg of *Asterias forbesii* and its changes following fertilization. Entry of the electrode into the egg causes a sudden appearance of a —60 mV membrane potential, which rapidly decreases to —30 mV. The previously steady potential decreases by 5 mV, as soon as the sperm contacts the egg. Subsequently, the potential again increases and remains steady at —40 mV, until the electrode is removed. From Tyler *et al.* (1956b).

It would be interesting to extend these studies to the eggs of other animals also and to check whether the release of K+ is preceded by a transient uptake of Na+ as in the stimulated nerve. This experiment, at least in the case of marine eggs, is difficult owing to the high concentration of Na+ in the outer medium and the very low Na+ content of the egg. An observation by Brooks (1939), however, indicates an accumulation of Na+ in the *Urechis* egg following fertilization, which may be taken as an indication that in the egg the same condition prevails as in the nerve. Although not strictly related to the problem of fertilization, it would be interesting to find out whether or not the concentration of Na+ increases during the course of development. Indeed, it has been found that Na$^+$ accumulates in the nucleus and that it is necessary for nuclear protein synthesis (Allfrey *et al.*, 1961; Naora *et al.*, 1962).

7. EXPERIMENTS AND HYPOTHESES AS TO THE ROLE OF THE CORTICAL LAYER IN THE ACTIVATION OF THE EGG

The two best known theories which emphasize the role of the egg cortex in fertilization are the fertilizin theory of Lillie and the lysin theory of J. Loeb (best summarized in 1916).

As previously mentioned in this section, according to Lillie the reaction of the ovophyle groups of the fertilizin molecules with the egg receptors is the basis of egg activation. On the other hand, according to Loeb (1913), the spermatozoon when reacting with the egg cortex injects, so to speak, a substance which causes a "surface cytolysis" which results in the release of the activating substance. The surface cytolysis, however, is a transient phenomenon interrupted by a "correcting" factor. In the hypothesis favored by Runnström (1949) the key to the activation is the breakdown of an enzyme-inhibitor complex present in the egg cortex. This breakdown may be caused by some factor introduced by the spermatozoon, which binds the inhibitor and thus releases the enzyme. The inhibitor, according to Runnström (1949), is a mucopolysaccharide similar to or identical with the jelly-coat substance. The hypothesis presented by the writer (Monroy, 1956, 1957b) involves a modified lysin theory and is based on some experiments carried out by Monroy (1953) and Maggio and Monroy (1955), using a model system. These experiments show the ability of live sea urchin spermatozoa to release phospholipids from the lipovitellin of the hen's egg. These phospholipids break down and release lysophosphatides (as revealed by the appearance of a hemolytic activity) which then undergo further hydrolysis (disappearance of the hemolytic activity). It has been suggested that the sperm lipases may activate egg lipases at the point of contact thus giving rise to an autocatalytic reaction which spreads through the surface layers of the egg. Furthermore, this may bring about the breakdown of the lipoprotein complex. A similar interpretation has been advanced by Yamamoto (1961) as the first step in the activation of the fish egg. The disappearance of the cortical birefringence following fertilization has been cited by the writer as evidence in favor of this interpretation. The next step in the hypothesis is of a more speculative character: It is thus suggested that during this reaction phospholipids are set free and by further degradation they release lysophosphatides, which are presumed to be the activating factor.

The presence of lysolecithin in the newly fertilized sea urchin eggs has recently been shown chromatographically; no lysolecithin is present in unfertilized eggs. A relevant increase of choline is also observed in conjunction with fertilization (Numanoi, 1959a). In *in vitro* experiments it can be shown that the addition of spermatozoa to a homogenate of unfertilized eggs results in the formation of lysolecithin (Numanoi, 1959b). At present, it is difficult to say whether these experimental results have any bearing on the problem of the activation or whether they are intermediate steps in metabolic processes other than the activation proper or just artifacts due to the *in vitro* conditions. Nevertheless, these results open the way to a new experimental approach to the problem.

Although each of the hypotheses that have just been presented has some evidence in its favor, they are all more or less speculative, and the nature of the activating reaction still remains only a matter of conjecture. Important developments in the study of the role of the cortex in the activation of the egg might come from serological experiments. In his studies on the surface antigens of the sea urchin egg Perlmann (summarized in 1959) has indicated the presence of an antigen, called activation or A-antigen, whose determinants seem to be chiefly carbohydrates, which may play an important role in the process of activation. When eggs are treated with an antiserum containing the anti-A antibodies, they undergo activation. However, attempts to confirm the ability of such antisera to activate the egg (Tyler, 1959; Tyler *et al.*, 1961) have not been successful. Furthermore, the situation is complicated by the fact that normal rabbit and sheep sera are known to bring about activation of some sea urchin eggs, (Runnström *et al.*, 1944). Experiments along these lines are certainly worthwhile pursuing, since they may yield very important results.

B. *The Metabolic Reaction*

1. Oxygen Consumption in Relation to Fertilization

The metabolic studies on fertilization were inaugurated by the classic work of Warburg (summarized in 1911) on the respiration of the fertilized sea urchin egg.

Warburg discovered that within the first hour after fertilization the rate of oxygen consumption of the sea urchin egg had undergone a six- to sevenfold increase. This observation thus appeared to support Loeb's hypothesis (best summarized in 1916) which regarded the increase in the rate of oxidation as one of the fundamental steps in fertilization or parthenogenetic activation. However, when these observations were extended to the eggs of other animals, not only were some found in which no change in the rate of O_2 uptake takes place following fertilization, but in some others the oxygen consumption even appeared to decline (see Table III). The significance of these differences is still largely unexplained, and various interpretations have been advanced. Special importance has been attached to the condition of the nucleus at the

TABLE III
THE RATIO OF O_2 UPTAKE IN FERTILIZED AND UNFERTILIZED EGGS[a]

Organism	Stage of maturation at time of fertilization	Ratio[b] $(-O_2f)/(-O_2u)$	References
Nereis succinea	Germinal	1.3	Barron (1932)
Mactra laterialis	vesicle	1.8	Ballentine (1940)
Urechis caupo		1.2	Tyler and Humason (1937)
Nereis limbata		1.35–1.45	Whitaker (1931c)
Cumingia tellinoides		0.45	Whitaker (1931b)
Chaetopterus variopedatus	Metaphase of the first	0.53	Whitaker (1933a)
Marthasterias glacialis	maturation	1.0	Borei (1948)
Saxostrea commercialis	division	1.0	Cleland (1950)
Sabellaria alveolata		1.1	Fauré-Fremiet (1922)
Ciona intestinalis		1.0	Holter and Zeuthen (1944)
Ciona intestinalis		1.5	Tyler and Humason (1937)
Ciona intestinalis		2.0	Lentini (1961)
Phallusia mamillata		2.0	Lentini (1961); Minganti (1957)
Rana temporaria	Metaphase of	1.0	Zeuthen (1944)
Bufo bufo	the second	1.0	Stefanelli (1938)
Fundulus heteroclitus	maturation	16.7	Boyd (1928)
Fundulus heteroclitus	division	1.0	Philips (1940)
Oryzias latipes		1.0	Nakano (1953)
Fucus vesiculosus	Maturation	1.9	Whitaker (1931a)
Strongylocentrotus purpuratus	completed	3.7	Tyler and Humason (1937)
Psammechinus miliaris		3.6	Borei (1948)
Paracentrotus lividus		4.7	Brock et al. (1938)
Arbacia punctulata		4.5	Ballentine (1940)

[a] From a table by Rothschild (1956b), with additions.
[b] O_2 uptake of fertilized eggs $(-O_2f)$; O_2 uptake of unfertilized eggs $(-O_2u)$.

time of fertilization (whether in the germinal vesicle stage, or arrested at the metaphase of the first or second maturation division, or fully matured), as a factor influencing the direction of the respiratory change following fertilization. In particular, it has been suggested that a great increase of respiration only takes place in those eggs, like the sea urchin eggs, which were fertilized after completion of maturation. Here again, however, more extensive investigations did not support the general validity of this hypothesis.

Upon examining eggs of the second group in Table III (fertilized at the metaphase of the first maturation division) we find some (*Cumingia, Chaetopterus*) in which, as a result of fertilization, a temporary decline in respiration occurs and others in which no change seems to take place. Holter and Zeuthen (1944), using the sensitive diver technique, observed no change in the eggs of *Ciona intestinalis* of the North Sea. On the other hand, employing the conventional Warburg technique, Tyler and Humason (1937) recorded a ratio of 1.5 (along the Pacific coast), and Lentini (1961) observed a ratio close to 2 (in the Mediterranean). Evidently, apart from differences in the techniques employed there seem to be conditions, other than the stage reached in maturation, that influence the respiratory response to activation. Furthermore, for the interpretation of the data collected in Table III it must be noted that only some of the data refer to observations made within the first 10 minutes after fertilization (e.g., Whitaker's data on *Nereis, Cumingia,* and *Chaetopterus*). Most of the others, however, are average values of oxygen consumption during the first or the first and second hours after fertilization. In most cases, the measurements only were started some time after fertilization; therefore, the changes occurring at fertilization have been missed. Undoubtedly, there are a number of technical difficulties which hamper the measurement of the respiratory exchanges of the eggs immediately upon fertilization. However, when these measurements have been successful, interesting information has been obtained. For example, in the experiments of Whitaker (1933a, b) on the egg of *Chaetopterus* he was able to show a sudden drop of about 50 % in the rate of oxygen consumption in the unfertilized egg within the first 5–10 minutes following fertilization (Fig. 12). Between 1 and 2 hours afterward (completion of the first cleavage) respiration begins to increase, and at about the fourth hour it has regained the prefertilization level. A converse type of change takes place in the sea urchin egg and serves as an illustration of the pitfalls inherent in such experiments (Laser and Rothschild, 1939) (Fig. 13).

Upon fertilization the rate of oxygen consumption suddenly increases. Within 10 minutes after fertilization, however, the rate of respiration falls back to values only slightly higher than in the unfertilized egg and then starts to increase quite rapidly. The sudden rise in oxygen consumption is accompanied by a correspondingly rapid and strong production of CO_2 which compensates for the manometric depression due to the utilization of oxygen (Fig. 13). Hence, if no special precautions are taken, a false impression is created—that during the first 10 minutes following fertilization respiration ceases altogether (Laser and Rothschild, 1939). Unequivocal demonstration of the transient jump in the rate of oxygen consumption immediately after fertilization has been given by Ohnishi and Sugiyama (1963) using a polarographic method. The initial

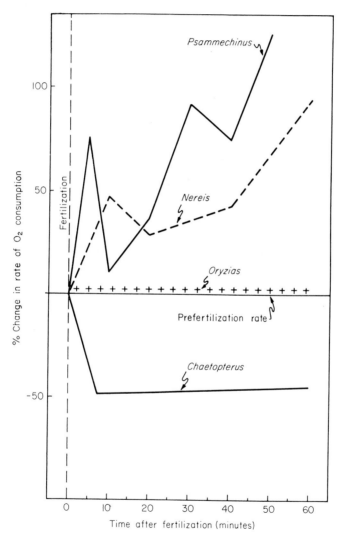

FIG. 12. A composite diagram indicating the changes in the rate of oxygen consumption in the egg during the first 60 minutes following fertilization. *Psammechinus:* data of Laser and Rothschild (1939); *Nereis* and *Chaetopterus:* data of Whitaker (1931c, 1933a); *Oryzias:* data of Nakano (1953).

overshoot in the rate of oxygen consumption is probably also present in *Nereis* (Whitaker, 1931c) (Fig. 12).

Research along these lines was discouraged by the observation of Borei (1948, 1949) that the rate of oxygen consumption in the un-fertilized egg of *Psammechinus miliaris* declines after removal from the ovary. Borei claimed that the result of fertilization was only to bring the rate of oxygen consumption back to the level the ripe egg had in

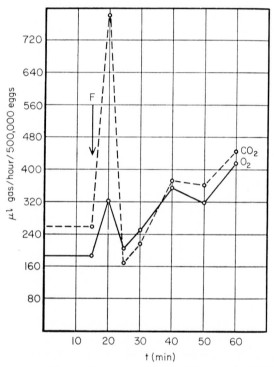

Fɪɢ. 13. CO_2 production and O_2 consumption following fertilization in the egg of *Psammechinus miliaris*; (F) insemination. From Laser and Rothschild (1939).

the gonad. Hence, if the egg could be fertilized immediately after re-moval from the gonad no change in the oxygen consumption ought to be observed. However, a re-examination of the question using extensive material (Yasumasu and Nakano, 1963) has shown that in all the sea urchin eggs examined there is no appreciable decline in the respiration of the unfertilized egg after several hours and fertilization is invariably followed by a sudden increase in the rate of oxygen consumption (Fig. 14). Most likely, the material studied by Borei is peculiar in this respect. It must be remembered that the egg of the *Psammechinus miliaris* of the Swedish west coast is the only one failing to exhibit the transient disappearance of the cortical birefringence upon fertilization (for a discussion, see Monroy, 1957b). Since the Swedish *Psammechinus* lives in water in which the salinity is very low close to the surface and increases progressively with depth, these conditions might be responsible for influencing the metabolism of the egg. It would be interesting to determine "if" and "how" this occurs.

Finally, the work of Tyler and Humason (1937) on the echiuroid worm *Urechis caupo* illustrates how the general condition of the animal may influence the type of respiratory response of the egg upon fertilization. The rate of respiration of the unfertilized eggs of *Urechis* is, in

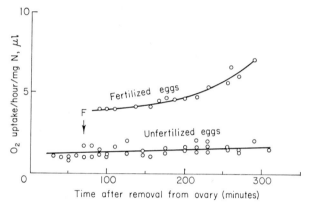

FIG. 14. Oxygen uptake in unfertilized and fertilized eggs of *Hemicentrotus pulcherrimus*; (F) insemination. From Yasumasu and Nakano (1963).

fact, considerably higher when the eggs are obtained from freshly collected animals. On the other hand, measurements taken on newly fertilized eggs show a remarkable uniformity in the rate of oxygen consumption, which is more or less intermediate between the highest and the lowest values. This means that as a result of fertilization the rate of oxygen consumption in this animal tends to a certain value which is independent of the prefertilization values. This finding is in agreement with the suggestion of Whitaker (1933b) that "the changes in the rate of oxygen consumption at fertilization by the different species of eggs, differing both in direction and magnitude, appear to be such as to bring the rate, when development is initiated, to about the same rate, which is also the rate of other comparable normally growing cells."

It must be stressed that only measurements of oxygen consumption do not take one very far. In fact, when a change is observed, it is a certain indication that a metabolic change has occurred within the egg which, among other things, has somehow influenced the respiratory system. The absence of a respiratory change, on the other hand, does not allow one to conclude that such a change has not occurred. A clear demonstration of this is given by the *Bufo* egg in which the rate of oxygen consumption does not undergo any change following fertilization (Stefanelli, 1938), but the respiratory quotient decreases from near unity to 0.66 thus indicating a change in the type of substrates utilized (Brachet, 1945). The study of the respiratory quotient may supply a great deal of additional interesting information. Determinations of the respiratory quotient, however, in the presence of sea water are technically difficult and open to serious objections (see Laser and Rothschild, 1939; Rothschild, 1956a). The data thus far available are quite unsatisfactory and do not allow one to draw even tentative conclusions as to whether or not any change occurs in the substrates utilized by the egg before and after fertilization. This is indeed a very important and still unanswered question.

2. Carbohydrate Metabolism and the Question of the "Fertilization Acid"

When a sudden demand for energy arises in an organism, the carbohydrates are thought of as the most likely candidates for fuel. Our knowledge of carbohydrate metabolism in the sea urchin egg has been summarized in detail by Rothschild (1956b) and the question has since progressed very little. From unfertilized eggs of *Paracentrotus* a glycoprotein, with glucose as the only carbohydrate component, has been isolated (Monroy and Vittorelli, 1960) which disappears within 5 minutes after fertilization. This is paralleled by a 20 % decrease of the total amount of polysaccharides in the trichloroacetic acid (TCA)-soluble fraction, whereas the total amount of carbohydrates does not undergo any significant change. At the same time a striking increase of glucose 6-phosphate, of fructose diphosphate, and of triose phosphate occurs (Aketa *et al.*, 1964). The low level of these esters in the unfertilized egg is certainly a limiting factor of the oxidative utilization of carbohydrates. It seems likely then that in the unfertilized egg there is a block of the pathway leading from glycogen to glucose 6-phosphate and which is released upon fertilization. Since the phosphorylase reaction is considered as the key step in the regulation of glycogenolysis (see Axelrod, 1960), it is suggested that in the unfertilized egg the phosphorylase is inhibited, activation occurring upon fertilization. The increased availability of hexose monophosphates, probably as a result of activation of the shunt may hence be involved in the increased rate of respiration that follows fertilization. That the shunt is the predominant pathway of glucose utilization in the sea urchin egg is demonstrated by a number of experiments (Lindberg and Ernster, 1948; Keltch *et al.*, 1956; Krahl, 1956) and its increased activity following fertilization is indicated by the increase of the concentration of TPNH (triphosphopyridine nucleotide, reduced form) during the first 1–3 hours of development (Krane and Crane, 1960, in *Arbacia* and *Spisula*). The importance of this pyridine nucleotide for the synthetic processes is worth mentioning here.

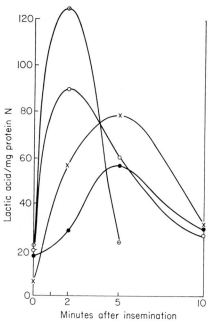

FIG. 15.   Transient production of lactic acid (in μg per mg protein N) in the egg of *Hemicentrotus pulcherrimus* following fertilization. The diagram indicates the time course of the phenomenon in four different experiments. From Aketa (1957).

On the other hand, a transient formation of lactic acid has been demonstrated in the egg of some sea urchin species upon fertilization (Fig. 15) (Aketa, 1957). This indicates that during the first few minutes after fertilization there may be a transient period during which the glycolytic pathway of carbohydrate utilization is pre-eminent, only to become immediately thereafter of minor, if of any, importance. There is, however, evidence that in later stages of development glycolysis again becomes important (Krahl, 1956). Anyway, what we lack at present is a comprehensive view of the time sequence and the linkage of all these metabolic events.

In particular, the question remains as to the significance of the sudden and transient increase in the oxygen consumption immediately following fertilization in sea urchin and probably also in *Nereis* eggs. As a working hypothesis it might be suggested that this increased rate may be caused by a transient uncoupling of the oxidative phosphorylation.

Another early event observed in the fertilization of the sea urchin egg that has also given rise to a number of discussions is the sudden production of an acid. This phenomenon was first described by Ashbel (1929) and extensively analyzed by Runnström (1933). The nature of the acid has been and still is a matter of discussion. The work of Runnström (1933) ruled out the possibility of lactic acid, and later work by Yčas (1950) dismissed the intermediates of the Krebs cycle. Although not dismissing the idea entirely, Aketa (1957) is not inclined to consider the existence of a link between the previously mentioned transient formation of lactic acid and the fertilization acid.

Mehl and Swann (1961) have offered the suggestion that the displacement of the CO_2 from the sea water is not due to the "production" of an acid but rather "to the changes in the number or strength of acidic and basic ionizing groups attached to the egg, resulting from changes in the state of certain proteins. This material may be on the outermost surface of the egg, outside the permeability membrane. If, on the other hand, it is inside the egg, the very high ionic flux suggests that the permeability membrane must break down completely for a few minutes after fertilization." But again Aketa (1963) has observed a release of $SO_4^=$ from the eggs immediately following fertilization and suggests that the fertilization acid may actually be sulfuric acid. According to Aketa, the breakdown of the acidic mucopolysaccharides of the cortical granules is responsible for the release of $SO_4^=$. Indeed, when the rupture of the cortical granules is inhibited, no acid production occurs.

3. THE CYTOCHROME SYSTEM AND THE METABOLIC BLOCK OF THE UNFERTILIZED EGG

For a more direct analysis of the respiratory metabolism of the egg a study of the isolated mitochondria, which are the site of the respiratory enzymes, has been undertaken by Maggio and her colleagues (Maggio and Ghiretti-Magaldi, 1958; Maggio, 1959; Maggio and Monroy, 1959; Maggio et al., 1960). First, they were able to show that the mitochondria of the unfertilized sea urchin egg contain a complete and operating system of cytochromes a_1, a_3, b, and c (Fig. 16) which is very similar to that of mammals (Maggio and Ghiretti-Magaldi, 1958). This observation is quite important because it settles the question of whether or not a cytochrome system is present in the sea urchin eggs and whether it is

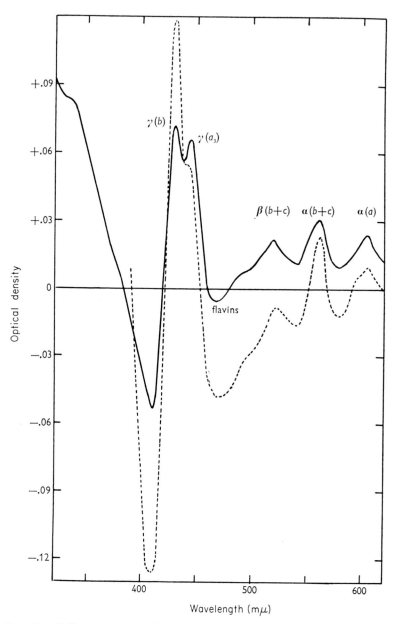

FIG. 16. Difference spectra (reduced minus oxidized) of a mitochondrial suspension of unfertilized eggs of *Sphaerechinus granularis* showing the peaks of the various cytochromes. (Solid line) reduction with succinate; (dotted line) reduction with dithionite. From Maggio and Ghiretti-Magaldi (1958).

similar to that typical in mammals (for a detailed summary of the question, see Rothschild, 1956b). It further strengthens the results of Robbie (1946) and Rothschild (1949), indicating that the respiration of the unfertilized sea urchin egg is reversibly inhibited by carbon monoxide and cyanide, thus proving that the cytochrome system is actually functioning, though at a low level.

The activity of the cytochrome oxidase was found to undergo only a small increase following fertilization (Maggio, 1959). However, since these determinations were carried out on mitochondrial preparations, and the cytochrome oxidase activity was referred to their protein content, there is a chance that the result might have been biased by a different degree of contamination of the preparation with nonmitochondrial material (for a discussion, see Monroy and Maggio, 1964). These experiments should be repeated, once a method to obtain clean preparations of mitochondria has been found. Anyway they indicate that the respiratory change observed *in vivo* does not depend on a sudden increase of cytochrome oxidase activity. Runnström (summarized in 1956) had previously suggested that in the unfertilized sea urchin egg there are structural factors which prevent the respiratory enzymes from coming into contact and reacting with their substrates (what would now be called compartmentation). In particular Runnström (1933) suggested that in the unfertilized egg the cytochrome oxidase is relatively "unsaturated" with reducing substrate; as development proceeds, the amount of saturation increases. This suggestion has recently been supported by observations on the ability of the egg to oxidize CO (Black et al., 1958; Black and Tyler, 1959a, b). It was shown that the respiratory rate of unfertilized eggs of sea urchin (Runnström, 1930; Lindahl, 1938; Rothschild, 1949), *Urechis* (Rothschild and Tyler, 1958), and ascidians (Minganti, 1957) is increased by CO. The work of Black et al. (1958) has now shown that this can be accounted for by the oxidation of CO to CO_2 operated by the cytochrome oxidase. Following fertilization, both in the eggs of *Urechis* and of *Strongylocentrotus*, the rate of CO oxidation in light increases. The experiments of Black and Tyler (1959b) on mitochondrial preparations of *Strongylocentrotus* eggs indeed show that the ability to oxidize CO increases with the increase of electron transfer. However, when this activity becomes very high, the CO oxidation decreases because CO acts as an inhibitor of cytochrome oxidase (see Breckenridge, 1953). Indeed, parallel to the increase in respiration during the course of development, the percent increase of gas uptake in the presence of CO in light decreases and there is a progressive increase of the inhibition in the dark. These results certainly favor the theory that the operation of the cytochrome system is progressively increased as development proceeds. Should it be proved that the activity of the cytochrome oxidase actually does not change during development (see previous discussion), then the most plausible interpretation of these results would be a changed compartimentation, as originally suggested by Runnström. New data pertinent to this subject have been obtained recently. In unfertilized sea urchin eggs an inhibitor of cytochrome oxidase has been identified (Fig. 17) which disappears or becomes considerably less active during the first few minutes following fertilization (Maggio and Monroy, 1959; Maggio *et al.*, 1960). Neither the nature of the inhibitor nor the process whereby it is removed

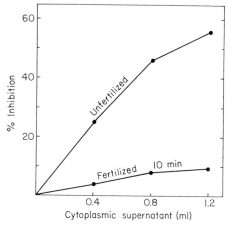

FIG. 17. Inhibitory effect of the cytoplasmic supernatant (supernatant after removal of particulates by ultracentrifugation) of unfertilized and fertilized eggs of *Paracentrotus lividus* on the cytochrome oxidase activity of mouse liver mitochondria. From Maggio and Monroy (1959).

are known; we only know that it is a heat- and alkali-labile, low molecular, nitrogen-free substance, the activity of which depends on the availability of SH groups. It acts competitively by interfering with the reoxidation of cytochrome oxidase. Whether or not this is the only factor which interferes with the activity of respiratory enzymes in the sea urchin egg is difficult to say. Nevertheless, it is clear that a block acting at the end of the chain of the electron-transport system will inevitably impair the energy-yielding systems as well. In connection with this it may be mentioned that Immers and Runnström (1960) studying the effect of dinitrophenol on the oxygen consumption of unfertilized and fertilized sea urchin eggs suggested that one of the causes of the increase in respiration following fertilization may be the increased availability of phosphate acceptors. In fact, it is known (Lardy and Wellman, 1952;

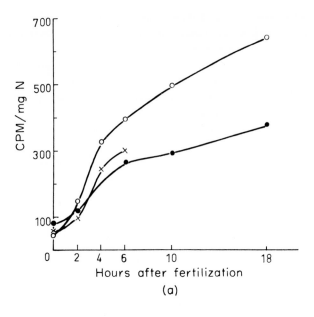

(a)

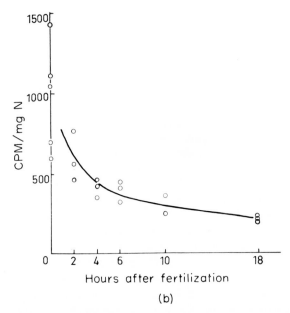

(b)

FIG. 18. Uptake of S³⁵-methionine by the mitochondria of developing *Paracentrotus lividus* (*a*) and parallel decrease of the radioactivity of the TCA-soluble fraction (*b*). Loading of the unfertilized eggs with the labeled amino acid by injection into the body cavity of the female. From Nakano and Monroy (1958b).

Slater and Hülsmann, 1959) that the availability of ADP (adenosine diphosphate) is the rate-limiting factor of oxygen consumption in the cells. Scarano (personal communication, 1963) has shown that in the unfertilized egg there is an accumulation of ATP (adenosine triphosphate) and little ADP. During the first 30 minutes following fertilization a decrease of ATP and an increase of ADP occurs, while AMP (adenosine phosphate) remains constant. Hence, the low ADP concentration may be one of the most important factors responsible for the low rate of respiration in the unfertilized sea urchin egg.

That the metabolic block of the unfertilized egg is largely due to some extramitochondrial factor is also shown by the following experiments.

The unfertilized sea urchin egg is able to take up labeled amino acids but very little, if any, incorporation occurs in the proteins. In particular, neither uptake nor incorporation occurs in the mitochondria. A few minutes after fertilization or parthenogenetic activation, a lively uptake of amino acids is observed in the mitochondria (Fig. 18), which is followed somewhat later by incorporation into the mitochondrial proteins (Nakano and Monroy, 1958b; Nakano et al., 1958; Giudice and Monroy, 1958). However, if the isolated mitochondria are tested in an in vitro system for their ability to incorporate amino acids into their proteins (Giudice, 1960), incorporation is observed also in the proteins of the mitochondria of the unfertilized egg. Actually, this ability is greater in the mitochondrial preparations of unfertilized eggs than in those of later developmental stages. Whether this decline is an artifact or a real one is at present dubious. These experiments again suggest that an extramitochondrial metabolic block may be operative in the unfertilized egg and that it impairs all the processes, which, like protein synthesis, require a large amount of energy.

4. THE INITIATION OF PROTEIN SYNTHESIS

The unfertilized sea urchin egg is able to carry out a number of synthetic processes. This is demonstrated for example by its ability to utilize glucose for the synthesis of glutamic and aspartic acid, alanine, and serine (Monroy and Vittorelli, 1962). It has also been shown that the unfertilized egg is able to utilize S^{35}-methionine for the synthesis of S^{35}-glutathione (Nakano and Monroy, 1958a). As soon as the egg is fertilized, a lively incorporation begins in the total proteins (i.e., in the total TCA-precipitate fraction) as well as in the subcellular fractions (Monroy, 1960; Giudice et al., 1962; Monroy and Vittorelli, 1962) thus indicating the beginning of a protein synthesis and/or turnover (Fig. 19). This raises the question of why the protein-synthesizing apparatus does not work in the mature unfertilized egg. In other words, there is the possibility that the various parts of the system, although present and potentially active, cannot function because of some factor foreign to the system, such as the presence of inhibitors or the lack of an energy supply. Conversely, some of the elements of the system might be either lacking or inactive. With *in vitro* experiments, Hultin and Bergstrand (1960) and Hultin (1961) have shown that the ribosomes isolated from

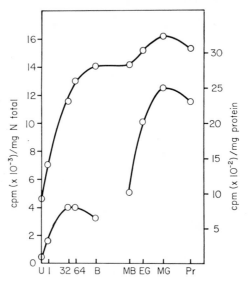

Fig. 19. Total uptake of C^{14} from glucose in the TCA-soluble fraction (upper curve and values on the left ordinate) and incorporation in the proteins (lower curve and values on the right ordinate) of eggs and embryos of *Paracentrotus lividus*. The eggs and the embryos were cultured in sea water containing 1 μc of C^{14}-D-glucose (U) per ml for 1 hour and processed immediately afterwards. (U) Unfertilized eggs; (1, 32, 64) 1-, 32-, and 64-cell stage; (B) early blastula; (MB) mesenchyme blastula; (EG) early gastrula; (MG) midgastrula; (Pr) prism. From Monroy and Vittorelli (1962).

unfertilized eggs display a poor ability to incorporate amino acids into the proteins, whereas this activity is markedly enhanced following fertilization. Hence, they have postulated an activation, interpreted as a structural rearrangement, of the ribosomes following fertilization which enables the ribosomes to acquire this capacity. Soon afterwards it was shown that ribosomes of unfertilized eggs can be stimulated by polyuridylic acid (poly-U) to synthesize polyphenylalanine (Tyler, 1962, 1963; Nemer, 1962b; Wilt and Hultin, 1962). This suggested that the difference between ribosomes of unfertilized and fertilized eggs may be that the former lack attached messenger RNA (mRNA). This suggestion was strengthened by the finding (Monroy and Tyler, 1963) that in the unfertilized egg ribosomes are mostly in the 73 S condition (monosomes), but soon after fertilization ribosomal aggregates (polysomes) begin to appear. The quantity of polysomes increases during the course of development. Recent work has shown that polysomes are indeed the active units engaged in protein synthesis (Marks *et al.*, 1962; Warner *et al.*, 1963; Wettstein *et al.*, 1963; Gierer, 1963; Gilbert, 1963), and there is evidence that they consist of ribosomes held together by a molecule of mRNA. We seem thus to be confronted with the alternative (a) either mRNA is lacking in the unfertilized egg and begins to be produced immediately following fertilization, or (b) mRNA is already present in the unfertilized egg but is unable to interact with the ribosomes.

The presence of mRNA in the unfertilized sea urchin egg was indicated by the fact that in actinomycin-treated eggs, in spite of a strong inhibition of RNA synthesis, protein synthesis proceded (at least quantitatively) unimpaired until the blastula stage (Gross and Cousineau, 1963; Gross *et al.*, 1964). More cogent evidence is that butyric acid activation stimulates protein synthesis in nonnucleated halves of unfertilized eggs (Brachet *et al.*, 1963; Denny and Tyler, 1964). This experiment rules out the possibility of a nuclear-dependent RNA synthesis stimulated by activation. It leaves, however, the possibility open of a mRNA synthesis directed by cytoplasmic DNA. RNA extracted and purified from unfertilized sea urchin eggs has now been proved to be able to stimulate amino acid incorporation into proteins by rat liver ribosomes (Maggio *et al.*, 1964). The same RNA, and also RNA from rat liver nuclei, which is very active on liver ribosomes, failed to stimulate ribosomes from unfertilized eggs. We seem thus to be led again to the conclusion that the crux of the problem lies in some structural peculiarity of the ribosomes of the unfertilized egg that are unable to interact with any mRNA and yet are stimulated by poly-U.

No one can fail to appreciate the importance of obtaining an answer to this question. Another problem which is certainly more difficult to answer but no less important is whether the sperm nucleus is in any way active in the synthesis of mRNA before it fuses with the egg nucleus.

These observations, while drawing attention to the changes that fertilization may bring about in the activity of the nucleus, certainly call for more extensive investigations of the metabolism of the nucleic acids before and after fertilization.

5. THE INITIATION OF DNA SYNTHESIS

The most important result of fertilization is certainly the activation of the nucleus. Two aspects of this activation may be considered: one concerns the beginning of the synthesis of specific messenger RNA to direct differentiation; the other concerns the resumed ability of the nucleus to synthesize DNA.

The basic mechanisms responsible for the activation of the nucleus escape us entirely. The activation is likely to occur very soon after fertilization. Indeed, in the sea urchin egg synthesis of some nonribosomal, non-4S RNA begins immediately after fertilization (Gross and Cousineau, 1963; Nemer, 1963; Wilt, 1963; Gross et al., 1964). In Drosophila, there is genetic evidence of gene activation very soon after fertilization. For example, the suppressor of erupt locus is activated within 8 minutes after fertilization (Glass and Plaine, 1950). Anyway, we still know far too little on this important question.

The work carried out in recent years by Scarano and his colleagues that has led to the discovery of the aminopyrimidine deoxynucleotides deaminase (Scarano's enzyme) (Scarano, 1958; Scarano et al., 1962a,b) presents a new approach to the problem of the control of DNA metabolism. It seems likely that the deaminase reactions catalyzed by Scarano's enzyme which convert the 5'-deoxycytidylic acid (dCMP) into 5'-deoxyuridylic acid (dUMP) and the 5'-methyldeoxycytidylic acid (MedCMP) to 5-thymidylic acid (dTMP) may be just two steps in the pathway of the interconversion of pyrimidine deoxynucleotides (Scarano and Maggio, 1959a, b). The three enzymes, deaminase, reaminase, and methylase, which are probably involved in this pathway may regulate the relative concentrations of the pyrimidine deoxynucleotides for optimal DNA synthesis. Now, it has been shown that in the unfertilized egg the deaminase is more active than the enzyme(s) reaminating the dUMP (Scarano and Caserta, unpublished observations, quoted by Scarano and Maggio, 1959b). The result would be an accumulation of dUMP which not only upsets the equilibrium of the deoxynucleotides in the pool, but, during the first two divisions, is also very poorly utilized for the synthesis of thymidylic acid (see Nemer, 1962a). This situation has to be taken into consideration as one of the factors responsible for the blocking of the DNA synthesis in the unfertilized egg. Upon fertilization, the dUMP-reaminating enzyme(s) might be activated, thus overcoming the action of the dCMP deaminase and resulting in the formation of the optimal amount of dCMP for DNA synthesis (see also Monroy and Maggio, 1964). This might be another of the key blocks of metabolism in the unfertilized egg. It must also be mentioned that recently Scarano et al. (1962b, 1963) have shown that the deaminase is an allosteric enzyme (see Monod et al., 1963). The allosteric effectors, deoxythymidine triphosphate (dTTP) and deoxycytidine triphosphate (dCTP), would regulate the activity of the enzyme, and this feedback mechanism would regulate the biosynthesis of deoxythymidine mono-phosphate (dTMP).

It must finally be mentioned that one of the most interesting and intriguing peculiarities of the egg is its high content of cytoplasmic DNA (for a review see Brachet, 1960). Almost nothing is known about this type of DNA, except that it may have a lower molecular weight than nuclear DNA (Brachet and Quertier, 1963). Cytoplasmic DNA is usually considered as a kind of store to be utilized for the synthesis of nuclear DNA during early development (cf. Chapter 1 of this volume). Without denying this, the possibility of a genetic function of cytoplasmic DNA must be seriously considered (see also Brachet, 1960).

6. Physicochemical Changes of Some Egg Proteins upon Fertilization

Another interesting point concerns the changes that take place in some of the proteins of the egg upon fertilization. Work in this field was initiated by Mirsky (1936) who described the "coagulation" of a protein fraction in the sea urchin egg taking place right after fertilization. The saline-soluble proteins of the unfertilized and newly fertilized sea urchin egg have been studied by a variety of chemical and physicochemical methods in our laboratory (summarized by Monroy, 1957a, b). These observations have all led to the conclusion that at least some of the proteins of the egg undergo some kind of structural rearrangement in conjunction with fertilization.

The electrophoretic analysis of saline extracts of eggs of *Paracentrotus* and of some of the fractions obtained by precipitation with ammonium sulfate showed a decrease in solubility of one fraction during the first few minutes following fertilization (Monroy, 1950). In *Arbacia* the change was not as conspicuous as in *Paracentrotus* (Monroy and Mon-roy-Oddo, 1951). It was later shown that the fraction which is precipi-tated at 50 % saturation of ammonium sulfate from a saline extract (1 M of LiCl) of *Arbacia* eggs upon treatment with urea undergoes a viscosity increase which is larger for the fraction prepared from fertilized than from unfertilized eggs. Furthermore, as a result of the urea treat-ment a greater number of phenolic groups become exposed in the former than in the latter (Ceas *et al.*, 1955). Also, in the stimulated nerve fiber changes have been detected indicating a molecular rearrangement of some of the constituent proteins and have been described under the admittedly vague heading of "reversible denaturation." In this case, there is evidence for an unmasking of amino side groups (Ungar *et al.*, 1957).

Following the pioneering work of Rapkine (1931) a considerable amount of work has been devoted to determining whether in the sea urchin egg as a result of fertilization free and protein-bound SH groups undergo any variation. In fact, it is known that the unmasking of SH groups is considered as one of the best indications of protein denaturation. Conflicting results have been cleared up recently by the work of Sakai and Dan (1959) and Sakai (1960). They have been able to show that the fluctuations of the SH groups which follow fertilization (decreasing from fertilization until the fusion of the pronuclei and then rising) depend on the interchange of the —SH $\rightleftarrows$ —S—S— groups of a protein fraction; this, however, does not involve any unmasking of masked or sluggishly reacting groups. Therefore, these results taken all together, though strongly suggestive of configurational changes of some egg proteins following fertilization, do not provide any information as to their nature.

An activation of proteolytic enzymes also follows fertilization (Lundblad, 1949, 1952, 1954a, b; Lundblad and Lundblad, 1953; Maggio, 1957) and this may largely be responsible for at least some of the observed changes. It can certainly account for the observed increase in the nonprotein amino nitrogen within the first 10 minutes after fertilization (Örström, 1941; Ricotta, 1956) which may indicate the splitting off of some protein end groups. Further, it may also account for the lowered sensitivity to trypsin of some of the egg proteins following fertilization (Giardina and Monroy, 1955; D'Amelio, 1955).

There is some evidence that the density of the sea urchin egg undergoes a sudden increase following fertilization [from 1.068–1.088 to 1.091–1.095 gm/ml (Salzen, 1957)]. This, together with the transient wrinkling (or even permanent shrinkage) which accompanies fertilization suggests a changed affinity of the protein molecules for water. Actually, it may even be supposed that the configurational changes taking place in the proteins may simply be secondary to a rearrangement of their hydration sheath (for the theory, see Klotz, 1958).

The squeezing of a liquid from the egg at fertilization which is such a widespread and probably general occurrence (Section IV,A,3) may also be viewed as a result of this phenomenon and of the accompanying volume changes. Proton magnetic resonance studies might provide useful information for the interpretation of these early events of fertilization.

7. Changes in the Distribution of Ions

Wide changes in the distribution of some ions have also been observed in conjunction with fertilization. The transient release of K^+ observed in the sea urchin egg at fertilization has already been described (Tyler and Monroy, 1959). It has also been observed (Monroy and

Tyler, 1958; Tyler and Monroy, 1959) that in the unfertilized egg only about one-fourth of the total K^+ is exchangeable, whereas following fertilization all or almost all of the intracellular K^+ becomes readily exchangeable (Fig. 20). During the first 10 minutes following fertilization Ca^{++} also appears to be released from a bound to an ionic form (Mazia, 1937); furthermore, both Ca^{++} and Mg^{++} appear to leak out of the egg (Örström and Örström, 1942; Monroy-Oddo, 1946). Although

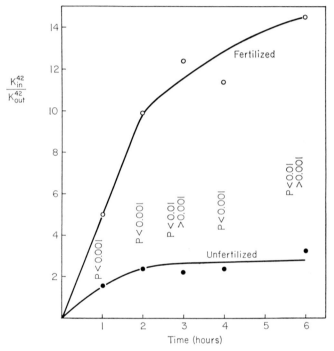

FIG. 20. Ratio of internal (K_{in}) to external (K_{out}) potassium in unfertilized and fertilized eggs of *Arbacia punctulata* at various times after being placed in sea water containing K^{42}. From the data of Tyler and Monroy (1959).

the interpretation favored by the writer is a change in the binding sites owing to the chemical and physicochemical rearrangement of the protein molecules, other interpretations, such as changes in the compartmentation within the egg, are admittedly possible, and further work is necessary to clear up this important question.

8. EVIDENCE FOR THE BUILDING UP OF INHIBITORS DURING MATURATION

In spite of the very scanty comparative data, there is no doubt that the unfertilized egg is a cell whose potentialities are activated as a result of fertilization. The investigations carried out on the respiration of the ripening oocytes of the sea urchin (Lindahl and Holter, 1941) and of the teleostean fish *Oryzias latipes* (Nakano, 1953) indicate a gradual decrease in the rate of oxygen consumption as maturation progresses (Fig. 21). The oocytes are also able to incorporate labeled amino acids into their proteins, but mature eggs are unable to do so (Monroy and Maggio, 1964). From the experiments of Esper (1962) in which *Arbacia* females were sacrificed at various time intervals following the injection of C^{14}-glucose, it seems that the ability to incorporate amino

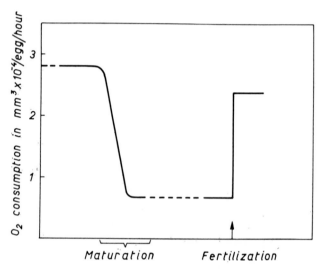

Fig. 21.   Changes in oxygen consumption during maturation and following fertilization in the oocytes of *Paracentrotus lividus*. From Lindahl and Holter (1941).

acids into the proteins is only abolished during the latest phases of maturation. However few and preliminary, these observations suggest that the metabolic block is established during maturation. Different conditions prevail among various animals regarding the state of the egg when it is shed from the gonad and ready for fertilization; they range from the fully ripe egg of the sea urchin to the egg with intact germinal vesicle, such as the eggs of the starfish and of the annelids. The fact that the process of maturation reaches completion before fertilization only in the eggs of very few animals suggests that the inhibiting factor may reach the threshold concentration at different stages during maturation or even before maturation is started at all. Indeed, very little is known of the biochemistry of the maturation of the egg, and yet it is very likely that the study of this process would yield important results for the understanding of the apparently different metabolic response of the egg to fertilization.[1]

V. Tentative Conclusions

The work carried out in the last few years, namely since the publication of Rothschild's book (1956b) and of the writer's review (Monroy, 1957b), has produced a number of new facts which have somewhat modified and increased our insight into the problem of the basic mechanisms underlying the activation of the egg. Physiological and morphological work, especially with the use of the electron microscope has contributed much to the understanding of the sperm-egg interactions and the processes whereby the spermatozoon enters the egg. Such interaction is indeed a highly specific phenomenon involving the fusion of two cells and its study may have general implications extending far beyond the problem of fertilization.

Recent work has also shown striking similarities between the early events of fertilization and the process of nerve stimulation to such an extent that it may be suggested that egg activation is basically a process of cell stimulation. It has long been known that fertilization is accompanied in the eggs of all animals by a number of cortical changes, and the electron microscope has shed new light on these changes. Indeed, a thorough rearrangement of the structural and molecular organization of the cortical layer of the egg takes place upon fertilization. By analogy with what is known of the physiology of the nerve cell, these changes are primarily responsible for electrical phenomena. In most animals the cortex is the site of the polyspermy-preventing mechanism, but its molecular basis is still a matter of conjecture. The cortex of the egg has been considered as the site of the origin of the sparking reaction of activation and, indeed, there is circumstantial evidence that this may be so, although the nature of this reaction is purely hypothetical. There is no need to emphasize that the discovery of the molecular basis of this reaction may be of fundamental importance.

The metabolism of the fertilized egg has been investigated intensely

---

[1] Recent work (Monroy and Tolis, 1964) indicates that in the egg of the starfish *Asterias forbesii* until the formation of the second polar body there is no significant difference between unfertilized and fertilized eggs as to the rate of uptake of labeled amino acids and their incorporation into proteins. Then both the rate of uptake and of incorporation start increasing rapidly in the fertilized eggs, whereas in the unfertilized eggs no change or even a decline is observed. In the eggs of *Spisula solidissima*, in which maturation is elicited by fertilization, uptake and incorporation of labeled amino acids undergo a marked increase soon after the breakdown of the germinal vesicle.

since the pioneering work on the respiratory changes in the egg at fertilization. That the egg before fertilization is in some way a blocked system is almost a tautology. The main point is that, at least as far as the sea urchin egg is concerned, the block involves the energy-yielding systems; hence, all the reactions requiring a large amount of energy are also inhibited. The accumulation of inhibitory substances during maturation seems to be the most likely explanation and, indeed, one such inhibitor has been identified. However, how such inhibitors are produced during the final phases of maturation and how they are inactivated or disposed of by the egg following fertilization still remains to be discovered. It would certainly be of the utmost importance to find out to what extent such inhibitors occur in unfertilized eggs; here again the necessity for comparative studies is emphasized.

Although the evidence is still rather preliminary, a number of data point to the nucleus of the unfertilized egg as also being in an inhibited condition. Repressor substances manufactured by the egg in the later phases of maturation would inhibit both the metabolic activities residing in the cytoplasm and the genetic activity of the nucleus. The key reaction of fertilization would thus be the removal of the repressor(s), releasing at the same time the cytoplasmic metabolic activities and the activity of the nuclear genetic system.

ACKNOWLEDGMENTS

The original work of the author and his collaborators referred to in this chapter has been aided by grants from the Consiglio Nazionale delle Ricerche, the Rockefeller Foundation, and the National Institutes of Health, U. S. Public Health Service (RG-06211).

The author wishes to express his indebtedness to his friends and colleagues C. R. Austin, L. and A. Colwin, R. Maggio, E. Nakano, G. Ortolani, A. B. Pardee, J. Pasteels, E. Scarano, and A. Tyler for reading part or all of the manuscript, for stimulating discussions and critical advice, and for permitting the use of data and illustrations from their unpublished work.

REFERENCES

Afzelius, B. A. (1956). *Exptl. Cell Res.* 10, 257.
Aketa, K. (1957). *Embryologia (Nagoya)* 3, 267.
Aketa, K. (1963). *Exptl. Cell Res.* 30, 93.
Aketa, K., Bianchetti, R., Marré, E., and Monroy, A. (1964). *Biochim. Biophys. Acta* 86, 211.
Allen, R. D. (1954). *Exptl. Cell Res.* 6, 403.
Allfrey, V. G., Meudt, R., Hopkins, J. W., and Mirsky, A. E. (1961). *Proc. Natl. Acad. Sci. U. S.* 47, 907.
Ashbel, R. (1929). *Boll. Soc. Ital. Biol. Sper.* 4, 492.
Austin, C. R. (1956). *Exptl. Cell Res.* 10, 533.

Austin, C. R. (1961). "The Mammalian Egg." Blackwell, Oxford, England.
Austin, C. R., and Bishop, M. W. (1958). *Proc. Roy. Soc.* **B149**, 241.
Axelrod, B. (1960). *In* "Metabolic Pathways" (D. M. Greenberg, ed.), Vol. I, p. 97. Academic Press, New York.
Ballentine, R. (1940). *J. Cellular Comp. Physiol.* **15**, 217.
Banta, A. M., and Gartner, R. A. (1914). *Biol. Bull.* **27**, 259.
Barron, E. S. G. (1932). *Biol. Bull.* **62**, 42.
Berg, W. E. (1950). *Biol. Bull.* **98**, 128.
Bernstein, G. S. (1952). *Biol. Bull.* **103**, 285.
Bielig, H. J., and Dohrn, P. (1950). *Z. Naturforsch.* **5b**, 316.
Bishop, D. W. (1951). *Biol. Bull.* **101**, 215.
Bishop, D. W., and Metz, C. B. (1952). *Nature* **169**, 548.
Bishop, D. W., and Tyler, A. (1956). *J. Exptl. Zool.* **132**, 575.
Black, R. E., and Tyler, A. (1959a). *Biol. Bull.* **117**, 443.
Black, R. E., and Tyler, A. (1959b). *Biol. Bull.* **117**, 454.
Black, R. E., Epstein, S., and Tyler, A. (1958). *Biol. Bull.* **115**, 153.
Bolst, A. L., and Whiteley, A. H. (1957). *Biol. Bull.* **112**, 276.
Borei, H. (1948). *Biol. Bull.* **95**, 124.
Borei, H. (1949). *Biol. Bull.* **96**, 117.
Boyd, M. (1928). *Biol. Bull.* **55**, 92.
Brachet, J. (1945). "Embryologie chimique." Masson, Paris.
Brachet, J. (1960). "The Biochemistry of Development." Pergamon Press, New York.
Brachet, J., and Quertier, J. (1963). *Exptl. Cell Res.* **32**, 410.
Brachet, J., Ficq, A., and Tencer, R. (1963). *Exptl. Cell Res.* **32**, 168.
Braden, A. W. H. (1952). *Australian J. Sci. Res.* **B5**, 460.
Braden, A. W. H., Austin, C. R., and David, H. A. (1954). *Australian J. Biol. Sci.* **7**, 391.
Braun, A. C., and Wood, H. N. (1962). *Proc. Natl. Acad. Sci. U. S.* **48**, 1776.
Breckenridge, B. (1953). *Am. J. Physiol.* **173**, 61.
Brock, N., Druckrey, H., and Herken, H. (1938). *Arch. Exptl. Pathol. Pharmakol. Naunyn-Schmiedeberg* **188**, 451.
Brooks, S. C. (1939). *Proc. Soc. Exptl. Biol. Med.* **42**, 557.
Ceas, M. P., Impellizzeri, M. A., and Monroy, A. (1955). *Exptl. Cell Res.* **9**, 366.
Cleland, K. W. (1950). *Proc. Linnean Soc. N.S. Wales* **75**, 282.
Colwin, A. L., and Colwin, L. H. (1955). *J. Morphol.* **97**, 543.
Colwin, A. L., and Colwin, L. H. (1958). *Biol. Bull.* **115**, 348.
Colwin, A. L., and Colwin, L. H. (1960). *J. Biophys. Biochem. Cytol.* **7**, 321.
Colwin, A. L., and Colwin, L. H. (1961). *J. Biophys. Biochem. Cytol.* **10**, 255.
Colwin, A. L., and Colwin, L. H. (1963). *J. Cell Biol.* **19**, 477.
Colwin, A. L., Colwin, L. H., and Philpott, D. E. (1957). *J. Biophys. Biochem. Cytol.* **3**, 489.
Colwin, L. H., and Colwin, A. L. (1956). *Biol. Bull.* **10**, 243.
Colwin, L. H., and Colwin, A. L. (1960). *J. Biophys. Biochem. Cytol.* **7**, 315.
Colwin, L. H., and Colwin, A. L. (1961). *J. Biophys. Biochem. Cytol.* **10**, 231.
Colwin, L. H., and Colwin, A. L. (1963). *J. Cell Biol.* **19**, 501.
Cornman, J. (1941). *Biol. Bull.* **80**, 202.
Corrias, L., and Novarini, L. (1950). *Monit. Zool. Ital.* **57**, 94.
D'Amelio, V. (1955). *Experientia* **11**, 443.
Dan, J. C. (1950). *Biol. Bull.* **99**, 412.

Dan, J. C. (1952). *Biol. Bull.* **103**, 54.

Dan, J. C. (1956). *Intern. Rev. Cytol.* **5**, 365.

Dan, J. C. (1960). *Exptl. Cell Res.* **19**, 13.

Denny, P. C., and Tyler, A. (1964). *Biochem. Biophys. Res. Commun.* **14**, 245.

Endo, Y. (1961). *Exptl. Cell Res.* **25**, 383.

Esper, H. (1962). *Biol. Bull.* **123**, 476.

Fauré-Fremiet, E. (1922). *Compt. Rend. Soc. Biol.* **86**, 20.

Fol, H. (1878-1879). *Mem. Soc. Phys. Hist. Nat. Geneve* **26**, 89.

Folkes, B. F., Grant, R. A., and Jones, J. K. N. (1950). *J. Chem. Soc.* **440**, 2136.

Giacosa, P. (1882). *Z. Physiol. Chem.* **7**, 40.

Giardina, G., and Monroy, A. (1955). *Exptl. Cell Res.* **8**, 466.

Gierer, A. (1963). *J. Mol. Biol.* **6**, 148.

Gilbert, W. (1963). *J. Mol. Biol.* **6**, 374.

Giudice, G. (1960). *Exptl. Cell Res.* **21**, 222.

Giudice, G., and Monroy, A. (1958). *Acta Embryol. Morphol. Exptl.* **2**, 58.

Giudice, G., Vittorelli, M. L., and Monroy, A. (1962). *Acta Embryol. Morphol. Exptl.* **5**, 113.

Glaser, O. (1921). *Am. Naturalist* **55**, 368.

Glass, B., and Plaine, H. L. (1950). *Proc. Natl. Acad. Sci. U. S.* **36**, 627.

Gray, J. (1928). *J. Exptl. Biol.* **5**, 362.

Gross, P. R., and Cousineau, G. H. (1963). *Biochem. Biophys. Res. Commun.* **10**, 321.

Gross, P. R., Malkin, L. I., and Moyer, W. A. (1964). *Proc. Natl. Acad. Sci. U. S.* **51**, 407.

Hadek, R. (1963). *J. Ultrastruct. Res.* **8**, 161.

Hagström, B. E. (1956a). *Exptl. Cell Res.* **10**, 24.

Hagström, B. E. (1956b). *Exptl. Cell Res.* **10**, 740.

Hagström, B. E. (1956c). "The Role of the Jelly Coat and the Block to Polyspermy in the Fertilization of Sea Urchins." Almqvist & Wiksell, Uppsala.

Hagström, B. E. (1956d). *Exptl. Cell Res.* **11**, 306.

Hagström, B. E., and Hagström, B. (1954). *Exptl. Cell Res.* **6**, 491.

Hartmann, M., and Schartau, O. (1939). *Biol. Zentr.* **59**, 571.

Hartmann, M., Schartau, O., Kuhn, R., and Wallenfels, K. (1939). *Naturwissenschaften*, **27**, 433.

Hartmann, M., Schartau, O., and Wallenfels, K. (1940). *Biol. Zentr.* **60**, 398.

Harvey, E. N., and Danielli, J. F. (1936). *J. Cellular Comp. Physiol.* **8**, 31.

Hathaway, R. R. (1959). *Biol. Bull.* **117**, 395.

Hathaway, R. R., and Metz, C. B. (1961). *Biol. Bull.* **120**, 360.

Hiramoto, Y. (1959a). *Embryologia (Nagoya)* **4**, 219.

Hiramoto, Y. (1959b). *Exptl. Cell Res.* **16**, 421.

Hiramoto, Y. (1962). *Exptl. Cell Res.* **27**, 416.

Hiyama, N. (1949a). *Tohoku J. Exptl. Med.* **50**, 373.

Hiyama, N. (1949b). *Tohoku J. Exptl. Med.* **50**, 379.

Hiyama, N. (1949c). *Tohoku J. Exptl. Med.* **50**, 385.

Holter, H., and Zeuthen, E. (1944). *Compt. Rend. Trav. Lab. Carlsberg Ser. Chim.* **25**, 33.

Hultin, T. (1961). *Exptl. Cell Res.* **25**, 405.

Hultin, T., and Bergstrand, Å. (1960). *Develop. Biol.* **2**, 61.

Immers, J., and Runnström, J. (1960). *Develop. Biol.* **2**, 90.

Ishida, J., and Nakano, E. (1947). *Dobutsagaku Zasshi* **57**, 117.
Ishida, J., and Nakano, E. (1950). *Annotationes Zool. Japon.* **23**, 43.
Ishikawa, M. (1954). *Embryologia* (*Nagoya*) **2**, 57.
Ito, S. (1960). *Kumamoto J. Sci. Ser. B* **5**, 61.
Ito, S., and Maeno, T. (1960). *Kumamoto J. Sci. Ser. B* **5**, 100.
Kacser, H. (1955). *J. Exptl. Biol.* **32**, 451.
Keltch, A. K., Krahl, M. E., and Clowes, G. H. A. (1956). *J. Gen. Physiol.* **40**, 27.
Klotz, I. M. (1958). *Science* **128**, 815.
Krahl, M. E. (1956). *Biochim. Biophys. Acta* **20**, 27.
Krane, S. M., and Crane, R. K. (1960). *Biochim. Biophys. Acta* **43**, 369.
Krauss, M. (1950). *Science* **112**, 759.
Kusa, M. (1951). *J. Fac. Sci. Hokkaido Univ. Ser. VI* **10**, 151.
Lardy, H. A., and Wellman, H. (1952). *J. Biol. Chem.* **195**, 215.
Laser, H., and Rothschild, Lord (1939). *Proc. Roy. Soc.* **B126**, 539.
Lentini, R. (1961). *Acta Embryol. Morphol. Exptl.* **4**, 209.
Lillie, F. R. (1914). *J. Exptl. Zool.* **16**, 523.
Lillie, F. R. (1919). "Problems of Fertilization." Univ. Chicago Press, Chicago, Illinois.
Lillie, R. S. (1916). *Am. J. Physiol.* **40**, 267.
Lindahl, P. E. (1938). *Naturwissenschaften* **26**, 709.
Lindahl, P. E., and Holter, H. (1941). *Compt. Rend. Trav. Lab. Carlsberg Ser. Chim.* **24**, 49.
Lindberg, O., and Ernster, L. (1948). *Biochim. Biophys. Acta* **2**, 471.
Loeb, J. (1913). "Artificial Parthenogenesis and Fertilization." Chicago Univ. Press, Chicago, Illinois.
Loeb, J. (1916). "The Organism as a Whole." Putnam, New York.
Lundblad, G. (1949). *Nature* **163**, 643.
Lundblad, G. (1950). *Exptl. Cell Res.* **1**, 264.
Lundblad, G. (1952). *Arkiv. Kemi* **4**, 537.
Lundblad, G. (1954a). *Arkiv. Kemi* **7**, 127.
Lundblad, G. (1954b). *Arkiv. Kemi* **7**, 169.
Lundblad, G., and Lundblad, I. (1953). *Arkiv. Kemi* **6**, 387.
Lundblad, G., and Monroy, A. (1950). *Arkiv. Kemi* **2**, 343.
Maeno, T. (1959). *J. Gen. Physiol.* **43**, 139.
Maeno, T., Morita, H., and Kuwabara, M. (1956). *Mem. Fac. Sci. Kyushu Univ. Ser. E* **2**, 87.
Maggio, R. (1957). *J. Cellular Comp. Physiol.* **50**, 135.
Maggio, R. (1959). *Exptl. Cell Res.* **16**, 272.
Maggio, R., and Ghiretti-Magaldi, A. (1958). *Exptl. Cell Res.* **15**, 95.
Maggio, R., and Monroy, A. (1955). *Exptl. Cell Res.* **8**, 240.
Maggio, R., and Monroy, A. (1959). *Nature* **184**, 68.
Maggio, R., Aiello, F., and Monroy, A. (1960). *Nature* **188**, 1195.
Maggio, R., Vittorelli, M. L., Rinaldi, A. M., and Monroy, A. (1964). *Biochem. Biophys. Res. Commun.* **15**, 436.
Marks, P. A., Burka, E. R., and Schlessinger, D. (1962). *Proc. Natl. Acad. Sci. U. S.* **48**, 2163.
Mazia, D. (1937). *J. Cellular Comp. Physiol.* **10**, 291.
Mehl, J. W., and Swann, M. M. (1961). *Exptl. Cell Res.* **22**, 233.

Mercer, E. H., and Wolpert, L. (1962). *Exptl. Cell Res.* **27**, 1.

Messina, L. (1954). *Pubbl. Staz. Zool. Napoli* **25**, 454.

Messina, L., and Monroy, A. (1956). *Pubbl. Staz. Zool. Napoli* **29**, 266.

Metz, C. B. (1945). *Biol. Bull.* **89**, 84.

Metz, C. B. (1957). In "Physiological Triggers" (T. Bullock, ed.), p. 17. Am. Physiol. Soc., Washington.

Metz, C. B. (1962). *Proc. Conf. Immuno Reprod., La Jolla, 1962* p. 107. Population Council, New York.

Metz, C. B., and Donovan, J. E. (1949). *Biol. Bull.* **97**, 257.

Minganti, A. (1948). *Nature* **161**, 643.

Minganti, A. (1951). *Pubbl. Staz. Zool. Napoli* **23**, 58.

Minganti, A. (1954). *Ric. Sci.* **24**, 1658.

Minganti, A. (1955). *Exptl. Cell Res. Suppl.* **3**, 248.

Minganti, A. (1957). *Acta Embryol. Morphol. Exptl.* **1**, 150.

Minganti, A. (1958). *Boll. Zool.* **25**, 55.

Minganti, A., and Azzolina, G. (1956). *Ric. Sci.* **25**, 2103.

Minganti, A., and D'Anna, T. (1957). *Ric. Sci.* **27**, 3052.

Minganti, A., and D'Anna, T. (1958). *Ric. Sci.* **28**, 2090.

Minganti, A., and Vasseur, E. (1959). *Acta Embryol. Morphol. Exptl.* **2**, 195.

Mirsky, A. E. (1936). *Science* **84**, 333.

Mitchison, J. M. (1952). *Symp. Soc. Exptl. Biol.* **6**, 105.

Monné, L., and Hårde, S. (1951). *Arkiv. Zool.* [2] **1**, 487.

Monod, J., Chengeux, J.-P., and Jacob, F. (1963). *J. Mol. Biol.* **6**, 306.

Monroy, A. (1945). *Experientia* **1**, 335.

Monroy, A. (1947). *J. Cellular Comp. Physiol.* **30**, 105.

Monroy, A. (1948a). *Experientia* **4**, 353.

Monroy, A. (1948b). *Arkiv. Zool.* **40A** (21).

Monroy, A. (1950). *Exptl. Cell Res.* **1**, 92.

Monroy, A. (1953). *Experientia* **9**, 424.

Monroy, A. (1954). *Pubbl. Staz. Zool. Napoli* **25**, 188.

Monroy, A. (1956). *Exptl. Cell Res.* **10**, 320.

Monroy, A. (1957a). In "The Beginnings of Embryonic Development" (A. Tyler, R. C. von Borstel, and C. B. Metz, eds.), p. 169. Am. Assoc. Advan. Sci., Washington, D. C.

Monroy, A. (1957b). *Intern. Rev. Cytol.* **6**, 107.

Monroy, A. (1960). *Experientia* **16**, 114.

Monroy, A., and Maggio, R. (1964). *Advan. Morphogenesis* **3**, 95.

Monroy, A., and Monroy-Oddo, A. (1946). *Pubbl. Staz. Zool. Napoli* **20**, 46.

Monroy, A., and Monroy-Oddo, A. (1951). *J. Gen. Physiol.* **35**, 245.

Monroy, A., and Montalenti, G. (1947). *Biol. Bull.* **92**, 151.

Monroy, A., and Ruffo, A. (1947). *Nature* **159**, 603.

Monroy, A., and Tolis, H. (1964). *Biol. Bull.* **126**, 456.

Monroy, A., and Tosi, L. (1952). *Experientia* **8**, 393.

Monroy, A., and Tyler, A. (1958). *Biol. Bull.* **115**, 339.

Monroy, A., and Tyler, A. (1963). *Arch. Biochem. Biophys.* **103**, 431.

Monroy, A., and Vittorelli, M. L. (1960). *Experientia* **16**, 56.

Monroy, A., and Vittorelli, M. L. (1962). *J. Cellular Comp. Physiol.* **60**, 285.

Monroy, A., Tosi, L., Giardina, G., and Maggio, R. (1954). *Biol. Bull.* **106**, 169.

Monroy, A., Vittorelli, M. L., and Guarneri, R. (1961). *Acta Embryol. Morphol. Exptl.* **4**, 77.

Monroy-Oddo, A. (1946). *Experientia* **2**, 371.

Montalenti, G. (1949). *Pubbl. Staz. Zool. Napoli* **22**, 6.

Montalenti, G., and Schartau, O. (1942). *Pubbl. Staz. Zool. Napoli* **19**, 48.

Morgan, T. H. (1923). *Proc. Natl. Acad. Sci. U. S.* **9**, 170.

Motomura, I. (1954). *Sci. Rept. Tohoku Univ. Fourth Ser.* **20**, 213.

Nakano, E. (1953). *Embryologia (Nagoya)* **2**, 21.

Nakano, E. (1954). *Japan. J. Zool.* **11**, 245.

Nakano, E. (1956). *Embryologia (Nagoya)* **3**, 89.

Nakano, E., and Monroy, A. (1958a). *Experientia* **14**, 367.

Nakano, E., and Monroy, A. (1958b). *Exptl. Cell Res.* **14**, 236.

Nakano, E., and Ohashi, S. (1954). *Embryologia (Nagoya)* **2**, 81.

Nakano, E., Giudice, G., and Monroy, A. (1958). *Experientia* **14**, 11.

Naora, H., Naora, H., Izawa, M., Allfrey, V. G., and Mirsky, A. E. (1962). *Proc. Natl. Acad. Sci. U. S.* **48**, 853.

Nemer, M. (1962a). *J. Biol. Chem.* **237**, 143.

Nemer, M. (1962b). *Biochem. Biophys. Res. Commun.* **8**, 511.

Nemer, M. (1963). *Proc. Natl. Acad. Sci. U. S.* **50**, 230.

Numanoi, H. (1959a). *Sci. Papers Coll. Gen. Educ. Univ. Tokyo* **9**, 285.

Numanoi, H. (1959b). *Sci. Papers Coll. Gen. Educ. Univ. Tokyo* **9**, 297.

Ohnishi, T., and Sugiyama, M. (1963). *Embryologia (Nagoya)* **8**, 79.

Örström, Å. (1941). *Z. Physiol. Chem.* **271**, 1.

Örström, Å., and Örström, M. (1942). *Protoplasma* **36**, 475.

Osanai, K. (1960a). *Sci. Rept. Tohoku Univ. Fourth Ser.* **26**, 69.

Osanai, K. (1960b). *Sci. Rept. Tohoku Univ. Fourth Ser.* **26**, 77.

Pasteels, J. J. (1963). *Bull. Classe Sc. Acad. Roy. Belg.* **49**, 329.

Pasteels, J. J., and de Harven, E. (1962). *Arch. Biol. (Liege)* **73**, 465.

Perlmann, P. (1959). *Experientia* **15**, 41.

Pfeffer, W. (1884). *Untersuch. Bot. Inst. Tübingen* **1**, 363.

Philips, F. S. (1940). *Biol. Bull.* **78**, 256.

Picken, L. E. R., and Rothschild, Lord (1948). *J. Exptl. Biol.* **25**, 227.

Popa, G. T. (1927). *Biol. Bull.* **52**, 238.

Rapkine, L. (1931). *Ann. Physiol. Physicochim. Biol.* **7**, 382.

Reverberi, G. (1935). *Pubbl. Staz. Zool. Napoli* **15**, 175.

Ricotta, C. M. (1956). *Naturwissenschaften* **43**, 258.

Robbie, W. A. (1946). *J. Cellular Comp. Physiol.* **28**, 305.

Rothschild, Lord (1949). *J. Exptl. Biol.* **26**, 100.

Rothschild, Lord (1952). *Intern. Rev. Cytol.* **1**, 257.

Rothschild, Lord (1956a). *J. Exptl. Biol.* **33**, 155.

Rothschild, Lord (1956b). "Fertilization." Methuen, London.

Rothschild, Lord, and Barnes, H. (1953). *J. Exptl. Biol.* **30**, 534.

Rothschild, Lord, and Swann, M. M. (1949). *J. Exptl. Biol.* **26**, 164.

Rothschild, Lord, and Swann, M. M. (1951). *Exptl. Cell Res.* **2**, 137.

Rothschild, Lord, and Swann, M. M. (1952). *J. Exptl. Biol.* **29**, 469.

Rothschild, Lord, and Tyler, A. (1954). *J. Exptl. Biol.* **31**, 252.

Rothschild, Lord, and Tyler, A. (1955). *Exptl. Cell Res. Suppl.* **3**, 304.

Rothschild, Lord, and Tyler, A. (1958). *Biol. Bull.* **115**, 136.

Runnström, J. (1928). *Protoplasma* **4**, 388.
Runnström, J. (1930). *Protoplasma* **10**, 106.
Runnström, J. (1933). *Biochem. Z.* **258**, 257.
Runnström, J. (1949). *Advan. Enzymol.* **9**, 241.
Runnström, J. (1956). *Pubbl. Staz. Zool. Napoli* **28**, 315.
Runnström, J., and Monné, L. (1945). *Arkiv. Zool.* **36A** (18).
Runnström, J., Tiselius, A., and Vasseur, E. (1942). *Arkiv. Kemi Mineral. Geol.* **15** (16).
Runnström, J., Monné, L., and Broman, L. (1943). *Arkiv. Zool.* **35A** (3).
Runnström, J., Monné, L., and Wicklund, E. (1944). *Nature* **153**, 313.
Runnström, J., Hagström, B. E., and Perlmann, P. (1959). *In* "The Cell" (J. Brachet and A. E. Mirsky, eds.), Vol. 1, p. 327. Academic Press, New York.
Sakai, H. (1960). *J. Biophys. Biochem. Cytol.* **8**, 609.
Sakai, H., and Dan, K. (1959). *Exptl. Cell Res.* **16**, 24.
Salzen, E. A. (1957). *Exptl. Cell Res.* **12**, 615.
Scarano, E. (1958). *Biochim. Biophys. Acta* **29**, 459.
Scarano, E., and Maggio, R. (1959a). *Arch. Biochem. Biophys.* **79**, 392.
Scarano, E., and Maggio, R. (1959b). *Exptl. Cell Res.* **18**, 333.
Scarano, E., Bonaduce, L., and De Petrocellis, B. (1962a). *J. Biol. Chem.* **237**, 3742.
Scarano, E., Geraci, G., Polzella, A., and Campanile, E. (1962b). *Boll. Soc. Ital. Biol. Sper.* **38**, 1360.
Scarano, E., Geraci, G., Polzella, A., and Campanile, E. (1963). *J. Biol. Chem.* **238**, 1556.
Schartau, O., and Montalenti, G. (1941). *Boll. Soc. Ital. Biol. Sper.* **16**, 460.
Schulz, F. N., and Becker, M. (1935). *Biochem. Z.* **280**, 217.
Slater, E. C., and Hülsmann, W. C. (1959). *Ciba Found. Symp. Regulation Cell Metab.* p. 58.
Spiegel, M. (1951). *Anat. Record* **111**, 128.
Stefanelli, A. (1938). *Arch. Sci. Biol. (Bologna)* **24**, 411.
Sugiyama, M. (1951). *Biol. Bull.* **101**, 335.
Sugiyama, M. (1953a). *Biol. Bull.* **104**, 210.
Sugiyama, M. (1953b). *Biol. Bull.* **104**, 216.
Sugiyama, M. (1956). *Exptl. Cell Res.* **10**, 364.
Suzuki, R. (1958). *Embryologia (Nagoya)* **4**, 93.
Suzuki, R. (1959a). *Embryologia (Nagoya)* **4**, 359.
Suzuki, R. (1959b). *Annotationes Zool. Japon.* **32**, 105.
Suzuki, R. (1960). *Japan. J. Zool.* **12**, 465.
Suzuki, R. (1961). *Japan. J. Zool.* **13**, 77.
Swyer, G. I. M. (1947). *Biochem. J.* **41**, 413.
Szollosi, D. G., and Ris, H. (1961). *J. Biophys. Biochem. Cytol.* **10**, 275.
Tyler, A. (1939a). *Proc. Natl. Acad. Sci. U. S.* **25**, 317.
Tyler, A. (1939b). *Proc. Natl. Acad. Sci. U. S.* **25**, 523.
Tyler, A. (1940). *Biol. Bull.* **78**, 159.
Tyler, A. (1941). *Biol. Bull.* **81**, 190.
Tyler, A. (1946). *Proc. Soc. Exptl. Biol. Med.* **62**, 197.
Tyler, A. (1948). *Physiol. Rev.* **28**, 180.
Tyler, A. (1949). *Am. Naturalist* **83**, 195.
Tyler, A. (1950). *Biol. Bull.* **99**, 324.

Tyler, A. (1953). *Biol. Bull.* **104**, 224.
Tyler, A. (1956). *Exptl. Cell Res.* **10**, 377.
Tyler, A. (1959). *Exptl. Cell Res. Suppl.* **7**, 183.
Tyler, A. (1962). *Proc. Conf. Immuno. Reprod. La Jolla, 1962* p. 13. Population Council, New York.
Tyler, A. (1963). *Am. Zool.* **3**, 109.
Tyler, A., and Fox, S. W. (1940). *Biol. Bull.* **79**, 153.
Tyler, A., and Hathaway, R. R. (1958). *Biol. Bull.* **115**, 369.
Tyler, A., and Humason, W. D. (1937). *Biol. Bull.* **73**, 261.
Tyler, A., and Metz, C. B. (1955). *Pubbl. Staz. Zool. Napoli* **27**, 128.
Tyler, A., and Monroy, A. (1955). *Biol. Bull.* **109**, 370.
Tyler, A., and Monroy, A. (1959). *J. Exptl. Zool.* **142**, 675.
Tyler, A., Burbank, A., and Tyler, J. S. (1954a). *Biol. Bull.* **107**, 303.
Tyler, A., Burbank, A., and Tyler, J. S. (1954b). *Biol. Bull.* **107**, 304.
Tyler, A., Monroy, A., and Metz, C. B. (1956a). *Biol. Bull.* **110**, 184.
Tyler, A., Monroy, A., Kao, C. Y., and Grundfest, H. (1956b). *Biol. Bull.* **111**, 153.
Tyler, A., Seaton, A., and Signoret, J. (1961). *Am. Zool.* **1**, 394.
Ungar, G., Aschheim, E., Psychoyos, S., and Romano, D. V. (1957). *J. Gen. Physiol.* **40**, 635.
Vasseur, E. (1947). *Arkiv. Kemi Mineral. Geol.* **25B** (6).
Vasseur, E. (1949). *Acta Chem. Scand.* **2**, 900.
Vasseur, E. (1950). *Acta Chem. Scand.* **4**, 1144.
Vasseur, E. (1952). *Acta Chem. Scand.* **6**, 376.
Vasseur, E. (1954). "The Chemistry and Physiology of the Jelly Coat of the Sea Urchin Egg." Kihlströmstryck, Stockholm.
Vasseur, E., and Immers, J. (1949). *Arkiv Kemi* **1**, 253.
Wada, S. K., Collier, J. R., and Dan, J. C. (1956). *Exptl. Cell Res.* **10**, 168.
Warburg, O. (1911). "Über die Oxydationen in lebenden Zellen nach Versuchen am Seeigelei." Rössler & Herbert, Heidelberg.
Warner, J. R., Knopf, P. M., and Rich, A. (1963). *Proc. Natl. Acad. Sci. U. S.* **49**, 122.
Wettstein, F. O., Staehelin, T., and Noll, H. (1963). *Nature* **197**, 430.
Whitaker, D. M. (1931a). *J. Gen. Physiol.* **15**, 167.
Whitaker, D. M. (1931b). *J. Gen. Physiol.* **15**, 183.
Whitaker, D. M. (1931c). *J. Gen. Physiol.* **15**, 191.
Whitaker, D. M. (1933a). *J. Gen. Physiol.* **16**, 475.
Whitaker, D. M. (1933b). *J. Gen. Physiol.* **16**, 497.
Whiteley, A. H., and Chambers, E. L. (1960). *Symp. Germ Cells Develop. Pallanza* p. 387.
Wilt, F. H. (1963). *Biochem. Biophys. Res. Commun.* **11**, 447.
Wilt, F. H., and Hultin, T. (1962). *Biochem. Biophys. Res. Commun.* **9**, 313.
Wolpert, L., and Mercer, E. H. (1961). *Exptl. Cell Res.* **22**, 45.
Yamamoto, T. (1961). *Intern. Rev. Cytol.* **12**, 361.
Yanagimachi, R. (1957). *Zool. Mag.* (*Tokyo*) **66**, 222.
Yanagimachi, R., and Kanoh, Y. (1953). *J. Fac. Sci. Hokkaido Univ. Ser. VI* **11**, 487.
Yasumasu, I., and Nakano, E. (1963). *Biol. Bull.* **125**, 182.
Yčas, M. (1950). Quoted by Rothschild (1956b).
Zeuthen, E. (1944). *Compt. Rend. Trav. Lab. Carlsberg Ser. Chim.* **25**, 191.
Zotin, A. I. (1958). *J. Embryol. Exptl. Morphol.* **6**, 546.

Part II

BIOCHEMICAL PATTERNS IN EMBRYOS

Chapter 3

MORPHOGENETIC SIGNIFICANCE OF BIOCHEMICAL PATTERNS IN SEA URCHIN EMBRYOS

TRYGGVE GUSTAFSON

Department of Developmental Physiology
The Wenner-Gren Institute for Experimental Biology
University of Stockholm
Stockholm, Sweden

I. General Introduction

The main problems of embryonic development are how the cells of an embryo become biochemically and structurally different, how the relative number of the different cells becomes properly adjusted, how their spatial distribution is determined, and how they form tissues and organs of a characteristic shape. Since all the cells of an embryo can be assumed to contain the same genes as the zygote nucleus, embryonic differentiation may appear as somewhat of a paradox. To circumvent this theoretical difficulty sometimes one has assumed that during the course of development the nuclei undergo various irreversible changes, e.g., that they lose some of their genetic information. Observations on the egg of *Ascaris* seemed to lend some support for this view (cf. Boveri, 1910). A classic experiment of Boveri with sea urchin eggs, however, indicated that the nuclei of the first blastomeres are equivalent (cf. Boveri, 1910). Later on various investigators working with nuclear transplantation into enucleated amphibian eggs have shown that the nuclei of rather advanced regions of the embryo are genetically equivalent to that of the zygote (cf. King and Briggs, 1956). In spite of some evidence for irreversible nuclear changes within the endodermal region, one is inclined to assume that such changes are not a general phenomenon.

An alternative interpretation of the process of differentiation can be based upon studies of the polytene chromosomes of certain insects (cf. Beerman, 1956) and of the so-called lampbrush chromosomes in the vertebrate oocyte, particularly in the amphibians (cf. Callan, 1963). According to these studies the activity of the different genes is turned on and off at certain stages of development. The control of these changes appears to be brought about by cytoplasmic or at least extrachromosomal factors, for instance, hormones (cf. Karlson, 1963). The microbiologists have provided us with important ideas about the nature and mode of operation of such control factors. The diagram in Fig. 1 is an example of how one can try to integrate the results of a great number of different microbiological experiments (cf. Jacob and Monod, 1961). According to this interpretation the transcription of the genetic information is controlled by metabolites in the cell. The applicability of this concept to the differentiation or at least temporary changes in the enzymatic activities of animal cells has been debated. There is, however, a number of experiments which favor the idea that substrate-induced enzyme formation and product repression as well as so-called catabolite repression really occur in embryos, adult organisms, as well as in explanted tissues and cells

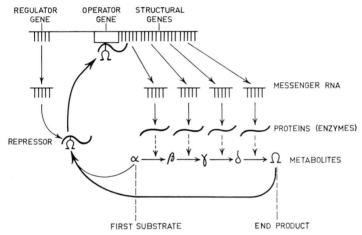

Fig. 1. Interpretation of the mechanism of regulation of the activity of a set of structural genes (an operon). An end product, Ω, in the metabolic sequence catalyzed by a series of enzymes reacts with a repressor which then becomes active and blocks the operator site of the operon thereby preventing the release of messenger RNA from the structural genes. In the presence of an excess of the substrate, α, the activation of the repressor fails.

cultivated *in vitro* (cf., e.g., Kato and Moog, 1958; Pitot and Periano, 1963; Schimke, 1964; Eliasson, 1963, 1965). It is not necessary, however, to rely entirely on enzyme induction and repression. Complex enzyme systems such as that in Fig. 2 (cf. Kacser, 1960), have the ability to operate in alternative ways. The critical factor that determines the choice between the metabolic patterns can be the concentration of a single metabolite.

How an induction-repression mechanism or a choice mechanism of the type just mentioned can bring about the elaboration of a stable metabolic pattern is outside the scope of this review. Jacob and Monod (1963), however, suggested various models for such a stabilization. A tendency to stabilization also occurs in the model outlined in Fig. 2 where

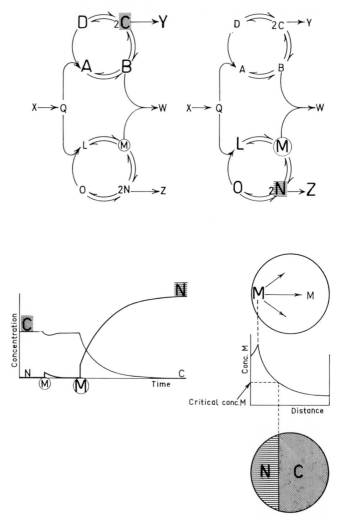

FIG. 2.   Diagram of the mode of regulation of a complicated metabolic system
where the metabolic flow can be funneled into two alternative directions. The letters
indicate various intermediary metabolites. The two alternative metabolic patterns are
characterized by a high concentration of C, respectively, or N. The first pattern is
realized when the concentration of the metabolite M is low and tends to stabilize itself,
even if a small amount of M is added. If the concentration of M exceeds a critical
level the pattern changes into the C type which tends to be stable. In an egg or
embryo where M is produced at one pole and a concentration gradient appears, the
N pattern becomes established within one region, sharply delineated from a region
with a C pattern. Based upon Kacser (1960).

enzyme synthesis is not necessarily involved. The elaboration of various cellular structures may also have a stabilizing effect upon the metabolic properties of a cell.

The general conclusion one can draw from investigations is that it is possible to account for differentiation without assuming irreversible changes of the nuclei and that metabolites of a cell can determine the choice between different metabolic patterns. Differentiation is accordingly not a genetic but an epigenetic process. This was already pointed out by Driesch on the basis of experiments on the development of sea urchin blastomeres separated during early cleavage stages (Driesch, 1891, 1892).

If an egg shows regional biochemical differences which lead to a localized production of diffusible control substances, one may visualize how it may become subdivided into two or more zones with different biochemical characteristics (cf. Fig. 2). The basic requirement for such a subdivision has been observed in most eggs. Egg cells often exhibit clear cytoplasmic differences along their animal-vegetal and dorsoventral axis before fertilization or at least after that event. So is the case in many eggs with an abundance of yolk and pigment, for instance in many amphibians, where the visible differences are in part only indicators of more important physiological ones. In other cases the polarity becomes overt as a result of cytoplasmic rearrangements which start upon fertilization, as for instance in the ascidian egg. In some eggs the polarity stands out more clearly after staining with a suitable agent. The cytoplasm may then exhibit different colors in the animal and vegetal region (cf. Spek, 1931). This phenomenon has sometimes been considered indicative of a pH difference between these regions or, alternatively, a difference in the properties of the proteins or other components to which the dye molecules become linked (see Ling, 1962). In this article we shall consider the problem of the sea urchin egg in which the polarity is not too evident.

II. The Polarity of the Sea Urchin Egg

The growing sea urchin oocyte is attached to the ovarial wall by its vegetal pole (Lindahl, 1932a). The polarity thus can be looked upon theoretically as an expression of the polarity of the cells of the germ epithelium. It may also become established as a result of polar differences with respect to the transport of nutrients to the egg, e.g., from the wall of the ovarium or from migrating "nurse" cells which cover the free surface of the growing oocyte as described by Lindahl (1941). Local differences in the oxygen and carbon dioxide content can also influence the growing oocyte. The origin of the animal-vegetal polarity is not too difficult to visualize, although we must admit that we know very little about the actual basis of this event. The origin of the dorsoventral polarity is, on the other hand, more difficult to visualize. It has often been claimed that this polarity is determined by the entrance point of the sperm. The sperm entrance may, however, be determined by the polarity of the egg (Runnström, 1962) which may give a false impression about the role of the sperm in this respect.

More important than theoretical possibilities is the real evidence for a physiological polarity of the sea urchin egg. The shape of the oocyte and the egg often suggests that a structural polarity already occurs before fertilization. The formation of the polar bodies at the animal pole is another indicator of polarity. The so-called micropyle through the jelly coat, which can be easily demonstrated at the animal pole, is still another indicator. In this case, however, we are dealing with a layer that appears to be secreted by the oocyte as a continuous envelope, but the micropyle formation seems to depend upon the formation of a protrusion from the egg that penetrates and perforates the jelly coat (Lindahl, 1941). In some eggs, particularly in *Echinocardium*, the animal pole of the mature egg forms a protrusion (Gustafson, 1952) which might be related to the one just discussed (Fig. 3b). In the egg of *Paracentrotus*, particularly the form from the Mediterranian, another indicator of polar differences can be observed. During maturation or shortly afterward the cortical pigment thus collects into a subequatorial band (Fig. 3a) (Boveri, 1901b). A ring-like zone can also be observed in the egg of *Brissopsis* when it has been kept for some hours in sea water (Gustafson, 1960). Observations by means of dark field illumination made by Runnström (1928b) show that the pigment ring in *Paracentrotus* is more or less paralleled by a ring which stands out owing to its yellow color. Observations on the development of giant polar bodies (Gustafson, 1946) indicate that the animal-vegetal polarity is already established at the time of maturation. Giant polar bodies thus have a strong tendency to ectodermal development.

Some sea urchin eggs also show evidence for a dorsoventral polarity even before fertilization. Eggs of *Echinocardium cordatum* treated with various SH-compounds and other agents undergo a local shrinkage that results in the formation of two concavities (Fig. 3b), the larger of which seems to correspond to the future ventral side (Gustafson, 1952). The evidence for this relation is only indirect, however. The concavities disappear at the time of fertilization and cannot be induced after that time, but if the fertilized eggs are kept in cyanide solutions or under anaerobic conditions two similar concavities appear, the larger of which corresponds to the future ventral side as can be concluded on the basis of vital staining experiments (Foerster and Öhrström, 1933). Furthermore, treatment of the unfertilized egg with anionic detergents prevents the formation of the prefertilization concavities or reverses them if they have already been induced (Gustafson, 1952), and if the eggs are left to develop in solutions

(a)

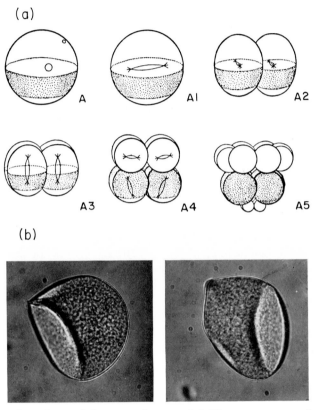

(b)

FIG. 3. The polarity of the sea urchin egg. (a) The pigment ring of the egg of *Paracentrotus lividus* (somewhat thinner than the zone indicated) and the pattern of cleavage up to the 16-cell stage. After Hörstadius (1928). (b) Eggs of *Echinocardium cordatum* in which the formation of two (occasionally one) concavity has been induced by treatment with an SH-compound. The large concavity probably corresponds to the presumptive ventral side. Note the tip which corresponds to the animal pole. From Gustafson (1952).

of these detergents, the dorsoventrality may become "weeped out" and the larvae become radial (Gustafson and Sävhagen, 1950). It also seems as if the sperm preferentially penetrates at the future ventral side and that the elevation of the fertilization membrane tends to start at the site of the concavities (Runnström, 1962). In summary, these observations suggest that the egg has an animal-vegetal as well as a dorsoventral polarity.

The nature of the polar differences of the egg is a rather obscure problem. There is thus no clear-cut evidence of biochemical or ultrastructural differences between the animal and vegetal half of the unfertilized egg. This, of course, does not mean that such differences are not likely to be detected in the future. One is, however, inclined to assume that the essential differences are confined to the cortical layer of the egg. Centrifugation of the sea urchin egg, which brings about a drastic redistribution of the yolk and other granules as well as of the clear cytoplasm thus does not affect the animal-vegetal polarity of the egg (Runnström, 1926; Lindahl, 1932b; Pease, 1939) or its sensitivity to lithium ions that bring about a shift in the proportions of the germ layers (Hörstadius, 1953). The dorsoventrality of the larva differs from the animal-vegetal polarity in the sense that it can be affected by centrifugation, but a careful analysis, particularly by Pease (1939), indicates that the ventral side is predetermined by some property of the egg cortex and that centrifugation can only shift the ventral side to a certain extent.

Raven (1961) considers the polarity of the *Limnaea* egg as related to the phospholipid composition of the cell surface, a concept that fits with a number of observations on the effect of lithium ions on phospholipid colloids (cf. Geilenkirchen, 1964). That the lipids of the cortex play a role in this connection is in line with the conclusion of Runnström (1928b) that the yellow subequatorial ring mentioned above corresponds to a region where the lipid layers of the cortex are particularly thick. Another observation in line with this concept is that anionic detergents, which bring about radialization (Gustafson and Sävhagen, 1950) and also animalization, are likely to interfere with the architecture of the cell membrane. The effect of a local stretching of the egg surface on the dorsoventral polarity of the egg (Lindahl, 1936) may also be discussed in terms of changes in the structure of the egg membrane.

III. The Dynamics of Determination

A. *Prospective Significance of the Different Regions of the Egg*

One can raise the question how specific and detailed the polar differences of the egg cortex are. Do we have to look upon the egg as a mosaic of distinctly different areas with the destination to develop into ectoderm, endoderm, and so on? The question may seem unnecessary and is only heuristic. To answer this question we have to consider the prospective significance of the different regions of the egg. This question can be answered on the basis of vital staining experiments (cf. Hörstadius, 1935).

Some conclusions can also be drawn from time-lapse cinematographic observations, for instance, on the developing egg of *Echinocardium* where the pigment cell fraction of the secondary mesenchyme can be traced at an early mesenchyme-blastula stage (Gustafson and Wolpert, 1962). Figure 4 gives a diagrammatic summary of our knowledge within this field. It has to be emphasized that the vegetal region is overscaled in the diagram and that some of the borders are merely to be considered as extrapolation of our knowledge. The normal development of an egg into a pluteus larva is summarized in Fig. 5.

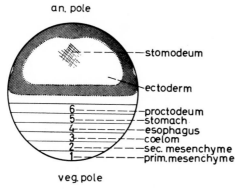

FIG. 4. A map of the presumptive regions of the egg. All the zones indicated have not yet been mapped by vital staining technique (cf. Hörstadius, 1935), and the diagram should be considered as an extrapolation from available results. The relative proportions of zones 1–6 are overscaled for convenience. The stippled zones correspond to thickened regions of the ectoderm but must be considered as entirely schematic.

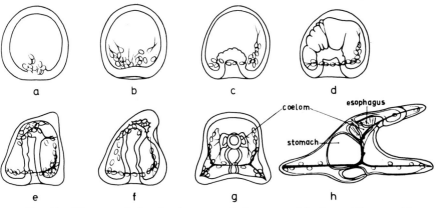

FIG. 5. Diagram of the development of the sea urchin larva (*Psammechinus miliaris*) from the mesenchyme blastula stage (a) to an early pluteus stage (h); (c–f and h) larvae in profile, (g) larva seen from the ventral side.

B. *Dynamics of Determination of the Sea Urchin Egg As Studied by Means of Microsurgical Experiments. The Double Gradient System.*

The zones in the diagram in Fig. 4 only indicate the prospective significance of the different zones. Classic experiments of Boveri, Driesch, Zoja, Terni, Selenka, and later investigators (cf. Hörstadius, 1935) have shown that the borders between the zones can be shifted. A systematic and detailed study of these borders can be based on fragments obtained by means of microsurgical operations. The formation of giant polar bodies (Gustafson, 1946) can be considered as a kind of natural microsurgical experiment before fertilization (cf. Hörstadius, 1937).

As is well known to every embryologist, animal halves develop into an ectodermal vesicle with an enlarged animal plate (Figs. 6, a–c; 7). The size of this plate and the further development of the larvae is, however, quite variable. The vegetal half, on the other hand, gives rise to a larva with mesentoderm and mesenchyme but has a more or less ovoid shape (Hörstadius, 1935, 1939). The polarity thus determines the sequence of the organ rudiments along the egg axis but does not rigidly determine their relative size and other features. Experiments with meridional egg fragments also indicate that dorsoventrality is rather labile during cleavage stages (Hörstadius and Wolsky, 1936; cf. Gustafson and Sävhagen, 1950).

The significance of the different zones of the egg is gradually determined as development proceeds. The dynamics of this determination has been studied extensively by Hörstadius (1935) who began his work by an investigation of the development of animal and vegetal halves from eggs where the third cleavage furrow was equatorial or slightly deflected from this level. A number of such experiments indicated that the vegetal material of the egg has a tendency to normalize the development of the animal material and vice versa. The investigations were carried on by microsurgical fragmentation of the egg at various levels along the animal-vegetal axis at the 16- to 64-cell stages and by recombination of fragments of different origin. These experiments showed that the intensity of the vegetal tendency decreases along this axis, being most pronounced in the micromeres. The experiments also showed that the intensity of the animal tendency has a graded distribution along the axis, being strongest at the animal pole. It was therefore concluded that development is controlled by two oppositely directed and mutually antagonistic gradients, an animal and a vegetal, a concept outlined by Runnström (1928a). A normal development occurs when the two gradients are properly adjusted, whereas the animal regions show an excessive development when the animal tendency dominates, the vegetal regions when the vegetal tendency is too strong (Fig. 6). When the animal or vegetal tendency dominates one speaks about animalization, respectively, or vegetalization.

One can, of course, ask if the increase in the animal tendency toward the animal pole is merely the result of a decrease in the vegetal one. Both the animal and the vegetal tendency are, however, aggressive in the sense that they try to extend at the expense of the other. The interaction of the animal and vegetal region is supposed to be mediated by diffusing animal and vegetal substances. Different attempts to affect the develop-

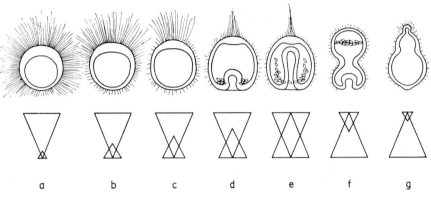

FIG. 6. Diagram of sea urchin larvae of about the same age but varying in the animal and the vegetal tendencies. (e) Normal gastrula, (a–d) larvae animalized to a varying extent, (f–g) larvae vegetalized to a different extent; in (g) the ectoderm is reduced to a small knob. The hypothetical double gradient system corresponding to each larva is indicated. Animalization can be brought about by a reduction of the amount of vegetal material or by treatment with various chemical agents such as SCN treatment before fertilization or treatment with o-iodosobenzoic acid or 2,5-thiomethylcytosine during cleavage stages. Vegetalization can be brought about by lithium or chloramphenicol treatment during cleavage.

ment with extracts from cells or whole larvae of a vegetal type have, however, failed (Hörstadius and Strömberg, 1940; Berg and Cheng, 1962).

C. Interference with the Double Gradient System by Means of Chemical Agents

Chemical agents of various kinds bring about the same change in development as microsurgical experiments (cf. Fig. 6). The earliest and most well-known experiment of this kind is that of Herbst on the influence of lithium ions added to the sea water (Herbst, 1892). These ions somehow bring about a shift of the ectoderm-endoderm border and also of other borders (cf. Fig. 6, f and g). The most dramatic effect can be described as a decrease of the size of the ectoderm and a corresponding increase of the mesendoderm. In extreme cases the ectoderm may be completely suppressed. In connection with these disturbances there is also a disturbance of the process of invagination. Unfortunately, such disturbances have often been misinterpreted as an expression of vegetalization. An exogastrula may develop, however, although the relative size of the organ rudiments is quite normal. Other substances, for instance thiocyanate, bring about an excessive development of the ectoderm at the expense of the endomesoderm, i.e., animalization, if applied at the proper time (see Lindahl, 1936; Runnström and Thörnblom, 1938). Animal and vegetal halves treated with these various agents can be completely normalized if the concentrations and periods of treatment are carefully controlled (Hörstadius, 1936a; von Ubisch, 1929). A combined treatment with substances with antagonistic effects may also completely counterbalance each other (cf. e.g., Lindahl, 1936; Gustafson and Hörstadius, 1956).

Theoretically these chemical agents could exert their effects in many different ways, for instance by interfering with the structural or biochemical polarity of the egg before or after cleavage has started, by increasing or decreasing the production of various control substances, or by directly affecting the system that responds to these control substances. That animal cells from a Li-treated larva have the same effect as micromeres (Hörstadius, 1936b) may indicate that the formation of the vegetal control substances is involved. The situation is, however, still quite obscure.

D. *Dorsoventrality in Relation to the Double Gradient System*

The dorsoventral development has been ascribed sometimes to the operation of a separate gradient system (cf. Czihak, 1961). In many cases, however, one has observed a close relation between the animal-vegetal gradient system and the dorsoventral development. Vegetalized larvae thus have a less pronounced dorsoventrality than normal larvae (Lindahl, 1936), and radializing agents generally influence the determination along the animal-vegetal balance (cf. Hörstadius and Gustafson, 1954). One may therefore suggest that the dorsoventrality depends upon a somewhat altered steepness of the animal and vegetal gradient along the ventral side. The most characteristic expression of a strong animal tendency, the great adhesion between the cells of the animal plate, is also a characteristic feature of the ciliated band that surrounds the oral side. This band, in fact, is a direct extension of the animal plate, and its close relation to the animal trend of development can be seen from the type series of Hörstadius describing the features of animal halves of different animal strengths (Hörstadius, 1935, 1936b). A strengthening of the animal tendencies in this type series is thus correlated with a broadening of the band, until it finally forms a thick plate in direct contact with and forming a part of the animal plate (cf. larvae B and D in Fig. 7). One may therefore conclude that the ventral side is characterized by rather strong animal properties. This concept will play a great role in the later discussion.

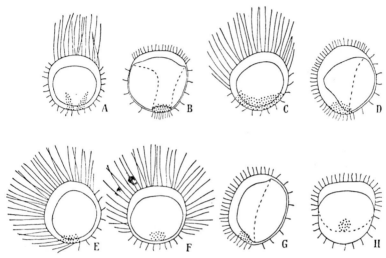

FIG. 7. The development of animal halves isolated at the 16-cell stage. The vegetal region has been marked by vital staining immediately after isolation. In B the ciliated band extends from the animal plate. In D and G the ciliated band and the animal plate form a continuous plate which covers the ventral side and is a direct continuation of the animal plate. The larvae with long stereocilia, A, C, E, and F, are somewhat younger than those with only short cilia. After Hörstadius (1936b).

E. *Feedback Relations within the Gradient System*

This description of the dynamics of the determinative gradients is only a first approximation. There are also interactions between various levels within each of the gradients. Removal of the material which normally forms the primary mesenchyme and skeleton results in the formation of a larva which has a fairly normal skeleton as was already shown by Boveri (1901a). According to Boveri's interpretation the strong skeleton-forming tendency of the most vegetal region suppresses a weaker skeleton-forming tendency in the adjacent region. It was, in fact, this observation that led Boveri to the assumption that the development of the egg is controlled by some graded processes, a conclusion which was also in agreement with the observations of the time course of the chromatin diminution in the *Ascaris* egg. The observations that an implantation of a great number of micromeres into an animal fragment does not lead to

an excessive development of the primary mesenchyme and that strongly
vegetalized larvae have a fairly normal number of primary mesenchyme
cells are also in line with the concept that the amount of primary mesenchyme is controlled by some kind of feedback mechanism. Another indication of a vegetal feedback control is that the number of pigmented
secondary mesenchyme cells is only slightly increased in vegetalized
larva, the increased pigment production mainly owing to an increase in
pigment production per cell. Also the secondary mesenchyme as a whole,
which plays a great role during the invagination of the archenteron, seems
to be governed by a feedback control. The region that undergoes a
primary invagination in a strongly vegetalized larva thus hardly or just
slightly exceeds the size of the normal invagination, although the size of
the mesendoderm as a whole is considerably increased (Gustafson and
Wolpert, 1963b). Also the size of the coelom seems to be governed by a
feedback control, as the size of the coelom in a vegetalized larva does
not greatly exceed that of a normal one (cf. Gustafson and Wolpert,
1961). The border between the ectoderm and endoderm, on the other
hand, is easily shifted as already mentioned. All these results are in line
with the conclusion of Lindahl (1936) that the mass of a particular tissue
is more difficult to increase, the smaller its distance to the vegetal pole.

The development of the animal region is also governed by a feedback control. Removal of most animal cells thus results in the formation
of a larva with a fairly normal animal plate, as if the presence of an
animal plate suppresses a similar activity further down the gradient
(Hörstadius, 1935). A strongly animalized larva may, in fact, obtain two
plates, one at each pole, as if the animal plate exerts some restriction on
the extension of the plate even if the animal strength permits development of an animal plate all over the surface (cf. Fig. 8) (Lindahl, 1936).
The occurrence of vegetalized larvae with a small extra ectoderm in the
vegetal region in addition to the small ectoderm in the animal region also
suggests that the ectoderm produces inhibitory substances that tend to
suppress the ectoderm-forming processes in the vicinity (cf. Gustafson
and Lenicque, 1952; Gustafson, 1954).

The ventral side also seems to emit some inhibitory agent that suppresses the development of a similar structure in the same larva. Separation of the ventral and the dorsal side of the larva microsurgically (Hörstadius and Wolsky, 1936) or by means of a constriction (Hörstadius,
1938) or a dorsoventral elongation of the blastula (Lindahl, 1936) abol-
ishes or decreases this inhibition, and each half can therefore develop
its own ventral side. If we consider the ventral side as a region where the
animal properties extend downward, it is possible that the inhibitions
exerted by the ventral side are related to those exerted by the animal
plate.

The basis for the inhibitions within each of the gradients is obscure. However, this type of inhibition is rather widespread among animals as well as plants. It certainly plays an important role in connection with the regulation of the size of organs and must be considered in regeneration experiments. Treatment of embryos with extracts of brain or blood and so on, in fact, tends to inhibit the development of the corresponding tissues (Lenicque, 1959). A hypothesis concerned with such substances has been formulated by Rose (1957) and Weiss (1947), although the details in their interpretations vary. The problem occurs if these control substances are different from and more specific than the substances that mediate the interaction between the gradients. Studies of the morpho-

Fig. 8. Strongly animalized larva having two plates with stereocilia. Animalization was brought about by means of SCN treatment before fertilization. From Lindahl (1936).

genetic behavior of the cells in the different zones along the animal-vegetal axis suggest that there is a gradual transition between cells of high adhesion in the animal plate and cells with low adhesion in the primary mesenchyme, although the cellular adhesion can show a change with time (Gustafson, 1961; Gustafson and Wolpert, 1963b). Such a picture may be in line with the assumption that the feedback inhibitions are mediated by the same pair of control substances that mediate the interactions between the gradients. This is, however, a quite theoretical consideration. More information might be obtained from studies on the time pattern of the interactions.

F. Time-Space Pattern of Interactions

It is for many reasons important to find out when the different types of interactions occur. Experiments with implantation of micromeres into animal halves at different times of development have shown that the sensitivity of the animal halves gradually decreases, but that it persists longer in halves that are detached from vegetal halves in early stages (Hörstadius, 1936a). Similar conclusions about the time course of determination can be drawn from studies on the effect of chemical agents which interfere with development. The most sensitive period for the lithium agent is from the 16-cell stage and 3–4 hours later (Lindahl, 1940), although the effect may be enhanced if the treatment is extended after that period (Hörstadius, 1936a). For other agents the sensitive period has not been investigated to the same extent as in the case of Li. In general, however, the sensitive period is restricted to the early cleavage stages. Thiocyanate is an important exception, since it can only bring about animalization if applied before fertilization for some hours (Lindahl, 1936). Glucose and other sugars are also exceptional in that they affect the development of the ectoderm after hatching (Hörstadius, 1959). Experiments with actinomycin C and mitomycin C (Markman, 1963) also indicate that the transcription of the information from the genetic material in some regions at least can be disturbed in rather advanced stages of development, leading to morphogenetic disturbances, particularly within the endomesoderm.

When discussing the influence of the vegetal region one also has to consider the topological aspect. Experiments with animal halves isolated at various stages of development followed by implantation of micromeres indicate that the determination proceeds from the vegetal pole toward the animal, the most animal region keeping its sensitivity longer than the more vegetal (Hörstadius, 1936a). This is in keeping with the idea that a morphogenetic factor spreads from the vegetal pole. One may suggest that this factor causes a change that is incompatible with the elaboration of the ectodermal differentiation. After this period the agent may not be so effective, although it is still produced (Hörstadius, 1936a). Lithium treatment may then either increase the production and hence the radius of action of the vegetal substances, or it may retard the ectodermal differentiation so that a larger region becomes affected by the vegetal control substances. When Li is applied after the most sensitive period, the animal region may be so close to its final differentiation that none of these mechanisms can be effective. A prolongation of a Li treatment that starts early may, however, cause a considerable change in both senses and so decrease the size of the ectoderm. That the effect of Li is enhanced by a number of substances such as amino acid analogs (Gustafson and Hörstadius, 1955) has to be considered with their possibilities in view.

As already mentioned it might be appropriate to consider if interaction within each gradient is mediated by substances different from those that mediate the interactions between the gradients. If they are different it is not necessary to assume that both types of interactions are coexistent. The former ones may thus occur in more advanced stages than the latter ones. Removal of the primary mesenchyme cells that have been formed already is thus followed by a transition of the secondary mesenchyme into skeleton-forming cells Fukushi (1962). After what has been said about the gradation of the morphogenetical properties of the cells during differentiation and the possibility that the vegetal influences, according to the sugar experiments also the animal influences, might continue in later stages it seems attractive, however, to think that we are dealing with just one pair of interactions.

The formation of the hypothetical animal and vegetal substances and other possible mediators of interaction and the fact that development can be altered by various chemical agents make it self-evident that the postulated gradients which control morphogenetic development have a biochemical basis. In order to understand these gradients we have to consider many steps in a causal chain such as the polarity of the eggs, the nature of the interactions during the period of primary determination of the germ layers, later interactions, and the gradual establishment of the final biochemical differences between the germ layers. Although the plasticity of the system gradually decreases, the biochemical activities of the different germ layers can shed some light on the processes in preceding stages.

IV. Total Changes in Biochemical Activities

A. *Over-All Respiratory Changes*

As a basis for a discussion of the regional biochemical differences within the developing sea urchin embryo it is suitable to look at some of the over-all biochemical changes of the embryo. Studies on the respiration of intact eggs and larvae by Lindahl (1939a, 1942) have shown that respiration increases during cleavage stages. Another rise starts at the onset of gastrulation, i.e., when the primary mesenchyme cells begin to enter the blastocoel (Fig. 9). A detailed study of the respiration of a smaller number of eggs by means of the Cartesian diver technique shows that the early rise is not steady but has a microstructure that can be related to the mitotic cycles (Fig. 10) (cf. Holter and Zeuthen, 1957). However, this does not rule out the main conclusion that an over-all respiratory rise occurs. The respiratory quotient, RQ, of the newly fertilized egg is about 0.7. On the assumption that this respiratory fraction remains constant during cleavage Lindahl and Öhman (1938) calculated the RQ of the increasing fraction and found that it has the value 1 which indicates that it corresponds to the oxidation of carbohydrates.

With this as a point of departure one may try to discuss the significance of the respiratory changes.

B. Over-All Changes in the Hexose Monophosphate Shunt

For various reasons (cf. Hörstadius and Gustafson, 1947), one was led to believe that the carbohydrate oxidation during cleavage stages did not follow the glycolytic and citric acid cycle pathway but the pathway of the hexose monophosphate shunt. This conclusion agrees with the observations that the activity of the glucose-6-phosphate dehydrogenase

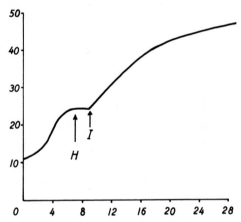

FIG. 9.   Changes in the rate of respiration during development of the sea urchin larva. H, Hatching; I, start of gastrulation. Ordinate: O_2 consumption in mm^3 per mg N and 60 minutes. Abscissa: hours of development. From Lindahl (1939a).

and the 6-phosphogluconate dehydrogenase shows a strong increase during cleavage stages (Fig. 11) (Bäckström, 1959b, 1963b). It is further supported by investigations on the fate of glucoses variously labeled with C^{14} (Bäckström et al., 1960). The work of Isono (in press) is also in agreement with this conclusion (Fig. 12). The strong fixation of CO_2 during cleavage stages which indicates a lively formation of TPNH (triphosphopyridine nucleotide, reduced form) has also been used as an

FIG. 10.   Changes in the rate of respiration in relation of the number of nuclei. (a) Aggregate nuclear volume during development. The corresponding developmental stages can be obtained from (b), the counts of visible nuclei during development. The scale is logarithmic, but the number of nuclei corresponding to developmental stages are indicated for each maximum ○, theoretical points. ●, observations. (c) Correlation of respiration and nuclear counts. Diver constant $V = 6.2$ μl; number of eggs, 170. ●, observed nuclear counts from control vessel batch; △, observed nuclear counts from diver batch; ○, theoretical points; ○——○ times for maximum nuclear counts; ←→ times for minimum nuclear counts. Gap in respiration curve indicates resetting of manometer. From Holter and Zeuthen (1957).

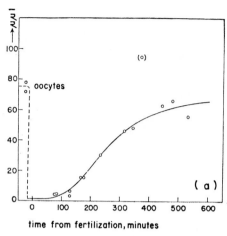

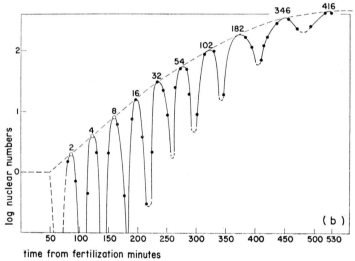

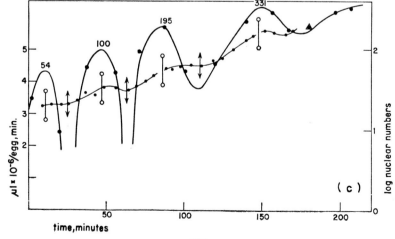

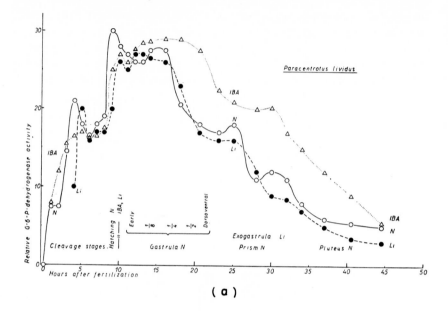

(a)

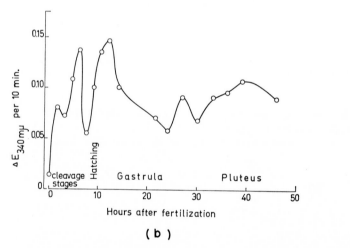

(b)

Fig. 11.   Changes in the activity of glucose-6-phosphate dehydrogenase (a) and 6-phosphogluconate dehydrogenase (b) in developing eggs of *Paracentrotus lividus*. Zero refers to unfertilized eggs. In (a) a comparison has been made between normal larvae (N), larvae vegetalized by means of lithium (Li), and larvae animalized by means of o-iodosobenzoic acid (IBA). (a) From Bäckström (1959b), (b) from Bäckström (1963b).

argument in favor of the role of the hexose monophosphate shunt (Hultin, 1953a). The early suggestion of Hörstadius and Gustafson (1947) have therefore, as it seems, turned out to be correct.

The interruption of the respiratory rise in the blastula can be correlated with a drop in the activity of the two shunt enzymes, a drop that is not contradictory to the results of Isono. Later there is a second main

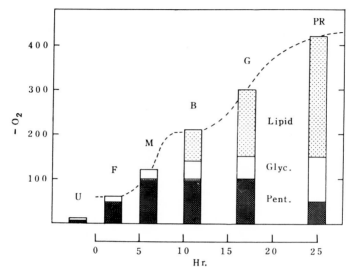

FIG. 12. Changes in the oxidation of carbohydrates and lipids in the developing sea urchin egg (*Anthocidaris crassipina*). Ordinate: O_2 uptake (μliter per 10^6 embryos per hour). Abscissa: hours after fertilization (embryos cultivated at 20°C). U, Unfertilized eggs; F, fertilized eggs; M, morula stage; B, swimming blastula stage (hatching at 9 hours); G, gastrula stage; PR, prism stage. Black zone (Pent.): respiration dependent on carbohydrate breakdown via the pentose phosphate cycle. White zone (Glyc.): respiration dependent on the carbohydrate breakdown via the Embden-Meyerhof pathway and the Krebs cycle. Dotted zone (lipid): respiration dependent on lipid breakdown. Dashed line: changes in the rate of oxygen uptake. From Isono (in press).

peak in the activity of the shunt enzymes followed by some smaller fluctuations (Bäckström, 1959b, 1963b).

It is evident that the changes in the shunt activity can only partially account for the changes in the respiratory activity. One has therefore to look at other processes that might shed light upon the over-all respiratory changes.

C. Over-All Changes in Mitochondrial Activities

The mitochondrial population has a rather constant density during cleavage stages. A certain rise in mitochondrial stainability has, however, been recorded during this period (Fig. 13) (Gustafson and Lenicque, 1955). This indicates that the mitochondria undergo a certain change during this period, a conclusion that is further supported by other observations (see below). The early changes in the respiratory intensity

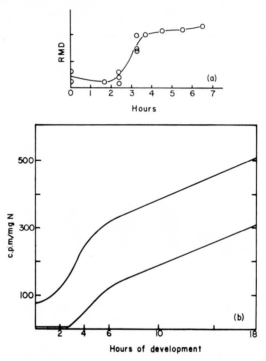

FIG. 13. (a) Changes in the relative number of Nile blue sulfate stainable granules during early cleavage and blastula stages of *Psammechinus miliaris*. Individual counts of two separate experiments plotted together. RMD, relative density of the particulate population. Sample sectors chosen by chance with regard to the polarity of the egg. The 32-cell stage was reached at 3 hr., 15 min. From Gustafson and Lenicque (1955).

(b) Incorporation of S^{35}-methionine in mitochondria during development of *Paracentrotus lividus*. The upper curve gives the total incorporation into the mitochondrial fraction, the lower curve the amount of S^{35} recovered in mitochondrial proteins (cf. Nakano and Monroy, 1958).

may, of course, have some relation to these changes. The mitochondrial population, however, undergoes its most dramatic change at the onset of gastrulation, which may account for part of the second rise in respiratory activity. The evidence for this change in mitochondrial activity is multifold. There is thus a strong increase in succinic and malic dehydrogenase and some other enzymes that may reflect the mitochondrial activity (Gustafson and Hasselberg, 1951) (Fig. 14A). Lindahl's studies on the effect of CO on respiration also indicate that there is a rise in cytochrome oxidase (Lindahl, 1939b). For unknown reasons this rise did not reveal itself in analyses of cytochrome oxidase activity in homogenates (Deutsch and Gustafson, 1952). It has, however, been suggested that this result does not reflect the actual condition in the living material, but that it may be influenced by the method of homogenization, by structural changes of the mitochondria, or by the presence of inhibitory substances which affect the enzymatic assay in crude homogenates (cf. Maggio and Monroy, 1959; Maggio et al., 1960). That mitochondria show a strong increase in activity and even a change in activity at the onset of gastrulation is also supported by the work of Hultin (1953b,c) (Fig. 14B). Further support for this conclusion is the observation of Isono (in press) that the oxidation of lipids shows a strong increase at this stage of development (Fig. 12). Changes in the relation between succinic dehydrogenase and transaminase activity of the mitochondria also indicate that the mitochondrial populations of the gastrula may be more efficient with regard to respiratory activity than that in the unfertilized egg (Black, 1964). Mitochondrial counts on vital stained larvae by Gustafson and Lenicque (1952; Fig. 14C) as well as counts on homogenates by Shaver (1956) give a direct evidence for the concept that the number of mitochondria increase at the onset of gastrulation, and electron microscopy work of Berg and co-workers (1962; Berg and Long, 1964) indicate that the mitochondria change their appearance in the early gastrula, a conclusion which was also drawn by Shaver.

D. Mechanism of Control of the Respiratory Rise

There is evidently strong support for the conclusion that the second rise in respiratory activity partly reflects an increase in mitochondrial activities (Gustafson and Hasselberg, 1951), at least more than the early rise. One has, however, to keep in mind that part of the second rise may also correspond to a transient increase in the hexose monophosphate shunt activity.

Another approach to the significance of the respiratory curve has been made by Immers and Runnström (1960) who studied the respiration of larvae treated with 2,4-dinitrophenol. Addition of dinitrophenol brings about a dramatic increase of the respiratory activity and changes the general shape of the respiratory curve so that a distinct minimum can be seen at the time of the plateau during normal development (Fig. 15). As dinitrophenol releases the respiratory control to the same extent as addition of the phosphate acceptor ADP (adenosine diphosphate), the conclusion was drawn that the respiratory intensity is controlled by the rate of consumption of ATP (adenosine triphosphate), which to a great extent reflects the rate of protein synthesis. As pointed out by these authors this is in good agreement with the studies of Kavanau (1954) on the changes in free amino acids and proteins of the embryo (Fig. 16). The occurrence of two main waves of protein synthesis during development is also in agreement with studies on the isotopic labeling of developing sea urchin eggs (cf. Monroy, 1963). The second strong rise in respira-

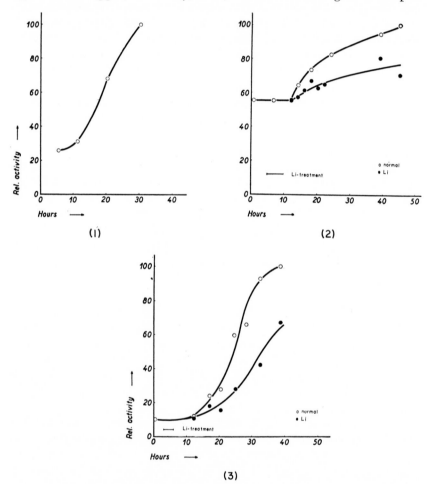

Fig. 14A.   Biochemical and structural changes at the time of gastrulation. Changes in the relative activity of succinic dehydrogenase (1), apyrase (2), and glutaminase (3); (1) and (3) refers to *Psammechinus miliaris* and (2) refers to *Paracentrotus lividus*. Open circles refer to the normal development, filled-in circles to larvae vegetalized by means of lithium treatment during early cleavage. From Gustafson and Hasselberg (1951).

tion would then correspond to the intensified protein synthesis that starts at the onset of gastrulation, that was particularly emphasized by Gustafson and Hasselberg (1951) and that partly corresponds to the synthesis of mitochondrial enzymes.

To sum up all these observations one may emphasize that the basis for the respiratory changes appears to be complex. The first rise appears to correspond to the first wave in shunt enzymes and to a lesser degree to a change in the mitochondrial population. The second rise can reflect to

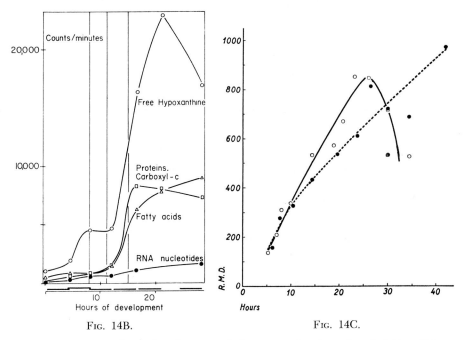

FIG. 14B.   FIG. 14C.

FIG. 14B. Biochemical and structural changes at the time of gastrulation. Rate of incorporation of labeled acetate into various fractions of the embryo of *Psammechinus miliaris* at different stages of development. Embryos at different stages of development kept for 4 hours in sea water containing 1-C14-acetate. Specific activities (counts per minute per 15 mg BaCO3 per cm2) of fractions, subsequently isolated from the embryos. Vertical lines indicate hatching, appearance of mesenchyme cells, and start of invagination. The periods of isotope treatment are indicated by horizontal lines at the bottom of the figure. From Hultin (1953c).

FIG. 14C. Biochemical and structural changes at the time of gastrulation. Mitochondrial counts in larvae of *Psammechinus miliaris* vitally stained with Nile blue sulfate. A strong rise in the number of stainable mitochondria occurs at the onset of gastrulation (mesenchyme blastula stage). Open circles refer to normal development, filled-in circles to larvae vegetalized by means of lithium treatment during early cleavage stages. RMD indicates the relative density of the population of stainable mitochondria. From Gustafson and Lenicque (1952).

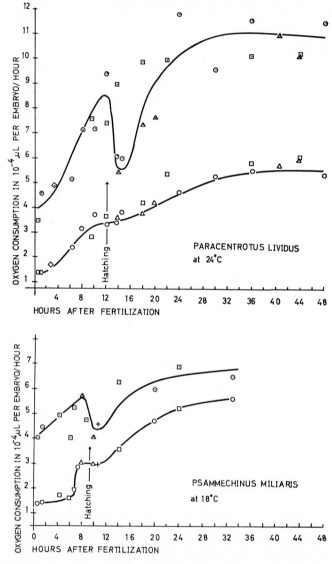

Fɪɢ. 15.　Changes in oxygen consumption in normal sea urchin larvae and in larvae treated with 2,4-dinitrophenol. Lower curves, the normal respiratory rates in different stages of development from fertilization to the pluteus stage. Upper curves, corresponding values for the respiratory rates released by addition of 2,4-dinitrophenol to the final concentration of $5 \times 10^{-5} M$ (*Paracentrotus*) or $1 \times 10^{-4} M$ (*Psammechinus*). From Immers and Runnström (1960).

a certain extent the transient second peak in shunt activity and the following smaller fluctuations, but mainly a strong rise in mitochondrial
enzymes. The respiratory control may reflect to a great extent the rate
of protein synthesis, which shows a peak during cleavage stages and a

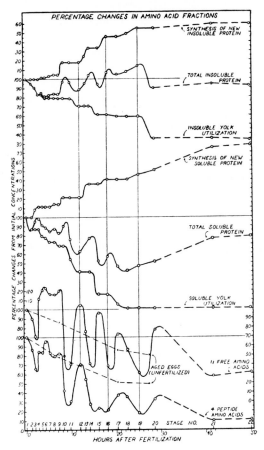

FIG. 16.   Average percentage changes of the amino acids from their values in the
unfertilized egg (all amino acids are weighted equally). Cysteine is omitted from the
free amino acid curve. The curve for peptide amino acids represents cysteine, histidine, phenylalanine, and tyrosine. From Kavanau (1954).

second one at the onset of gastrulation. We have to admit that these
studies do not as yet account quantitatively for all the fractions that make
up total respiration, but they have given us some concepts to pursue
further.

E. *General Approach to the Time-Space Pattern of the Changes in Bio-chemical Activities*

The next question we have to discuss is the spatial distribution of the changes discussed. For practical reasons we will postpone the discussion of those investigations that may seem most straightforward, namely, respiratory measurements on isolated animal and vegetal halves. It seems more suitable to examine the possible role of the processes concerned for the animal and vegetal trend of development in relation to the effects of lithium on whole embryos.

The first rise in respiration, the first peak in the hexose monophosphate shunt enzymes, and the first wave in protein synthesis occur during a period when the development can be affected by Li and when micro-surgical studies have shown that the size of the ectoderm is determined. As the early rise in respiration is interrupted by Li and the extent of the reduction of the size of the ectoderm is proportional to the extent of the deletion of the respiratory rise, one may draw the conclusion that the processes reflected by this rise play a role for the ectodermal development and that they have their highest intensity in the animal region. As an early deletion of the respiratory rise is followed by a decrease in the rate of mitochondrial elaboration, one can also suggest that there is a causal relation between the early and some of the late changes, the former ones being a prerequisite for the later ones, which can also be expected to be focused to the animal region. Finally, one may expect that the second shunt wave and some of the early and late anabolic processes are focused to the vegetal region. This highly theoretical section only has the purpose to define what one may have to look for in these studies.

V. The Reduction Gradients

A. *The First (Animal-Vegetal) Reduction Gradient*

Information about the localization of dehydrogenase activities can be obtained by observations of the rate of reduction of Janus green, methylene blue, and tetrazolium dyes in vital stained larvae kept under anaerobic conditions. Such observations have been performed by Child (1936, cf. 1941a), Hörstadius (1952, 1955), Lallier (1958), Bäckström (1959c), and others. According to these studies the animal region of early cleavage and blastula stages has a stronger reducing activity than the vegetal region so that one can speak about an animal-vegetal reduction gradient (Fig. 17). That this reducing activity varies in proportion to the size of the future ectoderm was shown by Hörstadius who found that the gradient is less steep in blastulae that develop from animal fragments

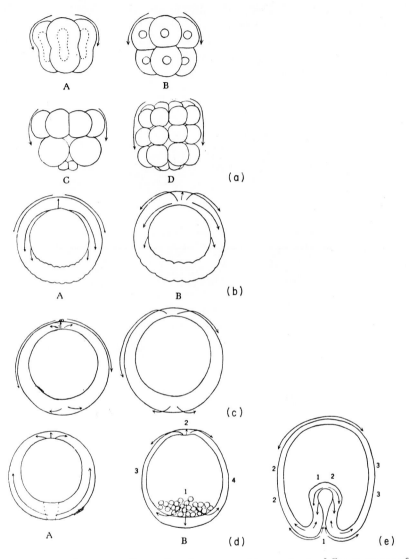

FIG. 17. Reduction gradients of various sea urchin species in different stages of development. From Child (1941a). (a) A-D, reduction gradient in early cleavage stages of *Strongylocentrotus franciscanus*; arrows indicate the direction of progress in reduction. (b) Reduction gradient in early blastulae. A, *Strongylocentrotus excentricus*; B, *Dendraster excentricus*. (c) Reduction gradients in late blastulae of *Patiria*; reduction more rapid on one side, presumably the ventral side. (d) Reduction gradients (A) in late blastula and (B) in mesenchyme blastula of *Strongylocentrotus purpuratus*. (e) Reduction gradients in mid-gastrula of *Patiria*.

isolated at the 16-cell stage and also in larvae subjected to treatment
with animalizing agent, whereas an early implantation of micromeres as
well as lithium treatment tends to confine the intense reducing activity
to the animal region (Figs. 18 and 19).

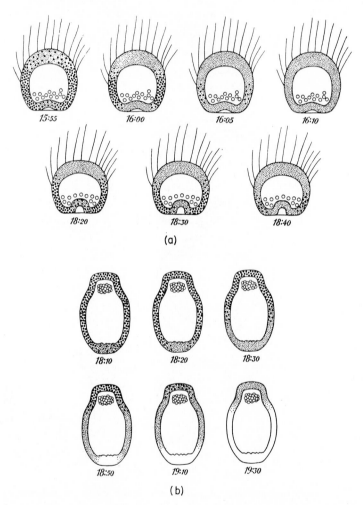

Fig. 18.   Reduction gradients (Janus green reduction) in animalized and vegetalized larvae of sea urchins. Large dots, blue; small or no dots, the color has faded
to varying extents. Figures indicate time of observations. (a) Reduction gradients in
larvae animalized by means of trypsin. The animal gradient is much stronger than
the vegetal one. (b) Reduction gradient in larvae vegetalized by means of lithium
treatment. No animal reduction gradient is present here. Mesenchyme cells displaced
toward the animal pole. From Hörstadius (1955).

B. *Biochemical Basis of the First Reduction Gradient*

The activity underlying the enhanced reducing activity of the animal region may be rather complex. As the first peak of the hexose monophosphate shunt enzymes occurs during the early cleavage stages, one may

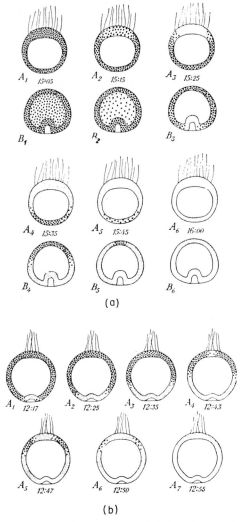

FIG. 19. (a) Reduction gradients in animal (A) and vegetal (B) halves of the same age stained equally and observed in the same reduction chamber. (b) Reduction gradients in animal halves with implanted micromeres by means of which a vegetal-animal reduction gradient has been induced. For an explanation of the symbols, see Fig. 18. From Hörstadius (1952).

guess that it largely reflects the shunt activity. Studies on the autoreduction of a tetrazolium stain where the formazan produced was extracted
and determined spectrophotometrically gave a curve that closely resembled that of the two shunt enzymes up to the time of hatching (Bäckström, 1963a) (Fig. 20), which indicates that the shunt is involved. Still
one may be somewhat hesitant about the nature of the rate-limiting factor
for the supposed shunt gradient. Investigations of Li-treated larvae do
not show any striking retardation in the first rise of glucose-6-phosphatase
that could be expected (Bäckström, 1959b). The reduction gradient
would therefore correspond to a gradient with respect to the activity of

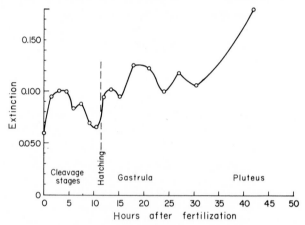

Fig. 20.   Autoreduction of a tetrazolium dye, 2-(p-indophenyl)-5-phenyltetrazo-
lium chloride, in larvae of *Paracentrotus lividus*. The formazan produced is extracted
by means of acetone and read spectrophotometrically. From Bäckström (1963a).

the whole enzyme system within the cells. For instance, one could assume
that the supposed shunt gradient reflects the rate of reoxidation of TPNH
which is generated during the first two steps of the shunt reaction. This
nucleotide chiefly occurs in the reduced form in the cell, and its reoxidation would therefore be of rate-limiting significance for the shunt reaction
as a whole. There are a number of different pathways for this reoxidation, some of which are known from the sea urchin embryo. One of these
is involved in the fixation of CO_2 (Hultin and Wessel, 1952), another in
the reduction of glutathione (cf. Bäckström, 1959c). An important pathway is also one in which the respiratory chain is involved. This pathway is slow, but can be accelerated if lactate is supplied, since lactic
dehydrogenase mediates the transfer of the TPNH hydrogen to DPN
(diphosphopyridine nucleotide) and the DPNH (dihydro form) is
readily oxidized via the respiratory chain. The observation that lactate,

pyruvate, and propanediol phosphate, which can, in fact, be looked upon as a potential lactate, have an animalizing tendency (Hörstadius and Gustafson, 1947), is in agreement with the concept that an animal-vegetal shunt gradient plays a role for the determination of the size of the ectoderm and that reoxidation of TPNH is a rate-limiting factor.

In order to test this idea Bäckström (1959c) studied the reduction of blue tetrazolium-treated larvae in buffer solutions to which TPN, DPN, and substrates for TPN- and DPN-dependent dehydrogenases were added. The generation of TPNH and DPNH in these systems were then reflected by the deposition of blue formazan. The reduction gradient also appeared in this system quite as in living Janus green-stained larvae. That the rate-limiting factor was not the total amount of triphosphopyridine dinucleotide present was shown by the addition of TPN. That DPN can mediate the reduction was shown in experiments where DPN was added. The rate-limiting factor could therefore be a TPNH-DPN transhydrogenase or a diaphorase, but also any other step in the respiratory chain. The observation of Czihak (1963) on the early regional variations of the Nadi reaction (cf. Child, 1941b, 1944) might be consistent with this idea. It is, however, also possible that the rate-limiting factor is the rate of ATP consumption during anabolic processes within the embryo. It therefore seems possible that the shunt activity, at the same time as it may play a role for the anabolic processes, is also favored by the anabolic processes. The factor that may first focus the processes to the animal region may thus be an early difference, for instance, in the cytochrome oxidase demonstrated by Czihak and Child, but the realization of the increase may also be influenced by factors interfering with any of the steps in the mutually dependent steps just mentioned.

That thiocyanate treatment of the unfertilized egg under good aerobic conditions, particularly in the presence of pyocyanine (Runnström and Thörnblom, 1938) brings about an animalization may theoretically be interpreted as due to the generation of S—S bonds that could serve as acceptors of hydrogen of reduced glutathione that is generated by the glutathione reductase in the presence of TPNH. That reduced glutathione enhances the vegetalizing effect of Li (Runnström, 1956) may also be in line with this interpretation and also the fact that o-iodosobenzoic (Runnström and Kriszat, 1952) and oxidized lipoic acid (Wolfson and Fry, 1965) have an animalizing effect. The situation is, however, still quite complex and obscure, and one should be cautious not to press the available data too much, without a detailed knowledge of the mode of control of the shunt. One may have to restrict the conclusions to the statement that the animal-vegetal reduction gradient may partly reflect a gradient in shunt activity that may be involved in the determination of the animal trend of development.

C. *The Second (Vegetal-Animal) Reduction Gradient*

In the late blastula a second, vegetal-animal, reduction gradient appears (Figs. 17–19). This gradient is related to the development of the mesendoderm. It is thus more pronounced in larvae subjected to treatment with Li as well as in isolated vegetal halves, whereas it is more or less absent in animalized whole larvae and in isolated animal halves where it appears, however, if micromeres were implanted at an early stage of development. The appearance of this gradient can be correlated with the second rise in shunt activity (Fig. 11) (Bäckström, 1959c) and it is hoped that this is not a coincidence.

D. *General Considerations*

To sum up, the correlation between the two peaks in shunt activity and the two reduction gradients appears to be striking. As already mentioned, however, the situation may be rather complex. The limiting factor may be the intensity of various anabolic processes and the enzymatic basis of the reduction may also change as development proceeds. It may be noted in this connection that from the time of gastrulation the reduction of tetrazolium blue becomes affected by the addition of DPN (Bäckström, 1959c). The primary mesenchyme is also characterized by a strong DPN diaphorase (Czihak, 1962b).

VI. Gradients in Ribonucleic Acid and Protein Synthesis

The reducing activity of the animal region is proportional to the rise in mitochondrial enzymes at the onset of gastrulation. We may recall that this rise is retarded in vegetalized embryos (Gustafson and Hasselberg, 1951) (see Fig. 14A). It therefore seems probable that the early shunt activity plays a role for the later anabolic activities of the larvae. If so, one might assume that the first reduction gradient corresponds to an animal-vegetal gradient in anabolic processes in the blastula but particularly at the onset of gastrulation, whereas the second reduction gradient plays a role for processes that start somewhat later in the vegetal region. It may be appropriate to ask about the nature of this dependence. An answer to this question might help us to look for specific gradients in anabolic processes.

The hexose monophosphate shunt gives rise to pentose phosphate and can therefore be assumed to play a role for the synthesis of nucleic acids, RNA (ribonucleic acid) as well as DNA (deoxyribonucleic acid). Since the sea urchin egg seems to contain a cytoplasmic DNA precursor which is used in early stages of rapid cleavage, one could expect that the shunt activity mainly plays a role for the synthesis of RNA. Certain studies in fact indicate that there is a slight increase in RNA during cleavage stages (Elson et al., 1954; Bäckström, 1959a), and this increase as well as the late DNA increase were both inhibited by Li treatment (Elson et al., 1954). Other investigators, however, have been unable to show any changes in RNA. This might indicate that the formation of new messenger RNA occurs at the expense of RNA already present in the cytoplasm. There is, in fact, a decrease in the cytoplasmic pyronine staining (Markman, 1961a) which would indicate that this latter assumption is correct. As emphasized by Tocco et al. (1963) nothing excludes, however, that RNA is synthesized from nucleotides formed de novo and that the decrease in cytoplasmic RNA could reflect a DNA synthesis. Incorporation experiments with glycine (Scarano and Kalckar, 1953), carbon dioxide (Hultin, 1953a), and formate (Hultin, 1957) are in line with this assumption, and so are the experiments of Tocco et al. (1963) on P^{32} incorporation into RNA, those of Nemer (1962), as well as those of Markman mentioned below.

Although we may be on the wrong track regarding the role of the shunt, we may still have come to a strategic question. That synthesis of RNA really occurs during early development of the sea urchin can be concluded from incorporation experiments with labeled adenine. This incorporation shows an increase during two phases (Markman, 1960) (Fig. 21). Before fertilization the incorporation is low. After fertilization there is an increase until the early blastula stage. After a plateau a second and stronger increase occurs, namely at the onset of invagination, probably followed by a slight transient depression during gastrulation and a rather constant rate of incorporation during the development of the gastrula into a prism larva. This incorporation, of course, reflects the synthesis of RNA as well as DNA. Experiments with ribonuclease-treated material has made it possible, however, to obtain a general picture of the synthesis of RNA, and when the isotopic labeling and ribonuclease treatment is carried out in combination with radioautography, information can also be obtained about the regional intensities of the RNA synthesis (Markman, 1961a) (Fig. 22). These studies have shown that the adenine incorporation into RNA is stronger in the animal region of the 8-hour blastula than in the rest of the larva. At this stage the most vegetal region already has a slightly stronger incorporation than the adjacent region. This vegetal incorporation is particularly clear in the mesenchyme blastula. There is evidently a good correlation between the first, animal-vegetal, reduction gradient and the early adenine incorporation in the animal

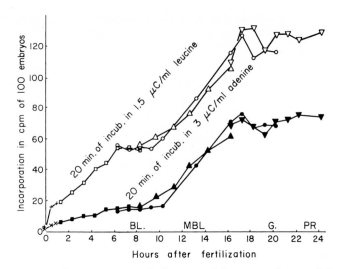

FIG. 21. Rate of incorporation of adenine and leucine in larvae of *Paracentrotus lividus*. BL, blastulae; MBL, mesenchyme blastulae; G, gastrulae; PR, prisms. From Markman (1960).

FIG. 22. Regional differences in the rate of incorporation of adenine into larvae of *Paracentrotus lividus* as studied by means of autoradiography. A, Early blastula stage, about 8 hours after fertilization. (a) Outline of a section with nuclei. The shadowed area shows the annular zone with area units and its relation to the section. (b) Autoradiogram of the section. Shadowed area corresponds to the zone with area units projected on the photograph of the autoradiogram. (c) Histogram showing the regional differences. Each pair of columns are obtained from one area unit. In the histogram the annular zone has been opened at the vegetal pole and straightened out horizontally. Consequently, the vegetal pole is at the ends and the animal pole at the center of the histogram. Thin columns give grain number and filled parts record the decrease of grain number following the treatment with ribonuclease. Broad columns show the number of nuclei and the curve illustrates the thickness of the body wall. (d) Similar histogram showing intracellular distribution of the grains in the different embryonic regions. Each pair of columns gives the number of grains within a nucleus (filled column) and the mean number within the same area of adjacent cytoplasm (open columns). B, Histograms showing regional differences in adenine incorporation in later stages of development. (a) Mesenchyme blastula 14 hours after fertilization. (b) Gastrula 20 hours after fertilization. The downward-directed columns refer to the invaginated part of the gastrula and the top of the archenteron is thought to have been opened. From Markman (1961a).

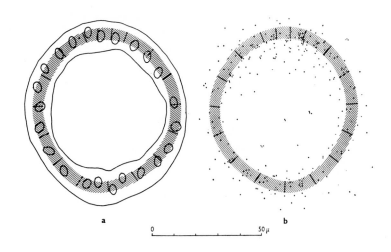

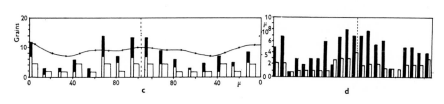

A

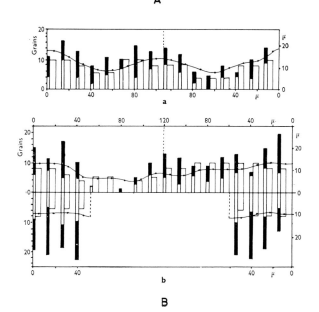

B

region as well as between the second, vegetal-animal, reduction gradient and the later adenine incorporation in the vegetal region, although the latter incorporation starts before the second reduction gradient becomes distinct (cf. Agrell, 1958).

Studies on the incorporation of labeled adenine into animal and vegetal halves isolated at the 16-cell stage and exposed to adenine 10 to 20 hours after fertilization are in excellent agreement with the general view about the relation between the reduction gradients and RNA synthesis. The RNA labeling is thus most marked in the animal half where it increases in activity. The vegetal halves show a weaker labeling at 10 hours but a much stronger labeling at 20 hours.

The results of the radioautographic studies were extended in a more quantitative way by means of Geiger counter readings of the total incorporation in animal and vegetal halves during cleavage and mesenchyme blastula stages. These observations fully supported the conclusions of the radioautographic studies (Markman, 1961b).

Further information about the details of labeling showed that the RNA synthesis involved is concentrated to the nuclei, both in the animal and the vegetal region (Markman, 1961a). This indicates that the RNA synthesis reflects the formation of messenger RNA. This observation concurs with the observation on the stainability of the nuclei by means of the Hale reaction with and without treatment with ribonuclease (Immers, 1956a,b; Markman, 1957).[1] These experiments, in fact, indicate that the nuclei of the mesenchyme blastula are rich in RNA, whereas the vegetal region has not as yet begun to synthesize RNA at a considerable rate. In animalized larvae the region with Hale-positive nuclei is larger than in normal larvae (cf. Fig. 23 which refers to a gastrula studied by a similar technique). In vegetalized larvae, on the other hand, the region with Hale-positive nuclei is reduced in proportion to the extent of the reduction in size of the future ectoderm (Immers, 1956b). An early occurrence of Hale-positive nuclei is thus a characteristic feature of the animal trend of development. No observations of the Hale reaction in the vegetal region of more advanced stages have been reported as yet, although one would anticipate that this reaction will appear here also. It may be mentioned in this connection that the increased Hale reaction seemed to be correlated with a decreased pyronine staining of the cytoplasm, but the

---

[1] The Hale reaction is based upon the reaction of strongly acidic groups with colloidal trivalent iron, the site of binding of which is then demonstrated by means of a color reaction. Sulfate and phosphate groups are easily demonstrated by this reaction, and the disappearance of the reaction after pretreatment of the section with ribonuclease indicates that the positive reaction is due to ribonucleic acid.

significance of this decrease is not clear after what has been said above about the DNA synthesis. The cytoplasmic RNA may thus be consumed to a great extent for synthesis of DNA.

One could expect that the gradient in nuclear RNA synthesis is paralleled by a gradient in protein synthesis. This question has been

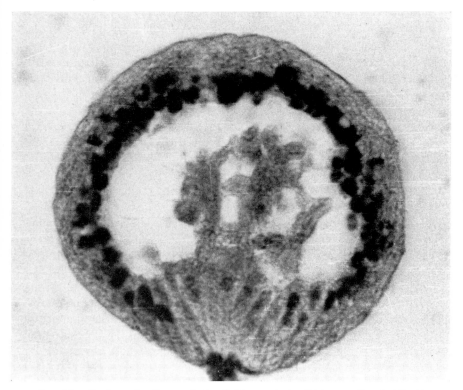

Fig. 23. Section of a *Paracentrotus lividus* gastrula, 24 hours after fertilization, somewhat animalized owing to cultivation in sulfate-free sea water, fixed in Carnoy's fluid, stained by the Ritter and Oleson technique, and photographed using an Ilford light filter No. 205. The stained ester-bound sulfate groups and unsubstituted phosphate groups of nucleic acids appear black in the photograph; sulfate groups are in the exterior rim of the archenteron, phosphate groups in the nuclei. From Immers (1956b).

studied by means of incorporation of labeled leucine with the same radioautographic and Geiger counter techniques as used for adenine incorporation, both on whole embryos and on animal and vegetal halves isolated at an early cleavage stage (Markman, 1961a). The results of these studies may be summarized briefly by saying that the adenine incorporation into RNA is indeed paralleled by gradients in protein synthesis, first by an animal-vegetal gradient and then, partially overlapping with this, a vegetal-animal gradient (Fig. 24).

VII. Mitochondrial Gradients

A. *Regional Differences in Mitochondrial Stainability*

The gradients in adenine and leucine incorporation can be expected to be paralleled by gradients in enzyme synthesis. The strong rise in the mitochondrial enzymes that occurs at the onset of gastrulation might therefore be expected to be composed of at least two fractions, first an increase in the animal region, then an increase in the vegetal one. This was, in fact, already suggested on the basis of comparisons between the rate of formation of mitochondrial enzymes in normal and vegetalized larvae (Gustafson and Hasselberg, 1951) (Fig. 14A). Observations on vital stained material by Gustafson and Lenicque (1952) indicated that these suggestions were correct. The rise in the number of Nile blue sulfate-stainable mitochondria started in the animal region so that a gradient could be observed (Fig. 25a,b). In vegetalized material the gradient was considerably depressed, whereas it was less steep in animalized material. Studies on animal and vegetal halves also showed that the number of stainable mitochondria is higher in the animal half than in the vegetal (Lenicque *et al.*, 1953) (Fig. 25c). The conclusion that the micromeres emit an inhibitor for protein synthesis was supported by observations of animal halves in which micromeres had been implanted during early cleavage stages. The first mitochondrial population was not stable but showed a decrease (Gustafson and Lenicque, 1952). Simultaneously new populations of stainable mitochondria appeared in the vegetal region (Fig. 25d). These populations appeared in several waves corresponding to different regions of the mesendoderm.

As a main conclusion these studies indicate that the vegetal region exerts an inhibiting effect on anabolic processes in the rest of the larva. The same conclusion about the distribution of anabolic processes and the inhibition exerted by the micromeres has been drawn by Runnström (1957) and Markman (1961a) on the basis of observations of larvae with

---

Fig. 24.   Regional differences in the rate of incorporation of leucine in larvae of *Paracentrotus lividus* as studied by means of radioautography. A. Early blastula stage, about 8 hours after fertilization. The legend to Fig. 22A applies to this figure apart from the fact that the thin columns in (c) refer to incorporation to leucine. B. Histograms showing regional differences in leucine incorporation in later stages of development. (a) Mesenchyme blastula, 14 hours after fertilization. (b) Prism stage, 24 hours after fertilization. The downward-directed columns refer to the invaginated part of the larva as in Fig. 22B (b). From Markman (1961a).

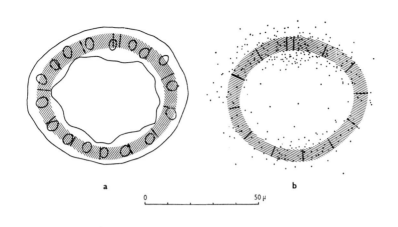

a   b

0   50 μ

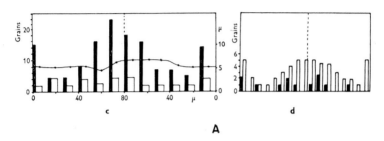

c   d

A

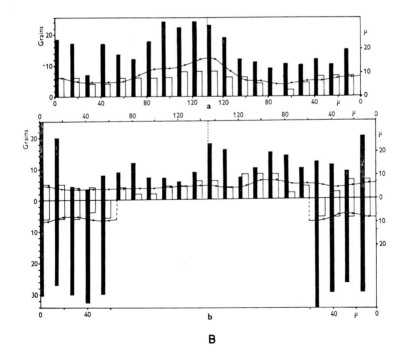

a

b

B

179

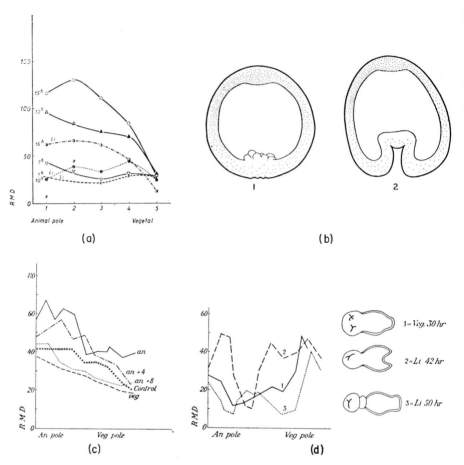

Fig. 25. Distribution of stainable mitochondria in larvae of *Psammechinus miliaris*. (a) Nile blue sulfate-stainable mitochondria in whole larvae of different ages; ages indicated to the left of each single curve. Li refers to larvae vegetalized by means of lithium treatment during early cleavage stages. RMD, relative density of the population of stainable mitochondria. From Gustafson and Lenicque (1952). (b) Janus green B-stainable mitochondria in (1) mesenchyme blastula and (2) early gastrula, both seen in profile. From Czihak (1962b). (c) Nile blue sulfate-stainable mitochondria in late blastulae-early gastrulae in isolated animal (an) and vegetal (veg) halves as well as in animal halves with 4 (an + 4) or 8 (an + 8) implanted micromeres. Control refers to whole intact larva. RMD, as in (a). From Lenicque *et al.* (1953). (d) Nile blue sulfate-stainable mitochondria (1) in an isolated exogastrulated vegetal half at an age of 30 hours; (2) in a whole egg treated with lithium during cleavage stages, observed at an age of 42 hours; (3) in lithium-treated larva at an age of 50 hours. RMD, as in (a); (2) and (3) from Gustafson and Lenicque (1952). From Lenicque *et al.* (1953).

the phase-contrast microscope, with the Hale reagent, and with radio-autographic methods.

B. *Mitochondrial Stainability As Related to the Physiological State of the Mitochondria*

The stainability of the mitochondria varies (Gustafson and Lenicque, 1952). When the gradient first appears the stainability is weak, and this is also the case in the vegetal region when stainable mitochondria just appeared. The conclusion was therefore drawn that the mitochondrial stainability reveals a gradual maturation of the mitochondrial population.

A mitochondrial maturation is by no means unique for the sea urchin embryo. Electron microscopy observations thus indicate that the mito-chondria of the amphibian embryo undergo a similar change (Eakin and Lehmann, 1957; Karasaki, 1959; Weber and Boell, 1962). The mitochon-dria in early stages of development are spherical and poor in cristae ac-cording to Karasaki, whereas elongated typical mitochondria appear as development proceeds in the neural plate region as one of the first signs of neural induction. Studies on the specific activities of cytochrome oxi-dase, ATPase (adenosinetriphosphatase), acid phosphatase, and cathep-sin in mitochondria from homogenates of *Xenopus* embryos and larvae by Weber and Boell (1962) also showed that the specific activity of each of the four enzymes changes during development, each one showing an individual pattern characteristic for the region of the embryo studied. A correlation could also be observed between the fine structure of the mito-chondria and the level of enzymatic activity. Liver mitochondria have few cristae and a relatively low cytochrome oxidase activity, whereas the opposite holds true for the mitochondria from muscles.

C. *Criticism of the Concept of Mitochondrial Gradients*

The results of Gustafson and collaborators on mitochondrial develop-ment has been met by some criticism by various authors. This criticism was, however, not directed against the results on the over-all changes but against the claims about the regional differences. Most of the authors have overlooked, however, that the differences observed by Gustafson and collaborators were considered to reflect differences in the physiological properties of the mitochondria as revealed by their stainability. It may be appropriate to discuss certain of the results of other authors in some detail.

Cytological observations on fixed and stained material by Mori *et al.* (1958) indicated that there is no gradient in the total number of mito-chondria in the gastrula. A regional difference could be observed, however, in the mitochondrial population, the mitochondria in the vegetal region being larger than those within the ectoderm.

Studies by Shaver (1956) were in agreement with the rise in mitochondrial number at gastrulation and also showed the drop in mitochondrial number that followed this rise as observed also by Gustafson and Lenicque in their studies. (This drop was restricted to the ectoderm which comprises a large fraction of the normal embryo. The drop would therefore also be noticeable by counts in a homogenate of whole larvae.) Shaver (1956) could, however, not observe any gradient in the number of mitochondria in vital stained material when Janus green or Nile blue sulfate was used, but the vegetal mitochondria appeared larger than those in the animal region.

The use of Nile blue sulfate for the detection of mitochondria has been criticized by Shaver. The mitochondrial gradient could, however, be reproduced by means of Janus green, but this dye was avoided for several reasons. In preliminary studies the mitochondria during cleavage stages showed a rather poor Janus green stainability, an observation also made by Shaver (1956). This led the authors to look for another stain. Furthermore, Janus green is reduced under anaerobic conditions, which might affect the mitochondria counts in larvae kept under a cover slip. The selection of Nile blue sulfate was justified on the basis that the mitochondria in the ciliated band of the pluteus, which is rich in mitochondria, are also stained by Janus green. The authors have also been able to reproduce their results by means of various other stains that have been reported in the literature as used for mitochondrial staining.

It has been suggested (Shaver, 1956) that the counts of Gustafson and Lenicque were influenced by the presence of lipid droplets which also take up the stain used. If this explanation is valid, it seems remarkable that the results of Shaver and those of Gustafson and Lenicque are in agreement with respect to the over-all changes in mitochondrial number. The claim that lipid droplets make the mitochondrial counts difficult may be correct in the case of *Strongylocentrotus* which is rich in lipid droplets, although this source of error would not be important if the shape and intensity of coloration of the granules is considered. In any case, the lipid droplets that do occur in *Psammechinus* are rather few and, in addition, more faintly stained than the mitochondria. Furthermore the lipid droplets are spherical and rather immobile, whereas the mitochondria are more or less dumbbell-shaped and move considerably. Lipid droplets, furthermore, do not swell upon prolonged staining, whereas the mitochondria do, probably or partly owing to an impairment of their oxidative phosphorylation which is known to bring about a swelling.

Another suggestion by Shaver (1956) was that the vegetal region of the larvae is more easily compressed than the animal region. This could give the erroneous impression of differences in the density of the mitochondrial populations. All precautions were made, however, to avoid this obvious source of error. The gradient could, in fact, be observed without any compression of the larvae below the cover slip. Furthermore, the strong gradients which were observed by Gustafson and Lenicque (1952) could not possibly be due to a flattening.

D. *Electron Microscopy Investigations on the Mitochondrial Populations*

In early gastrulae of *Lythechinus anamesus* fixed in buffered osmium solution Berg *et al.* (1962) could not find any evidence of a gradient in the number of mitochondria. In the vegetal region, however, the mitochondria were larger than those in the animal cells, an observation which coincides with that of Mori *et al.* (1958) and Shaver (1956). The relatively short penetration of the cristae into the interior as well as the complete lack of a matrix, however, suggested that the original condition of the mitochondria had been altered by swelling and extraction. In a further study by Berg and Long (1964) comparisons were therefore made of the mitochondria in embryos of various stages including vegetalized animal halves fixed, dehydrated, and embedded in a series of different ways. In this work the difference in size between the animal and vegetal regions could be confirmed with larvae fixed in buffered osmium solutions as well as with freeze-substitution, which probably preserves the original structure better than the osmium fixation. It therefore seems likely that the differences observed reflect regional differences in size within the living embryo. The observations also suggested that the number of cristae in the large vegetal mitochondria is higher than in the smaller animal mitochondria, although this result was not stressed. Vegetalization of animal half-embryos indicated that the difference in size of the mitochondria between the animal and vegetal region is proportional to the extent of vegetalization. The difference in size of the mitochondria persisted at least throughout gastrulation, but an increase in the proportion of rod-shaped mitochondria increased at the late gastrula stage in agreement with the observations of Shaver on vital stained material.

Preliminary observations by Berg and Long on the cytochrome oxidase in animal and vegetal half-embryos indicated that the region with large mitochondria had a higher cytochrome oxidase activity and therefore probably a more intense energy metabolism. This does not, however, fit with the observations of Child (1941b, 1944) with the Nadi reagent which revealed a stronger reaction in the animal region of the early gastrula. These results which were also confirmed by Berg and Long were, however, considered by these authors to be influenced by the toxicity of the reagents since other less toxic reagents did not reveal this gradient.

Czihak (1962b) using the same species as Gustafson and Lenicque, *Psammechinus miliaris*, has been able to confirm the observations of Gustafson and Lenicque about the occurrence of regional differences in the mitochondrial population (Fig. 25b). His results, in fact, agree with those of Gustafson and Lenicque in the sense that the mitochondrial number is higher in the animal region, more precisely at the oral region, an observation that could be deduced from the data published by Gustafson and Lenicque (1952), although the detailed shape of the pattern was not commented on further. Czihak concluded that the mitochondrial maximum can be correlated with the oral region. This conclusion will be discussed further later on in connection with the relation between the animal-vegetal and dorsoventral polarity.

Berg and Long (1964) carried out some observations of the mitochondria during early developmental stages. In the 16-cell stage no regional difference in size could be observed between the animal and vegetal regions. The mitochondria in early stages were also reported to be spherical or oval, a conclusion in agreement with the observations by Shaver (1956) with the phase-contrast microscope. Some elongated mitochondria were also seen, but their frequency of occurrence as well as the degree of elongation was identical in the animal and vegetal regions. In some of the sections, however, a number of irregular mitochondria were seen, particularly in the vegetal cells, that may be after all a faint indication of a regular difference between these two regions. Furthermore, the impression was obtained that the mitochondria undergo certain changes between the 16-cell stage and the early gastrula. The number of cristae as well as the over-all mitochondrial size thus appeared to increase. In the ectoderm the size was reported to be 24% larger than in the 16-cell stage, in the vegetal region the increase in size would be still greater. This result was, however, not emphasized since it was considered possible that the mitochondria in the later stages were more susceptible to swelling during the osmium fixation which was used in this series of investigations. This could give the erroneous impression of an increase in size with possibly more countable cristae. It was, however, not excluded that the changes were real.

E. *Physiological Changes of the Mitochondrial Populations*

To synthesize these observations with some data of other investigators it is quite clear that the mitochondria undergo a change as development proceeds. This change appears to start during cleavage stages as suggested by the electron microscopy studies. The elaboration of the mitochondria during the early cleavage stages is in agreement with the observations of Guidice and Monroy (1958) and Nakano and Monroy (1958) on the incorporation of labeled amino acids in the mitochondria that starts immediately after fertilization or even after artificial activation (Nakano et al., 1958) and follows the main course of the early respiratory rise. It also agrees with the strong incorporation of P^{32} orthophosphate into mitochondrial RNA (Tocco et al., 1963) during early stages. The slight increase in mitochondrial stainability during the early cleavage stages reported by Gustafson and Lenicque (1955) may be another aspect of this change. The most dramatic change in the mitochondrial population, however, occurs at the onset of gastrulation as revealed by the rise in the activity of various mitochondrial enzymes and by a change in the relative proportion of succinic dehydrogenase and deaminase (Black, 1964) as well as by a strong increase in stainability of the mitochondria and changes in the intensity of various metabolic processes referred to earlier. The increase in size length and possibly in the number of cristae observed by Berg and Long (1964) may be particularly strong at this stage, although the data do not present any detailed conclusions; however, see the observations of Shaver (1956) concerning the change in size. The dramatic change in the mitochondrial properties at gastrulation is in agreement with the observations of Harvey (1946) on the appearance of "new" mitochondria in the gastrula of larvae developing from egg fragments, from which the mitochondria have been more or less removed by means of high-speed centrifugation.

The studies discussed above also indicate that there are regional differences in the physiological properties of the mitochondria, i.e., a gradient with respect to stainability and size. The disagreement between the various authors is, as mentioned above, somehow connected with the criteria used. In one case the stainability was used, in the other cases the structure and size in fixed material, and so on. Gustafson and Lenicque called the unstainable mitochondria "precursors" and spoke about a gradual change in this property. The other authors used different criteria and defined the different mitochondrial types with methods that were not available to the present author in 1951. The disagreement therefore seems to a certain extent to be a semantic one. It is the purpose of the following section to analyze this question further. One may, however, emphasize that Czihak (1962b) was able to understand that the mitochondrial differences observed by Gustafson were considered to be related to the physiological properties of these organelles.

If there is a mitochondrial gradient one might anticipate that it should reveal itself by respiratory measurements on animal and vegetal halves, even in early developmental stages when the mitochondrial populations undergo certain changes. The observations of Holter and Lindahl (1940),

however, failed to show a respiratory difference between animal and vegetal fragments. This observation, however, should not be misinterpreted.
Respiration does not reflect the actual number of mitochondria in a tissue.
Mitochondrial respiration is thus limited by the rate at which ADP har-
vests the energy-rich phosphate bonds produced in the oxidative phosphorylation (cf. Immers and Runnström, 1960). A better indicator of a mitochondrial gradient could be obtained if the respiratory control is abolished
by means of an uncoupling agent such as 2,4-dinitrophenol. Under these
conditions the animal halves have a higher rate of respiration than the
vegetal ones, which is consistent with the ideas about an animal-vegetal
gradient in mitochondrial development (Hörstadius et al., 1964). In addition, these observations give important information about the meaning of
the regional differences in stainability, structure, and size of the mitochondria. The per cent rise in respiration in the animal fragments is thus higher
than in the vegetal ones, which indicates that the control enacted by
oxidative phosphorylation in normal larvae is higher in the animal region
than in the vegetal one. In other words the stainability, size, and structural
differences in the gastrula could reflect a difference in the maturity of the
mitochondria with respect to the ability to perform oxidative phosphorylation as well as with respect to their content of respiratory enzymes. It
may be mentioned that mitochondria undergo a swelling when the oxidative phosphorylation is impaired, and it is possible that mitochondria in
which the oxidative phosphorylation is still weak have a larger volume
than more mature mitochondria.

One may ask if the difference in oxidative phosphorylation is the
basis for the gradient in stainability observed by Gustafson and Lenicque
(1952). The generally accepted hypothesis for mitochondrial staining
with Janus green is that the agent is kept in the green, oxidized form
within the mitochondria, whereas it is reduced within the cytoplasm
(Lazarow and Cooperstein, 1953). This interpretation, however, presumably only reflects part of the truth. Another aspect of the stainability of
the mitochondria is probably that the mitochondria actively accumulate
the vital stain and therefore become more strongly colored than the
cytoplasm. That cyanide and anaerobiosis prevent the coloration of the
mitochondria could therefore have a complex background, since an
inhibition of respiration also leads to a deletion of the oxidative phosphorylation and therefore of the supposed active uptake of the stain.

In order to test the idea about the importance of the oxidative phosphorylation the author has carried out staining experiments with Chang
liver cells treated with 2,4-dinitrophenol, pentachlorophenol, and rote-
none in doses large enough to stop the oxidative phosphorylation before
they were exposed to Janus green under aerobic conditions. These re-

sults showed that the stainability is quite dependent on oxidative phosphorylation (Gustafson, 1963).

Similar experiments were performed with sea urchin gastrulae which after treatment with the agents concerned were stained with Janus green or Nile blue sulfate (Gustafson, 1963, 1964). These results also showed that the stainability of the mitochondria of the gastrula is related to the oxidative phosphorylation. In spite of strong staining of the cytoplasm there was no differential staining of the mitochondria. Furthermore, these observations showed that there was no accumulation of stain in fat droplets and no precipitation of the stain by other cellular components.

It would be interesting to know more about the mechanism of the mitochondrial staining. One might suggest that the stain is precipitated within the mitochondria by calcium ions which the mitochondria is also able to accumulate actively. In any case the stainability does not have much to do with the ability of the stain to become reduced within the cytoplasm. Other stains can therefore be used provided one makes sure that other inclusions are not stained in the same way and that the staining is inhibited by a deletion of the oxidative phosphorylation. Many investigators have, in fact, used dyes other than Janus green such as dahlia violet, Nile blue sulfate, pinacyanol, and rhodamine B (cf. Conn, 1946; Cowdry, 1918, 1948; McClung Jones, 1950; Romeis, 1948). It is interesting to see that all these compounds contain diethylamine groups (cf. Cowdry, 1948) whereas Janus black, which has no such groups, is not a suitable mitochondrial staining. The role of the diethylamine groups in this connection remains obscure, although this group is also characteristic of a number of pharmacologically active agents.

VIII. The Relation between the Animal-Vegetal and the Dorsoventral Polarities

An important observation which may indicate a heterogeneity of the mitochondrial population even in the early cleavage stage has been reported by Czihak (1963). Berg (1958) studied the oxidation of reduced cytochrome c in animal and vegetal halves by means of spectrophotometry. According to this investigation animal halves isolated in the 16-cell stage had the same activity as vegetal fragments. In later stages the isolated animal halves had a 40% higher activity than the vegetal ones. Czihak (1963) extended these studies to cytochrome oxidase by the use of the indophenol blue reaction and to studies of the rate of oxidation of the stain. The specificity of the reaction was tested by means of cyanide and azide treatment. This study showed that the animal region has a somewhat higher activity than the vegetal one and that the highest activity occurs in the oral region of the animal area. This area, in fact, corresponded to the region where Czihak found a maximum in mitochondria in the gastrula (Fig. 25b). The observations that the oral side has a higher activity than the dorsal is also consistent with the observations of Child (1941b).

That the maximum in the reaction both in early and in later stages occurs within the ventral region fits well with the fact that the oral side can be considered to have stronger animal properties than the dorsal side, a concept that is well illustrated by observations of the detailed structure of isolated animal halves and the effect of Li on the dorsoventrality as mentioned earlier (Section III,D). The animal halves of type B and C of Hörstadius (1936b), in fact, show that the animal plate goes down on the ventral side (cf. Fig. 7). In a recent paper by Markman (1963) it was also mentioned that the strongest labeling of RNA and proteins occurred on this side. That the physiological activity of the mitochondria plays a role in the development of the ventroanimal region is supported by various observations (cf. Czihak, 1963). Cyanide has thus a certain vegetalizing effect on the larvae (MacArthur, 1924; Hörstadius and Strömberg, 1940) at least in combination with Li (Runnström, 1933), and Child (1948) reported a strong vegetalization by means of azide. Pease (1941, 1942), furthermore, reported that in experiments with a localized treatment of the egg both these inhibitors caused a shift of the ventral side to the least inhibited region.

IX. General Conclusions Concerning the Activities within the Ectoderm

The general picture one may obtain by summing up all the different observations discussed previously is that the animal-vegetal or rather ventroanimal-vegetal gradient favors the early onset of anabolic processes within the future ectoderm region. In studies of whole larvae the processes may reveal themselves by the early peak in hexose monophosphate enzymes and an autoreduction in a tetrazolium compound, a rapid rise in respiratory intensity, the first rise in ribonucleic acid synthesis, the first peak in protein synthesis, and probably by some changes in the mitochondria. The causal chain may be very long and entangled. An increase in the hexose monophosphate shunt may, for instance, stimulate the formation on RNA and hence the protein synthesis, but these anabolic processes may, in turn, act on the respiratory activity including the shunt by making ADP available. The anabolic processes can be visualized as preparing the region concerned for the almost explosive anabolic activity connected with the formation of mature mitochondria at the time of gastrulation, when the number of "resting" nuclei increases. Part of this sudden process is probably reflected by the second respiratory rise and the second peak in protein synthesis demonstrated by various authors. The topography of these changes reveals itself by gradients in the intensity of various processes and in the distribution of mitochondria of different stainability, size, and structure.

The rapidity of the anabolic processes in the animal region may be due to differences in the properties of the cortex and may reflect themselves during early cleavage stages by the stronger Nadi reaction of the ventroanimal region. The cortex may, however, also influence the processes in a rather indirect way by determining the size of the cells and their nucleic acid metabolism as has been suggested by Agrell (1956). This may influence the mitotic pattern and the length of the period during which the nucleus can influence the anabolic processes in the cells during cleavage stages (cf. Agrell, 1956).

The size of the ectoderm seems to be determined by the processes that determine the intensity of the anabolic processes. This coincides with the recent observation of Hörstadius (1963) that chloramphenicol brings about vegetalization. The ectoderm corresponds to the region where the mitochondria first attain a strong stainability with all that this tells about the possible state of these organelles. It is, however, clear that all this is only a first approximation. More information will be gained by investigating those processes, which determine the vegetal tendencies.

X. The Vegetal Activities

The second reduction gradient, the incorporation of labeled adenine and leucine into the vegetal region, and the later appearance of stainable mitochondria in the endoderm suggests that the vegetal region is partly characterized by the same processes as the animal region, although they start somewhat later. These processes may be reflected by part of the second peak in shunt activity and tetrazolium autoreduction, by part of the second peak in protein synthesis, and by part of the second respiratory rise. That the process of differentiation starts relatively late in the vegetal region appears to be in line with the observation of Markman (1963) that the morphogenetic activities of the mesendoderm can be affected by actinomycin C treatment in the late blastula. It is, however, quite clear that all this is only a first approximation. Some of the processes in the vegetal region are qualitatively different from those in the ectoderm. One may point at the formation of a skeleton by the primary mesenchyme and the formation of an acid-soluble pigment by some of the secondary mesenchyme cells. The vegetal region also has a stronger alkaline phos-

phatase activity than the ectoderm, a difference that becomes marked at
the time of gastrulation when the total activity of the enzymes increases
(Mazia et al., 1948; Gustafson and Hasselberg, 1950; Flickinger, 1957;
Hsiao and Fujii, 1963). The primary mesenchyme is furthermore characterized by a distinct cytochrome c reductase activity and the esophagus
has a high esterase activity (Czihak, 1962b). The second reduction gradient also showed a response to the addition of DPN in the experiments of
Bäckström (1959c) on tetrazolium reduction.

One can speculate about the basis of the differences between the ectoderm and the mesendoderm. Gustafson and Lenicque (1952) suggested
that the ectodermal region emits inhibitors that specifically prevent regions from differentiating at a later stage to form an ectoderm, a concept
that is in line with the general ideas of Weiss (1947) and Rose (1957).
This is also consistent with the observation that a strongly vegetalized
larva, which has a small ectoderm, sometimes forms a second ectoderm
in the vegetal region (Gustafson and Lenicque, 1952) and that a strongly
animalized larva often has two ciliated plates, one in the animal region
and one in the vegetal region (Lindahl, 1936). One has, however, to consider the possibility that the specificity of the different vegetal regions is
directly influenced by the properties of the cortex.

One of the first indications reported about specific animal-vegetal
metabolic differences can be traced back to the observation by Herbst
(1904) that the animal development is somehow favored in larvae cultivated in sulfate-free sea water if one overlooks the fact that they have a
radial tendency. This effect was studied later by Lindahl (1936) and
others. In animal halves cultivated in sea water the extent of animalization
was also increased although, curious though it may seem, the vegetalized
halves showed an enhanced vegetalization (Runnström et al., 1964).
Studies on the incorporation of radioactive sulfate indicate that the incorporation starts during cleavage and shows a number of distinct peaks
as development proceeds (Immers, 1961a). Various observations indicate
that this incorporation partly corresponds to the formation of sulfated
mucopolysaccharides (Immers, 1961b). Radioautographic studies show
that sulfate is incorporated in the whole of the larva, i.e., in the animal
region as well as in the vegetal one. Histochemical studies by means of the
Hale reagent show that the sulfate groups are masked in most of the
larva. In the vegetal region, however, mucopolysaccharides with unmasked sulfate groups could be detected (Fig. 26). These mucopolysaccharides were partly located around the primary and secondary mesenchyme cells, in the cavity of the early coelom, and in the endodermal
cavity.

The incorporation studies and the Hale reaction showed many inter-

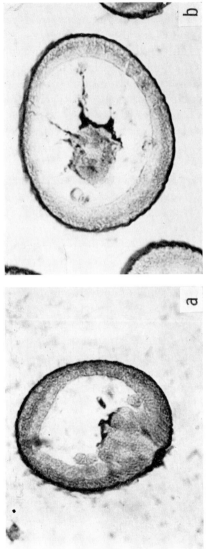

Fig. 26. Distribution of sulfated mucopolysaccharides in larvae of *Paracentrotus lividus* stained by the Ritter-Oleson method. The acid polysaccharides with unsubstituted sulfate groups appear black in the photograph. (a) Larva 17 hours after fertilization, in early invagination. (b) Gastrula 21 hours after fertilization, sectioned transversely through the vegetal region. From Immers (1961b).

esting details. The incorporation of sulfate groups is paralleled by an incorporation of amino acids. On the basis of this observation Immers suggested that the mucopolysaccharides play some role for the protein metabolism, for instance, as acceptors of newly produced proteins or as inhibitors of proteolytic enzymes. These functions could be of importance for the animal region as well as for the vegetal region. An indication of this is that lack of sulfate, although it brings about an animalization, results in some anomalies in the nuclei of the animal region (Immers, 1961b; Runnström et al., 1964). The sulfate can also play a role in the formation of the vegetal substances active during the period of primary determination of the germ layers. It is also very likely that the unmasked mucopolysaccharides that are extruded from the vegetal cells play a role in the decrease of adhesion between the cells and, as emphasized by Immers, in the development of the pseudopodal activity.

If one tries to make a general picture of the vegetal metabolism at the onset of the mesenchyme blastula stage one can, as a point of departure, start with a supposed additional role of the sulfate that was suggested by Lindahl (1936) before the interest became focused on the mucopolysaccharides. Lindahl suggested that the vegetal region is the site of a strong degradation of proteins. That a strong degradation of yolk occurs in the primary mesenchyme is quite evident since the early primary mesenchyme is devoid of yolk granules. Lindahl suggested that the sulfate is needed for a detoxication of aromatic waste products formed in the vegetal region as a result of a protein combustion. Ten Cate (1952), on the basis of this, suggested that the oxidation of aromatic amino acids is connected with the formation of a collagen-like protein in the mesenchyme cells, which might serve as a matrix for the skeleton. This interpretation is well in line with many observations. The role of a particular type of protein synthesis in the most vegetal region, even starting during early cleavage stages, is indicated by an early treatment of these stages with ethionine. This treatment resulted in various anomalies in the primary mesenchyme and the skeleton formed by them as well as a disturbance of gastrulation (Bosco and Monroy, 1960). That proline and hydroxyproline, both important building blocks for collagen, have a vegetalizing action on animal halves should not be stressed in this connection, since many other amino acids have a similar weak effect (Gustafson and Hörstadius, 1957). That an analog of ascorbic acid, glucoascorbic acid, enhances the animalization of animal halves (Gustafson and Hörstadius, 1955) and that ascorbic acid enhances the effect of Li (Runnström, 1956) indicates that these compounds are more interesting as ascorbic acid is considered to play a role in the synthesis of collagen. Bäckström (1956, 1957) was able to lend some support to the role of ascorbic acid in the vegetal region by showing that the ascorbic acid content increased very strongly in the advanced gastrula producing both a soluble and an insoluble fraction, the latter of which was shown to be localized particularly in the vegetal area. The alkaline phosphatase of this region could also play a role in the formation of collagen-like proteins. The abundant formation of unmasked mucopolysaccharides in the vegetal region may also be looked upon as an aspect of the formation of connective tissue substances in this region. The pigment production referred to above might also be related to the metabolism of aromatic amino acids, although the details of their formation are not known.

One might object that the assumed production of collagen-like proteins and pigment is restricted to certain specialized cells. Morphogenetic studies, however, indicate that the mesenchymal properties, if we are allowed to use this vague terminology, extend far outside the mesenchyme proper (Gustafson, 1961; Gustafson and Wolpert, 1963b). All the derivatives of the archenteron wall are thus characterized by the presence of mesenchymal elements, particularly the coelom, the sphincter regions of the endoderm, and the wall of the proctodaeum (Gustafson, 1963, 1964). The mucopolysaccharides also occur far outside the mesenchyme region proper. The close relation between the different cell types is also indicated by the ability of the secondary mesenchyme to compensate for the loss of primary mesenchyme cells when they are removed (Fukushi, 1962). The observation that the skeleton-forming cells in *Echinocardium* pluteus apparently change into pigment cells after the skeleton has been laid down in the advanced pluteus (Gustafson, 1964) also indicates that the cells are not too distantly related.

To sum up these observations it seems clear that the vegetal area in part undergoes the same changes as the ectoderm and in part also is the site of quite characteristic types of anabolic processes which may be related to the formation of collagen-like proteins and mucopolysaccharides.

Another gradient with respect to the properties of cellular inclusions has been reported by Gustafson and Lenicque (1952), concerning the pigment granules in the pigment cell fraction of the secondary mesenchyme. The pigment cells in a vegetalized exogastrula are distributed along the ectoderm as well as along the archenteron wall. The pigment granules, however, have a different stainability in the various regions. In the most animal region they have a great affinity for Nile blue sulfate and similar dyes, and their normal red color is completely covered by these dyes which attain a black appearance. In the vegetal regions, on the other hand, they do not take up any stain at all and remain red. In intermediate zones there is a series of transitions in the appearance of the pigment granules. These granules may show a thin red crescent, a thick red crescent, or may be red throughout, apart from a small spot at the periphery, the rest of the granules being black. The size of the dye-up-taking area is related to the position of the pigment cell along the animal-vegetal axis, the more animal cells having granules with a larger dark area. The significance of this phenomenon is still unknown. One might guess that the pigment granules are derived from mitochondria and that their dye accumulation is an active process. One may also guess that the development of the pigment cells and particularly of their granules is influenced by the cells to which they are attached by means of their pseudopods. Contact with an ectoderm cell having an intense oxidative phosphorylation may hence influence the capability of the granules to form the dye-uptaking area, whereas contact with a region that is less mature does not have this effect.

XI. Biochemical Activities and Morphogenesis

The concept that the biochemical activities within the developing sea urchin egg show a variation along gradients seems to concur with the observations on the morphogenetic behavior of the individual cells. This behavior can be described to a great extent as a reflection of the adhesion between the cells and their ability to show pulsatory and pseudopodal activity (see reviews by Gustafson, 1961, 1964; Gustafson and Wolpert, 1963b).

It seems that one can arrange the morphogenetic behavior of the cells along a spectrum with a high adhesion between the cells at one end and a very low adhesion at the other, and with all transitions in between the two. The animal plate of the gastrula is thus characterized by a high cellular adhesion as can be concluded from its strong contacts. A high adhesion also characterizes the ciliated band which extends from the animal plate and surrounds the ventral side and which in strongly ani-malized animal larvae forms a plate continuous with the animal plate. The adhesion of the rest of the ectoderm is somewhat lower than in the regions just mentioned. At the vegetal pole of the late blastula the adhesion is very low as indicated by the detachment of the primary mesenchyme cells into the blastocoel. A rather low adhesion is also characteristic of the early endomesoderm, although it is not so low as that in the primary mesenchyme area of the wall and varies from zone to zone. The decrease in adhesion can be correlated with a pulsatory activity of the cells and the ability to form pseudopods. These two lat-ter activities seem to be closely related, since cells with a strong pulsatory activity later on have a lively pseudopodal activity. The ability to form pseudopods, however, seems to decrease more rapidly in the direction of the animal pole than the pulsatory activity.

The time course of the changes in adhesion can be correlated to some extent with the biochemical gradients and their time pattern. The changes in adhesion start in the ectodermal regions where there is an increase in adhesion, particularly in the regions of the ciliated band and the animal plate, as can be concluded from the gradual appearance of a dorsoventral shape of the larva. A new phase in the morphogenetic activities starts at the vegetal pole and spreads upward through zone after zone (cf. Fig. 4) and is manifested by a decrease in adhesion, a pulsatory and pseudopodal activity with the restrictions mentioned earlier. These activities play an important role in the release of the primary mesenchyme, in the process of invagination, and in coelom formation. In further development, however, the adhesion apparently increases within the entomesoderm.

One could summarize these observations by saying that the animal development is characterized by the acquirement of epithelycytic properties by the cells. In contrast the vegetal regions exhibit amebocytic and mechanocytic properties or simply exhibit mesenchymal properties to a varying extent, ranging from the typical appearance of the free mesenchyme cells to the mesothelial type of coelom cells, to the more epithelial type of endoderm cells. This general pattern of distribution of the properties concerned seems to be a rather general feature of developing embryos as emphasized by Willmer (1960).

If one tries to discuss these changes in terms of their relation to the metabolic gradients one has to consider both the animal and vegetal processes and the concept that these changes are similar in part but have a different time pattern and are qualitatively different. It is tempting to suggest that the adhesion is related to the oxidative phosphorylation of the cells. The low adhesion that characterizes many cancer cells might also reflect a defective phosphorylation (cf., e.g., Valentine, 1955). Furthermore, the adhesion of leucocytes decreases when glycolysis is inhibited (Garvin, 1961), and the variation in the malignancy of pathological leucocytes seems to be correlated with a decrease in their adhesiveness. In addition, the adhesion between the ectodermal cells within the ciliated bands is particularly high at their outer and inner ends, and the outer contact points are regularly in close contact with mitochondria that might supply the energy needed for the maintenance of the contacts (Larje, 1963, 1964). That animal regions are so strongly affected by respiratory inhibition and thereby show a decrease in contact so that the cell sheet disintegrates may also indicate that the strong cell contacts are based upon an active energy metabolism. The strong anabolic processes that seem to characterize the animal region, e.g., the activity of the cilia, may rapidly exhaust the available ATP when respiration is blocked. The decrease in the contact in the vegetal regions may be due to a slower development of the energy-supplying mechanism and to the onset of anabolic processes that consume the ATP available for maintenance of cell contacts. The decrease in adhesion may, however, also reflect the formation of mucopolysaccharides in this area. These substances may cover the cell surfaces and tend to separate the cells.

The relation between low adhesion and the pulsatory and pseudopodal activity may also reflect changes in the cell surface (cf. Immers, 1961b). The ability of the pseudopodal tips to attach at the contact points between the ectoderm cells (Gustafson, 1963) could indicate that the adhesiveness of these points can also be used by other cells, the energy metabolism of which is still defective. It is, however, also possible that the adhesion of the mesenchyme cells is determined by the presence of mucopolysaccharides in certain zones of the ectoderm (see Motomura, 1960; Okazaki et al., 1962). All these points are to be considered as a preliminary attempt to formulate some ideas and observations as a basis for further experiments and considerations.

The further development of the larva results in a shape of increasing complexity. It seems, however, that the morphogenetic activities of the cells that bring about these changes are of the same type as during gastrulation (cf. Gustafson and Wolpert, 1963a,b). If so, one could assume that the biochemical activities also are closely related to those in the gastrula.

How sharp borders between the different organ rudiments are established in a gradient system is an important problem. The diagram in Fig. 2, however, shows how one can visualize the basis for such a subdivision.

XII. General Conclusions

Studies on enzyme synthesis in simple systems such as cultures of bacteria and mammalian cell strains are likely to give us much information about fundamental mechanisms of differentiation, but it is quite evident that they can tell us little about the way in which the various processes are integrated during the formation of an embryo. The use of the sea urchin embryo for the investigation of such problems is quite advantageous as the system can be influenced by various factors that promote one or the other trend of development. In addition, this embryo compared with the vertebrate embryo is comparatively simple. In spite of this, our insight into the biochemical background of sea urchin development is rather fragmentary and too few trained biochemists have devoted their time to a study of this material. This may be due partly to the complexity of the problem which forces us to discuss it in terms that have little meaning for the biochemist. We are, in fact, faced with a system which, like all other embryos, consists of various regions in close contact with each other and which interact and undergo rapid changes. The situation, however, is not hopeless.

The classic microsurgical experiments have provided us with a rather detailed set of data that have been summarized in terms of the double gradient concept. It seems, however, that the interactions within the egg in the more advanced stages of development are more complicated and may involve feedback mechanisms, but nothing is known about the relationship between the early and the supposedly late interactions. To begin with it may be advisable therefore to restrict the problem to the development of the ectoderm and the mesendoderm as a whole. If we do so it seems possible to find a biochemical counterpart to the gradients as suggested by the microsurgical experiments. The general picture indicates that the animal tendency promotes the synthesis of ribonucleic acid and proteins, whereas the vegetal principle seems to counteract the onset of these processes for a while. The time pattern of early protein synthesis will therefore be different in the animal and vegetal regions. This time difference may play a great role in the development of biochemical specificity in the two regions as the more advanced region may prevent the development of a similar specificity in regions that become active later on. This picture is no doubt oversimplified. It seems quite likely that the vegetal principle in a more direct way switches the vegetal cells into a different direction of development. Our knowledge is, however, too fragmentary to permit us to build up a picture of this process.

Unfortunately, it is difficult to obtain large amounts of material on the individual cell types of the sea urchin embryo. We are forced therefore to compare the biochemical changes in normal embryos with those in embryos where development has been disturbed by treatment with animalizing or vegetalizing substances. Another approach is to study the activities of individual cell groups in situ. The reduction gradients certainly deserve a further analysis by means of more quantitative methods, and microradioautographic methods will also be of great help in the future. Ultrastructural studies of mitochondria and other organelles offer another promising approach. Studies of the ultrastructure of a mitochondrium, however, can only give a very vague idea about the physiological activities of the organelle. An analysis of the factors that govern the uptake of vital stains into the mitochondrium seems to give important hints as to the nature of some of these activities. Another promising approach to the problem of differentiation is, of course, to make use of various agents that in a more or less well-defined way interfere with the biochemical activities of the cells, particularly agents which interfere with nucleic acid and protein synthesis. Treatment of the eggs for short periods of time with these agents could at least give us some information about the time pattern for the transcription of the genetic code.

The problem of linkage between the biochemical events and the actual formation of the shape of the embryo is immensely complicated. It seems encouraging, however, that in this case also the activities can be arranged along a gradient in a way similar to those suggested by biochemical and microsurgical experiments.

REFERENCES

Agrell, I. (1956). *In* "Bertil Hanström Zoological Papers in Honor of his Sixty-Fifth Birthday" (K. G. Wingstrand, ed.), p. 27. Zoological Institute, University of Lund, Lund, Sweden.

Agrell, I. (1958). *Arkiv Zool.* 11, 435.

Bäckström, S. (1954). *Arkiv Zool.* 6, 527.

Bäckström, S. (1956). *Exptl. Cell Res.* 11, 322.

Bäckström, S. (1957). *Exptl. Cell Res.* 13, 333.

Bäckström, S. (1958). *Exptl. Cell Res.* 14, 426.

Bäckström, S. (1959a). *Arkiv Zool.* 12, 339.

Bäckström, S. (1959b). *Exptl. Cell Res.* 18, 347.

Bäckström, S. (1959c). *Exptl. Cell Res.* 18, 357.

Bäckström, S. (1963a). *Acta Embryol. Morphol. Exptl.* 6, 235.

Bäckström, S. (1963b). *Exptl. Cell Res.* 32, 566.

Bäckström, S., Hultin, K., and Hultin, T. (1960). *Exptl. Cell Res.* 19, 634.

Beerman, W. (1956). *Cold Spring Harbor Symp. Quant. Biol.* 21, 217.

Berg, W. E. (1958). *Exptl. Cell Res.* 14, 398.

Berg, W. E., and Cheng, A. C. (1962). *Acta Embryol. Morphol. Exptl.* 5, 167.

Berg, W. E., and Long, N. D. (1964). *Exptl. Cell Res.* 33, 422.

Berg, W. E., Taylor, D. A., and Humphreys, W. J. (1962). *Develop. Biol.* 4, 165.

Black, R. E. (1964). *Exptl. Cell Res.* 33, 361.

Bosco, M., and Monroy, A. (1960). *Acta Embryol. Morphol. Exptl.* 3, 53.

Boveri, T. (1901a). *Verhandl. Phys.-Med. Ges. Würzburg* [N.F.] 34, 145.

Boveri, T. (1901b). *Zool. Jahrb. Abt. Anat. Ontog. Tiere* 14, 630.

Boveri, T. (1910). *Festschr. R. Hertwig* 3, 131.

Callan, H. G. (1963). *Intern. Rev. Cytol.* 15, 1.

Child, C. M. (1936). *Arch. Entwicklungsmech. Organ.* 135, 426.

Child, C. M. (1941a). "Patterns and Problems of Development." Univ. of Chicago Press, Chicago, Illinois.

Child, C. M. (1941b). *Proc. Natl. Acad. Sci. U.S.* 27, 523.

Child, C. M. (1944). *Physiol. Zool.* 17, 129.

Child, C. M. (1948). *J. Exptl. Zool.* 107, 1.

Conn. H. J. (1946). "Biological Stains," 5th ed. Biotech. Publ., Geneva, New York.

Cowdry, E. V. (1918). *Contrib. Embryol. Carnegie Inst. Wash.* 8, 39.

Cowdry, E. V. (1948). "Laboratory Technique." Williams & Wilkins, Baltimore, Maryland.

Czihak, G. (1961). *Arch. Entwicklungsmech. Organ.* **153**, 353.
Czihak, G. (1962a). *Fortschr. Zool.* **14**, 238.
Czihak, G. (1962b). *Arch. Entwichlungsmech. Organ.* **154**, 29.
Czihak, G. (1963). *Arch. Entwicklungsmech. Organ.* **154**, 272.
Deutsch, H. F., and Gustafson, T. (1952). *Arkiv Kemi* **4**, 221.
Driesch, H. (1891). *Z. Wiss. Zool.* **53**, 160.
Driesch, H. (1892). *Z. Wiss. Zool.* **55**, 1.
Eakin, R. M., and Lehmann, F. E. (1957). *Arch. Entwicklungsmech. Organ.* **150**, 177.
Eliasson, E. (1963). *Exptl. Cell Res.* **30**, 74.
Eliasson, E. (1965). In press.
Elson, D., Gustafson, T., and Chargaff, E. (1954). *J. Biol. Chem.* **209**, 285.
Flickinger, R. A. (1957). *Biol. Bull.* **112**, 21.
Foerster, M., and Öhrström, Å. (1933). *Trav. Sta. Biol. Roscoff* **11**, 63.
Fukushi, T. (1962). *Bull. Marine Biol. Sta. Ashamushi, Tohoku Univ.* **11**, 21.
Garvin, J. E. (1961). *J. Exptl. Med.* **114**, 51.
Geilenkirchen, W. L. M. (1964). *Exptl. Cell Res.* **34**, 463.
Giudice, G., and Monroy, A. (1958). *Acta Embryol. Morphol. Exptl.* **2**, 58.
Gustafson, T. (1946). *Arkiv Zool.* **38A** (4).
Gustafson, T. (1952). *Arkiv Zool.* **3**, 273.
Gustafson, T. (1954). *Intern. Rev. Cytol.* **3**, 277.
Gustafson, T. (1961). In "Biological Structure and Function" (T. W. Goodwin and O. Lindberg, eds.), Vol. 2, p. 497. Academic Press, New York.
Gustafson, T. (1963). *Exptl. Cell Res.* **32**, 570.
Gustafson, T. (1964). In "Primitive Motile Systems in Cell Biology" (R. D. Allen and N. Kamiya, eds.), p. 333. Academic Press, New York.
Gustafson, T. (1960, 1963, 1964). Unpublished material.
Gustafson, T., and Hasselberg, I. (1950). *Exptl. Cell Res.* **1**, 371.
Gustafson, T., and Hasselberg, I. (1951). *Exptl. Cell Res.* **2**, 642.
Gustafson, T., and Hörstadius, W. (1955). *Exptl. Cell Res.* Suppl. 3, 170.
Gustafson, T., and Hörstadius, S. (1956). *Zool. Anz.* **156**, 102.
Gustafson, T., and Hörstadius, S. (1957). *Pubbl. Staz. Zool. Napoli* **29**, 407.
Gustafson, T., and Lenicque, P. (1952). *Exptl. Cell Res.* **3**, 251.
Gustafson, T., and Lenicque, P. (1955). *Exptl. Cell Res.* **8**, 114.
Gustafson, T., and Sävhagen, R. (1950). *Arkiv Zool.* **42A** (10).
Gustafson, T., and Wolpert, L. (1961). *Exptl. Cell Res.* **22**, 509.
Gustafson, T., and Wolpert, L. (1963a). *Exptl. Cell Res.* **29**, 561.
Gustafson, T., and Wolpert, L. (1963b). *Intern. Rev. Cytol.* **15**, 139.
Gustafson, T., and Wolpert, L. (1962). Unpublished data.
Harvey, E. B. (1946). *J. Exptl. Zool.* **102**, 253.
Herbst, C. (1892). *Z. Wiss. Zool.* **55**, 446.
Herbst, C. (1904). *Arch. Entwicklungsmech. Organ.* **17**, 306.
Hörstadius, S. (1928). *Acta Zool.* (Stockholm) **9**, 1.
Hörstadius, S. (1935). *Pubbl. Staz. Zool. Napoli* **14**, 251.
Hörstadius, S. (1936a). *Arch. Entwicklungsmech. Organ.* **135**, 1.
Hörstadius, S. (1936b). *Arch. Entwicklungsmech. Organ.* **135**, 40.
Hörstadius, S. (1937). *Biol. Bull.* **73**, 295.
Hörstadius, S. (1938). *Arch. Entwicklungsmech. Organ.* **138**, 197.
Hörstadius, S. (1939). *Biol. Rev. Cambridge Phil. Soc.* **14**, 132.

Hörstadius, S. (1952). *J. Exptl. Zool.* 120, 421.
Hörstadius, S. (1953). *Pubbl. Staz. Zool. Napoli* 24, 45.
Hörstadius, S. (1955). *J. Exptl. Zool.* 129, 249.
Hörstadius, S. (1959). *J. Exptl. Zool.* 142, 141.
Hörstadius, S. (1963). *Develop. Biol.* 7, 144.
Hörstadius, S., and Gustafson, T. (1947). *Zool. Bidr. Uppsala* 25, 271.
Hörstadius, S., and Gustafson, T. (1954). *J. Embryol. Exptl. Morphol.* 2, 216.
Hörstadius, S., and Strömberg, S. (1940). *Arch. Entwicklungsmech. Organ.* 140, 409.
Hörstadius, S., and Wolsky, A. (1936). *Arch. Entwicklungsmech. Organ.* 135, 69.
Hörstadius, S., De Vincentis, M., and Runnström, J. (1964). In preparation.
Holter, H., and Lindahl, P. E. (1940). *Compt. Rend. Trav. Lab. Carlsberg Ser. Chim.* 23, 249.
Holter, H., and Zeuthen, E. (1957). *Pubbl. Staz. Zool. Napoli* 29, 285.
Hsiao, S. C., and Fujii, W. K. (1963). *Exptl. Cell Res.* 32, 217.
Hultin, T. (1953a). *Arkiv Kemi* 5, 267.
Hultin, T. (1953b). *Arkiv Kemi* 5, 543.
Hultin, T. (1953c). *Arkiv Kemi* 5, 559.
Hultin, T. (1957). *Exptl. Cell Res.* 12, 518.
Hultin, T., and Wessel, G. (1952). *Exptl. Cell Res.* 3, 613.
Immers, J. (1956a). *Arkiv Zool.* 9, 367.
Immers, J. (1956b). *Exptl. Cell Res.* 10, 546.
Immers, J. (1961a). *Arkiv Zool.* 13, 561.
Immers, J. (1961b). *Exptl. Cell Res.* 24, 356.
Immers, J., and Runnström, J. (1960). *Develop. Biol.* 2, 90.
Isono, N. In press.
Jacob, F., and Monod, J. (1961). *J. Mol. Biol.* 3, 318.
Jacob, F., and Monod, J. (1963). In "Cytodifferentiation and Macromolecular Synthesis" (M. Locke, ed.), p. 30. Academic Press, New York.
Kacser, H. (1960). *Symp. Soc. Exptl. Biol.* 14, 13.
Karasaki, S. (1959). *Embryologia (Nagoya)* 4, 247.
Karlson, P. (1963). *Perspectives Biol. Med.* 6, 203.
Kato, Y., and Moog, F. (1958). *Science* 127, 812.
Kavanau, L. (1954). *Exptl. Cell Res.* 7, 530.
King, T. J., and Briggs, R. (1956). *Cold Spring Harbor Symp. Quant. Biol.* 21, 271.
Lallier, R. (1958). *Experientia* 14, 309.
Larje, R. (1963, 1964). In preparation.
Lazarow, A., and Cooperstein, S. J. (1953). *J. Histochem. Cytochem.* 1, 234.
Lenicque, P. (1959). *Acta Zool. (Stockholm)* 40, 141.
Lenicque, P., Hörstadius, S., and Gustafson, T. (1953). *Exptl. Cell Res.* 5, 400.
Lindahl, P. E. (1932a). *Arch. Entwicklungsmech. Organ.* 127, 300.
Lindahl, P. E. (1932b). *Arch. Entwicklungsmech. Organ.* 135, 69.
Lindahl, P. E. (1936). *Acta Zool. (Stockholm)* 17, 179.
Lindahl, P. E. (1939a). *Z. Vergleich. Physiol.* 27, 136.
Lindahl, P. E. (1939b). *Z. Vergleich. Physiol.* 27, 233.
Lindahl, P. E. (1940). *Arch. Entwicklungsmech. Organ.* 140, 168.
Lindahl, P. E. (1941). *Acta Zool. (Stockholm)* 22, 101.
Lindahl, P. E. (1942). *Quart. Rev. Biol.* 17, 213.
Lindahl, P. E., and Öhman, L. O. (1938). *Biol. Zentr.* 58, 179.

Ling, G. N. (1962). "A Physical Theory of the Living State: The Association-induction Hypothesis." Ginn (Blaisdell), Boston, Massachusetts.
MacArthur, J. W. (1924). Biol. Bull. Marine Biol. Lab. 46, 60.
McClung Jones, R., ed. (1950). "McClungs Handbook of Microscopical Technique," 3 ed. Harper (Hoeber), New York.
Maggio, R., and Monroy, A. (1959). Nature 184, 68.
Maggio, R., Aiello, F., and Monroy, A. (1960). Nature 188, 1195.
Markman, B. (1957). Exptl. Cell Res. 12, 424.
Markman, B. (1960). Exptl. Cell Res. 23, 197.
Markman, B. (1961a). Exptl. Cell Res. 23, 118.
Markman, B. (1961b). Exptl. Cell Res. 25, 224.
Markman, B. (1963). Arkiv. Zool. 16, 207.
Mazia, D., Blumenthal, G., and Benson, E. (1948). Biol. Bull. 95, 250.
Monroy, A. (1963). Ann. Biol. Animale Biochim. Biophys. 2, 289.
Mori, S., Takashima, Y., Yano, K., Kojo, T., Hashimoto, K., and Fujitani, N. (1958). Bull. Exptl. Biol. (Japan.) 8, 65.
Motomura, I. (1960). Bull. Marine Biol. Sta. Asamushi, Tohoku 10, 165.
Nakano, E., and Monroy, A. (1958). Exptl. Cell Res. 14, 236.
Nakano, E., Guidice, G., and Monroy, A. (1958). Experientia 14, 11.
Nemer, M. (1962). J. Biol. Chem. 237, 143.
Okazaki, K., Fukushi, T., and Dan, K. (1962). Acta Embryol. Morphol. Exptl. 5, 17.
Pease, D. C. (1939). J. Exptl. Zool. 80, 225.
Pease, D. C. (1941). J. Exptl. Zool. 86, 381.
Pease, D. C. (1942). J. Exptl. Zool. 89, 329, 347.
Pitot, H. C., and Periano, C. (1963). J. Biol. Chem. 238, 1911.
Raven, C. P. (1961). "Oogenesis." Macmillan (Pergamon), New York.
Romeis, B. (1948). "Mikroskopische Technik." Leibniz Verlag, München.
Rose, S. M. (1957). Biol. Rev. Cambridge Phil. Soc. 32, 351.
Runnström, J. (1926). Arkiv Zool. 18(4).
Runnström, J. (1928a). Acta Zool. (Stockholm) 9, 365.
Runnström, J. (1928b). Arch. Entwicklungsmech. Organ. 113, 556.
Runnström, J. (1933). Arch. Entwicklungsmech. Organ. 129, 442.
Runnström, J. (1956). Exptl. Cell Res. 11, 660.
Runnström, J. (1957). Arkiv Zool. 10, 523.
Runnström, J. (1962). Exptl. Cell Res. 27, 485.
Runnström, J., and Kriszat, G. (1952). Exptl. Cell Res. 3, 497.
Runnström, J., and Thörnblom, D. (1938). Acta Biol. Latvica 8, 97.
Runnström, J., Hörstadius, S., Immers, J., and Fudge-Mastrangelo, M. (1964). Rev. Suisse Zool. 71, 24.
Scarano, E., and Kalckar, H. M. (1953). Pubbl. Staz. Zool. Napoli 24, 188.
Schimke, R. T. (1964). J. Biol. Chem. 239, 136.
Shaver, J. R. (1956). Exptl. Cell Res. 11, 549.
Spek, J. (1931). "Allgemeine Physiologie der Entwicklung und Formbildung." Thieme, Leipzig.
Ten Cate, G. (1952). In "Proceedings of the Symposium on the Biochemical and Structural Basis of Morphogenesis," p. 108. E. J. Brill, Leiden.
Tocco, G., Orengo, A., and Scarano, E. (1963). Exptl. Cell Res. 31, 52.
Valentine, W. N. (1955). Ann. N.Y. Acad. Sci. 59, 1003.

von Ubsich, L. (1929). *Arch. Entwicklungsmech. Organ.* **117**, 80.
Weber, R., and Boell, E. J. (1962). *Develop. Biol.* **4**, 452.
Weiss, P. (1947). *Yale J. Biol. Med.* **19**, 235.
Willmer, E. N. (1960). "Cytology and Evolution." Academic Press, New York.
Wolfson, N., and Fry, D. S. (1965). *Exptl. Cell Res.* **28**, 66.

Chapter 4

MORPHOGENETIC SIGNIFICANCE OF BIOCHEMICAL PATTERNS IN MOSAIC EMBRYOS

J. R. Collier

Department of Biology
Rensselaer Polytechnic Institute
Troy, New York
and
The Marine Biological Laboratory
Woods Hole, Massachusetts

I. Introduction

The members of several invertebrate groups (nemertines, annelids, mollusks other than cephalopods, and ascidians) produce eggs which are designated as mosaic eggs because the early blastomeres, when reared in isolation, show a striking capacity for self-differentiation. The term "mosaic egg" has been used for a long time, and its continued use will, no doubt, be preferred by some; however, for those eggs other than the ascidians, the term "spiralian," also of long usage, has the advantage as it is a descriptive term, though inapt, which has not gathered a variety of theoretical implications. As an experimental system the spiralian egg provides the most definitive criteria of differentiation available to the embryologist—it is a self-differentiating system operating within a rather broad range of circumstances free of alterations imposed by the external environment and the juxtaposition of neighboring cells. Further, determination occurs early in development, and this separates temporally the determinative process from the final stage of differentiation. This precocious determination occurs at a time when an individual cell may be readily isolated from its neighbors and permits a more refined analysis of the chemistry of determination as opposed to those chemical changes which form the final products of differentiation. The present consideration of the spiralian and ascidian eggs will be restricted mainly to the work of the last decade with emphasis on the chemical embryology.

II. Experimental Embryology

The experimental embryology of the spiralian egg, indeed much of the field in general, has as foundation the cell-lineage studies initiated by C. O. Whitman in 1878 and continued by E. B. Wilson, E. G. Conklin, F. R. Lillie, and others during the last decade of the past century. This work was at first centered on the origin of the germ layers and the homology of organs in different animal groups; however, experimental embryology developed concurrently and as a part of the work in comparative embryology in the blastomere separation and defect experiments of W. Roux, O. Hertwig, H. Driesch, E. B. Wilson, and H. E. Crampton. The extent to which experimental work pervaded the thinking of the late nineteenth century embryologists is reflected by Conklin's statement in his classic paper (1897) on the embryology of Crepidula, ". . . when all the world shakes eggs; it may be hazardous to risk an opinion . . . which is not based on experimental work."

Experimental embryology of the spiralian egg is well illustrated by the work of Clement (1952, 1956, 1960, 1962) on the egg of the marine mud snail Ilyanassa obsoleta. This form is particularly suited for experimental work because blastomeres can be successfully isolated, the isolates can be reared without much difficulty, and the embryo develops into a veliger larva that has a number of well-defined organs. Much of the following account of early development is derived from Conklin's work (1897) with Crepidula; the applicability of the cell-lineage of Crepidula to the Ilyanassa embryo has been considered by Clement (1952).

Prior to the first cleavage, the Ilyanassa egg forms at the vegetal pole a cytoplasmic bulge that is designated the polar lobe. Actually, three such lobes form, but it is the third one, which occurs at the first division, that is of particular interest because it can be removed without killing the egg. As the first division progresses the third polar lobe goes into one of the blastomeres, now called CD, which is then larger than the AB blastomere. At the next division each blastomere divides, and a small fourth polar lobe emerges from the CD blastomere and enters the D blastomere. The A, B, and C cells are now of equal size, and the D, slightly larger.

The third cleavage separates four micromeres from the yolk-laden macromeres. These are the first quartet of micromeres, 1a–1d, and the descendants of this cell line form the ectoderm of the head vesicle, apical and posterior cell plates, part of the velum, the cerebral ganglia and commissures, the cerebropedal connective (probably the pedal ganglia also), and the eyes.

The fourth cleavage separates from the macromeres a second quartet of micromeres, 2a–2d, which give rise to the larval mesoblast, and in conjunction with the cells of the third quartet, which are formed by the sixth cleavage, produce all ectodermal organs posterior to the first row of velar cells. The fifth cleavage is the division of the first quartet of micromeres. By the seventh cleavage, the division of the second quartet micromeres, the embryo consists of 24 cells. At the eighth cleavage only one cell, 3D, divides and produces the 4D and the mesentoblast, 4d. Bilaterality is initiated when the 4d later divides into right and left mesentoblasts; in subsequent divisions the mesoblastic and enteroblastic components of this cell line are completely segregated. The mesoblastic derivatives of the 4d cell produce the mesodermal bands from which all of the mesoderm posterior to the stomodeum, including the larval heart, is formed; the derivatives of the enteroblasts in conjunction with the macromeres form the larval digestive system.

The significant landmarks of the later development of the *Ilyanassa* embryo are schematically indicated in Fig. 1; for a detailed account of gastropod development, Conklin's paper (1897) is without equal. Werner's paper (1958) should be consulted also for the anatomy and development of the *Crepidula* veliger.

In 1896 H. E. Crampton observed that removal of the polar lobe from the *Ilyanassa* egg prevented the formation of the mesentoblast and mesodermal bands. Clement (1952) confirmed this and observed that this operation produced a partial larva which lacked a foot, organized shell, complete velum, and other structures. He also showed that removal of the polar lobe altered the rate of cell division in the fourth quartet. In a series of experiments in which he removed the 4d cell soon after its appearance, Clement (1960) demonstrated that all of the morphogenetic influence of the polar lobe was not confined to the mesentoblast. In twelve embryos deprived of the mesentoblast there was

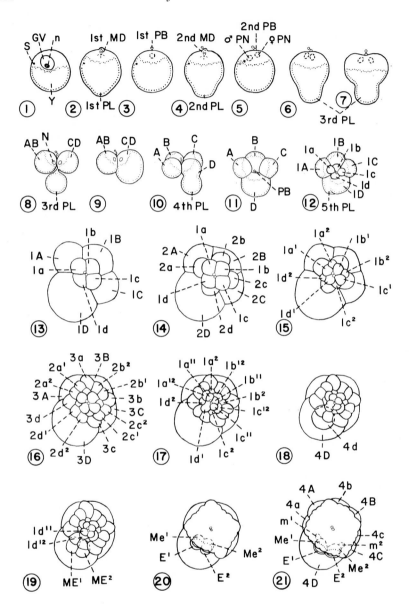

FIG. 1.   Cell-lineage and development of *Ilyanassa*.

(1) Fertilized egg before breakdown of germinal vesicle. (2) Appearance of first polar lobe during first maturation division. (3) Egg becomes spherical again. (4) Appearance of second polar lobe during second maturation division. (5) Egg becomes spherical once more. Male pronucleus moves toward female pronucleus. (6) Appearance of third polar lobe. (7) Animal pole flattens as first cleavage begins. (8) Trefoil stage: third polar lobe almost completely constricted from CD blasto-

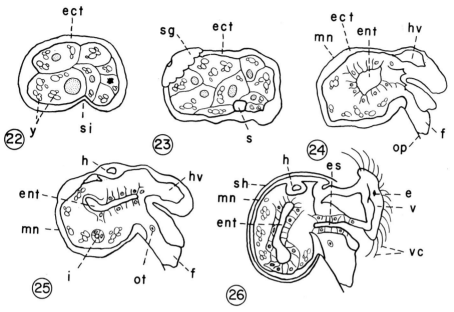

mere. (9) First cleavage completed. (10) Appearance of fourth polar lobe during second cleavage. (11) Four-cell stage seen from animal pole. (12) Slight constriction of D blastomere produces fifth polar lobe at third cleavage. (13) Enlargement of (12) showing first quartet of micromeres, 1a–1d. (14) Division of macromeres to give second quartet of micromeres, 2a–2d. (15) Division of first quartet of micromeres. (16) Division of second quartet of micromeres. Division of macromeres to give third quartet of micromeres. (17) Second division of first quartet of micromeres, excepting 1d[1]. (18) Fourth division of D macromere to produce 4d, the mesentoblast. (19) Division of 1d[1]. Division of mesentoblast produces first bilaterality. (20) Division of mesentoblasts only shown. (21) Division of the primary mesoblasts from the mesentoblasts. Fourth division of A, B, and C blastomeres. (22) Three-day embryo. Invagination for stomodeum present. (23) Four-day embryo. Stomodeum and shell gland present. (24) Five-day embryo. (25) Six-day embryo. (26) Seven-day embryo.

EXPLANATION OF FIG. 1: This figure was compiled from the work of Conklin (1897), Morgan (1933, 1936), Clement (1952), and Collier (1965b). In the cell-lineage portion yolk is indicated by dotted outlines, in the older embryos (22–26) by ovals. Yolk representation, however, is omitted from (13–21). Nuclei are omitted in most of the figures; in (22–26) those shown are stippled. The polar bodies in the cell-lineage drawings indicate the position of the animal pole. The older embryos are presented in sagittal section, the anterior to the right. They were reared at 20°C.

KEY TO ABBREVIATIONS: dg, digestive gland; e, eye; ect, ectoderm; en, endoderm; ent, enteron; es, esophagus; evs, everted stomodeum; f, foot; GV, germinal vesicle; h, heart; hv, head vesicle; i, intestine; is, internal shell fragment; MD, maturation division; m, muscle fibers; mn, mantle; N, nucleus; n, nucleolus; op, operculum; ot, otocyst; PB, polar body; PL, polar lobe; PN, pronucleus; rm, retractor muscle; S, sperm head; s, stomodeum; sg, shell gland; sh, shell; si, stomodeal invagination; st, stomach; v, velum; vc, velar cilia; vp, velar pigment; y, yolk.

neither heart nor intestine; however, normal development of a velum, eyes, cerebral ganglion, foot, operculum, statocysts, stomodeum, esophagus, and shell was observed. This clearly indicates that part of the morphogenetic influence of the polar lobe is transmitted to cells other than the mesentoblast.

Clement (1962) has extended this work by removing the D macromere of the *Ilyanassa* embryo at successive cleavage stages. By this technique he studied the development of the following blastomere combinations: ABC, ABC + 1d, ABC + 1d + 2d, ABC + 1d + 2d + 3d, ABC + 1d + 2d + 3d + 4d. From the development of these isolates, Clement has concluded that the 4D macromere has no morphogenetic influence and that structures dependent on the polar lobe are not determined at the same time, e.g., the external shell is weakly determined when the second quartet of micromeres is formed, the velum, eyes, foot, and shell are determined when the third quartet of micromeres appears, and determination of the heart and intestine occurs when the 4d cell is formed. Clement concludes that the influence of the polar lobe on the heart and intestine may be attributed to cytoplasmic segregation, while an inductive mechanism is probably involved in the formation of the velum, eyes, foot, and shell. Recently, Clement (1963) observed the developmental effect of the microsurgical removal of the micromeres 1a, 2a, 2b, 2c, 2d, 3a, 3b, 3c, 3d, and 4d from the *Ilyanassa* embryo. With the exception of 2b, which has little or no effect on differentiation, each of the above micromeres was found to have a specific effect on development. Clement's experimental analysis of the development of *Ilyanassa* is illustrated in Fig. 2.

Raven (1952) observed that lithium treatment of the *Limnaea* egg caused a defective invagination of the archenteron and that wherever the archenteron contacted the ectodermal cells the shell gland appeared. From these observations he concluded that the archenteron exerts an inductive influence on the formation of the shell. Similarly, Hess (1956a, b) observed delayed invagination of the endoderm in exogastrulae of *Bithynia* with a parallel delay in formation of the shell gland. Clement (1962) was doubtful that the developing shell gland in *Ilyanassa* made contact with the endodermal cells, and Collier and McCann-Collier (1964) have shown that neither the invaginating archenteron nor the small-celled endoderm come into contact with the shell gland in *Ilyanassa*. The shell development may be influenced by contact of the 3D macromere with adjacent blastomeres after the formation of the third quartet and before the appearance of the mesentoblast. If an inductive influence is mediated at this time, it certainly involves a different sequence of events than those observed for *Limnaea* and *Bithynia*.

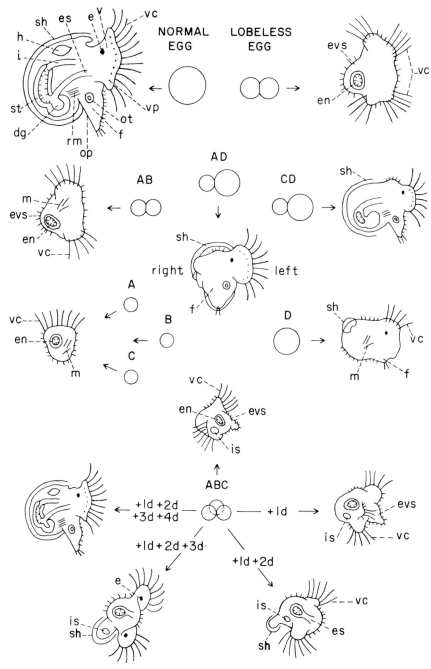

FIG. 2.   Summary of blastomere isolation experiments with *Ilyanassa* (redrawn from Clement, 1956, 1962). For key to abbreviations see Fig. 1.

Rattenbury and Berg (1954) followed the development of lobeless eggs and isolated blastomeres of the *Mytilus* egg and found a progressive transfer of determinative factors by the polar lobes to the D quadrant. They noted that determinative factors for the apical tuft were localized by the first polar lobe to the CD cell and then to the D cell without entering the second polar lobe, which appears at second cleavage. The capacity for forming a shell gland was segregated into the CD cell by the first polar lobe. A stomodeum was observed to develop in only the CD isolate; however, removal of either the first or second polar lobe had no effect on the differentiation of the stomodeum. Velar cells were present in both AB and CD isolates.

In *Limnaea stagnalis* Hess (1957) observed the formation of a stomodeum and shell gland in half-embryos which were derived from either the AB or CD cell. Morrill and Gottesman (1960), working with *Limnaea palustris*, killed one blastomere at the 2-cell stage and found that 2.5 % of the single blastomeres hatched as normal snails. These results indicate that the first cleavage in *Limnaea* may not involve the segregation of materials essential for differentiation, or if it does there is a margin of error in segregation of approximately 2.5 %.

Costello (1945a) studied the development of isolated blastomeres of the *Nereis limbata* eggs; his results indicated ". . . from the first through the fifth cleavage, and probably later, the development of *Nereis* corresponds, in many of its features, to a mosaic-work of self-differentiating cells." Costello was successful in performing the difficult task of progressive blastomere isolation up to the 16-cell stage; his analysis of these isolates showed no evidence of interaction between the blastomeres during the first four cleavage periods. Further, he considered the possibility that the differences in the development of the AB and CD cells may have resulted from differential injury at a specific time during the mitotic cycle, but, after separating these two isolates at the 2-cell stage and later at the 4-cell stage, he found no evidence of differential injury. This paper also includes a concise account of the cell lineage and normal development of *Nereis* and, most particularly, a critical evaluation of the idea of organizers and morphogenetic substances in annelid development.

Recent work on the development of isolated blastomeres of spiralian eggs has added examples of their capacity for self-differentiation, and the observations of Clement (1962) on the *Ilyanassa* embryo have pointed out the possible role of cellular interactions during early cleavage of these eggs. While additional cases of cellular interaction in the early cleavage of the spiralia are likely to be found, it should not detract from the experimental advantages offered by the mosaic features so clearly demonstrated in certain aspects of early development. Clearly, all eggs have, to varying degrees, both mosaic and regulatory qualities; to characterize a particular egg by one or the other of these two attributes of development adds nothing to our understanding of embryogenesis.

A comprehensive review of the earlier studies of blastomere isolation is given by Wilson (1925). Morgan (1927) also considers this topic. Clement (1956, 1962), Costello (1945a, 1955), and Watterson (1955) discuss more recent work in this field.

Raven (1963) has modified his earlier hypothesis of the operation of a continuous gradient-field in the egg of *Limnaea stagnalis*. He states (Raven, 1963, p. 131) his present view as follows: "We therefore have come to the conclusion that this field has a mosaic character in the sense that there must be, besides continuous variations, also discontinuous, stepwise variations in the structure and properties of the cortex." Raven attributes the mosaic character of this field to the asymmetrical location of six subcortical patches, distinguished by their staining characteristics, which correspond to the juxtaposition of follicle cell nuclei within the oocyte. Whether the organization responsible for differentiation resides in the cortex or the endoplasm, these findings are of interest because they suggest that the follicle cells may play an important part in the organization of the egg cytoplasm. Nevertheless, it is difficult to reconcile the results of Morrill and Gottesman (1960), described above, with the idea that all six of these subcortical areas of cytoplasm described by Raven play an essential role in differentiation unless it is assumed that all six areas were contained in a single blastomere in those cases, 2.5 %, in which one of the first two blastomeres produced a normal snail.

Morrill (1963a) centrifuged eggs of *Limnaea stagnalis* and observed the development of antipolar fragments after the formation of giant polar bodies. He found that a normal snail was produced in thirteen out of thirty-five cases, 37 %, after removal of 19.8–37.7 % of the animal cortex and 8.4–23.2 % of the animal-pole cytoplasm. While he did not state the number of normal snails which developed from those cases in which the maximal amount of the cortex was removed, it is clear that at least 19.8 % of the cortex can be removed without impairing differentiation. In any event, the indifferent loss of this much of the cortex raises some doubt of Raven's contention (1942, 1943, 1945, 1963) that the cortex exerts a major organizing influence, maximal at the animal pole, on the differentiation of the *Limnaea* egg. If the cortical organization resides, however, *entirely* within the six subcortical "patches" of cytoplasm described by Raven (1963, Fig. 6), then it is possible that removal of 20 % of the cortex would not include the critical area nearest the animal pole; although removal of 40 % of the cortex would include at least one, probably two, and most of a third of these critical cytoplasmic areas. Thus, it is important to know what percentage of normal snails develops from eggs in which 40 % of the cortex is removed. Even though Morrill (1963a) observed that 8.4–23.2 % of the animal-pole plasm and its granular constituents were also removed from the egg by giant polar body formation, this is unimportant in discerning the role of the cortex since normal development did occur after removal of these amounts of the cortex and the animal-pole cytoplasm.

Reverberi and Ortolani (1962) studied the development of un-fertilized *Ascidia malaca* egg fragments obtained by cutting. The non-nucleated fragment developed upon fertilization, and from a series of operations which involved meridional, equatorial, and oblique equal sections of the egg, they observed that both halves developed into normal larvae, except for distortions or reductions in the tail. They concluded that there was no "preconstituted architecture" present in the *Ascidia* egg and that it is an "isotropic system." These conclusions renew the controversy of Driesch (1895) and Conklin (1905). This problem was also considered by Dalcq (1932, 1935), Reverberi (1931), and Ortolani (1958). Conklin (1905) found that the individual blastomeres of *Cynthia partita* gave rise to partial embryos and concluded that the ooplasm of the ascidian egg is not totipotent. It should be noted, how-ever, that Conklin's results were obtained by differential injury, with the injured blastomere remaining next to the surviving cell; whereas, Reverberi and Ortolani's results (1962) were based on cut fragments of unfertilized eggs. As pointed out by Dalcq (1960), a careful cytological study of the larvae obtained from egg fragments should be pursued; un-fortunately, the recent work of Reverberi and Ortolani did not include a study of sectioned larvae. The details required for a definitive answer to the questions posed by Reverberi and Ortolani are not available.

Reverberi *et al.* (1960) have made an extensive analysis, by defect and transplantation experiments, of brain formation in *Ascidiella aspersa* and *Phallusia mamillata*. They concluded that the notochord and archen-teric roof are causal factors in the determination of the neural system.

III. Developmental Mechanics

A. *Mechanism of Cleavage*

Consideration of cleavage of the spiralia reveals the ineptness of the term "spiral cleavage." If a spiral pattern is visualized, as suggested by Wilson (1892), the alternation of direction of the cleavage plane results in two opposed spirals. Lillie (1895) pointed out that the radii are inclined rather than curved and suggested the expression "oblique cleavage." Kofoid's suggestion (1895) of "alternating cleavage" is descriptive of the early cleavage sequence, but is not applicable since there are cases in which the plane of division is in the same direction in different quadrants. Although different terms were originally urged, usage has established "spiral cleavage," and as pointed out by Conklin (1897, p. 177) ". . . if taken apart from its colloquial meaning, the word spiral clearly and specifically designates a particular kind of cleavage which needs a distinctive and technical name. . ."

Spiral cleavage emphasizes the inequality of cleavage and the regular alternation of cleavage planes. Unequal cleavage often occurs in the first and generally in the third and subsequent divisions of the spiralian egg. Conklin (1897) observed a dexiotropism of the nuclei and protoplasmic areas after the first cleavage in *Crepidula*, which indicates a disposition toward spiralization established before or during the first cleavage; the spiral form of cleavage is unequivocally present by the third division.

Although the role of the asters and spindle as active forces in cell division has been variously acclaimed, with recent evidence to the contrary (Hiramoto, 1956, 1958), there remains general agreement that these structures are the immediate determinants of the plane of cleavage. Reviews by Gray (1931), Dan (1943, 1960), Wolpert (1960), and Mazia (1961) consider this point in detail.

The primary concern here is: What factors are responsible for the orientation and reorientation, in the case of the alternation of cleavage planes, of the mitotic apparatus? Particularly relevant are the observations of Dan *et al.* (1952) that asymmetrical asters appear in the isolated mitotic apparatus from cleaving eggs of *Spisula solidissima*. Dan (1960) has confirmed this observation in the living eggs, following centrifugation, of *Spisula saghalensis*, *Mactra sulcataria*, *M. veneriformis*, and *Perinereis cultrifera*. Dan and Nakajima (1956) isolated the mitotic apparatus during the formation of micromeres in the egg of the sea urchin *Hemicentrotus pulcherrimus* and observed that the asters of the micromeres were truncated and smaller than the asters of the macromeres. Agrell (1958) made a similar observation on a section of the cleavage of *Psammechinus miliaris*. These data, as do many others, center attention on the asters as the determinative element in the origin and positioning of the mitotic apparatus.

Kojima (1959a) centrifuged *Urechis unicinctus* eggs and found that vitally stained granules were displaced to the centrifugal portion of the egg; cleavage and ciliation were confined to that half of the egg. Kojima (1959b) also studied granules in the eggs of five species of sea urchins and found that after treatment with cleavage inhibitors (colchicine and iodoacetamide) the granules were fewer in number and uniformly dispersed in the cytoplasm; they did not form at all when cleavage was inhibited by 2,4-dinitrophenol. Another interesting observation reported from this work was that in refertilized eggs the vitally stained granules do not gather around supernumerary sperm nuclei, but do become associated with the asters later formed by supernumerary sperm.

In general, the asters are equal and central in equal division, unequal and/or eccentric in unequal division. That this arrangement is not entirely related to the volume of the cytoplasmic area in which the aster initially forms is shown by Lillie's observations (1901) on the unequal cleavage of the egg of *Unio*. The spindle is formed in the exact center of the egg and just before metaphase moves to one side of the egg. Lillie (1912) pointed out that the inequality of the first cleavage in *Nereis* was foreshadowed in early prophase by the inequality of the asters; in this case the central bodies of the sperm amphiaster were also unequal. Conklin (1902) studied cytoplasmic movements associated with the formation of the first three quartets of micromeres in *Crepidula*. He found that prior to division the spindle was displaced peripherally and the cell divided unequally in the proper laeotropic and dexiotropic directions in accordance with the displaced asters.

Costello (1961) has reported his observations of the centrioles at the metaphase of the first and second meiotic division and the first cleavage in the egg of the acoel *Polychoerus carmelensis*. These centrioles are slightly curved rods; this allowed Costello to establish that they were oriented at right angles to each other and to the axis of the mitotic spindle. Costello (1961, p. 310) proposed the following hypothesis: "(a) The orientation of the centrioles at any given division determines the position in which the daughter centrioles will separate from each other. (b) The path of separation of daughter centrioles determines the position of the main axis of the spindle for the next division. (c) The axis of the spindle determines the relative positions of the daughter cells with respect to each other. (d) This arrangement of the daughter cells is maintained, for a time at least, by the primary cell connective, of which the spindle remnant is the significant portion. (e) These relations obtain in the absence of secondary intervening factors."

Costello (1961, p. 303) in his statement, "The physico-chemical nature of the forces that orient the centrioles is as yet unknown," (it should be added that the "biological" forces operating in the orientation of the centrioles are also unknown) recognizes that this hypothesis fails to deal with the basic mechanism responsible for the determination of the cleavage plans. Nevertheless, his treatment of the subject returns attention to a long-neglected problem and emphasizes that the core of the problem lies in the elucidation of those factors responsible for the asymmetrical location and growth of the division centers.

Dan (1960) reported a single observation in the centrifuged egg of *Spisula saghalensis* which is most suggestive and deserves further attention. After centrifugation of the *Spisula* egg Dan (1960, p. 331) observed that ". . . the aster which was lying closer to the yolk mass formed by the centrifuging first extended its rays into the yolk mass so that it looked, for a while, as if this aster was going to form the CD blastomere. But the rays of this aster soon disappeared, and the rays of the farther aster invaded the area and took possession of it, becoming the CD cell. The above fact indicates that the ray formation corresponds to the setting up of the territory for an aster." This result suggests heterogeneity of the division centers, i.e., each center has a preference for a particular kind of cytoplasm. The evidence supporting the role of the division center (centriole, centrosome, and asters) in determining the cleavage plane suggests that Dan's observation may be the key point for further investigation of this problem.

B. *Ooplasmic Segregation*

Costello (1945b, 1948) has suggested that the Teorell diffusion effect may provide an explanation for the localization of visible cytoplasmic components "and a parallel but invisible segregation of the 'ooplasmic stuffs'" in marine eggs.[1] He adopted the term ooplasmic segregation for this type of cytoplasmic localization. Costello is chiefly concerned with the precleavage localization of ooplasmic materials, but presumably means to include postcleavage events as he points out that ooplasmic segregation in *Nereis* is not well advanced until just before the third cleavage. He states (Costello, 1948, p. 663), "The fact that certain ova, under experimental conditions, may show various degrees of differentiation without cleavage indicates that neither the mitotic mechanism, nor cleavage, nor the cleavage pattern, nor cell boundaries are of essential importance."

The view that ooplasmic segregation occurs by a process other than, but in synchrony with, cleavage stems from Lillie's report (1902, 1906) of differentiation without cleavage following KCl treatment of the *Chaetopterus* egg. These eggs developed cilia in the absence of nuclear and cytoplasmic divisions; however, the pattern of ciliation was not normal and chromosomal replication did occur. Other aspects of differentiation

---

[1] Teorell (1935, 1937) predicted that the continuous diffusion of a substance across a permeable membrane into a confined volume that is small in comparison to the external volume would establish a diffusion potential that would affect the distribution of electrolytes and electrically charged particles within the confined volume.

reported by Lillie are less clear, and in the strictest sense this experiment demonstrated only that compartmentation of the cytoplasm is not necessary for formation of cilia.

The main point to be made here is that this experiment does not dissociate the mechanism(s) of ooplasmic segregation and determination of the cleavage plane. Because the mechanism(s) responsible for both events are unknown, it may be argued that those factors which segregate cytoplasmic materials may also be the same ones that determine the orientation of the mitotic apparatus and the cleavage plane. That a mitotic apparatus failed to form in KCl-treated eggs does not preclude the operation of the factors responsible for its orientation. From this viewpoint it is not clear that ooplasmic segregation and the determination of the cleavage plane are unrelated and that the latter event is not of essential importance to ooplasmic segregation.

An observation of Lehmann (1956) on the cleavage of the 2d and 4d cells in the centrifuged *Tubifex* egg indicates that cleavage does play a role in ooplasmic segregation. He found that shifting of the granules in the 2d and 4d cells of the *Tubifex* egg by centrifugation had no effect on differentiation, but disturbance of the division mechanism which altered the size of the cells altered their differentiation. From this it would seem that the mitotic apparatus plays a direct role in ooplasmic segregation by apportionment of cytoplasmic materials.

The saltatory movements of metachromatic granules in the *Spisula* egg and yolk granules in the *Cistenides* egg described by Rebhun (1960, 1963b) are clearly related to ooplasmic segregation. He has reported a radial orientation of the ergastoplasm with respect to the mitotic centers and postulated that the forces responsible for this orientation emanate from the centers and that the ergastoplasm is the force-transmitting structure in cells which have saltatory particle movements. While Rebhun did not offer any further explanation of the forces involved, it appears that his observations are pertinent to the movement and localization of particles during early development.

C. *Polar Lobe Formation*

Wolpert (1960) suggests that a regional relaxation of the cell membrane with a concomitant increase in internal pressure in the egg could account for polar lobe formation. This scheme is similar to Wolpert's explanation for the formation of the polar body, to which it is more suited because of the small size of the polar body, and involves the assumption that the asters determine, though not necessarily by actual contact, the area of the egg surface that relaxes. This explanation is inapplicable to polar lobe formation because Wilson (1904, p. 52) using *Dentalium* showed that enucleated, nondividing vegetal halves formed polar lobes corresponding with the division rhythms of the nucleated half.

The sequence of events in induced ameboid movements in the *Spisula* egg, as described by Rebhun (1963a, Figs. 14–18) suggests that the contraction of the egg surface, which is initiated in the animal half and progresses toward the vegetal half of the egg, may account for polar lobe formation.

Dan and Dan (1942) have made a detailed study of the surface changes associated with polar lobe formation in the *Ilyanassa* egg.

IV. Ultrastructure

Within the past several years the ultrastructure of a number of spiralian and ascidian eggs has been studied. The following discussion is by no means a review of all the work in this area.

The egg surfaces of several forms [*Limnaea* (Recourt, 1961); *Barnea* (Pasteels and de Harven, 1962); *Mytilus* (Humphreys, 1962a; Dan, 1962); *Spisula* (Rebhun, 1962); *Hydroides* (Colwin *et al.*, 1957); *Pectinaria gouldi* (Lambson and Austin, 1963)] show numerous microvilli anchored in the vitelline membrane. That the microvillar surface is continuous with the bilamellate cell membrane is most clearly shown for the egg of *Barnea candida* by Pasteels and de Harven (1962). Microvilli are not visible in the electron micrographs of the eggs of *Ciona intestinalis* and *Styela barnharti* (Mancuso, 1962; Berg and Humphreys, 1960), though present in oocytes of *Molgula manhattensis* (Kessel and Kemp, 1962).

The bulk of each microvillus is removed from the egg surface by adherence to the vitelline membrane (Humphreys, 1962a; Rebhun, 1962; J. C. Dan, 1962) as the cleavage furrow moves away from the membrane; however, that portion of the microvillus which extends across the perivitelline space, approximately one-third of its length in *Spisula* (Rebhun, 1962), is available to supplement the area of the cell membrane in the cleavage furrow (see Fig. 3). The assumption generally made is that new membrane is formed as the cleavage furrow advances, but breaking of a microvillus at any point along its length and reformation of the cell membrane by coalescence of the broken surface will result, upon stretching, in an increase in the area of the cell membrane. These events do not involve formation of new membrane, rather a redistribution of pre-existing membrane material. From Rebhun's data (1961) calculations can be made which show that the surface area of the portion of the microvillus which extends from the egg surface to the midpoint of the perivitelline space, i.e., 0.17μ from the egg surface, contains approximately 1.7 times the surface area of the entire egg. [Humphreys (1962a) has calculated the total surface area of the intact microvilli in the *Mytilus* egg.] The membranous area of the microvillus would eventually be depleted as they are not reformed on the opposed surfaces of blastomeres after cleavage (Rebhun, 1962, Fig. 11). Nevertheless, this source of membrane material would probably be available during several cleavages since all cells during the early cleavage of mollusks and annelids have a free surface, i.e., a surface not opposed by an adjacent cell. This situation prevails until the formation of the mesodermal bands is initiated, which is the 52-cell stage of *Crepidula*.

The idea of microvilli as a source of "reserve" membranous material is significant since it provides new membrane material during early cleavage without protein synthesis. The pertinent aspects of protein synthesis will be discussed in Section VI.

Except for the presence of cortical granules and a general sparsity of mitochondria and lipid droplets in the subsurface of the spiralian egg [*Spisula* (Allen, 1958, personal communication from Rebhun); *Mytilus* (Humphreys, 1962a; Mancuso, 1960; J. C. Dan, 1962); *Barnea* (Pasteels and de Harven, 1962)] it is difficult to make a case for the existence of a structurally differentiated cortex. The cortex, the cytoplasmic area within 1–2 μ of the inner surface of the cell membrane, of these eggs contains, as does the endoplasm, smooth membranous vesicles and small granules [15 mμ in *Mytilus* (Humphreys, 1962a); "smaller than ribosomes" in *Barnea* (Pasteels and de Harven, 1962)]. The subsurface of the *Limnaea* (Elbers, 1959), *Ciona*, and *Styela* eggs (Berg and Humphreys, 1960) is structurally undifferentiated.

The cortex of the eggs of *Spisula*, *Mytilus*, and *Barnea* (Allen, 1958; Humphreys, 1962a; Pasteels and de Harven, 1962) contain numerous large cortical granules. In *Mytilus* they are spherical or oval particles which are partially confined by a membrane, have a diameter of 0.8 μ, and contain a dense mass of 10 mμ particles; in *Barnea* the cortical granules are 0.4–0.6 μ in diameter, enclosed by a double membrane, and contain fine granules which are later dispersed in the endoplasm. The cortical granules of *Barnea* are PAS (periodic acid-Schiff) positive after salivary digestion and are metachromatic in the living egg, thus judged

---

Fig. 3. Ultrastructure of *Spisula* egg. Electron micrographs courtesy of Dr. Lionel I. Rebhun.

A. Electron micrograph of a *Spisula* egg stratified by centrifugation at metaphase and allowed to begin redistribution of egg contents. l, lipid layer; uh, upper hyaline zone consisting of elements of the endoplasmic reticulum (ER); mv, multivesicular bodies; m, mitochondria; vm, vitelline membrane. Note radial orientation of the ER from the upper hyaline toward mitochondrial layer. Other work indicates that the convergent point of the oriented ER is the centrosome.

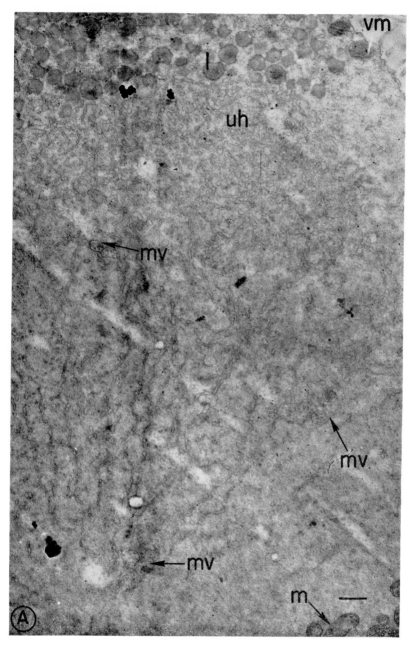

(For Figs. 3B and 3C, see pages 220 and 221.)

to contain mucopolysaccharides (Pasteels and de Harven, 1962). Following treatment with sperm extract, the cortical granules of *Spisula* and *Barnea* disperse in the endoplasm; those of *Mytilus* (Humphreys, 1962a) disappear (final disposition not described). That the contents of the cortical granules of these eggs, unlike those of the ubiquitously studied sea urchin egg, are ultimately dispersed in the cytoplasm is of interest

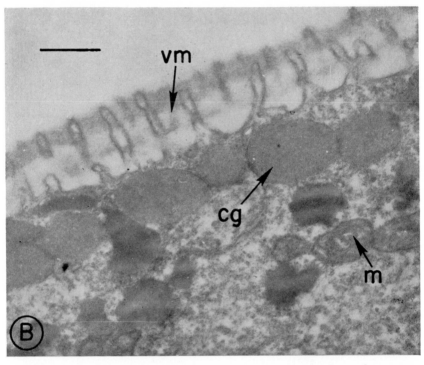

Fig. 3B.   Electron micrograph of the surface of an unfertilized *Spisula* egg. VM, vitelline membrane. It consists of microvilli projecting through a clear space about 0.25 μ into two denser layers, an inner light and an outer dense amorphous layer. In other electron micrographs, these layers appear fibrous, with fibers parallel to egg surface. CG, cortical granules. They are arranged in a single layer immediately below the plasmalemma; m, mitochondrion.

and probable significance. The role of the cortical granule material in development has not been considered. Does it constitute a source of mucoprotein or protein and mucopolysaccharide for utilization in the formation of cilia and early mesenchyme cells?

The most informative papers on the ultrastructure of the endoplasm of the spiralian and ascidian eggs are those of Rebhun (1960, 1961, 1963b) on *Spisula solidissima, Otala lactea,* and *Cistenides gouldi,* Berg and

Humphreys (1960) on *Ciona intestinalis* and *Styela barnharti*, Humphreys (1962a) on *Mytilus edulis*, and Recourt (1961) on *Limnaea stagnalis*.

Rebhun (1961, p. 208) has described for the *Spisula* and *Otala* eggs "four classes of membranous elements of the ergastoplasm . . . These are annulate lamellae, yolk nuclei in the form of spherical whorls or endo-

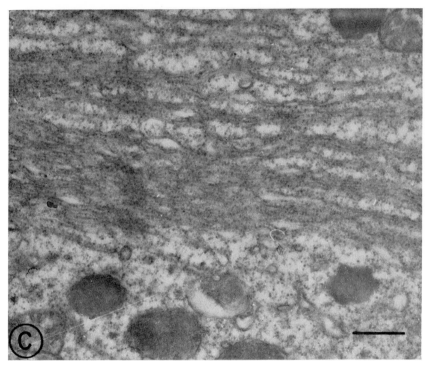

FIG. 3C.   A bundle of parallel cisternae of the ER in an unfertilized *Spisula* egg. Note numerous attached and free ribosomes.

plasmic reticulum, and isolated vesicles or cisternae." The last are basophilic vesicles coated with 150-Å particles and are distinct from the smooth-surfaced vesicles which he considers derived from Golgi bodies or micropinocytosis vacuoles. The reality of the ergastoplasm, its relation to the nuclear envelope, and its origin are carefully discussed. Rebhun's electron micrographs are the clearest and most informative available for the spiralian egg, and the original papers should be consulted.

Humphreys (1962a) described large vesicles surrounded by and containing 15-mμ particles in the centripetal half of the centrifuged *Mytilus* egg; the centrifugal half contains only smaller vesicles and the 15-mμ particles. A similar system of vesicles and granules was also found in the eggs of *Styela* and *Ciona* by Berg and Humphreys (1960), although the *Styela* egg appears to have a more typical ergastoplasm than *Ciona*. Recourt (1961) depicts some membranous elements of the ergastoplasm and the Golgi bodies in the *Limnaea* egg.

The application of electron microscopy to cytoplasmic specification was initiated by Lehmann (1950, 1954) in his studies of the *Tubifex* egg. This work with *Tubifex* has also been pursued by Weber (1958, 1960) who found that the pole plasm was rich in mitochondria and "chromidia" (rough-surfaced, membranous vesicles) which probably correspond to an undifferentiated ergastoplasm, whereas the endoplasm contained only few mitochondria and chromidia. The fine structure of the cytoplasm of the 2d (ectoblast) and the 4d (mesoblast) cells was rich in mitochondria and chromidia and thus identifiable with the pole plasm(s) of the egg, but the cells were indistinguishable on the basis of their cytoplasmic ultrastructure. Although he was able to discern some quantitative and topographical differences, as previously reported by Lehmann (1958), in the distribution of mitochondria and chromidia between the ecto-, meso-, and entoblast cells, it is difficult to attribute the direction of developmental areas to these features. In comparing the 2d and 4d cells of *Tubifex*, Weber's statement (1960, p. 238), "Therefore, one is led to the conclusion that the segregation of the morphogenetic potentialities, characteristic to the pole plasm escapes the resolving power of the electron microscope," seems to be a fair appraisal of the general use of electron microscopy on the problem of embryonic localization.

Similar studies on the ascidian egg have also been initiated by Berg and Humphreys (1960) and Mancuso (1962).

A significant feature of Weber's work with the *Tubifex* egg is the demonstration of the association of "chromidia" with the nuclear membrane and preferentially at regions where the "nuclear reticulum" contacts the nuclear membrane. This relationship suggests a route by which nuclear products may be transferred to the cytoplasm, a view expressed by Gay (1955) for the *Drosophila* salivary glands; see also Rebhun (1961) for discussion of this point.

Reverberi and Mancuso (1961) and Humphreys (1962b) prepared electron micrographs of the fertilized egg and 2-cell stage of *Mytilus edulis*. Reverberi and Mancuso found no significant differences among the cytoplasmic constituents of the AB and CD blastomeres and the polar lobe. Humphreys concluded that there was a variable distribution of the yolk and lipid in the polar lobe but that the numerical density of mitochondria per unit area of cytoplasm was the same in the polar lobe as in the whole egg; he (Humphreys, 1962b, p. NN-10) observed that, "A screen of flattened vesicles becomes aligned in a plane connecting the inner margins of the surface constriction between the polar lobe and the rest of the egg" and, "During the latter half of cytokinesis the complex of flattened vesicles is not seen." It is interesting to guess that these vesicles may be related to the segregation of materials essential for differentiation.

The presence of isolated vesicles, either smooth or coated with particles, and an abundant population of granules approximately 150 Å in diameter and presumably basophilic is a feature common to all eggs investigated. Whereas some eggs have an elaborate endoplasmic reticulum, its absence in others enforces the conclusion that the system of vesicles and granules is sufficient ultrastructural refinement for the initiation of development. Needed next is a series of electron micrographs of selected stages of later development whereby changes in the ergastoplasm, if they occur, could be correlated with differentiation.

Even though ultrastructural studies promise a remarkable increase in our knowledge of differentiation, one should realize that the ergastoplasmic structures resolved by the electron microscope are gross compared to the stereochemical requirements for the synthesis of a specific protein. When proteins become adequately characterized it should be possible to relate specific protein synthesis to a given area of the ergastoplasm. If two proteins were defined in terms of their rate of incorporation of two or more amino acids, their intracellular sites of synthesis could be detected by a combination of electron microscopy, autoradiography, and double isotopic labeling. This approach would provide a meeting ground for biochemical and ultrastructural studies. The synthesis of a protein is a first step; a second step involves the combination of proteins to form a structure or functional molecule, and this is the level of organization at which ultrastructural studies properly combined with biochemical experiments may contribute significantly.

V. Chemical Cell-Lineage

Chemical cell-lineage describes an area of research devoted, for the most part fruitlessly, to the search for chemical differences pertinent to differentiation among the early blastomeres of the spiralian egg. The localization of mitochondria and other cytoplasmic inclusions is considered in this section because of their enzymatic and molecular constituents.

The role of mitochondria in development has been relentlessly pursued, and more exhaustively in the spiralian and ascidian eggs than in other forms; in recent years studies of the enzymes associated with the mitochondria have been given parallel attention. Most of the work on mitochondria and respiratory enzymes has been reviewed by Brachet (1960), Reverberi (1957, 1961), Raven (1958), and Weber (1960), and for this reason only a few selected papers will be discussed here.

Reverberi (1958) has studied mitochondrial distribution in the egg of *Dentalium* by staining with Janus green and the Nadi reaction. He finds that the mitochondria are initially localized in the polar lobe; during cleavage some of the mitochondria are distributed to the animal pole of each macromere, the 2d cell, and the perinuclear area of all the micromeres, perhaps with a greater concentration in the 2d and 3d micromeres. In the *Dentalium* larva mitochondria appear localized in the apical plate cells which form the apical tuft and the three principal rows of trochoblasts which give rise to the prototrochal cilia. Reverberi (1958, p. 86) concludes, "The polar lobe can be considered as a device for the transmission of mitochondria to the mesodermic organs," and, "The results which follow removal of the polar lobe from the egg can well be explained if one takes into account the peculiar distribution of the mitochondria and their physiological function as energy generators." These conclusions are questionable when it is recalled that the localization of mitochondria described by Reverberi is confined to ectodermal cells (apical plate cells and trochoblasts) and all three rows of trochoblasts, with prototrochal cilia, develop in the lobeless egg (Wilson, 1904, Figs. 32 and 33, also p. 26). If the mitochondria contained in the second polar lobe of *Dentalium* are ultimately localized in the trochoblasts and the trochoblasts develop normally after removal of the polar lobe, then the conclusion that the mitochondria of the second polar lobe are unessential for differentiation of the trochoblasts is inescapable.

Berg and Humphreys (1960) have made an important contribution in their study of the fine structure of the eggs of *Styela barnharti* and *Ciona intestinalis*. They confirmed Conklin's identification (1931) of "small spherules" in the *Ciona* egg as mitochondria and pointed out that the "yellow mitochondria" described by Conklin for *Styela partita* were actually lipid droplets in *Styela barnharti*. The lipid droplets were invariably associated with mitochondria and upon centrifugation the lipids carried mitochondria along with them; however, they suggest that the low centrifugal force necessary to displace the lipids would leave many unattached mitochondria in their original position.

If this contention of Berg and Humphreys is correct, as it likely is, then Conklin's interpretation of his centrifugation experiments with *Styela* and *Ciona* should be reconsidered. In any event, if it is required to remove or shift all of the mitochondria in order to reach a decision concerning their role in embryogenesis, then the question is likely to remain unresolved. On the other hand, if the possibility of the reformation of mitochondria by an egg once they have been removed is resolved a reasonable approach to this problem may be expected. Specifically, how many mitochondria remain in an area after an isolation or centrifugation experiment and how many mitochondria are present in the differentiated structure under consideration?

The work of Berg and Humphreys (1960) shows the feasibility of this approach in that they were able to count the number of mitochondria in meridional and equatorial sections of the ascidian egg. From an average value of three sections they report a localization of mitochondria and lipid droplets in the posterior blastomeres of the *Styela* egg and of mitochondria and large membranous vesicles in the posterior blastomeres of *Ciona*. A significant feature of this work was that these authors developed a way of orienting and embedding single eggs, so that serial sections could be cut in any desired plane.

La Spina (1961) fragmented unfertilized eggs of *Ciona intestinalis* and *Ascidia malaca* by centrifugation; she found that only the centrifugal fragments of *Ciona* formed a normal larva, whereas both fragments of *Ascidia* produced normal larvae. Regarding the results with *Ciona*, she states (La Spina, 1961, p. 324), "The fact that this centripetal fragment does not develop is probably due to its lack of mitochondria." It is also probable that the failure of the clear fragment to develop resulted from a qualitatively unequal distribution of hyaloplasm. The distribution of the germinal vesicle or its contents after breakdown is not clear from La Spina's paper (1961).

Berg (1956, 1957) demonstrated by enzymatic assay in homogenates of isolated blastomeres that cytochrome oxidase and succinate dehydrogenase activity was significantly greater in posterior blastomeres than anterior cells of the embryo of *Ciona intestinalis*. Berg (1957) reported briefly some previously unpublished results on the cytochrome oxidase activity of the AB and CD cells of *Mytilus edulis* in which he found an activity ratio, AB/CD, of 0.98 ± 0.03 after correction for volume differences. He pointed out that localization of oxidases occurs in some spiralian eggs but that it is not a feature common to all forms.

Weber (1958), working with the *Tubifex* egg and using microchemical methods, showed that the cytochrome oxidase activity of the ectomesodermal region is three times higher than that of the endodermal region. Weber (1960) reported the pertinent result that the endodermal region of the *Tubifex* embryo consistently fails to stain with the indophenol blue reagent, yet they contain measurable cytochrome oxidase activity. Further, he cited unpublished results of Lehmann and Mancuso, which show that the perinuclear mitochondria may be stained cytochemically in dissected entoblasts—a vagary of cytochemical methods that should be kept in mind.

The significance of the localization of mitochondria and respiratory enzymes in various cells of the spiralian egg is obscure. To establish that the mitochondrial or enzyme content of early blastomeres bears a causal relationship to the developmental capacity of a cell it must be shown that a blastomere deficient in these components cannot compensate for this deficiency by synthesizing the mitochondria or enzymes at a later stage in its developmental history. It is possible that the localization of mito-chondria and respiratory enzymes is a case of *precocious differentiation* and that these materials are related to larval physiology, particularly locomotion, and/or postlarval development rather than to embryogenesis. In those cases in which mitochondria are localized in certain blastomeres, an occurrence which is not universal among the spiralian and ascidian eggs, these particular cells are most frequently destined to give rise to locomotor systems.

In a number of invertebrate eggs some particulates stain meta-chromatically *in vivo* with dilute solutions of methylene blue and toluidine blue. These particulates have been designated α- and β-granules; whether there are two distinct types of particles or one is the precursor of the other has been argued. Rebhun (1958, 1959) from his work with the *Spisula* egg, takes the view that they are two types of granules. Pasteels and Mulnard (1957), working with the eggs of *Barnea* and *Gryphea*, and Mulnard (1958) with the *Chaetopterus* egg, have suggested that the α-granules are precursors to the β-granules; disagreement also exists as to the time when the β-granules are first formed (see Mulnard, 1958; Mulnard *et al.*, 1959).

Rebhun's view (1960) of the particles in the *Spisula* egg is: "(1) β particles are present from the unfertilized egg . . . and are attracted to asters whenever the latter are formed. . . . (2) α particles may be formed at any point in the mitotic cycle, but move into the asters only after pro-nuclear fusion, and then only if they have been formed prior to the time of assembly of the aster. . . . (3) Our staining results are neutral with respect to the relation between α and β particles postulated by the Belgian group. With respect to point 3, however, we feel that the electron microscope observations to be presented now lend support to the con-cept that β particles may be formed from a precursor (although we do not know what relation this precursor has to the α particles); therefore, we must mitigate the criticism we have previously leveled at this con-cept."

Rebhun (1960), from a study of electron micrographs of the centrifuged *Spisula* egg, has concluded that the granules are multivesicular bodies, circular to oblong in shape, of approximately 0.5 μ in diameter, surrounded by a single dense layer, and containing a number, anywhere from 3 to 40, of smaller bodies 250–500 Å in diameter. He discussed the probable functions of these particles and pointed out that their unequal distribution during cleavage suggests a role in differentiation (see Mulnard, 1958) and that they may have a role in the induction of the cleavage furrow as indicated by the work of Kojima (1959a, b) and Zimmerman and Marsland (1960).

Mulnard (1958) has presented evidence that the β-granules of the *Chaetopterus* egg contain mucopolysaccharides and acid phosphatase.

Tweedell (1962) has distinguished on the basis of staining with toluidine blue and nile blue sulfate and displacement by centrifugation two kinds of metachromatic granules in the egg of *Pectinaria* (*Cistenides*) *gouldii*. He has presented a careful description of the centrifuged *Pectinaria* egg and discussed the relation of the metachromatic granules to those described in *Spisula* and other forms.

Dalcq and Pasteels (1963), using cytochemical methods, have studied the distribution of a group of mononucleotide-phosphohydrolases in the eggs of *Barnea candida*, *Sabellaria alveolata*, *Psammechinus miliaris*, and *Ascidiella scabra*. They found that the polar lobe of *Sabellaria* stains intensely when ATP (adenosine triphosphate) is used as a substrate in the cytochemical procedure. The relations of these enzymes to the α- and β-granules were discussed.

Dalcq (1960) has recently reviewed the work on the occurrence of metachromatic granules in vertebrate, echinoderm, and spiralian eggs.

Durante (1957) found by histochemical procedures that acetylcholinesterase became localized in the tail-muscle cells during the development of *Ciona intestinalis*. Durante (1958) also found that treatment of embryos with eserin resulted in a negative histochemical test for cholinesterase and retarded motility, but had no effect on the structural differentiation of muscle. These observations are of interest because they indicate the early appearance of an enzyme during embryogenesis which has primarily, if not entirely, a larval function. This may be another example of precocious differentiation similar to the suggestion made for the early localization of mitochondria.

Using an immunodiffusion technique, Berg and Baker (1962) found four antigenic components in the egg of *Styela barnharti* and two in the egg of *Ciona intestinalis*. Their study of the distribution of these antigenic substances to the anterior and posterior blastomeres did not indicate any qualitative differences between these blastomeres.

Weber (1958) determined that the catheptic activity was evenly distributed between the ectomesodermal and the endodermal cells of *Tubifex*; these results are similar to the distribution of dipeptidase (Collier, 1957) among the early blastomeres and the polar lobe of the *Ilyanassa* embryo. In the latter work no differential in dipeptidase activity was detectable during the development of the AB, CD, and lobeless embryos.

Berg (1957) found that the posterior blastomeres at the 4-cell stage of *Ciona* contained more RNA (ribonucleic acid) than the anterior cells. Collier (1960) determined the RNA content of the egg, lobeless egg, polar lobe, AB and CD blastomeres of *Ilyanassa*. The concentration per cell and polar lobe was calculated using three different reference units for the cytoplasmic volume. A higher concentration of RNA was found in the AB blastomere. The meaning of this distribution is obscure; however, it appears that the polar lobe, which has a lower concentration of RNA than any of the isolates, is not a major factor in the quantitative segregation of RNA in the *Ilyanassa* egg. Although the possibility remains that the RNA of the polar lobe may be of qualitative significance because it contains enough RNA to account for template molecules to direct the synthesis of a number of different kinds of proteins. The higher concentration of RNA in the AB as compared to the CD blastomere demonstrates a mechanism of segregation of RNA which is independent of the polar lobe.

The chemical cell-lineage approach is based on the fact that the early blastomeres of the spiralian egg have different and specific developmental capacities when reared in isolation. This observation and the demonstration of nuclear equality in early development of the newt, frog, *Ascaris*, sea urchin, and insect eggs, and to the 8-cell stage for *Nereis* (Wilson, 1896; Morgan, 1910) has led to the point of view that the factors responsible for the diversity of early blastomeres reside in the cytoplasm. This emphasis on cytoplasmic components has imposed a restricted outlook on the embryology of the spiralian egg.

Nuclear contribution to the regional specification of the egg can be envisioned the following way. The mature annelid or molluskan egg is radially symmetrical along a polar axis, and its nucleus is eccentrically or centrally located along the polar axis. With respect to its chromosomal complement the nucleus must be asymmetrical since it is haploid or, in the case of the oocyte with a germinal vesicle, the homologous chromosomes are paired and constitute an asymmetrical arrangement. Considering that interphase chromosomes are frequently in contact with or close to the nuclear membrane, it is clear that any chromosomal product, e.g., nucleoli and nuclear ribosomes, could be asymmetrically distributed to the cytoplasm. [The description by Afzelius (1963) of annulated vesicles along the inner surface of the nuclear membrane in the dinoflagellate *Noctiluca* and the discharge of these vesicles (Fig. 6 from Afzelius, 1963) into the cytoplasm illustrates a mechanism whereby chromosomal products could be transported to the cytoplasm.] The general pattern of ooplasmic segregation is a displacement of materials from the polar axis toward the periphery; thus, an asymmetry initiated by the above process would be re-enforced by ooplasmic segregation. This pattern of cytoplasmic localization is strikingly illustrated by Lehmann's observation (1958) that after equatorial displacement of pole plasms in the centrifuged *Tubifex* egg, these pole plasms spread along the cortex in opposite directions and are finally located at the animal and vegetal poles.

Obviously, this scheme does not imply a qualitative distribution of chromosomes nor nuclear inequality; it does not minimize the role of cytoplasmic areas, such as the pole plasms of the eggs of *Dentalium, Ilyanassa,* and *Tubifex,* but attempts to envision a process by which the maternal genome can contribute to the specifications of the egg cytoplasm at an early stage.

None of these possibilities—cytoplasmic localization of materials synthesized under nuclear control from the oocyte, by accessory cells of the ovary, or by transcription of the egg genome just before cleavage— are mutually exclusive, and each presents questions which are pertinent and answerable. Answers can be sought by pulse-labeling nucleic acids or proteins in the oocyte, followed by a chase with nonisotopic metabolites, and subsequent radioautography of the egg. Clearly, any given cytoplasmic characteristic can be ultimately traced to a nuclear origin; the point to be made here is that experiments can now be designed to study the time when gene transcription establishes cytoplasmic organization.

VI. Nucleic Acid and Protein Synthesis

To study the causal relationship between protein synthesis and differentiation one must know (1) that there is a synthesis of new protein(s) at a particular stage, (2) the identity of the new protein(s), and (3) that the protein(s) are essential for the differentiation of a structure or physiological process. As an alternative to protein synthesis, the egg may contain preformed specific proteins which are utilized at a later period for differentiation. These two possibilities are not mutually exclusive, and the extent to which one or both are operative in embryogeny has not been critically established.

Generally, protein synthesis is correlated with RNA synthesis and/or RNA turnover. The causal relationship of the parallel synthesis of these two molecules will be dealt with in Section VII. The present concern is restricted to how much and what kind of information there is about the synthesis of these molecules in spiralian and ascidian embryos.

Cowden and Markert (1961) have made a cytochemical study of nucleic acid, protein, and mucopolysaccharides during oogenesis and development of *Ascidia nigra.* [Cowden (1961a, 1962) has made similar studies during oogenesis of several species of ascidians.] They found that neither nucleoli nor cytoplasmic accumulations of RNA appeared before the onset of metamorphosis, although an increase in the concentration of protein in the myogenic cells was observed prior to metamorphosis. Cowden's cytochemical study (1961b) of *Chiton tuberculatum* has shown that RNA synthesis occurs only in the prototrochal and apical plate cells before metamorphosis. Cowden and Markert (1961) suggest, ". . . that in this mosaic embryo the RNA templates necessary for premetamorphic development must be produced during oocyte growth, and are subsequently parceled out to the individual blastomeres. While this may not be a general mechanism in all mosaic development, it is improbable that synthesis of new RNA plays any role in the primary differentiation of the mosaic embryos so far studied." While this suggestion of Cowden and Markert agrees with their observation, the insensitivity of cytochemical methods for detecting RNA synthesis prevents any meaningful conclusions on this point.

In the *Ilyanassa* embryo (Collier, 1961a, b) net RNA synthesis, as determined microchemically with an 8.6 % coefficient of variation, begins between days 3 and 4 and continues throughout development; P^{32}-incorporation into RNA is extremely low during the first 2 days with the first increase occuring during day 3 and continuing until day 5. The incorporation of C^{14}-leucine into the proteins of the *Ilyanassa* embryo was correlated with the increase of P^{32}-incorporation, which occurred before any net synthesis of RNA was detected. For the first 6 days the DNA (deoxyribonucleic acid) content (Collier, 1965b) of the *Ilyanassa* embryo nearly doubles each day, except for a slight lag in synthesis between days 3 and 4 when net RNA synthesis begins.

These results show that RNA synthesis and increased amino acid incorporation into proteins begin 24 to 36 hours before and continue throughout morphological differentiation as first evidenced by the formation of the shell gland in the 4-day embryo.

During the first 2 days of development there is no major synthesis of proteins and RNA, but it is not clear whether there is slight or no synthesis of these molecules. As originally suggested (Collier, 1961a), it would appear that the low incorporation of P^{32} into the RNA would rule out early synthesis; however, the uptake of radioactive phosphorus is considerably less in the young embryo than at later stages of development, and the possibility that RNA synthesis proceeds from polynucleotide precursors which have a limited exchange with inorganic phosphorus prevents a decisive interpretation of this type of incorporation experiment.

From experiments with the *Ilyanassa* embryo carried out in the author's laboratory on the *in vivo* incorporation of C^{14}-uridine into RNA and of C^{14}-valine into protein, it was calculated that the minimal synthesis of RNA from the trefoil to the 25-cell stage would yield 3×10^6 molecules per cell. (These calculations were made from the assumption that the RNA had a molecular weight of 500,000 and a uridylic acid composition of 32.0 moles per cent.) This figure is for minimal synthesis, as are the calculations for protein synthesis given below, because it involves only the utilization of the radioactive precursor and does not take into account precursor contributions from the metabolic pool. Whether this synthesis of RNA is "turnover" or net gain cannot be decided. However, net synthesis of RNA is not required for protein synthesis, and this number of RNA molecules is sufficient for template function. These results mean that enough RNA molecules are available for a template function, not that they are such or that protein synthesis occurs. It must be pointed out that the incorporation of uridine into RNA could have occurred as terminal addition onto transfer RNA, via conversion of uridylate to cytidylate. Nevertheless, this approach serves to point out the requirements for a meaningful answer to the problem of nucleic acid synthesis in early embryogenesis. Also, Allfrey and Mirsky (1959) have shown that all nucleotides in RNA do not have the same stability; thus, the above consideration needs to be extended to include the other three nucleotides of RNA.

A similar series of experiments has been carried out on protein synthesis in the *Ilyanassa* embryo.[2] It was found that the 1-day embryo incorporated enough C^{14}-leucine to synthesize 2×10^{10} molecules per hour of protein of 35,000 molecular weight with an assumed leucine content of 9.0 %. This is equivalent to about 0.006 μg of protein or 3.2 % of the nonyolk protein content of the egg. A caution: these results may be misleading as Gale and Folkes (1955) found that the *in vitro* rate of incorporation of a single amino acid into bacterial protein was not correlated with the rate of net synthesis. While this difficulty may not exist for *in vivo* incorporation, it remains to be shown that it does not. The central question is whether this protein synthesis is "turnover" or net gain. Harris and Watts (1958) have shown that protein degradation in nondividing macrophage cells of the rabbit proceeds at the rate of

[2] See Collier (1965b).

30–35 % in 8 hours. These results cannot be applied to dividing cells of the molluskan embryo, but they illustrate an approach to the problem.

Tolis and Monroy (1963) observed an increase in incorporation of C^{14}-valine after fertilization in the *Spisula* egg and, although their observations were restricted to the 2-cell stage, these results may indicate protein synthesis during early development.

The incorporation of amino acids into a protein can mean one of the following: (1) a protein molecule is degraded and replaced by an identical molecule, (2) net synthesis occurs, or (3) a reserve protein, e.g., yolk protein, is degraded and its amino acids utilized to synthesize a different kind of protein. Differentiation occurs only with the latter two situations, one of which is a case of net protein synthesis and the other a special case of protein "turnover" that could result in the formation of a new protein. These three possibilities cannot be discerned by the incorporation of isotopically labeled amino acids, which is the only method sensitive enough to detect nonenzymatic protein formation during early development. If the proteins of oocytes, however, could be labeled and the isotopic amino acid could be completely removed from the metabolic pool, the problem could be investigated by following the exchange of labeled amino acids between the proteins and the precursor pool.

Morrill (1963b) has demonstrated a net protein gain, detected analytically just after day 2 with a continued increase throughout development, in the embryo of *Limnaea palustris* and has shown a corresponding decrease in the protein content of the capsule fluid which surrounds this embryo. His cytological observations indicate that "Beginning at the 40-cell stage the embryo begins to ingest capsule fluids—first in the ectodermal cells, then the archenteron and finally the larval liver cells and the gut." Morrill also studied the composition of the capsule fluid and separated by cellulose acetate electrophoresis eight protein, one esterase, and four polysaccharide components; by starch-gel electrophoresis, seven proteins; and by immunoelectrophoresis, seventeen antigenic substances. His opinion that the proteins of the capsule fluid come from the albumen gland is supported by the finding of all seventeen antigenic components of the capsule fluid in the albumen gland.

Morrill's extensive study of the protein metabolism of the *Limnaea* embryo has demonstrated an extraembryonic source of a substantial number of proteins and suggests that the embryo does not bear the entire burden of synthesizing the proteins required for differentiation. Not all embryos have capsular fluid, but a similar situation may exist in regard to yolk proteins. A demonstration that the intact proteins of the capsule fluid are utilized for differentiation would be extremely interesting.

The distribution of nine hydrolytic enzymes in the adult organs of *Limnaea* and the time of appearance during embryogenesis have been studied by Morrill and Dow (1962). Isozymes of each enzyme were identified electrophoretically in both adult tissues and the embryos. From these results it may be possible to relate the appearance of certain isozymes that appear during embryogenesis to particular adult organs because there is a correlation, though not a clear specificity, with the appearance of particular isozymes in a given organ or group of organs.

During the development of *Ilyanassa* Morrill (1961) has also assayed for ten hydrolytic enzymes and separated isozymes for each enzyme. A total of twenty-three electrophoretically mobile proteins were identified. Seven components were present at all stages of development, three were present only during the first 4 days, and thirteen components appeared after day 4 of development. Morrill (1963b) has also separated twelve antigens in the *Ilyanassa* embryo by immunoelectrophoresis. All but two of these antigens appear to be associated with the yolk.

An important feature of Morrill's work is that the electrophoretic separation of enzymatic proteins established the individuality of the protein, and in the case of new enzymes appearing during development, it is clear that there was net protein synthesis. The appearance of new proteins was correlated with the period of intense RNA synthesis and the formation of organ anlagen in the *Ilyanassa* embryo. Further, it appears that some enzymatic proteins present in the egg function throughout development, whereas others disappear early, still others are synthesized at later stages of embryogenesis.

Collier and McCann-Collier (1962) have estimated the DNA content of the *Ilyanassa* sperm, ovarian egg, and the 25-cell embryo by the diphenylamine reaction for deoxyribose. The DNA determinations were made on acid-precipitated material; even though this does not establish the presence of high molecular weight DNA, it does exclude the possibility that low molecular weight polynucleotides were measured. The ovarian egg contained about thirty-two times the amount of DNA expected on the basis of its chromosomal DNA. Synthesis of DNA was first detected in the 25-cell embryo; the DNA content was five times that expected from the number of cells present. Whether there is cytoplasmic DNA is not known. The uncertainties of the diphenylamine reaction have been considered. Of particular interest is the finding of excess DNA when DNA synthesis is initiated—a situation clearly different from those in the sea urchin, frog, and chick eggs (Hoff-Jørgensen, 1954), which also contain more DNA than expected from their chromosomal complements before DNA synthesis begins.

Until this work with the *Ilyanassa* embryo has been confirmed using a more reliable assay for DNA, it is not possible to reach any general conclusions. Yet, the apparent synthesis of more DNA than is required by the 25-cell embryo suggests that the DNA content of embryonic cells may not be constant for all cells.

VII. Mechanism of Gene Transcription

Jacob and Monod (1961) proposed a model for protein synthesis that involved the formation of a "cytoplasmic transcript" of the structural gene by an unstable polynucleotide messenger (see Chapter 8 in this volume for a detailed discussion of the model of Jacob and Monod). The finding by Nirenberg and Matthaei (1961) that amino acid incorporation into proteins in a cell-free system of *Escherichia coli* was dependent on the addition of a template or messenger RNA and the demon-

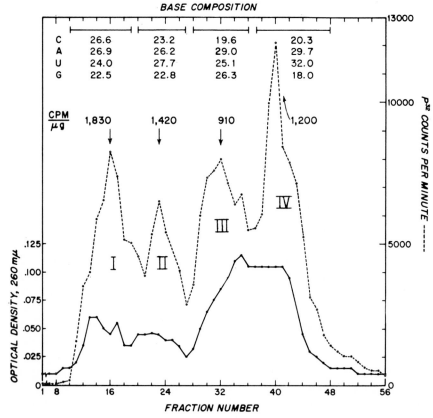

FIG. 4. Ribonucleic acids of the *Ilyanassa* embryo (Collier, 1965a). Base composition given as moles per cent.

stration of DNA-directed synthesis of RNA by an RNA polymerase in
E. coli by Chamberlain and Berg (1962) have established the value of
the messenger concept.

Applying the messenger concept to embryogenesis, one can envision
that differentiation depends on the sequential translation of the genome
into specific proteins via messenger RNA's. The protein may be an enzyme required for the production of a nonprotein end product or itself
the final product—a structural protein or a functional enzyme of a differentiated cell.

The following work (Collier, 1965a) with the *Ilyanassa* embryo from
the author's laboratory was undertaken with the view that the messenger
concept was applicable to embryogenesis and that the initial step was
to isolate and characterize a messenger polynucleotide.

TABLE I
NUCLEIC ACID BASE COMPOSITION OF THE *Ilyanassa* EMBRYO[a,b]

Material	C	A	U(T)	G	AU(T)	CG
DNA	16.9	32.5	33.1	17.1	66.0	34.0
Bulk RNA	20.4	29.4	25.6	24.5	55.0	44.9
Fractions						
I	26.6	26.9	24.0	22.5	50.9	49.1
II	23.2	26.2	27.7	22.8	53.9	46.0
III	19.6	29.0	25.1	26.3	54.0	45.9
IV	20.3	29.7	32.0	18.0	61.7	38.3

[a] Values given as moles per cent.

[b] C, cytidylate; A, adenylate; U(T), uridylate (thymidylate); G, guanylate;
AU(T), adenylate + uridylate (thymidylate); CG, cytidylate + guanylate.

Ilyanassa embryos of stages 4 to 5 (see Fig. 1 (23), (24)) were pulse-
labeled with P^{32}, homogenized, and the RNA separated and purified by
the phenol method of Scherrer and Darnell (1962). The RNA was sorbed
onto a methylated albumin column and eluted with a linear gradient of
NaCl. The elution sequence, base composition, and radioactivity profile
shown in Fig. 4 define four different RNA's. The order of elution shows
that fraction I is a low molecular weight RNA; its high cytidylate content indicates that it is transfer RNA. Similarly, the elution sequence of
the other three fractions (II, III, and IV) indicates that they have higher
molecular weights than fraction I; they are probably ribosomal RNA.
The correspondence in base composition of fractions II and III with
that of the bulk RNA (see Table I) also supports this conclusion. Of
the four RNA's fraction IV is judged to have the highest molecular
weight, and its unique base composition shows a closer similarity to
DNA (see Table I) than to any of the other fractions of RNA. It is therefore concluded that fraction IV is an informational RNA. This conclu-

sion is based solely on the similarity of base composition of this RNA fraction to that of DNA. The specific activity of the informational RNA suggests that its stability is comparable to that of the other RNA fractions. Experiments on the ability of this fraction to function as an informational RNA in protein synthesis are in progress.

The presence of informational RNA in the 4- to 5-day embryo is correlated with the stage of organ primordia formation. Informational RNA has also been isolated from the 3-day *Ilyanassa* embryo, which demonstrates that its synthesis precedes differentiation by 24 to 36 hours.

These studies represent a first step toward an understanding of the role of the gene in differentiation. It is hoped that further work will reveal additional details of how the genome controls embryogenesis.

VIII. Function of the Polar Lobe in Development

Berg and Kato (1959) found in the CD blastomere and the polar lobe of the *Ilyanassa obsoleta* egg a marked localization of acid-soluble materials with an ultraviolet absorption characteristic of purine and pyrimidine compounds. From the observation that the bulk of this material had a low chromatographic mobility they tentatively concluded that it was polynucleotide in nature.

Collier (1961a) found in the *Ilyanassa* egg that the concentration of total, acid-soluble, and phospholipid phosphorus was significantly greater in the polar lobe and CD blastomere than in the egg or AB cell. The acid-soluble fraction had an ultraviolet absorption curve characteristic of nucleic acid intermediates. Three components of this soluble fraction have been separated on DEAE (diethylaminoethanol) cellulose (Collier, 1965b). One of these components behaves chromatographically as a mixture of bases and nucleosides, whereas the other two components appear to be nucleotides and/or polynucleotides. It is hoped that further characterization of this acid-soluble fraction will lead to a clearer understanding of the role of the polar lobe in development.

An indirect approach to the study of chemical cell-lineage would be the determination of the effect of a particular defect experiment on the ability of the operated embryo to synthesize macromolecules; thus, a synthetic process could be followed rather than a search for minute quantities of materials. This approach has been favored in the author's laboratory; Collier (1961b) determined the incorporation of DL-leucine-1-C^{14} into the proteins of the normal and lobeless embryos of *Ilyanassa* and found that removal of the polar lobe definitely repressed the capacity of the embryo for incorporation of amino acids into protein. It was assumed that this incorporation of amino acids into protein represented net protein synthesis.

RNA and DNA synthesis have been studied in the lobeless embryo of *Ilyanassa* (Collier, 1965b), and the capacity for RNA synthesis, when adjustments were made for the cytoplasmic mass by using dipeptidase activity as a reference unit (Collier, 1957, 1961b), was found to be comparable to that of the normal embryo. The same results were obtained when the RNA content was expressed on a per cell basis. Removal of the polar lobe repressed, but did not block, DNA synthesis.

Collier (1965b) has shown that the *Ilyanassa* embryo between days 1 and 6 of embryogenesis utilizes 97.6 µµmoles of C^{14}-thymidine and 104.6 µµmoles of C^{14}-uridine for DNA synthesis. Therefore, uridine utilization for DNA synthesis is a major metabolic pathway in this embryo.

In summary, evidence has been presented for (1) the existence of a large pool of nucleic acid precursors in the egg, (2) the probable localization of a major part of this pool in the polar lobe, (3) the utilization of uridine as a major pathway in DNA synthesis, and (4) the removal of the polar lobe resulting in decreased protein and DNA synthesis, and a decrease in total RNA synthesis, but a per cell RNA content equivalent to that of the normal embryo.

From these findings it is suggested that the lobeless embryo fails to differentiate because it is deficient in nucleic acid precursors and that this deficiency of precursors in the lobeless embryo represses informational RNA synthesis selectively. This point of view implies that a separate component of the metabolic pool regulates the synthesis of informational RNA or that all RNA synthesis does not proceed from a common metabolic pool. The repression of DNA synthesis in the lobeless embryo may be related to the loss of uridylic acid (or its precursors) from the metabolic pool as the utilization of uridylic acid for DNA synthesis in the *Ilyanassa* embryo has been demonstrated (Collier, 1963). An alternative point of view is that the polar lobe contains an informational RNA, stable or unstable, that is essential for determination and/or differentiation.

Burdon's finding (1963) that the terminal addition of polyuridylic acid to existing ribosomal RNA by Landschutz tumor cell nuclei is DNA-dependent suggests that polyuridylate synthesis is gene-controlled. This possibility adds interest to the idea that informational RNA synthesis is regulated by a polynucleotide.

The alteration of the cleavage pattern of the D quadrant by removal of the polar lobe implies that an informational RNA is required for determination of the early cleavage pattern. Whether this informational RNA is preformed in the polar lobe, which contains approximately 7×10^8 molecules of RNA (calculated from the data of Collier, 1960), or is synthesized during early development cannot be decided at present. Some essential proteins are probably synthesized during early cleavage since it appears unlikely that the mere allocation of nucleotides, polynucleotides, or informational RNA to a cell would account for the disappearance of the distinctive features of the D quadrant in the lobeless embryo (see Clement, 1952).

The segregation of preformed materials, apart from nucleotides or informational RNA, by the polar lobe may also occur, but the present point of view is that the principal effect of removing the polar lobe is the disruption or prevention of informational RNA synthesis.

IX. Discussion

The embryology of the spiralian and ascidian eggs has been considered from the viewpoints of defect and isolation experiments, ultrastructure, and biochemistry. While the biochemical approach will probably be most extensively followed in the near future, additional study of the ultrastructure of embryos is also important; otherwise, there will be no structural reference for biochemical embryology. That there is still much value in properly executed defect and isolation experiments is shown by Clement's recent contributions (1962, 1963) in the field.

From a biochemical point of view a differentiated cell can be described in terms of its specific proteins; if this is taken as a starting point, further inquiries can be directed to the mechanisms of differentiations. The messenger concept of Jacob and Monod (1961) postulates that a particular nucleotide sequence of DNA produces an informational polynucleotide (RNA) that programs a population of ribosomes to form a specific protein. The demonstration of the applicability of this concept to embryogeny is an approach to the biochemical mechanisms of embryogeny, but not the solution to these problems. The fundamental questions of biochemical embryology are: What factors regulate the synthesis of a specific protein at a particular time in a certain cell or region of a cell, and what coordinates the first synthesis with subsequent syntheses? The major value of the messenger concept to embryology can be realized only by the isolation, characterization, and elucidation of the synthetic mechanism of informational RNA in *embryos*; only when such details are available can proper attention be given to the regulatory factors responsible for the coordinated synthesis of a number of proteins. While it is highly probable that the messenger concept is applicable to protein synthesis in embryos, efforts to establish this point by implication will not provide the information necessary for an understanding of the control mechanisms involved in development.

Diversity rather than uniformity of biochemical mechanisms should be looked for in embryogeny, as it might be expected that some of the macromolecules that characterize differentiation may exist preformed in the egg, others may arise as required for cell division, respiration, and cell movements, and still others may be synthesized at later stages of development. This diversity of synthetic patterns suggests that the informational molecules of the embryo may consist of a gamut of types with respect to stability, time of synthesis, and origin. The evidence discussed above for the occurrence in the *Ilyanassa* embryo of an informational RNA suggests that its rate of synthesis and stability is different from the rapidly synthesized and unstable messenger RNA described for *E. coli* (Spiegelman, 1963), neither does it correspond entirely to the postulated stable messenger of the mammalian reticulocyte (Marks *et al.*, 1962).

It may be envisioned that some of the informational RNA contained in the egg could have been formed during oogenesis, by the oocyte or some accessory cells of the ovary. [See Allen's observations (1961) of RNA-containing, cytoplasmic bridges between nurse cells and the oocyte in the egg of *Diopatra cuprea*.] These molecules, which may be stable and permanently attached to ribosomes, could control the protein synthesis required for functions that are correlated with differentiation. The production of a number of proteins, which may be specifically utilized in development, by the albumen gland of *Limnaea* (Morrill's work described above) suggests another diverse source of embryonic proteins that would involve transcription of a nongametic genome.

If there is a partial or complete transcription of the oocyte genome, as would be expected from the behavior of the lampbrush chromosomes in the germinal vesicle, what then is the fate of the corresponding genetic material, i.e., cistrons, on the homologous chromosomes introduced by the sperm at fertilization? Are the allelic cistrons of the sperm transcribed at a later time or is their transcription prevented? If it is assumed that such cistrons are controlled by repressors, then the differential action of the repressors on the maternal and paternal genome needs to be explained.

The possibility should not be overlooked that RNA-primed RNA synthesis plays a role in differentiation. An example of an RNA-primer is the terminal addition of cytidylic acid to soluble RNA. This soluble RNA shows considerable specificity in its requirements as it is not primed by nuclear nor ribosomal RNA (Hecht *et al.*, 1958). Also, Burdon and Smellie (1961) have demonstrated in ascites tumor cells that uridine incorporation into RNA is more effectively primed by nuclear than by cytoplasmic RNA. With polynucleotide phosphorylase purified from *Micrococcus lysodeikticus* and synthetic polyribonucleotides as primer, Nakamoto and Weiss (1962) have clearly demonstrated that polyribonucleotides can prime the incorporation of nucleotides into RNA. Majumdar and Burma (1963) have presented evidence for a soluble RNA-dependent, nonterminal incorporation of ribonucleotides into RNA by a partially purified enzyme of *Azotobacter vinelandii*. RNA-primed RNA synthesis could play a central role in the control of development; if this should be the case, it must be recognized that an extremely small number of molecules may be involved.

In the preceding section it was suggested that the absence of nucleotides or polynucleotides, brought about by the removal of the polar lobe, would prevent the synthesis of informational RNA. The existence of a fraction of mononucleotides and/or polynucleotides in the acid-soluble pool of the *Ilyanassa* embryo suggests that all RNA synthesis may not proceed from a single pool and that the ability of the embryo to utilize the polynucleotide pool would control informational RNA synthesis and, thereby, gene transcription. This is envisioned as an all-or-none type of control mechanism which would determine the beginning of differentiation, but would not select a limited set of genes responsible for the development of a specific structure. Before such a control system can be understood it is necessary to know whether the differentiation of a particular structure is controlled by the transcription of a limited number of genes or by the capacity of the cytoplasm to select specific informational RNA's presented by the transcription of all or many genes for translation into proteins. The determination of the extent to which these two alternatives, which are not mutually exclusive, are operative is necessary for an understanding of the control mechanisms of embryonic differentiation.

The problems discussed above were selected because they are of interest to the author. There are many other aspects of embryology of equal or greater pertinence, and it is hoped that they will all be vigorously attacked with the elegant experimental procedures now available to biologists. If in the past the embryo has been considered difficult experimental material, the refined biochemical methods available today should, if applied, hasten a reversal of this opinion. Finally, it is hoped that the experimental and analytical demonstration of biochemical events in embryos will prevail over a noncritical adoption of concepts developed from the analysis of other biological systems—that the problems of embryology must be solved by studying embryos is inescapable.

ACKNOWLEDGMENTS

The author expresses his appreciation to Marjorie M. Collier for the preparation of the figures and assistance in preparation of the manuscript.

Unpublished work of the author, presented in this article, was supported by grant A-3554, and the preparation of the manuscript was supported in part by grant AM08316-01 of the Division of Arthritis and Metabolic Diseases of the National Institutes of Health.

REFERENCES

Afzelius, B. (1963). *J. Cell Biol.* **19**, 229.
Agrell, I. (1958). *Arkiv Zool.* **11**, 435.
Allen, M. J. (1961). *Acta Embryol. Morphol. Exptl.* **4**, 219.
Allen, R. D. (1958). *In* "The Chemical Basis of Development" (W. D. McElroy and B. Glass, eds.), p. 17. Johns Hopkins Press, Baltimore, Maryland.
Allfrey, V., and Mirsky, A. E. (1959). *Proc. Natl. Acad. Sci. U. S.* **45**, 1325.
Berg, W. E. (1956). *Biol. Bull.* **110**, 1.
Berg, W. E. (1957). *Biol. Bull.* **113**, 365.
Berg, W. E., and Baker, P. C. (1962). *Acta Embryol. Morphol. Exptl.* **5**, 274.
Berg, W. E., and Humphreys, W. J. (1960). *Develop. Biol.* **2**, 42.
Berg, W. E., and Kato, Y. (1959). *Acta Embryol. Morphol. Exptl.* **2**, 227.
Brachet, J. (1960). "The Biochemistry of Development." Pergamon, New York.
Burdon, R. H. (1963). *Biochem. Biophys. Res. Commun.* **13**, 37.
Burdon, R. H., and Smellie, R. M. S. (1961). *Biochem. Biophys. Acta* **51**, 153.
Chamberlain, M., and Berg, P. (1962). *Proc. Natl. Acad. Sci. U. S.* **48**, 81.
Clement, A. C. (1952). *J. Exptl. Zool.* **121**, 593.
Clement, A. C. (1956). *J. Exptl. Zool.* **132**, 427.
Clement, A. C. (1960). *Biol. Bull.* **119**, 310.
Clement, A. C. (1962). *J. Exptl. Zool.* **149**, 193.
Clement, A. C. (1963). *Biol. Bull.* **125**, 375.
Collier, J. R. (1957). *Embryologia* (*Nagoya*) **3**, 243.
Collier, J. R. (1960). *Exptl. Cell Res.* **21**, 126.
Collier, J. R. (1961a). *Exptl. Cell Res.* **24**, 320.
Collier, J. R. (1961b). *Acta Embryol. Morphol. Exptl.* **4**, 70.
Collier, J. R. (1963). *Exptl. Cell Res.* **32**, 442.
Collier, J. R. (1965a). *Science* **147**, 150.
Collier, J. R. (1965b). Unpublished results.
Collier, J. R., and McCann-Collier, M. (1962). *Exptl. Cell Res.* **27**, 553.
Collier, J. R., and McCann-Collier, M. (1964). *Exptl. Cell Res.* **34**, 512.
Colwin, A. L., Colwin, L. H., and Philpott, D. E. (1957). *J. Biophys. Biochem. Cytol.* **3**, 489.
Conklin, E. G. (1897). *J. Morphol.* **13**, 1.
Conklin, E. G. (1902). *J. Acad. Nat. Sci. Phila.* [2] **12**, 1.
Conklin, E. G. (1905). *J. Exptl. Zool.* **2**, 145.
Conklin, E. G. (1931). *J. Exptl. Zool.* **60**, 1.
Costello, D. P. (1945a). *J. Exptl. Zool.* **100**, 19.
Costello, D. P. (1945b). *J. Elisha Mitchell Sci. Soc.* **61**, 277.

Costello, D. P. (1948). *Ann. N. Y. Acad. Sci.* **49**, 663.
Costello, D. P. (1955). *In* "Analysis of Development" (B. H. Willier, P. A. Weiss, and V. Hamburger, eds.), p. 213. Saunders, Philadelphia, Pennsylvania.
Costello, D. P. (1961). *Biol. Bull.* **120**, 285.
Cowden, R. R. (1961a). *Acta Embryol. Morphol. Exptl.* **4**, 142.
Cowden, R. R. (1961b). *Biol. Bull.* **120**, 313.
Cowden, R. R. (1962). *Trans. Am. Microscop. Soc.* **81**, 149.
Cowden, R. R., and Markert, C. L. (1961). *Acta Embryol. Morphol. Exptl.* **4**, 142.
Crampton, H. E. (1896). *Arch. Entwicklungsmech. Organ.* **3**, 1.
Dalcq, A. M. (1932). *Arch. Anat. Microscop.* **28**, 223.
Dalcq, A. M. (1935). *Compt. Rend. Soc. Biol.* **119**, 1421.
Dalcq, A. M. (1959). *Arch. Biol.* (*Liege*) **71**, 93.
Dalcq, A. M. (1960). *In* "Fundamental Aspects of Normal and Malignant Growth" (W. W. Nowinski, ed.), p. 305. Elsevier, Amsterdam.
Dalcq, A. M., and Pasteels, J. J. (1963). *Develop. Biol.* **7**, 457.
Dan, J. C. (1962). *Biol. Bull.* **123**, 531.
Dan, K. (1943). *J. Fac. Sci. Univ. Tokyo Sect. IV* **4**, 323.
Dan, K. (1960). *Intern. Rev. Cytol.* **9**, 321.
Dan, K., and Dan, J. C. (1942). *Cytologia* (*Tokyo*) **12**, 246.
Dan, K., and Nakajima, T. (1956). *Embryologia* (*Nagoya*) **3**, 187.
Dan, K., Ito, S., and Mazia, D. (1952). *Biol. Bull.* **103**, 292.
Driesch, H. (1895). *Arch. Entwicklungsmech. Organ.* **2**, 195.
Durante, M. (1957). *Acta Embryol. Morphol. Exptl.* **1**, 131.
Durante, M. (1958). *Acta Embryol. Morphol. Exptl.* **1**, 273.
Elbers, P. F. (1959). Over de Beginoorzaak van Het Li-effect in de Morphogenesis. Ph.D. thesis, Univ. Utrecht, Holland.
Gale, E. F., and Folkes, J. P. (1955). *Biochem. J.* **59**, 661.
Gay, H. (1955). *Proc. Natl. Acad. Sci. U. S.* **41**, 370.
Gray, J. (1931). "A Textbook of Experimental Cytology." Cambridge Univ. Press, London and New York.
Harris, H., and Watts, J. W. (1958). *Nature* **181**, 1582.
Hecht, L. I., Zamecnik, P. C., Stephenson, M. L., and Scott, J. F. (1958). *J. Biol. Chem.* **233**, 954.
Hess, O. (1956a). *Arch. Entwicklungsmech. Organ.* **148**, 336.
Hess, O. (1956b). *Arch. Entwicklungsmech. Organ.* **148**, 474.
Hess, O. (1957). *Arch. Entwicklungsmech. Organ.* **150**, 124.
Hiramoto, Y. (1956). *Exptl. Cell Res.* **11**, 630.
Hiramoto, Y. (1958). *J. Exptl. Biol.* **35**, 407.
Hoff-Jørgensen, E. (1954). *In* "Recent Developments in Cell Physiology" (J. A. Kitching, ed.), p. 79. Academic Press, New York.
Humphreys, W. J. (1962a). *J. Ultrastruct. Res.* **7**, 467.
Humphreys, W. J. (1962b). *In* "Proceedings of the 5th International Congress for Electron Microscopy" (S. S. Breese, ed.), Vol. 2, NN-10. Academic Press, New York.
Jacob, F., and Monod, J. (1961). *J. Mol. Biol.* **3**, 318.
Kessel, R. G., and Kemp, N. E. (1962). *J. Ultrastruct. Res.* **6**, 57.
Kojima, M. K. (1959a). *Embryologia* (*Nagoya*) **4**, 211.
Kojima, M. K. (1959b). *Embryologia* (*Nagoya*) **4**, 191.

Kofoid, C. A. (1895). *Bull. Museum Comp. Zool. Harvard Coll.* **27**, 33.
Lambson, R., and Austin, C. R. (1963). *Biol. Bull.* **125**, 364.
La Spina, R. (1961). *Acta Embryol. Morphol. Exptl.* **4**, 320.
Lehmann, F. E. (1950). *Arch. Julius Klaus-Stift. Vererbungsforsch. Sozialanthropol. Rassenhyg.* **25**, 611.
Lehmann, F. E. (1954). *Arch. Julius Klaus-Stift. Vererbungsforsch. Sozialanthropol. Rassenhyg.* **29**, 288.
Lehmann, F. E. (1956). Naturwissenschaften **43**, 289.
Lehmann, F. E. (1958). *In* "The Chemical Basis of Development" (W. D. McElroy and B. Glass, eds.), p. 73. Johns Hopkins Press, Baltimore, Maryland.
Lillie, F. R. (1895). *J. Morphol.* **10**, 1.
Lillie, F. R. (1901). *J. Morphol.* **17**, 227.
Lillie, F. R. (1902). *Arch. Entwicklungsmech. Organ.* **14**, 477.
Lillie, F. R. (1906). *J. Exptl. Zool.* **3**, 153.
Lillie, F. R. (1912). *J. Exptl. Zool.* **12**, 413.
Majumdar, C. and Burma, D. P. (1963). *Biochim. Biophys. Acta* **76**, 48.
Mancuso, V. (1960). *Rend. Ist. Super. Sanita* **23**, 793.
Mancuso, V. (1962). *Acta Embryol. Morphol. Exptl.* **5**, 32.
Marks, P. A., Burka, E. R., and Schlessinger, D. (1962). *Proc. Natl. Acad. Sci. U. S.* **48**, 2163.
Mazia, D. (1961). *In* "The Cell" (J. Brachet and A. E. Mirsky, eds.), Vol. 3, p. 77. Academic Press, New York.
Morgan, T. H. (1910). *Arch. Entwicklungsmech. Organ.* **29**, 205.
Morgan, T. H. (1927). "Experimental Embryology." Columbia Univ. Press, New York.
Morgan, T. H. (1933). *J. Exptl. Zool.* **64**, 433.
Morgan, T. H. (1936). *J. Exptl. Zool.* **74**, 381.
Morrill, J. B. (1961). *Am. Zoologist* **1**, 87.
Morrill, J. B. (1963a). *Exptl. Cell Res.* **31**, 490.
Morrill, J. B. (1963b). Personal communication. Biology Dept., Wesleyan Univ., Middletown, Connecticut.
Morrill, J. B., and Dow, E. N. (1962). *Biol. Bull.* **123**, 463.
Morrill, J. B., and Gottesman, D. M. (1960). *Anat. Record* **137**, 383.
Mulnard, J. (1958). *Arch. Biol. (Liege)* **69**, 645.
Mulnard, J., Auclair, W., and Marsland, D. (1959). *J. Embryol. Exptl. Morphol.* **7**, 223.
Nakamoto, T., and Weiss, S. B. (1962). *Proc. Natl. Acad. Sci. U. S.* **48**, 880.
Nirenberg, M. W., and Matthaei, J. H. (1961). *Proc. Natl. Acad. Sci. U. S.* **47**, 1588.
Ortolani, G. (1958). *Acta Embryol. Morphol. Exptl.* **1**, 247.
Pasteels, J. J., and de Harven, E. (1962). *Arch. Biol. (Liege)* **73**, 465.
Pasteels, J. J., and Mulnard, J. (1957). *Arch. Biol. (Liege)* **68**, 115.
Rattenbury, J. C., and Berg, W. E. (1954). *J. Morphol.* **95**, 393.
Raven, C. P. (1942). *Proc. Koninkl. Ned. Akad. Wetenschap.* **45**, 856.
Raven, C. P. (1943). *Acta Biotheoret.* **7**, 135.
Raven, C. P. (1945). *Arch. Neerl. Zool.* **7**, 91.
Raven, C. P. (1952). *J. Exptl. Zool.* **121**, 1.
Raven, C. P. (1958). "Morphogenesis; The Analysis of Molluscan Development." Pergamon, New York.

Raven, C. P. (1963). *Develop. Biol.* **7**, 130.

Rebhun, L. I. (1958). *Biol. Bull.* **115**, 325.

Rebhun, L. I. (1959). *Biol. Bull.* **117**, 518.

Rebhun, L. I. (1960). *Ann. N. Y. Acad. Sci.* **90**, 357.

Rebhun, L. I. (1961). *J. Ultrastruct. Res.* **5**, 208.

Rebhun, L. I. (1962). *J. Ultrastruct. Res.* **6**, 107.

Rebhun, L. I. (1963a). *Exptl. Cell Res.* **29**, 593.

Rebhun, L. I. (1963b). *In* "Symposium on the Cell in Mitosis" (L. Levine, ed.), pp. 67-106. Academic Press, New York.

Recourt, A. (1961). An electron microscopic study of oogenesis in *Limnaea stagnalis* L. Ph.D. thesis, Univ. Utrecht, Holland.

Reverberi, G. (1931). *Pubbl. Staz. Zool. Napoli* **11**, 168.

Reverberi, G. (1957). *In* "The Beginnings of Embryonic Development" (A. Tyler, R. C. von Borstel, and C. B. Metz, eds.), p. 319. Am. Assoc. Advan. Sci., Washington, D. C.

Reverberi, G. (1958). *Acta Embryol. Morphol. Exptl.* **2**, 79.

Reverberi, G. (1961). *Ric. Sci.* **31**, 263.

Reverberi, G., and Mancuso, V. (1961). *Acta Embryol. Morphol. Exptl.* **4**, 102.

Reverberi, G., and Ortolani, G. (1962). *Develop. Biol.* **5**, 84.

Reverberi, G., Ortolani, G., and Farinella-Feruzza, N. (1960). *Acta Embryol. Morphol. Exptl.* **3**, 296.

Scherrer, K., and Darnell, J. E. (1962). *Biochem. Biophys. Res. Commun.* **7**, 486.

Spiegelman, S. (1963). *Federation Proc.* **22**, 36.

Teorell, T. (1935). *Proc. Natl. Acad. Sci. U. S.* **21**, 152.

Teorell, T. (1937). *J. Gen. Physiol.* **21**, 107.

Tolis, H., and Monroy, A. (1963). *Biol. Bull.* **125**, 369.

Tweedel, K. S. (1962). *Biol. Bull.* **123**, 424.

Watterson, R. L. (1955). *In* "Analysis of Development" (B. H. Willier, P. A. Weiss, and V. Hamburger, eds.), p. 315. Saunders, Philadelphia, Pennsylvania.

Weber, R. (1958). *Arch. Entwicklungsmech. Organ.* **150**, 542.

Weber, R. (1960). *In* "Symposium on Germ Cells and Development," pp. 225-254. Inst. Intern. d'Embryol. Fond. A. Baselli.

Werner, B. von (1958). *Helgolaender Wiss. Meeresuntersuch.* **5**, 169.

Whitman, C. O. (1878). *Quart. J. Microscop. Sci.* **71**, 215.

Wilson, E. B. (1892). *J. Morphol.* **6**, 361.

Wilson, E. B. (1896). *Arch. Entwicklungsmech. Organ.* **3**, 19.

Wilson, E. B. (1904). *J. Exptl. Zool.* **1**, 1.

Wilson, E. B. (1925). "The Cell in Development and Heredity." Macmillan, New York.

Wolpert, L. (1960). *Intern. Rev. Cytol.* **9**, 321.

Zimmerman, A. M., and Marsland, D. (1960). *Ann. N. Y. Acad. Sci.* **90**, 470.

Chapter 5

BIOCHEMICAL PATTERNS IN EARLY DEVELOPMENTAL STAGES OF VERTEBRATES

E. M. DEUCHAR

Department of Anatomy
University College
London, England

I. Introduction: General Nature and Significance of the Biochemical Patterns

A. *The Main Events of Early Vertebrate Development and the Problems They Pose*

Vertebrates undergo initial processes of embryonic development that are essentially similar to those of most invertebrates. The fertilized egg divides, by the process known as "cleavage," into a number of cells of varying size called "blastomeres." These cells then carry out "gastrulation" movements by means of which the *mesoderm* cells (future skeleton, muscle, connective tissue, and vascular system) and *endoderm* cells (future gut epithelium) come to lie inside the *ectoderm* cells that will form the epidermis and central nervous system. The patterns of cleavage and of gastrulation vary in different classes of vertebrates and there is not space to describe them here, but Fig. 1 illustrates the process of gastrulation in those vertebrate forms referred to in the present chapter.

Subsequent events of vertebrate development differ considerably from those in invertebrates. The vertebrate nervous system forms dorsally as a tube, by the upfolding of a specialized area of ectoderm known as the "neural plate." This phase of "neurulation" is then followed by a prolonged and complex period of both tissue and organ formation, the details of which differ for each species. The most important general feature of these latter phases of development, as revealed by numerous grafting and culturing experiments from 1920 onward, is the dependence of the developing tissues on each other for their normal differentiation.

This chapter will be concerned chiefly with biochemical events during cleavage, gastrulation, and neurulation. The initial stages of differentiation, i.e., before the cells have many visible structural differences, have particular biochemical interest because it is then that the events which precede and cause the structural differences should be occurring, at the molecular level. As we shall see, many interesting biochemical differences have been observed between cells or groups of cells that are known to have different destinies in development. In reviewing the literature it has to be realized, of course, that evidence of *differences* between parts of the embryo have always been paid the most attention, whereas similarities have tended to be ignored as meaningless, because of what we already know from classic tissue transplantation work about the diverse future of the embryonic cells. It is the biochemical differences that seem important and that we may hope eventually to understand and even to manipulate. Thus, any study of the biochemistry of embryonic development involves the consideration of patterns of difference, either spatial, in the different parts of an embryo at a given stage, or temporal, in successive stages of development.

One might expect biochemical patterns in vertebrate embryos to be less stable than those in invertebrates. It used to be fashionable to describe vertebrate embryos as "regulative," owing to their remarkable ability to complete themselves and to develop into normal animals when parts of them have been removed or tampered with by experimenters, in apparent contrast to the so-called "mosaic" embryos of invertebrates. But,

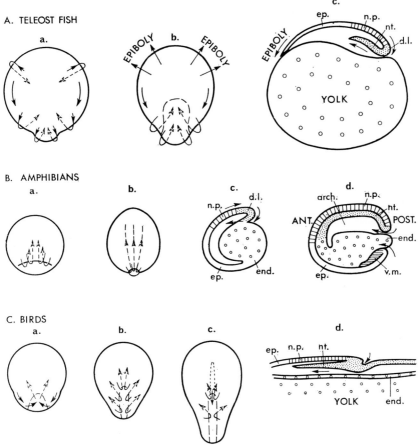

Fig. 1. Diagrams illustrating different types of gastrulation in vertebrates. (A) Teleost Fish: a, surface view of embryonic disc at early gastrula stage; b, same, at late gastrula stage; c, sagittal section of midgastrula stage. (B) Amphibians: a, external view of early gastrula; b, external view of late gastrula; c, sagittal section of early gastrula; d, sagittal section of late gastrula. (C) Birds: surface views of embryonic disc; a, early gastrula stage; b, midgastrula (definitive streak) stage; c, late gastrula (head process) stage. Full arrows indicate surface tissue movements; dotted arrows, movements of cells below surface; d, sagittal section of stage c.

Key to abbreviations: (arch.) archenteron, (d.l.) dorsal lip, (end.) endoderm, (ep.) epidermis, (n.p.) neural plate, (nt.) notochord, (v.m.) ventral mesoderm.

as more evidence gradually accumulates from experiments on invertebrate embryos, it becomes doubtful whether such a sharp distinction
should be made. The cells of vertebrate embryos certainly appear to be
more versatile, but the difference from invertebrates is one of degree
only. In biochemical terms, this versatility may be envisaged as caused
by alteration in the rates or directions of chemical reactions, resulting
from changes in environmental conditions. The regulative embryo presents no insoluble theoretical problems to the biochemist, although in
practice he finds it difficult material to deal with because of its change-
ability.

There is, however, an important contrast between vertebrate and invertebrate embryos that is not often remarked on, regarding the timing
of external events in relation to changes at the biochemical level. Vertebrate embryos do not start to gastrulate until several thousand cells are
present (e.g., 30,000 cells in the toad, *Xenopus laevis*). On the other hand,
many invertebrates gastrulate with only a few hundred cells. As an obvious result of the more numerous replications of DNA (deoxyribonucleic
acid) prior to gastrulation, DNA-dependent replications in the cytoplasm
have also taken place many more times in the vertebrate than in the
invertebrate gastrula. Consequently, the vertebrate has a far larger reserve of material with which to supplement a loss or adapt to a new
environment. This material is also distributed in many more cells. In the
invertebrate gastrula there may be only one cell representing a whole
organ or tissue; in the vertebrate gastrula there are many equivalent cells
of each type. The units with which the analyst deals in biochemical work
on vertebrate embryos will therefore be groups of cells rather than single
stem cells, and his results will be averages for the cells in any group. It
may not be easy to demarcate sharply the differences between various
cell groups; these have to be calculated on a statistical basis, and extremely accurate quantitative work is needed.

Overemphasis of the spatial patterns of biochemical differentiation in
the embryo leads, however, to the danger of becoming "unable to see the
wood for the trees." In order to avoid this, the following account attempts
to view the findings in the perspective of development as a whole.

B. *The Origins of Biochemical Patterns and Differentiation in the
    Vertebrate Embryo*

A *pattern* is the result of inhomogeneity, but the word also implies a
nonrandom distribution of the inhomogeneous materials, so that some
over-all unity is recognizable. In our present discussion, the over-all unity
is the fertilized egg, and inhomogeneities result from the distribution of
materials in its cytoplasm. Commonly, the distribution follows a quanti-

tative gradient, with the lightest materials at the upper (animal) pole and the heavy materials at the lower (vegetal) pole. Thus, the nucleus lies in a zone of clear cytoplasm near the animal pole, while mitochondria and ribosomes accumulate in an intermediate zone, and the yolk is densest near the vegetal pole. This arrangement of cytoplasmic components occurs in all yolky eggs, but surprisingly, it is seldom referred to in discussions of the causes of differentiation in vertebrate embryos. Only Dalcq and his school (see Dalcq, 1957) have persisted in emphasizing the importance of cytoplasmic gradients in amphibian eggs. Dalcq and Pasteels (1938) first suggested that an interaction between the original animal–vegetal (yolk) gradient of the egg and a dorsoventral gradient in the cortex initiated at fertilization determined the destinies of the cells of amphibian embryos. It was known from centrifugation experiments (Pasteels, 1940) that the correct distribution of particles is essential for normal development of the embryo. Abnormalities arise if the materials remain redistributed after centrifuging.

The reason why gradients in the egg contents have tended to be disregarded in recent considerations of the origins of biochemical patterns in vertebrate embryos is that transplantation experiments have long indicated that the fates of cells are not fixed until much later—after the end of gastrulation. It cannot be believed, therefore, that any critical steps in biochemical differentiation occur earlier than this. Most biochemical investigation has, in fact, been focused on the gastrula stage, particularly in amphibian embryos. There is, however, a danger that at this transition phase of cell determination conflicting experimental results will be obtained and confusion may arise. Those aiming at precise biochemical analysis would be better advised to begin their work with later stages, when tissue differences are clear-cut, before embarking on work with gastrulae for which the precision and sensitivity of their methods will be under most stringent test.

Many problems of differentiation are now, of course, being approached via electron microscopy too (cf. Weber, 1962). Valuable information can be gained in this instance by study of the cytoplasmic components in the uncleaved egg and early segmentation stages. But actually, the earliest biochemical events of importance to differentiation must take place even before this, during oogenesis, an era of development that lies outside the scope of the present chapter.

II. Reliability of the Methods of Observation

A. *General Considerations*

There are two radically different ways of making biochemical observations; one may either observe the end products of reaction in intact cells, using histochemical and cytochemical methods, or disrupt the cells and subject extracts of the cells to biochemical tests *in vitro*. Biologists tend to mistrust methods that begin with homogenization and end with a reaction in a test tube that seems far remote from events in the intact cell. On the other hand, biochemists prefer to study isolated cell components, because they can then control the reaction conditions much more precisely than in intact cells. Both types of procedures have advantages as well as imperfections. It must be realized, too, that additional inaccuracies may arise when any method is applied to an embryo instead of to the tissue with which the method was first used. Embryos are quite peculiar biochemically, in many ways that will be mentioned later. So it is unjustifiable to assume that they will respond "normally" to histochemical, cytochemical, or biochemical tests that have usually been devised for a limited number of adult tissues. As a corollary to this, reports of biochemical *peculiarities* in embryos are perhaps to be relied on more than reports of their similarities to adult tissues. It takes many repetitious experiments to establish an exception, whereas such checks are not always applied to results that seem to fit in with current findings.

In Sections II, B and C some further technical problems will be dealt with briefly.

B. *Histochemical and Cytochemical Methods*

1. GENERAL

Yolky vertebrate embryos present many difficulties for histochemical and cytochemical work.

First of all, special fixatives are necessary for the preservation of yolk, that may not suit some histochemical procedures. For instance, we have found that the Feulgen stain for DNA works best on embryos of *Xenopus laevis* if they are fixed in Carnoy, but this fixative gives very poor preservation of yolk. Again, in autoradiography the trichloroacetic acid fixative usually recommended has devastating effects on yolky embryonic tissues. Another problem is the high affinity of the yolk itself for a variety of stains. Even supposedly specific coloring agents may be adsorbed on yolk platelets so that any localization of color in other cytoplasmic components is obscured.

Conversely, a component of the embryonic cell that is sometimes most difficult to stain is the cell membrane. In earlier studies of the morphogenesis of the amphibian notochord (Mookerjee *et al.*, 1953) the cell membranes did not show up after routine staining methods and, at first, it was thought that they disappeared at a certain stage. This idea has since been found to be erroneous, however (Waddington and Perry, 1962).

2. Nucleic Acids: Differential Staining of DNA and RNA

The Unna-Brachet methyl green–pyronine technique has been used for differential staining of DNA and RNA (ribonucleic acid) in amphibian embryos. Recently, Baltus and Brachet (1962) have adopted an extremely sensitive fluorometric method for measuring DNA in these forms. The more spectacular, acridine orange fluorescent method has been used successfully to distinguish DNA and RNA in living rat embryos (Austin and Bishop, 1959). Other methods of measuring DNA and RNA concentrations in fixed tissues have been described by Davidson (1961). The Feulgen method has also been used successfully on embryonic cells.

Although the techniques mentioned are just as readily applicable to embryonic as to adult tissues, a major difficulty has arisen in their interpretation because of reports of large reserves of DNA-like material in the cytoplasm, e.g., in echinoderm, amphibian, and hens' eggs (Hoff-Jørgensen and Zeuthen, 1951; Zeuthen, 1952; Sze, 1953; Solomon, 1957a). There has been some skepticism about the validity of these findings, since the methods used to identify DNA were not fully diagnostic (cf. Chapter 1 of this volume). It has now been established, however, that there are thymidine-rich deoxyribonucleotides present in the cytoplasm, and their insolubility in cold trichloroacetic acid suggests a high molecular weight. Apparently, they are a source of DNA for the nuclei during cleavage, for there is very little increase in total DNA per embryo before the late blastula stage (Chen, 1960; Bristow and Deuchar, 1964), despite the rapid increase in the number of nuclei.

There have also been reports of Feulgen-positive material, assumed to be DNA, in the cytoplasm of fibroblasts (Chèvremont et al., 1960) and of plant cells (Gahan et al., 1962). So it is not unacceptable that cells of early embryos should possess cytoplasmic DNA too. Moreover, using a modified procedure, Brachet (personal communication, 1963) has obtained a positive Feulgen reaction in the cytoplasm of amphibian eggs. Recently, it has also been observed that the cytoplasmic DNA of oocytes of the frog, Rana catesbeiana, has the same base composition as that of the nuclei.

The nucleic acids of early embryos appear to have solubilities unlike those of adult tissue nucleic acids. Lu and Finamore (1963) have found that the RNA of carp eggs is relatively insoluble in 0.17 M sodium chloride solution; so is the RNA of amphibian eggs (Finamore and Volkin, 1958). Finamore (1962) noted that both RNA and DNA of amphibian embryos are more acid-soluble than the nucleic acids of adult tissue. These findings emphasize the need for care when applying histochemical methods to embryonic cells.

3. PROTEINS

a. Immunohistochemical Methods (for details see Chapter 7 of this volume). In these methods the antibody is revealed by coupling it to fluorescent material. The same difficulty may arise as in all histochemical procedures, namely, diffusion of the end product of the reaction from the original site where it was deposited. In embryos the possibilities of diffusion are great because the cells are fewer and larger than in adult tissues and there is little intercellular material. Diffusion across even a small number of the embryonic cells may encroach on some entirely different organ rudiment. Accurate localization is therefore especially important.

Holtzer *et al.* (1957) achieved high precision in locating skeletal myosin in the chick embryo and were able to show by means of labeled antibody that it was confined to the "A" bands of glycerol-extracted myofibrils. The ferritin–antibody coupling procedure (Singer and Schick, 1961) offers an even more precise method of localizing sites of antigen formation in cells at the electron microscope level. This might be applied profitably to embryonic tissues.

b. Enzyme Histochemistry. Because the absence of connective tissue makes the early embryo extremely fragile, enzyme histochemistry is difficult with embryonic material, particularly if frozen sections have to be used. Then, as already pointed out (Section II,A) the embryo may not react in quite the "standard" way to histochemical tests. A further difficulty is that enzyme concentrations tend to be extremely low in the early embryo prior to gastrulation (Løvtrup, 1955), so that tests applied to these stages have to be highly sensitive. The ultimate limits to histochemical sensitivity have hitherto been set by the degree of resolution of the light microscope, but we can now look to electron microscopy for higher degrees of resolution. Quite different principles are employed in electron microscopy, aiming not at color reactions but at the production of changes in density (i.e., in electron scattering). An example of this new approach is the ferritin–antibody coupling method mentioned previously. Methods for locating enzymes with the electron microscope are now being applied to embryonic material, because some are already available (e.g., Persijn *et al.*, 1961).

c. Detection of Collagen. There is no diagnostic histochemical test for collagen in adult tissues. It is especially difficult, therefore, to find evidence of possible collagen precursors in the embryo. "Reticulin" and "argyrophil fibers" may be found in the early connective tissue of embryos, and one may reasonably presume that these are precursors of collagen fibers. But we do not know yet how closely the structure of embryonic collagen resembles that of adult tissue collagen.

d. Hemoglobin. The orthodianisidine test (Owen *et al.*, 1958) for the catalase activity of hemoglobin has been used successfully on chick embryos by Hell (1964) and by O'Brien (1961a), who made the surprising observation that in erythroblasts the nucleolus was the earliest site of hemoglobin formation. There is no reason to doubt the validity of the test when applied to embryonic, as distinct from adult, cells; in these authors' works it has been applied in several ways, including application to hemoglobin isolated by electrophoresis. Tooze and Davies (1963) confirm that hemoglobin is found intranuclearly, but suggest that it enters from the cytoplasm.

4. Metabolites of Special Interest

a. Carbohydrates. Glycogen has been the main object of study in embryos, chiefly because of the reliable tests known for glycogen. It is possible, however, that materials exist in eggs and embryos that are closely related to glycogen, so as to react to tests for glycogen, but are not identical with it. Mammalian embryos are peculiar in that the placental glycogen differs from that of the mother (Huggett, 1929), and the embryo is also peculiar in metabolizing fructose instead of glucose, which leads one to think that other carbohydrate materials of the embryo may be unusual.

b. Special End Groups: SH Groups. Because it has long been thought that morphogenetic movements in embryos may be mediated by contractile proteins, much effort, led principally by Brachet and his school, has been devoted to demonstrating SH groups in embryonic tissue proteins. The nitroprusside test has been used as a standard for this. In the author's experience this is a difficult test to carry out convincingly on amphibian embryos, however. The apparently denser coloration of dorsal cells could be an optical effect due to their smaller size and, therefore, greater opacity. No attempts appear to have been made to support histochemical findings by biochemical SH assays—a serious omission when so many theoretical arguments have been put forward concerning the role of SH-containing enzymes in embryonic development (e.g., Brachet, 1963).

5. Autoradiography

The general principles in applying this technique to embryos are the same as for adult tissue. A fixative that will solubilize small molecules and leave proteins and nucleic acids intact is usually desirable, since labeled amino acids or labeled nucleic acid precursors are often used with the object of measuring their rate of uptake into protein or nucleic acid. Adult tissue is usually fixed in trichloroacetic acid (but see Section II,B,1).

Bouin's fixative, however, is preferable for studies on uptake of amino acid into embryonic proteins, since it gives better histological results, and it certainly removes all nonprotein-bound radioactivity from the tissue (Warshawsky and Droz, 1962; Deuchar and Herrmann, 1962). We have as yet no information on the solubility of radioactive materials in Smith's formol–bichromate which is the best fixative for very yolky eggs.

Cutting thin sections of embryos for autoradiography with tritium-labeled compounds is difficult and may necessitate using the imbedding media of electron microscopy instead of paraffin wax. It is, of course, now possible to carry out autoradiography in electron microscopy as well (Pelc et al., 1961).

The interpretation of results obtained with radioactive tracers is discussed in the following section.

C. Biochemical Methods

1. Use of Radioactive Metabolites

In measuring the rates of uptake of radioactive metabolites into components of tissues the usual aim is to obtain some idea of the rate of synthesis of those components. It cannot, however, be assumed that the rate of incorporation is a direct measure of the rate of synthesis without independent quantitative estimations of the increase of material, too (e.g., proteins: Herrmann and Schultz, 1958). It should also be noted when comparing the rate of uptake of a radioactive metabolite by different tissues, that the metabolite may not normally be used by these cells. It may be absorbed in the experiment simply because it is present in abnormally high concentration. Any metabolite supplied to an embryo that already contains yolk is an unnecessary excess. Its fate cannot be assumed to be the normal one for that metabolite. Preferably, the yolk of the developing oocyte should itself be labeled via its normal blood supply in the ovary.

A technical problem that arises, when postcleavage stages are used, is how to ensure that all cells have equal access to a tracer. If an intact amphibian embryo, for instance, is immersed in a solution containing the tracer, its outermost cells will necessarily become labeled fastest. If, on the other hand, in an attempt to overcome this difficulty the embryo is cut open (Friedberg and Eakin, 1949), the inner cells will become labeled fastest, because they lack the relatively impermeable "surface coat" characteristic of the outer cells (Holtfreter, 1943). The only procedure that avoids these difficulties is to disaggregate the cells before labeling them (cf. Giudice, 1962).

All these difficulties just mentioned are, of course, also avoided in cell-free systems, where conditions can be more uniform. Certain special problems arise, however, with embryonic material; these will be discussed next.

2. ISOLATION AND HOMOGENIZATION PROCEDURES

The small size of embryos and, consequently, small quantities of material available from them are a source of serious error unless rigorous precautions are taken. When enormous numbers of embryos have to be collected for a single analysis, hours may elapse before the final biochemical assay. In this time enzyme activities may fall and other properties may deteriorate, even when the preparations are kept chilled. There is also the problem of concentrating material that is collected "piecemeal." If dissections are performed in saline solution, a few drops of this solution are inevitably transferred with each embryo into the collecting vessel and may add up to a large volume in the end. Centrifuging is one way of compacting such samples; but then, further washes are necessary in order to replace the saline completely with extracting medium.

Homogenizing small samples of embryonic tissue without loss is difficult; a microhomogenizer is essential. The high proportion of lipid in the homogenate may produce a thick surface layer after centrifugation, and to collect the all-important microvolume of clear supernatant below this, it is advisable to use Carlsberg-type micropipettes (Linderstrøm-Lang and Holter, 1933).

After differential centrifugation of embryonic material, the resultant fractions have often been classified as "mitochondria," "ribosomes," and "supernatant" by comparison with adult tissue preparations. But it cannot be assumed that the components of embryonic cells exactly fit into adult categories. These particles "develop," just as the embryo does, and scrupulous checks, including observations with the electron microscope, are necessary to see what each centrifugal fraction contains. The current practice of designating particles by "S" numbers according to their sedimentation rate (cf. Brown and Caston, 1962) is preferable until we know more about the properties of these particles from different stages of animal development.

3. SPECIAL METHODS

a. Enzyme Assays. Moog (Chapter 6 of this volume) deals with this topic in detail, so only a few special points will be mentioned here.

The established principle of studies of enzyme activities *in vitro* is that assays are made under optimal conditions with the enzyme activity at a maximum. Many trials are necessary in order to discover those optimal conditions, and particularly large numbers of enzyme samples may be needed for these preliminary experiments. This may not be practicable with small amounts of embryonic material. A further complication is that each tissue may have different reaction characteristics [e.g., cathepsin activity in *Xenopus* embryos (Deuchar, 1958)]. These variables should be corrected for by establishing the Michaelis-Menten constant for the enzyme reaction in each tissue studied (cf. von Hahn and Herrmann, 1962).

It is also necessary to decide on the best units for expression of the enzyme activity. Most authors use activity units that apply only to the particular tissue they are studying, which makes their results difficult to compare with those of other workers. There seems to be a case for suggesting the adoption of some *universal* standard activity unit based on an adult tissue that is available in large quantities. If enzyme activities in embryonic tissues were expressed in, say, "rat liver units" they would more readily be comparable with adult tissues initially; then their special peculiarities could be investigated later.

b. Amino Acid Analyses. The standard methods for estimating small quantities of amino acids are either microbiological assay (Kuiken *et al.*, 1943) or paper chromatography (Consden *et al.*, 1944). Of these, paper chromatography is the most popular. Details are given by Léderer and Léderer (1955), and only a few remarks relevant to embryonic material need be added here.

Autolysis has to be guarded against far more scrupulously with embryos than with adult material, owing to the high activity of their proteolytic enzymes (Emanuelsson, 1955; Deuchar, 1958). Chilling at 0°C is not sufficient to prevent autolysis in tissues of *Xenopus laevis* embryos; an ice–salt bath followed by freeze-drying is advisable (Deuchar, 1956). Kavanau (1958) prefers an acetone-drying method for echinoderm embryos. A particularly convenient extractant of free amino acids is 70 or 80 % alcohol (Chen, 1956; Deuchar, 1956), since it disperses yolk lipids which tend to cause "streaking" on chromatograms, as well as counteracting the effects of salt ions from the saline in which the embryonic tissues were originally collected.

The precautions needed for accurate quantitative paper chromatography apply most emphatically to work with embryos, because it is often impossible to obtain many identical samples for comparison (minor chemical differences exist, even between different batches of eggs from the same female in *Xenopus*). The amino acids may also have different R_f values from those accepted as standard. There are relatively high concentrations of peptides in some embryos (Chen, 1956) which, together with the abundant lipid, tend to "clog" the chromatographic runs. The only reliable procedure is to add one known amino acid to each chromatogram of the embryonic material; then, the spot with greatly enhanced color pinpoints beyond all doubt the position of this amino acid *in this particular mixture*. It is also essential to follow identical procedures and timing in all experiments and to run control chromatograms of known amino acids every time too.

The reason for emphasizing these meticulous experimental precautions is that work of this kind on embryos, at the moment, has to be carried out against a background of ignorance with no reliable previous data for comparison. In this situation, it is preferable to aim at obtaining data which are mean values from a number of different experiments rather than using means of several samples in one experiment. Exact repetition of experimental procedures is therefore imperative.

D. Expression of Quantitative Data: Problem of the Basis of Reference

The accurate quantitation of biochemical patterns in embryos involves calculating, not merely the absolute values for quantities of substances or enzyme activities, but also their distribution, i.e., their concentration per unit of space. There are conflicting opinions, however, as to what is the most meaningful way to express "concentration" of the constituents in an embryo. Most embryos have cells of very unequal size, and to say that a large cell has less of a given substance per unit volume than a small cell may obscure the perhaps important fact that both cells have, in absolute terms, equal quantities of the substance. This difficulty can arise both with microscopic observations, where area units are used, and with biochemical observations, where total nitrogen or dry weight are most often used as bases of reference.

Consider first data obtained using the microscope: the rate of uptake of a radioactive metabolite is, for instance, usually expressed in terms of the number of grains per unit area on an autoradiograph. In comparing two regions of an embryo that have cells of different size we shall probably obtain higher counts per unit area where there are many small cells than where the cells are large and few. But, if we express the counts *per cell*, instead, this will almost certainly give the largest cells highest counts. Some compromise has to be made in order to obtain the correct emphasis of results.

In vitro observations on embryonic tissue may lose much meaning when expressed as ratios to "total nitrogen" or "dry weight." An imbalance of emphasis will arise if there are yolky cells at the vegetal pole, that are very much heavier and richer in nitrogen than cells at the animal pole. Yet one must take some account of these differences in cytoplasmic structure: they have most important effects on development. Although yolk is no longer considered metabolically inert, as it once used to be, it is known to have a quite peculiar and individual metabolism unlike that of the rest of the cytoplasm (cf. Panijel, 1950). This problem has been discussed further by Barth and Sze (1953), Boell and Weber (1955), D'Amelio and Ceas (1957) and the author (Deuchar, 1962).

In summation, it must be emphasized that all observations on embryonic tissues need special consideration with particular thought about the broader interpretations of the results. In attempting to fit data into the conventional terms of adult tissue analysis, one may fail to notice important peculiarities of the constantly changing, developing embryo. Those biochemical embryologists who express their data graphically against a time scale only and omit all mention of what morphological stage of development has been reached at any particular time are omitting the whole significance of their findings for the elucidation of classic embryology.

To avoid adopting too "abstract" an attitude toward patterns of biochemical events during development, Section III has been subdivided according to the different vertebrate groups and not the different biochemical processes. It is a long time since comparative biochemistry made its first great impact by emphasizing the similarities in make-up and metabolism throughout the animal kingdom (see Baldwin, 1949). This same preoccupation with comparisons dominated biochemical embryologists when Needham's great treatise (1931) was written. But it is more appropriate now to focus on the more detailed and accurate knowledge that has accumulated since then about relatively few "laboratory embryos" (fish, amphibians, chicks, and rodents) and to try to relate these biochemical findings to the morphological changes with which we know they must in some way or another be linked.

III. Biochemical Patterns of Special Interest in Each Vertebrate Group

A. *Fish*

1. INTRODUCTION

Very little is known about the biochemistry of fish eggs and embryos; they are not convenient "laboratory embryos," although they have interested physiologists for some time. The earlier literature has been reviewed by Needham (1931, 1942). Smith (1957) has reviewed more recent work on respiration and heat production, and Hayes (1949) has given a survey of the physiology and general chemistry of salmonid eggs.

Biochemical and ultrastructural events at the time of fertilization in fish have received particular attention; Monroy deals with this topic more fully in Chapter 2 of this volume, so it will receive only very brief mention here, along with the work on later stages.

2. BIOCHEMISTRY OF STAGES PRIOR TO GASTRULATION

Special attention has been focused on the "cortical alveoli" which are vesiculate bodies in the cortical cytoplasm of the egg. They have been described in some detail in the zebra fish *Oryzias latipes* (Aketa, 1954; Kusa, 1956; Nakano, 1956; Yamamoto, 1954, 1956, 1962) and are thought to consist of mucoprotein coated with a layer of lipid. At fertilization they break down, the wave of breakdown beginning at the region where the sperm entered, then extending to other regions. Shortly after this, the perivitelline space appears, while the outer membrane hardens under the influence of an enzyme in this fluid (Zotin, 1958). The contents of the perivitelline space have been believed to arise partly from the cortical alveoli, but Detlaff (1962) has shown that in sturgeon eggs a colloid material from the region of the animal pole contributes to the perivitelline fluid.

Movements of cytoplasm toward the future germ-disc region of the egg immediately after fertilization have been described by Vakaet (1955). These movements accentuate the polarity already present (see review by Clavert, 1962) and they have also been shown by Roosen-Runge (1938) using time-lapse filming. Nothing is known of their biochemical significance, nor of the composition of this particular cytoplasm. Arndt (1956) has followed the distribution of lipids at initial stages of development and notes that prior to cleavage lipid droplets lie beneath the germ disc. At the blastoderm stage there are some lipid droplets within the cells (Fig. 2) including, later on, the neural plate cells (cf. Spek, 1942).

3. GASTRULA AND NEURULA STAGES

The classic experimental work on fish embryos includes isolations and transplantations of tissue (for reviews, see Oppenheimer, 1958; Devillers, 1961). It has been shown, for instance, that the dorsal invaginating mesoderm induces neural tissue, as it does in amphibians. Special chemical properties of this mesoderm have therefore been looked for, but without any significant findings. Krammer (1950) reports that the invaginating cells are especially rich in lipid, but it is not known whether any of this material passes into the neural plate to cause the lipid accumulation that Arndt observed (1956). Devillers (1951) found that not only the invaginating cells but also the cells of the outer cell layer are rich in RNA. It has long been known that cells synthesizing protein are rich in RNA (cf. Brachet, 1949). A suggestion that in fish embryos there is a quantitative relation between RNA content and differentiation rate is given by the findings of Hisoaka and Hopper (1957) that the abnormal tissues that arise in zebra fish treated with barbiturates contain less RNA than normal tissues. Unfortunately, this work has not been taken further.

So far, we have very little information about changes in the proteins of early fish embryos. Ohi (1962) has attempted to separate the water-soluble proteins of cyprinoid embryos by electrophoresis and has observed the appearance of one new component on the second day, which predominates on the third day. It is not clear, however, what developmental stages these times represented; there is a need to extend the work with more precise extraction methods.

4. General Trends During Development

a. Enzyme Activities and the Utilization of Reserves. It appears that first carbohydrate, then protein, and last of all, fat are used as energy sources during the development of teleost fish. The abundant opalescent globules in the yolk sac of fish embryos are a visible result of the conservation of fats. They may partly account for the buoyancy of the embryos and of the young fish fry (Grodzinski, 1956). In fact, some fish embryos normally float downward underneath their yolk, e.g., the embryos of the blue gourami *Trichogaster trichopterus* (Hisoaka and Firlit, 1962).

Tatarskaia *et al.* (1958) concluded that the general pattern of respiratory metabolism in developing fish resembles that of other vertebrate embryos. Cleavage can occur in the trout embryo in the absence of oxygen (Devillers and Rosenberg, 1953), but gastrulation is blocked by lack of oxygen or by treatment with cyanide or azide (Devillers *et al.*, 1957). In this respect, fish embryos resemble amphibian embryos.

According to Hishida and Nakano (1954), mesoderm invagination in the zebra fish *Oryzias latipes* is accompanied by glycogen breakdown, again paralleling events in amphibia. The same authors observed an exponential rise of succinic oxidase and cytochrome oxidase activities during development comparable with that in the amphibian *Xenopus laevis* (Boell and Weber, 1955). Since these two enzymes are contained in mitochondria, their increased activity may simply reflect the increase in mitochondrial population, although in *Xenopus* it seems that there is also an increase in specific activity of the enzymes.

Tatarskaia *et al.* (1958) have studied phosphatase activities during the development of the sturgeon. They found only low levels of acid and alkaline phosphatase activity throughout development, but β-glycerophosphatase activity increased sharply at later stages.

b. Transfer of Material from the Yolk to the Embryo. This subject is dealt with fully by Williams (Volume II, Chapter 7).

Work with radioactive amino acids (Monroy *et al.*, 1961) on *Oryzias latipes* indicates that material at first passes slowly from the yolk into a low molecular weight pool, after closure of the blastopore. Later, when the blood circulation is established, there is a more rapid uptake into whole proteins of the embryonic tissues (cf. Fig. 2). Since the data of Sriramulu (1959a, b) and of Rizzoli (1957) indicate a general decrease of total free amino acid in embryo and yolk during development, the uptake into new protein of the embryo is evidently more rapid than the breakdown of yolk protein reserves.

Yolk breakdown apparently takes place chiefly in the yolk sac which, according to Van der Ghinst's histochemical evidence (1935) is a seat of intense peptidase activity. No biochemical assays of its peptidase activity appear to have been carried out, but by analogy with bird embryos (Borger and Peters, 1933) one would expect high values. Felix *et al.* (1936) have observed dipeptidase in fish eggs, but its localization (perhaps in the embryo?) was not traced. Lipases and esterases, the other enzymes that would be involved in yolk breakdown, have long been demonstrable in fish eggs (Needham, 1931). Recently, Berg and Creaser (1953) have also found inorganic polyphosphatase at the gastrula stage in the minnow *Pimephales notatus*. This enzyme activity is confined to the yolk sac, and they suggest that it is closely linked with yolk utilization.

c. Amino Acids. Holtfreter *et al.* (1950) have identified free and protein-bound amino acids in eggs and embryos of fish as well as a wide variety of other animals. They found no qualitative tissue or stage differences. More recently, Colas and Devillers (1962) have estimated cystine, aspartic acid, glutamic acid, glutamine, serine, and threonine quantitatively in embryos of the trout (*Salmo irideus*). They observed that aspartic and glutamic acids were always present in highest concentration and that valine and leucine did not appear until after gastrulation. These results resemble the findings in amphibian embryos (see Section III,B,4a). Roberts *et al.* (1957) concluded from a broad survey of many different tissues and animal species that each tissue has a characteristic and constant free amino acid pattern. If this is true, it is a question of salient interest to embryologists how early in development such characteristic patterns of free amino acids become established in the tissue primordia. So far, however, there are no data directly linking embryonic amino acid patterns with those of adult tissue in fish.

A few recent observations on abnormal tissue differentiation in fish are of special interest. Anders *et al.* (1962) noted that tumor-bearing strains of carp have abnormally high free amino acid concentrations in their tissues and that, surprisingly, their embryos show the same characteristic. It has been known for some time that tumors and tumor-bearing animals have abnormal free amino acid patterns (Roberts and Borges, 1955)—including a deficiency of glutamine—but, so far, there is no explanation of this phenomenon. Levy (1962) has induced tumors of the notochord in fish embryos by growing them in β-aminoproprionitrile, the well-known lathyritic agent, and teratomas have been described in the ovary of *Lebistes reticulatus* by Stolk (1959). The biochemistry of these abnormalities has not yet been investigated, however. The fish seem an excellent source of material for studies of the biochemical differences between normally and abnormally differentiating tissues, and investigations on these forms should be carried further.

5. Later Stages of Development: Special Proteins

Hemoglobin has been described in erythroblasts of the cichlid *Cichlosoma facetum* by Stolk (1961). The nuclei synthesize hemoglobin earlier than the cytoplasm. Colle-Vandevelde (1961) identified blood cells in *Lebistes* by the Unna-Brachet method and the benzidine reaction (O'Brien, 1961a). Two new hemoglobin types appear in fish hybrids (Manwell *et al.*, 1963b).

Another special protein, the hatching enzyme, has been shown by Ignat'eva (1959) to be produced in the sturgeon by an endodermal gland innervated by the palatine nerve. Explants of the gland will secrete the enzyme, in the absence of any nervous stimulation. Hatching enzymes have previously been identified in a number of other species of fish (see Needham, 1931), and more recently in *Fundulus* by Kaighn (1964).

6. Conclusion

There is still a wide-open field for biochemical work on fish embryos. The previous work, besides being scanty compared with that on the more readily obtainable forms, such as amphibians and chicks, is also uncoordinated owing to the widely different choice of material by different investigators. One cannot expect a marine fish to resemble very closely a fresh-water form in any points concerning its metabolism that affect its relationship to its environment. There are, in fact, many special environmental adaptations in this remarkably widespread vertebrate group; but these remain unilluminated by any of the biochemical findings so far. For instance, an especially interesting feature is the occurrence of viviparity in some forms, but no comparative biochemical studies have yet been made between embryos of closely related viviparous and oviparous species. Another topic of great interest to experimental embryologists that has not been elucidated at the biochemical level so far, is the role of the periblast in controlling morphogenetic movements (Trinkaus, 1949; and a review by Devillers, 1961).

The gaps in our information about the biochemical patterns in developing fish embryos are only too noticeable. An attempt, however, has been made to assemble some of the known facts in Fig. 2.

A. DISTRIBUTION OF LIPIDS

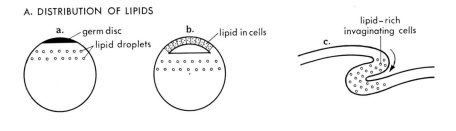

B. TRANSFER OF YOLK MATERIALS

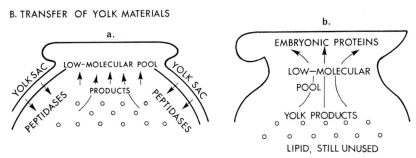

FIG. 2. Biochemical patterns in fish embryos. Diagrams represent sagittal sections. (A) Distribution of lipids: a, before cleavage; b, before gastrulation; c, invaginating tissues of gastrula. (B) Transfer of yolk materials to embryo: a, before blood circulation; b, after blood circulation.

B. *Amphibians*

1. INTRODUCTION

Because they are easy to handle and are usually available in large numbers at a time, amphibian embryos offer good material for biochemists. Having been favorite objects for experimental study for many years now makes them especially attractive for those who hope to elucidate problems of cell differentiation, since the fates of the cells and the times at which they normally become capable of independent differentiation are known very precisely. In amphibia more than in other groups, therefore, biochemical work has been aimed at showing patterns of difference between various regions of the early embryo. The literature is extensive and only those topics that have received special attention in recent years and that have not already been dealt with fully in Brachet's book (1960) will be discussed here. In order to maintain emphasis on the embryo as an individual organism, whose changing morphology biochemical investigators must always be trying to explain, the findings will be considered mainly under headings of the developmental stages as in the previous section.

2. BIOCHEMISTRY OF STAGES PRIOR TO GASTRULATION

The structure of the egg is dealt with in detail by Williams in Chapter 1 of this volume. Special mention may be made here, however, of the cortical layer because recently it has been subjected to some pioneering experimental work. Curtis (1962) succeeded in grafting pieces of the cortex of *Xenopus laevis* eggs and found that at the 8-cell stage the cortex of the "gray crescent" region opposite the point of sperm entry is able to induce the formation of a secondary embryo, when it is grafted ventrally into a host prior to its third cleavage. So this cortical material is already endowed with the properties later possessed by the dorsal lip cells of the gastrula, which arise from the gray crescent region. Curtis has suggested the existence of some type of "field" patterning in the cortex, but there is very little information so far about biochemical differences between the gray crescent and other regions of the cortex. Nass (1962) believes the special properties of the gray crescent cortex can be attributed to the phosphoprotein phosphatase activity of the pigment granules in this region. This enzyme is known to participate in yolk breakdown (Flickinger, 1956), but there is no obvious connection between this process and induction of a secondary embryo. The color of the gray crescent is caused by the particular proportion of pigment to yolk in this region.

It has been pointed out earlier (Section I,B) that the biochemical patterning of all embryos results to some degree from the original distribution of materials in an animal–vegetal gradient in the egg. Dalcq (1960) reviewing the results of rotation and other procedures that temporarily disarrange the egg contents, concludes that the position where the blastopore lip finally forms is determined by interaction between the yolk and the cortical material. On the other hand, Løvtrup and Pigon (1958) claim to have been able to control the future polarity of axolotl embryos by keeping them in glass tubes in which they have access to oxygen only at one side. Gastrulation usually took place with the dorsal lip nearest this side. They had rather few cases, however, and did not use a very precise method of limiting the oxygen supply. To explain the findings, Løvtrup (1958) argued that the gray crescent of the normal embryo is more permeable to oxygen than other regions and that this increased oxygen supply initiates the higher metabolic and morphogenetic activities of this region. Some data on permeabilities to oxygen are required in support of this idea, however.

Hardly any investigations have been made so far on patterns of difference between individual blastomeres at cleavage stages, perhaps because of prejudice that no differences of any permanent significance can exist at this early stage. The necessary first step to such investigations, i.e., to separate the blastomeres, can now be done quite easily with Versene (EDTA) (Curtis, 1957), so that it is possible to obtain isolates of each cell type for biochemical analysis. It is desirable that more work of this kind be undertaken. One interesting recent investigation may be mentioned; Baltus and Brachet (1962) have measured the DNA content of *Pleurodeles* embryos during cleavage using a new fluorometric method. They have confirmed that there is a large cytoplasmic reserve of DNA and that none is synthesized until the blastula stage.

3. GASTRULA AND NEURULA STAGES

These are the earliest stages at which different tissue primordia can readily be identified and isolated by dissection. They are also the crucial stages at which the cells become set along certain paths of differentiation that they will pursue even when isolated in culture. So there has been tremendous impetus to perform biochemical studies on them, and the consequent wealth of literature has had to be selected very rigorously here, owing to limits of space.

a. Properties of the Invaginating Region (see Fig. 3). In studies on the gastrula, it has been a matter of principle to look for special properties of the dorsal lip because of its remarkable inducing powers. Now that many other examples of "inductors," i.e., of tissues that influence the way in which an adjacent one develops, are known, we have less reason to suppose that the dorsal lip of the gastrula should have any unique properties or constituents, although it may well show quantitative differences from the rest of the gastrula. The first properties studied were respiration rate and RNA content. From the earlier work (see Brachet, 1960, for references) it appeared that both respiration rate and RNA content were high in the dorsal lip as compared with other parts of the gastrula. Barth and Sze (1953), however, later pointed out that the respiration rate of the dorsal lip is not as high as that of the dorsal ectoderm, although its respiratory quotient (RQ) is nearer unity than other regions. Some time ago Woerdeman (1933) suggested that glycogen breakdown was a speciality of the invaginating dorsal lip cells; but later Jaeger (1945) showed that breakdown of glycogen occurred ventrally too and, subsequently, interest in this metabolite has flagged.

The earlier findings on RNA distribution in the gastrula (see Fig. 3b),

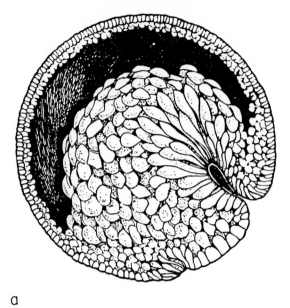

a

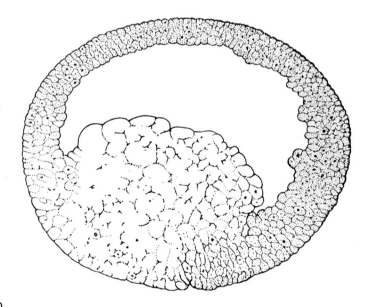

b

Fig. 3.   a and b.

on the other hand, have provoked further considerable thought and analysis. As mentioned previously (Section III,A,3), the presence of RNA in high concentration is taken as indicating active protein synthesis. Pfautsch (1960) has obtained interesting data on the distribution of RNA in gastrulae and neurulae of newt (*Triturus alpestris*) and axolotl (*Ambystoma mexicanum*) embryos (Table I). These data show the ectoderm to have a higher RNA content than the dorsal lip, in contradiction to previous findings. The values obtained by biochemical methods are probably to

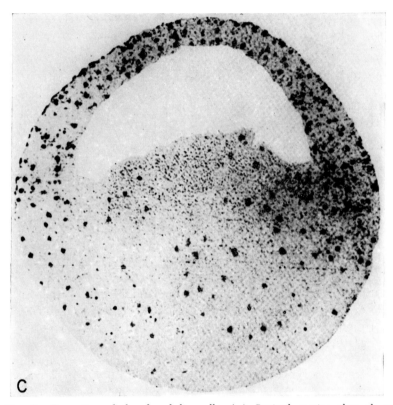

FIG. 3. Properties of the dorsal lip cells. (a) Sagittal section through early gastrula, showing foliate shape of the invaginating cells. From Waddington (1956). (b) Gradient of RNA concentration in the early gastrula. Density of stippling indicates concentration of RNA revealed by histochemical staining. Note that highest concentration appears to be in future neural ectoderm, although high concentration also appears in dorsal lip region. From Brachet (1949). (c) Uptake of $C^{14}O_2$ in the amphibian gastrula. In the autoradiograph the larger black spots indicate heavily labeled nuclei. Note that densest graining is in dorsal lip region. After Duspiva (1963).

be relied on more than the attempted quantitative comparisons made by histochemical methods in earlier work. So we may have to abandon the idea that the dorsal lip is any more substantially equipped for protein synthesis than the ectoderm—although it could be responsible for passing on this faculty to the ectoderm. In fact, Pfautsch found higher concentrations of RNA in ectoderm that had been underlain by mesoderm than in other parts of the ectoderm.

TABLE I

RNA and DNA Contents of Different Regions of the Amphibian Gastrula[a]

Region	RNA[b,c]		DNA[b,c]	
	Triturus alpestris	Ambystoma mexicanum	Triturus alpestris	Ambystoma mexicanum
Ectoderm not underlain by mesoderm	3.25 ± 0.04	2.51 ± 0.12	2.37 ± 0.09	2.34 ± 0.25
Ectoderm underlain by mesoderm	4.46 ± 0.27	4.48 ± 0.22	2.5 ± 0.22	5.45 ± 0.92
Dorsal blastopore lip	2.68 ± 0.1	—	1.47 ± 0.24	—
Archenteron roof	1.78 ± 0.07	—	1.18 ± 0.07	—

[a] After Pfautsch (1960).
[b] Expressed in µg/mg.
[c] Means from five determinations; ± standard errors of the means.

The connection between RNA and protein synthesis in embryos should now be expressed in terms of the current concepts that a "messenger RNA" which has its base sequence determined by DNA, determines the sequence of amino acids in proteins (see this volume, Chapter 8). RNA of the dorsal lip may be presumed to control the synthesis first of the proteins of the dorsal lip cells and then of the proteins of the neural plate, if it passes into these cells, by means of some messenger RNA. If so, it should eventually be possible with suitable techniques to isolate from embryos a short-lived RNA that possesses base sequences corresponding to the sequence of amino acids in some known protein of either the dorsal lip or the neural plate. The next step in the analysis of biochemical patterns in the gastrula is to study base sequences in RNA from different regions. Brown and Caston (1962) have succeeded in determining the base composition of RNA extracted from whole embryos of *Rana pipiens*. Brown and Littna (1964a, b) have characterized the RNA types obtained by density gradient centrifugation of extracts of *Xenopus laevis* embryos (see Chapter 9). Deuchar and Bristow (1965) have followed some base ratio changes in RNA of the neural plate and neural crest tissue in *Xenopus* embryos.

    b. Proteins (see also Chapters 7 and 9 of this volume). There is considerable evidence for the existence of characteristic patterns of protein distribution in the early embryo. Much work has been carried out in this field by Vyazow (1962), whose recent book on developmental immunology reviews the Russian literature. It has been known for some time that the proteins from different regions of both gastrulae and neurulae of amphibian embryos differ antigenically. Clayton (1953) showed that there is a clear correspondence between the time of appearance of serologically distinct proteins and the time of divergence in fate of the various tissues in the newt embryo (*Triturus alpestris*). Thus, ectoderm, mesoderm, and endoderm of the early gastrula already differ antigenically; by the end of gastrulation it is possible to distinguish differences between neural ectoderm and epidermis too. Spar (1953) has carried out similar studies on *Rana pipiens*. Inoue (1961a, b) undertook a more ambitious survey of the antigens in *Triturus* and *Hynobius* embryos throughout development and distinguished several stage-specific antigens. In an attempt to show antigenic differences between different cell types, he also tried growing cells in different antisera (Inoue, 1961c), but with no clear-cut results.

Radioactive amino acids provide another means of observing protein synthesis in the embryo (but with the reservations about interpreting uptake to mean actual synthesis, as mentioned in Section II,C,1). In amphibian gastrulae the dorsal lip cells have been found to take up amino acid and also $C^{14}O_2$ at higher rates than other regions (Sirlin and Waddington, 1954; Duspiva, 1963, Fig. 3c). The procedure in these cases was to immerse whole embryos in saline containing the tracer in solution, which may have given an unfair advantage in uptake to the dorsal lip cells, because these would lose the relatively impermeable "surface coat," as they invaginate. Ceas and Naselli (1958), however, introduced S^{35}-methionine into oocyte stages of *Discoglossus pictus* by injections into the adult female. The neurulae arising from these labeled oocytes showed radioactivity passing from soluble to insoluble (i.e., protein) material in the dorsal regions, whereas ventrally the trend was from insoluble (presumably reserve, yolk) material into soluble material. Unfortunately, their work was not continued, however, and they gave no data to prove conclusively if there was a net synthesis of new protein in the dorsal neurula tissue. Other observations on amino acid uptake at gastrula and neurula stages have all shown most rapid incorporation into dorsal regions (Friedberg and Eakin, 1949; Eakin *et al.*, 1951; Waddington and Sirlin, 1954). The methods used, however, do not rule out the possibility that the higher uptake is simply caused by the smaller size and greater exposed surface area of the dorsal tissues, and future work should preferably be carried out on cell disaggregates (cf. Giudice, 1962).

c. Yolk Breakdown in Different Regions. Before new proteins can be synthesized, the raw materials, which are gradually derived from the yolk, must be made available. So far, we have little data on the rates of yolk breakdown in different regions of amphibian embryos, and some of these appear to be in disagreement (see Duspiva, 1963, for review), mainly because of the different ways in which the data were expressed. D'Amelio and Ceas (1957) measured peptidase activity in different regions of the embryos of *Discoglossus pictus* and found maximal activity, per unit of "extractable" (i.e., saline-soluble) nitrogen, in the dorsal lip of the early gastrula. On the other hand, maximal activity was found ventrally in *Xenopus laevis*, when the data were expressed per cell, although expressing the data per unit of total nitrogen resulted in highest figures for dorsal regions (Deuchar, 1958). For reasons discussed in Section II,D, the total nitrogen reference basis seems meaningless. More relevant was the finding that much of the peptidase activity was contained in the yolk fraction after mild centrifugation, so that it seemed possible that catheptic enzymes were an integral part of the yolk platelets. Other enzymes, such as phosphoprotein phosphatase are also involved in yolk breakdown. Flickinger (1956, 1961) notes that solubilization of yolk with the help of this enzyme occurs earliest in the invaginating mesoderm of the gastrula and only later in the ectoderm.

Since the enzymes capable of yolk breakdown are abundantly present, a problem that arises is how their activity is limited, so that the right degree of breakdown occurs at the right moment in the right places. There must be some mechanism to maintain the correct ratio of concentrations of free amino acids and proteins, such that a decrease in the pool stimulates, whereas an increase in the pool inhibits, yolk breakdown. Flickinger (1949) states that addition of glycine or alanine to cultures of neural crest cells inhibits the breakdown of yolk in them, but this effect has not yet been confirmed by any other investigators. One also has to consider the factors acting upon enzyme activities. It seems possible that external environmental changes can limit peptidase activity. Rosenbaum (1960) found that autolysis could be prevented in embryos of *Rana pipiens* by submitting them to high oxygen pressures; the embryos remained intact for several days, although their development was blocked. Barth and Barth (1954) have suggested, from studies on extracts of amphibian embryos, that certain concentrations of ATP (adenosine triphosphate) inhibit the breakdown of yolk. It is doubtful, however, whether the normal localization of ATP in the embryo would support their idea. Ambellan and Webster (1962) and Deuchar (1960b) have suggested that ATP may play a part in the cell movements of neurulation and of somite segmentation, but neither of these processes is characterized by any hiatus of yolk breakdown. The result of the ATP treatment is believed to be caused by the presence of some myosin-like protein with ATPase activity, that is responsible for the contractions that the cells undergo. It has to be remembered, however, that because ATP is a source of energy-rich phosphate groups it is likely to promote a number of the energy-consuming activities of cells—contraction would be only one such activity.

Other recent investigations on yolk breakdown in amphibian embryos include Karasaki and Komoda's observations (1958) with the electron microscope of the structure of the crystal lattice in yolk platelets. An outer, less dense layer (possibly polysaccharide) persists, while the central region becomes polygonal, when yolk breakdown is occurring. The details of this process are described by Karasaki (1963).

4. GENERAL TRENDS DURING EARLY DEVELOPMENT

a. Distribution of Amino Acids. The free amino acids in embryos have a dual interest, since they are both the main products of yolk breakdown and the main raw materials used to make new proteins. Because yolk is broken down at different times in different regions and these regions also synthesize different proteins, one may expect to find regional differences in the concentrations of free amino acids.

Kutsky *et al.* (1953), Chen (1956), and Deuchar (1956) have measured free amino acid concentrations in amphibian embryos. The trends in aspartic acid concentration in embryos from cleavage stages to hatching agreed remarkably well in the three sets of data, although different species and methods were used (Fig. 4). A general feature in which the results also agreed was that glycogenic amino acids appeared in highest concentrations at early stages, but then decreased. In contrast, the "essential" amino acids (in mammalian terminology) were in low concentration initially, but gradually increased; their later increase in concentration was almost certainly attributable to yolk breakdown.

Comparisons of the free amino acid content of different regions in embryos of *Xenopus laevis* showed that dorsal regions had the highest total free amino acid concentration (Deuchar, 1956). The central nervous tissue at the late neurula stage contained the highest concentrations of glutamine and glutamic acid, which is interesting because brain tissue of a number of different animals has characteristically high concentrations of these two amino acids (Ansell and Richter, 1954). It is believed that the conversion of glutamic acid into glutamine may afford a means for removal of ammonia that otherwise accumulates in toxic concentrations because of the blood–brain barrier (Weil-Malherbe, 1953). It is remarkable that, even in these early embryos before any blood–brain barrier operates, an accumulation of the two characteristic amino acids should occur. Recently, Curtis and Watkins (1963) have found that glutamic acid has an excitatory effect on neurons and that glutamic acid and related compounds may function as transmitters.

Free valine is particularly concentrated in ventral regions and then in the heart and blood of *Xenopus* embryos. This may have some connection with hemoglobin synthesis, since valine is the N-terminal amino acid of the α- and β-polypeptide chains. Free leucine accumulates in the dorsal tissue of the neurula for a short period; then its concentration falls during

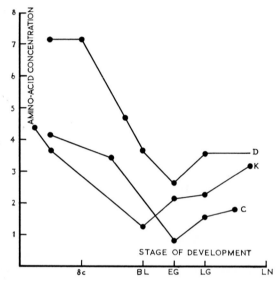

FIG. 4. Concentrations of free aspartic acid in amphibian embryos. Graph K, μmoles per 10,000 *Rana* embryos; data of Kutsky *et al.* (1953). Graph C, μg per 10 *Triturus* embryos; data of Chen (1956). Graph D, μg per 50 *Xenopus* embryos; data of Deuchar (1956). (8c) 8-cell stage, (BL) blastula, (EG) early gastrula, (LG) late gastrula, (LN) late neurula.

the time of somite formation. Subsequent investigations have shown (Deuchar, 1961) that leucine activation [the preliminary step toward its uptake into protein, according to the scheme of Hoagland *et al.* (1956)] predominates in somite mesoderm during this segmentation phase. If there is an uptake of leucine into protein, this would explain the fall in concentration of free leucine at this stage. Myosin contains a high percentage of leucine (Block and Weiss, 1956), so that the somite myoblasts should be in special need of leucine. There is some evidence supporting this idea; Lucy and Rinaldini (1959) noted that myoblasts of the chick embryo take up leucine preferentially from tissue culture media. Also, leucine analogs inhibit somite segmentation in explanted chick embryos

(Herrmann, 1953; Schultz and Herrmann, 1958), whereas leucine, on the other hand, speeds up the process of segmentation (Deuchar, 1960b).

Measurements of free amino acid concentrations at arbitrarily chosen stages of development are subject to the criticism that they tell nothing of the movements of these metabolites and that it is impossible to judge whether these free amino acids represent unwanted left-overs from previous protein synthesis or essentials accumulating for the proteins about to be synthesized next. In envisaging the pattern of events, then, these possible alternatives have to be considered, but the choice between them remains open at present.

b. Exchanges of Metabolites between Tissues. An important possibility for consideration is that transfer of amino acids or other essential metabolites may occur between adjacent tissues. Does one tissue act as "food supply" for another during development, and could this be a possible mechanism for the "inductions" that are so often observed? Wilde (1955, 1956) has suggested that phenylalanine may be synthesized from precursors in the archenteron roof mesoderm of the late gastrula and then passed on to the neural crest cells, which require it for their differentiation. He bases this suggestion on the fact that in cultures of neural crest cells differentiation is blocked by analogs of phenylalanine, unless archenteron roof cells are also present. He also claims to have converted ventral ectoderm into neural crest cells by treatment with phenylalanine. Biochemical evidence is still needed, however, to determine the fate of the metabolites added to his cell cultures; some radioactive labeling experiments are desirable.

Tracer techniques have been used in many attempts to find out what materials pass from inductors into induced neural tissue in amphibian embryos and explanted tissues. This subject is reviewed by Tiedemann (Volume II, Chapter 1). In many cases (Ficq, 1954; Sirlin et al., 1956; Kuusi, 1958) there was a passage of tracer into other host tissues besides the induced ectoderm, and it was not clear in what form it passed across the tissues. Later work (Flickinger et al., 1959; Vainio et al., 1962) using fluorescently labeled antibodies has established that serologically identifiable proteins pass from inducers into induced neural tissue, but it is not yet clear what significance the passage of these materials has. There is some scattered evidence from tissue culture work (see review by Lucy, 1960) that different cell types have differences in their amino acid requirements. The period of testing is often much longer than that of early embryonic differentiation, however, so that the same differential needs may not arise in the embryo.

Exchange of metabolites between cells in the embryo is dependent on morphogenetic movements, such as gastrulation, since each tissue must reach the right position in order to become adjacent to the one it influences; and also there is a causal relation between abnormal metabolism and abnormal movements. In cases of "gastrular block" resulting from treatments with inhibitory agents or from hybridization, the mesoderm fails to invaginate, and nucleic acid synthesis also is reduced (Chen, 1956). The analog 5-deoxyfluorouridine also blocks gastrulation (Tencer, 1961) suggesting again that RNA synthesis and these morphogenetic movements are linked. More must be learned, however, about the types of metabolism that govern the very different kinds of movement that gastrulating cells undergo. Gregg and Ornstein (1953) studied the effects of various metabolic inhibitors on invagination and epiboly, but obtained no noteworthy differences in effect, unfortunately, and the work was not pursued.

5. Later Stages of Development: Distribution of Proteins

a. Enzymes. Few enzyme activities have been studied comparatively between different regions of amphibian embryos, mainly because of the labor involved in collecting enough tissue for assays (cf. Section II,C,2). Cathepsin activity, for which there is a good microassay method (Duspiva, 1939), has been studied in *Rana esculenta* by Urbani (1955), in *Discoglossus pictus* by D'Amelio and Ceas (1957), and in *Xenopus laevis* by Deuchar (1958). The distributions of activities in the embryonic regions are shown in Fig. 4. Dipeptidase activity has also been estimated by Urbani (1955) and Pickford (1943), and leucine activation has been compared between dorsal and ventral halves of later stages of *Xenopus* embryos (Deuchar, 1961a). All the differences illustrated are quantitative; in no case is the enzyme activity confined to any one region. It has been suggested, however, by the work of Stearns and Kostellow (1958) that tryptophan peroxidase activity, which is confined to the liver in the adult, is already becoming restricted to endoderm cells by the end of gastrulation. According to their findings, at the end of gastrulation, only the endoderm cells respond to induction of the peroxidase activity by tryptophan. Others (e.g., Spiegel and Frankel, 1961) have not been able to confirm these findings, however.

The general trends of enzyme activities in amphibian development have been discussed by Løvtrup (1955) and Duspiva (1963) (also see Moog, Chapter 6 of this volume). Wallace (1961) gives details of enzyme activities in the citric acid cycle, Finamore (1955) of DNase and RNase activities, and Coleman (1962) of DNase I and II in *Rana pipiens* embryos. The activity of β-glucuronidase has been studied in *Xenopus* by Billett (1957). None of these data includes any reference to regional dif-

ferences, however, so they may be omitted from our present consideration of the spatial biochemical patterns at each developmental stage.

Weber and Boell (1962) have compared the activities of mitochondrial enzymes in different embryonic and larval tissues of *Xenopus
laevis*. They found that cytochrome oxidase, ATPase, acid phosphatase,
and cathepsin have characteristically different activities in each tissue
throughout development and they attempted to correlate these findings
with mitochondrial structure. Shen *et al.* (1955, 1956) followed the development of cholinesterase activity in various regions of the central nervous system of *Rana pipiens*. Using histochemical methods they have
shown very clearly that this enzyme activity appears at the same time as
the synapses between nerve cells. In the retina also, cholinesterase appears at each synapse layer as it forms.

b. Antigens. Inoue (1961a, b) has characterized some of the antigens in amphibians at later developmental stages (see Solomon, Chapter
7 of this volume). Denis (1961) has successfully used the cellulose acetate strip method (Kohn, 1961) to separate eleven distinct protein bands
which are present from early cleavage stages onward in *Pleurodeles
waltlii*. At the tailbud stage two of these protein bands disappear and
two new bands appear. These have not yet all been identified immunologically.

The lens has long been a favorite organ for serological study. Flickinger and Stone (1960) have found lens-type antigens in *Rana pipiens*
from the oocyte stage onward. Only later do some of these antigens become confined to the lens-forming cells. These results illustrate an important aspect of biochemical differentiation, namely, the gradual change
from widespread distribution of many common substances to restriction
of each type of substance to certain organ rudiments only.

Two other proteins that are readily identifiable serologically—actin
and myosin—have received special attention recently (Ogawa, 1960,
1961). Actin normally appears before myosin in development, but by X-
irradiation Ogawa was able to suppress actin formation in *Triturus pyrrhogaster* embryos, and found that myosin still appeared normally, so it
is clearly independent of actin.

c. Adrenalin. Caston (1962) observed that dopamine and noradren-
aline appear in the neural crest of the *Rana pipiens* embryo at stages 15
and 16 (late neurula), followed by adrenaline at stage 17 (tailbud). But
in isolated neural crest cells the adrenaline does not appear until the equivalent of stage 20 (hatching). This may be another facet of the metabolic
dependence of the neural crest on archenteron roof mesoderm, comparable to Wilde's claim with regard to phenylalanine. On the other hand,
it is common for differentiation to be retarded in explanted tissues. Evi-

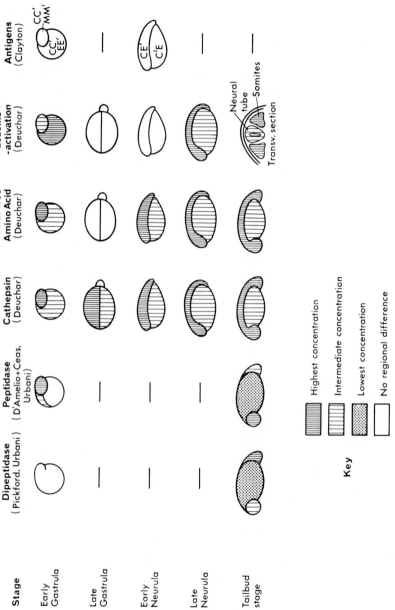

Fig. 5. Regional differences in early amphibian embryos. For literature references, see text. Antigen groups—C, C': common to ectoderm + mesoderm before, after gastrulation, respectively. E, E': ectoderm group before, after gastrulation, respectively. M, M': mesoderm group before, after gastrulation, respectively.

dently, their individual biochemical patterning normally receives some impetus from attachment to the whole embryo.

6. CONCLUSION

One must hope that before long more information will be obtained from electron microscopy on the patterns of molecular and supramolecular structure in different cell types of amphibian embryos. Karasaki and Komoda (1958), Eakin and Lehmann (1957), and Butschak (1960) have pioneered in this field, and Waddington and Perry (1962) have made a special study of the notochord. But it will require much more work with the rapidly improving methods to achieve reliable and reproducible results.

Figure 5 is presented as a summary of the regional biochemical patterns that are known to exist in early amphibian embryos.

C. *Reptiles*

Biochemical work on these forms is very scant, and there is an obvious need for more to be done. Apart from studies on nitrogen metabolism (see Volume II, Chapter 9) and on respiration, only a little experimental work has been undertaken and has been reviewed by Holder and Bellairs (1962). It is to be hoped that Maderson and Bellairs' successful culture method (1962) will encourage further work on early developmental stages.

D. *Birds*

1. INTRODUCTION

All remarks in this section will refer to embryos of the domestic hen, *Gallus domesticus*, since biochemical investigations have been confined almost entirely to this avian species.

Because they are much smaller and more difficult to dissect than amphibian embryos, less information is available concerning the early stages of development in birds than the later stages when the organs and tissues have formed. Biochemists have seldom dealt with embryos younger than 4 days, presumably because they felt that impossibly large numbers would be required. The information on early stages will therefore be dealt with in this section under two headings only.

2. PRIMITIVE STREAK STAGES

The early chick embryo can be grown successfully for up to 3 days in a damp-chamber, watch-glass culture; so it is readily amenable to experiments at this stage. The agar/saline medium of Spratt (1948) is satisfactory for biochemical work, because other nutrients may then be added in known concentrations. Less growth occurs on this medium, however, than on the classic plasma/embryo-extract clot (Waddington, 1932) or the albumen medium of New (1955). Spratt found that only glucose or an equivalent sugar was essential for short-term survival and

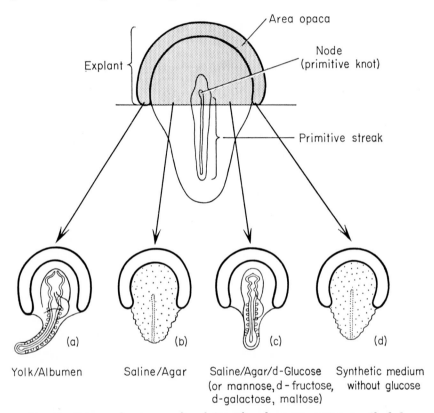

Fig. 6. Scheme showing results of Spratt's culturing experiments. Shaded area in top figures indicates the part of the embryo explanted. Lower figures are all drawn to the same scale (reduced by comparison with upper figure). Adapted from Spratt (1958).

differentiation (cf. Fig. 6). He also studied the effects of various metabolic inhibitors on anterior halves of blastoderms explanted on agar/saline/glucose and found that the brain was the most severely affected by all of them, except fluoride, which blocked the development of the heart. The mechanism of the fluoride effect is not known. In muscle it inhibits energy conversion by blocking the coenzyme enolase; so perhaps for the same reason, it blocks cell movements that are essential for the convergence of the heart-forming areas. De Haan (1958) found that agents, such as Versene and acetylcholine, which caused cell disaggregation, led to abnormal heart development and often resulted in embryos with bifid hearts because the convergence of the paired rudiments was blocked.

Spratt (see his review, 1958) carried out histochemical tests for enzyme activities *in situ* on the whole blastoderm and found that the node region (Fig. 6) gives the strongest reactions for dehydrogenases and cytochrome oxidase, besides basophilia, and reduction of Janus green. He concludes that the special properties of the node cells may be caused by a higher content of mitochondria, but does not appear to have verified this by any cytological study. At later primitive streak and neurula stages, the axial tissues show high enzyme activities as compared with more lateral parts. For instance, Billett and Mulerkhar (1958) found β-glucuronidase activity highest in axial tissues. Studies with radioactive methionine (Feldman and Waddington, 1955; Sirlin and Waddington, 1956) also show that the axial tissues incorporate these most rapidly into protein.

The previous findings indicate that biochemical patterns at these early stages embody quantitative rather than qualitative differences. It would be surprising if it were otherwise, because grafting work and tissue isolates on the chorioallantoic membrane (Lutz and Bernard, 1960; Rawles, 1936) show that the fates of the cells are not yet irrevocably determined and they are still interconvertible. Another aspect of the patterns has been brought to light by Ebert (1958) and his co-workers. They have shown that cardiac myosin gradually becomes restricted to cells of the heart rudiments only, at the head process stage, after previously having been distributed over the whole blastoderm. This gradual restriction of a special protein to one type of cell, after previously having been universally distributed, is comparable with what happens to lens antigens in amphibia (Section III,B) and emphasizes that cell differentiation involves specific protein losses as well as gains.

3. Two-Day-Old Embryos

a. Histochemistry. From 40–48 hours' incubation the process of neurulation in the chick is completed, and up to eighteen pairs of somites may form. The axial tissues are clearly distinct histologically and may be isolated by dissection for separate analysis. The histochemistry of their structure has been investigated in a number of classic studies which lie outside the scope of this account. To cite only one example of these, Ramon y Cajal's elucidation of the development of nerve fibers was derived from exhaustive study of the spinal cord in chick embryos (Ramon y Cajal, 1928). In recent work interest still focuses mainly on the central nervous system. The old problem of whether mitoses are really confined entirely to the ependymal layer of the spinal cord and, if so, whether the nuclei migrate out between their divisions was taken up again by Sauer and Chittenden (1959). They concluded from estimations of the DNA in individual nuclei that the idea is correct; only those nuclei next to the lumen of the spinal canal show the DNA increase characteristic of the premitotic phase. Another recent histochemical study of the early spinal cord is that of Catayée and Bonhomme (1961), who measured acid phosphomonoesterase activity in this tissue. According to their findings it is distributed throughout the thickness of the neural tube at first, then localized later in the extreme outer and inner layer and in the neural crest.

b. *Amino Acid Metabolism.* Studies by Feldman and Waddington (1955) and Sirlin and Waddington (1956) on methionine uptake have already been mentioned. Herrmann and Schultz (1958) measured the uptake of C^{14}-glycine into chick embryos that had been explanted into a medium containing the tracer. They found the following order in rate of uptake: primitive knot, spinal cord, somites, unsegmented somite mesoderm, brain, heart, and notochord. They did not include endoderm in their measurements, but later it was found (Deuchar and Herrmann, 1962) that the endoderm accumulates tracer very rapidly. Embryos which either have their endoderm removed or are explanted with their dorsal surface next the medium take up much less tracer than when the endoderm is in contact with the medium. This effect was observed both with glycine and with leucine, according to measurements of protein-bound radioactivity made by both biochemical methods and autoradiography.

The tissue differences referred to previously may be indications of differing rates of renewal of protein. It is particularly interesting that both the node region, which is still undergoing active proliferation and has not yet differentiated, and the endoderm, which is relatively undifferentiated at this stage, showed high glycine uptake. Comparisons of the free amino acid content of the various tissues of the 48-hour embryo (Deuchar, 1963a) suggest that the differences in rate of uptake are not caused by any amino acid concentration differences in the intracellular "pools" of the tissues. As in *Xenopus* embryos (Section III,B,4) only a few noteworthy differences in amino acid concentration were apparent. For instance, there were high concentrations of free glutamic acid and glutamine in the central nervous tissue, in accord with the findings in *Xenopus* embryos and in adult brain. Proteins of the extraembryonic area contained high concentrations of methionine, valine, and leucine, as well as detectable cysteine, like egg yolk. There were also high concentrations of protein-bound glycine in these extraembryonic tissues, as well as traces of hydroxyproline, suggesting an early synthesis of collagen here. A final interesting feature was that segmented somite mesoderm contained free valine and leucine, which were not detectable prior to segmentation. The evidence that leucine is required by segmenting somites has already been discussed (Section III,C,4,a). Besides observations by Rothfels (1954), Herrmann (1953), and Schultz and Herrmann (1958) that leucine analogs, particularly ω-bromoallylglycine, block somite segmentation, it has also been observed (Deuchar, 1961b) that leucine-activation activity is higher in the somite mesoderm than in other axial tissues of the chick embryo at 48 hours. Klein et al. (1962) note that leucine is an essential component of artificial culture media, and leucine added by itself speeds the rate of somite segmentation (Deuchar, 1960b). As remarked in Section III,B,4,a, Lucy and Rinaldini (1959) have shown that chick skeletal myoblasts take up more leucine from artificial culture media than other amino acids. So, collectively, the evidence suggests that myoblasts, in particular, may have a special need for leucine, perhaps using it for synthesis of myosin and other leucine-rich proteins.

It should be pointed out that other antimetabolites may also cause blockage of somite segmentation in chick embryos (Waddington et al., 1955; Billett and Perry, 1957). But in these cases, additional effects, particularly on the central nervous system, have been described. X-rays produce similar effects (Billett, personal communication, 1963).

c. Enzymes. Rudnick and Waelsch (1955) found glutamyltransferase activity in 48-hour chick embryos to be particularly active in the area opaca, then later in the yolk sac when this formed. According to Catayée and Bonhomme (1961) phosphomonoesterases are also confined to the yolk sac. Berg and Szekerczes (1962) have observed high trimetaphosphatase activity in the yolk sac. These are all indications that the yolk sac is an important organ of absorption, as has already been suggested from the work on amino acid uptake. Walter and Mahler (1958) concluded from experiments in which yolk and albumen were labeled radioactively in ovo that up to day 9 of incubation the chief source of protein for the embryo was the yolk.

d. Exchanges between Tissues. We know very little about the transfer of metabolites from one tissue to another in chick embryos. Sirlin et al. (1956), Waddington and Mulerkhar (1957), and Pantelouris and Mulerkhar (1957) showed passage of labeled amino acid from a grafted node into the neural tissue it induced; but it is not clear to what extent this occurs during normal development, nor how significant it is. They concluded that the transfer was mostly as free amino acid and not as protein.

4. General Developmental Trends

Mahler and associates (1958); Brand and Mahler (1959); Brand et al. (1960) made a detailed study of enzymes of the citric acid cycle and of respiratory pigments in the chick embryo. They observed that the respiratory pigments reached maximum concentrations in the embryo as a whole on day 4 of incubation, but that in the heart and liver their increase continued until day 14. Presumably the increases in the heart are secondary to those in the liver, since the liver is the site of hemopoiesis during this period. Enzymes of the citric acid cycle show a turning point at 3-days' incubation; after this the activities decline gradually until day 10. Newburgh et al. (1962) studying the relationship between certain dehydrogenase activities and cell proliferation between 40-and 88-hours' incubation, concluded that the decline in specific activity of glucose-6-phosphate dehydrogenase was caused by the appearance of cells with a new pattern of enzyme activity. Further details about enzyme activities in the chick are given by Moog (Chapter 6 of this volume).

Emanuelsson (1958, 1961a, b) estimated both DNA and RNA in chick embryos from 0- to 48-hours incubation, and concluded that there were alternating phases of cell proliferation and of differentiation during this period. But, since Solomon (1957b) found DNA-like material in the yolk of the hen's egg (cf. Section III,B,1), values obtained for DNA in yolky tissues may not parallel the numbers of nuclei present. Solomon concluded, however, that in early chick blastoderms the increase of DNA paralleled their rate of cell proliferation. Nucleic acid metabolism in chick embryos is considered in Chapter 9 of this volume.

5. Later Stages of Development: Proteins in Tissues and Organs

a. Absorption in Yolk Sac and Gut. We have already seen that the yolk sac endoderm of the chick is active in absorbing nutritive materials as early as the 48-hour stage. It contains highly active peptidases, too (Borger and Peters, 1933; Goldstein and Gintsbourg, 1936; Emanuelsson, 1955; Ito, 1957), so that it is certainly capable of digesting yolk proteins prior to absorbing them, although recent studies with the electron microscope (Bellairs, 1963) suggest that pinocytosis of protein may also occur in the cells of the yolk sac endoderm.

Moog has followed the increase and localization of alkaline phosphatase in the intestine as it develops from the yolk sac (see Chapter 6 of this volume), and Allenspach and Hamilton (1962) have observed alkaline phosphatase activity by histochemical methods in the developing esophagus.

b. Appearance of New Tissue Proteins. Chaube and Carter (1961) have separated electrophoretically a number of proteins, among them hypoxanthine dehydrogenase and lactate dehydrogenase, from the kidney of 15-day chick embryos. The mobilities of the two enzymes were shifted further in the positive direction, after injections of chlorothiazide into the embryo after 5-days' incubation. When the mechanism of the chlorothiazide effect is understood, this may throw light on how changing patterns of "isozymes" arise during embryonic development (Section IV,E,2). Proteins of embryonic liver and heart muscle have also been separated by electrophoresis (Philip and Vesell, 1962) and show a gradual change in pattern during development. Heart muscle proteins change little from 8 days onward, however; since the heart is the earliest organ to function in the embryo, it is not surprising that it should mature early biochemically.

The blood serum of the chick embryo has been studied extensively by electrophoretic and immunological methods (Marshall and Deutsch, 1950; Schechtman, 1948; Nace and Schechtman, 1948, 1953; D'Amelio and Salvo, 1961; Wilt, 1962). Further details are given by Solomon in Chapter 7 of this volume.

D'Amelio and Salvo (1961) found two hemoglobin components at 68-hours' incubation with mobilities higher than that of adult bird hemoglobin, so perhaps analogous to the "fetal hemoglobin" of mammals (Section III,E,3,*f*). They were able to detect three adult hemoglobin components (C_1, C_2, and C_3) from 88-hours' incubation onward. Since they had previously noted C_1 to be the only type detectable in isolated nuclei of bird erythrocytes, they suggested that C_1 forms intranuclearly in the embryo. O'Brien (1961a, b), however, described the first synthesis of hemoglobin in erythroblast nuclei of the area vasculosa much earlier, at 29–33 hours' incubation. He also found that treatment of explanted embryos with the purine analog, 8-azaguanine, at or before stage 8 (4-somite stage, Hamburger and Hamilton, 1951), blocked hemoglobin synthesis and concluded that the nucleic acid templates necessary for the initial synthesis are formed at this critical stage. Wilt (1962) has found that 8-azaguanine partially inhibits the uptake of H^3-leucine into the hemoglobin of chick embryos at this stage. He has also found similarities between the immunoelectrophoretic pattern of the globins in the 2- to 3-day embryo and that of the adult, although Manwell *et al.* (1963a) note the persistence of a distinct embryonic hemoglobin up to at least 5-days incubation in many different breeds of fowl.

c. Collagen in Connective Tissues. Collagen has come in for much study partly because its characteristic hydroxyproline content makes it easy to identify [for a review, see Harkness (1961); see also Chapter 7 of this volume]. Neuman (1950) observed the gradual accumulation of hydroxyproline in the proteins of chick embryos, especially in the extra-embryonic membranes; and Mitoma et al. (1959) showed that proline injected at 12-days' incubation is taken up into protein within 24 hours. They were among the first to observe that free proline, and not free hy-droxyproline, was the main source of the protein-bound hydroxyproline (cf. Green and Lowther, 1959). Ebert and Prockop (1962) have shown, using tritium-labeled proline, that in the chick embryo only one hydrogen atom is lost during the hydroxylation of proline. Tritiated (H^3-) proline injected into early chick embryos accumulates first in the notochord sheath and then in the dermatome and sclerotome cells of the somites, from the 3-day stage onward (Deuchar, 1963b). Osteoblasts in tissue culture also take up proline into collagen (Jackson and Smith, 1957). During embryonic development some collagen exists at first in a soluble form; Kivrikko (1963) followed the concentrations of hydroxyproline from 5- to 20-days' incubation, finding that the soluble and free fractions fall from 21 to 5 % of the total hydroxyproline, whereas the insoluble fraction rises from ca. 60 to ca. 90 %. There is a constant reserve of pep-tide-bound hydroxyproline, the function of which is not yet known. Mi-crosomes are the chief site of collagen synthesis (Prockop et al., 1962). Jackson (1956, 1958) has studied by electron microscopy the process of collagen formation in bone rudiments of the chick embryo.

Collagen precursors other than proline or hydroxyproline have also been studied. Rosenberg (1960) found that the maximum hexosamine concentration in chick embryos was reached on day 10, just before the main increase in collagen. Herrmann et al. (1958) used C^{14}-glycine to measure rates of collagen synthesis in chick embryonic tissues and found that the tracer equilibrated very slowly with collagen in the muscle of 12- to 16-day embryos. Adult collagen has also been found to have a very slow turnover rate (Thompson and Ballou, 1956; Neuberger et al., 1951; Neuberger and Slack, 1953).

Differentiation of the cornea and sclera in the eye involves collagen synthesis. In earlier experiments (Herrmann, 1960) it appeared that cor-neal mesenchyme cells were dependent on contact with the ectodermal epithelium for their ability to synthesize collagen; recently, however, this view has been retracted (Herrmann and Lebeau, 1962). The divergence in pattern of synthesis between the corneal and scleral mesenchyme is, as Herrmann has stressed, a particularly clear-cut example of a biochem-ical step in differentiation and would repay experimental analysis. Holt-zer et al. (Holtzer, 1961; Stockdale et al., 1963) have already gone far in analyzing the conditions necessary for synthesis of chondroitin sulfate by chondroblasts in culture; and there is, in general, a promising field for experimentation on collagen synthesis in cultured cells of chick embryos.

d. *The Nervous System* (see Moog, Chapter 6 of this volume). Rudnick and Waelsch (1955) followed the development of glutamyl transferase (GTF) activity in the brain and retina of the late chick embryo. GTF appears in the retina even when it is transplanted to heterotopic sites, and the activity is equally distributed throughout the retinal layers (Rudnick, 1959, 1963). Glutamine synthetase has also been demonstrated in the brain during the last week of incubation (Rudnick *et al.*, 1953).

The components of nervous tissue that have come under most biochemical study are the phospholipids, in which this tissue is particularly rich. Myelination, of special interest since it governs the onset of function, involves the appearance of particular phospholipids. Bensted *et al.* (1957) found that the main period of myelination in the spinal cord is from day 15 onward, although it is detectable before this, at 11 days (Peterson and Murray, 1955). Adams and Davison (1959) noted also a relative increase of esterified cholesterol in the central nervous system from day 14–18, apparently connected with myelination. Bieber *et al.* (1962) have distinguished lipid fractions in the chick embryo after 4, 6, 12, 14, and 18 days of incubation, containing either ethanolamine, choline, sphingosine, or inositol. The sphingomyelin content at least doubled between day 4 and day 18.

There have been several attempts to trace the precursors of cholesterol and to follow its synthesis in the chick embryo. Camerino and Wright (1962) showed that $2\text{-}C^{14}$-mevalonic acid injected into the yolk sac of the 6-day embryo is taken up into nonsaponifiable material of the embryo, and that 3 % goes into the brain. Fish *et al.* (1962) found that radioactivity from injected $1\text{-}C^{14}$-acetate accumulated in a large pool of desmosterol (2,4-dehydrocholesterol) which is evidently a main precursor of cholesterol in the embryo. From day 9–18, desmosterol makes up 11.2 % of the total brain sterol.

e. *The Glycogen Body.* This peculiar organ that appears in the roof plate of the lumbar spinal cord at 7- to 8-days' incubation remains a functional mystery. Watterson (1949) drew special attention to it, and Watterson *et al.* (1958) found that hypophysectomy of the embryo reduces the amount of glycogen stored here. But hormone effects are not directly demonstrable (Snedecor and Henrikson, 1959). Pieces of glycogen body isolated on the chorioallantois will start to store glycogen independently (de Gennaro, 1959). It is still unknown whether this glycogen store has any importance in embryonic metabolism.

6. Morphogenetic Significance of Subcellular Particles

Fell and her associates have for several years used organ culture methods to study the differentiation of skin under various conditions including treatment with excess vitamin A (recent summary, Fell, 1961). In the presence of excess vitamin A the epidermal layer secretes mucin instead of forming keratin. Investigating the biochemical mechanism of the vitamin A effect, Fell *et al.* (1962) showed that proteolysis occurs in the matrix surrounding cartilage cells when these are treated with vitamin A. Peptidases are released from the lysosomes of these cells. These findings raise the possibility, already suggested by Brachet *et al.* (1958), that lysosomal enzymes figure in the tissue regressions and cell deaths that normally occur during ontogeny (for review, see Glucksmann, 1951). Brachet *et al.* (1958) observed, for instance, that the regression of Muller's ducts in male chick embryos is associated with high activity of lysosomal hydrolytic enzymes.

It is to be hoped that, as differential centrifugation methods improve and more detailed examination of particles under the electron microscope becomes possible, the enzyme patterns of differentiating cells, both normal and abnormal, will become explicable in terms of the distribution and morphology of these particles. To return to an earlier theme (cf. Section I,B) it may again be noted that the initial distribution of particles must occur in the egg before cleavage, since they cannot cross cell boundaries. Any differences arising later must be the result of local changes in the number and/or morphology of the particles. Therefore, if such particles carry features specific to the various cell types, transplantation or injection of them into other tissues might be expected to cause some morphogenetic change. This possibility and its theoretical links with the selective uptake of particles by embryonic cells, as well as with the ability of viruses to induce tumors, has been discussed by Ebert and Wilt (1960). The use of subcellular particles alone as grafts has not yielded any definite effects so far.

7. Conclusion

It is not possible to make a brief summary of this section, because of the very wide range of biochemical problems that has been investigated in chick embryos. Their tissues and organs reach a much higher degree of maturity before hatching than those of amphibian larvae, and they offer much more convenient and accessible material than do mammal embryos for the investigation of problems of biological and medical interest. If one were to try to assemble a complete picture of biochemical events during ontogeny from the information available to date, it would be made up chiefly from what we know of early development in amphibians and of the later stages of both organ and tissue differentiation in the chick.

E. *Mammals*

1. INTRODUCTION

Once the mammalian embryo is implanted in the uterine wall, it is inaccessible to direct experimental attack. We therefore have to concern ourselves with the biochemistry of preimplantation stages and with such of the work on later stages as does not involve controversy about the so-called "placental barrier"—a topic that lies outside the scope of this chapter (see Chapter 8 of Volume II).

2. PREIMPLANTATION STAGES

a. Histochemical Studies. Dalcq and his co-workers have taken the lead in this field. The distribution of RNA, mucopolysaccharides, and alkaline phosphatase has been described in rodent embryos (Dalcq, 1957). Some of their findings on the egg and cleavage stages have been disputed

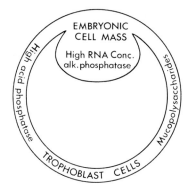

FIG. 7.   Biochemical patterns in the mammalian blastocyst. See text for further details.

(Austin, 1961). In the blastocyst they report that the cells of the embryonic knob (Fig. 7) are richest in RNA and in alkaline phosphatase, whereas mucopolysaccharides, on the other hand, are more highly concentrated in the trophoblast (and later in other extraembryonic membranes). The alkaline phosphatase activity is later highest in neural tissue. Extending this work Mulnard (1960) has shown that acid phosphatase activity accumulates in the same regions that are rich in mucopolysaccharides. Since acid phosphatase is present in lysosomes, its high activity may indicate that particularly large numbers of these particles are present in the embryonic membranes; their high peptidase activity (Gold-stein and Milgrom, 1935) also suggests this. The presence of mucopoly-saccharides may have some connection with the fact that connective tissue develops quite soon afterward in the cells derived from the tropho-blast. What the histochemical findings emphasize is that the cells of the future embryo differ biochemically from those of future extraembryonic tissues, at the earliest stage that they are grouped separately. This char-acteristic grouping in which the embryonic cells mass to one side of the blastocyst cavity, while the trophoblast cells become flattened and re-main as a peripheral epithelium, itself implies that the cells have some different intrinsic properties, which should eventually be explicable in biochemical terms. It may be added that Stegner (1960) studied in hu-man embryos the distribution of glycogen, glycoprotein, and DNA, as well as of acid mucopolysaccharides; he also found that the latter are localized in extraembryonic membranes.

b. *Experimental Work.* The broadest program of biochemical experi-ments embarked on so far is that of Lutwak-Mann and associates (Adams *et al.,* 1961). They have devised a rapid method of "screening" any pos-sibly teratogenic agent injected into pregnant female rabbits, by fixing the embryos at the blastocyst stage and examining them histologically as "flat-mount" preparations. Among the agents tested were: hormones, anti-mitotic agents, vitamin A, vitamin antagonists, and pyrimidine analogs—to name only the main types. It is premature to try to interpret any of the results in connection with special metabolic effects, but it has been shown that the embryonic knob cells are usually more severely affected than the trophoblast and that the effects are very rapid. The resistance of the trophoblast perhaps may be in some way related to its invasive properties, but so far we know little about these properties. Glenister (1961) has developed a method for culturing rabbit trophoblast tissue *in vitro,* but so far has not made experiments on this material.

Popp (1958) attempted an analysis of the utilization of C^{14} in early mouse embryos by growing either the blastocysts or the membranes con-taining implanted blastocysts in roller tubes, hanging-drop cultures, or capillary tubes, in a medium containing C^{14}-glucose. After short times the radioactivity in amino acids from hydrolyzates of protein from these em-bryos was observed. He noted a particularly high incorporation of C^{14} into yolk sac proteins even at late stages, indicating that this remains an important absorptive organ until late in gestation. Blastocysts incorpo-rated C^{14} chiefly into lactate, and none into glutamic or aspartic acids, suggesting that anaerobic metabolism predominated. This metabolism may not have been normal, however, for Popp was growing many of the blastocysts in highly anaerobic conditions—in sealed capillary tubes. It is a pity that he did not continue and improve his methods, for this was pioneering work that could have made possible many short-term biochemical investigations on mammal embryos even up to quite advanced stages—the oldest he used were very near birth, at 19 days.

Hansson and Garzo (1961) injected radioactive methionine and ethionine into pregnant female mice and found that the analog, ethionine, was not taken up into fetal protein under these conditions. The pattern of methionine uptake in the rat fetus (Proffit and Edwards, 1962) indicates the liver as the main absorptive organ, but ethionine distributes randomly, i.e., in the case of methionine, some selective absorption must take place.

Atlas et al. (1960) injected tritiated thymidine into pregnant female mice in an attempt to follow DNA synthesis in the blastocysts, but the tracer did not appear to have penetrated the embryos successfully. Only at 11 days did any embryonic cells besides the trophoblast become labeled, and then it was mainly the blood cells. The usual histochemical methods have been used to identify DNA (Dalcq and Pasteels, 1955), and there appears to have been no suggestion so far that any DNA is present in the cytoplasm of mammalian eggs.

It is clear from the preliminary nature of all the findings mentioned here that much more needs to be done to forward biochemical research on early mammalian embryos. People have been mistaken in thinking that a successful long-term culture method has to be devised first. In fact, many biochemical investigations need to last only a few hours. New and Stein (1964) have succeeded in growing rodent embryos for limited periods on plasma clots, so that the outlook for culture work along these lines is quite hopeful.

3. Later Stages of Development: Tissues and Organs

The organs of mammalian fetuses are amenable to biochemical analyses of the same kind as those applied to chick embryos, although not as much work has been done on them as on birds. Moog, in Chapter 6 of this volume, discusses enzyme activities, so only a few brief comments will be made on them here and particularly to those concerned in amino acid metabolism.

a. *The Liver.* Friedberg et al. (1948) have observed that fetal rat liver slices take up amino acid far more rapidly than does the adult liver, and according to Kafer and Pollak (1961), glutamic acid-alanine aminotransferase is more active in the liver of the rat embryo than in the adult liver. In some respects, however, the fetal liver is immature enzymatically. For instance, Kenney and Kletchmer (1959) noted that it cannot form tyrosine from phenylalanine, because it lacks phenylalanine hydroxylase.

b. Other Viscera. An enzyme of the kidney, leucine aminopeptidase, appears at 18 days in the rat (Hopsu *et al.*, 1961) and is first detectable in the juxtamedullary region in only a few nephron groups. It is interesting that Radde and McCance (1959) observed glutaminase activity in the mesonephros as well as the metanephros of the pig embryo. This supports the view held by many embryologists that the mammalian mesonephros functions, although it has only a transitory existence.

One particularly interesting aspect of enzyme development in fetal tissues has emerged from recent studies of lactic dehydrogenase (LDH) "isozymes" which, according to Markert and Ursprung (1962), are present in proportions characteristic for each tissue in the mouse embryo. Fine *et al.* (1963) have analyzed further the differences between these forms of LDH; and two main types of polypeptide subunits, H and M, governed by different genes, are now recognized. The enzyme exists as a tetramer,

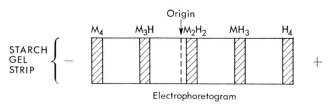

Fig. 8. Diagram of starch-gel electrophoretogram of lactic dehydrogenase isozymes. Adapted from Fine *et al.* (1963).

i.e., it can be H_4 or M_4, or hybrids can occur of the forms H_3M_1, H_2M_2, and H_1M_3. The higher the proportion of H subunits, the faster (toward the positive electrode) is the electrophoretic migration (Fig. 8). The LDH's of the tissues of the mouse embryo gradually acquire higher proportions of H during their development. The same trend occurs in other mammals too, but the human embryo is exceptional, with 99 % H in LDH at 6 weeks which decreases to between 60–70 % at 7 months. In adult human tissues H is only ca. 10 %. Wiggert and Villee (1964) found five LDH types in the human fetus, changing quantitatively. Creatine kinase isozymes have been studied in rat embryos by Eppenberger *et al.* (1964).

c. Brain. The Flexners and their collaborators (1953) took the lead in work on the biochemistry of brain development. They stressed that there is a critical period, around 41- to 46-days' gestation in the guinea pig, when several enzyme activities increase sharply in the cerebral cortex; at this time the neurons are maturing and a spurt of myelination also occurs. But there seems no obvious biochemical link between any of the enzyme activities and the myelination process. Recently, Flexner *et al.* (1960) have distinguished four LDH isozymes in the developing cerebral cortex of the mouse and the guinea pig.

The amino acid metabolism of the fetal brain, particularly glutamic acid metabolism, has been the object of much clinical research, because abnormalities in it give rise to some forms of idiocy (Walshe, 1953). The activities of glutamyl transferase, L-glutamic dehydrogenase, and glutamic-oxalacetic transaminase have been followed in fetal monkeys and pigs by Jolley and Labby (1960), who found mainly a steady increase in specific activities with advancing age. Glutamyl transferase showed the greatest increase, especially toward the end of gestation, and this increase was greater in the pig than in the monkey. The findings of Ansell and Richter (1954) that brain tissue is rich in free glutamic acid and glutamine have already been mentioned (Section III,B,4,a) as well as the possible role of glutamic acid as a transmitter (Curtis and Watkins, 1963). Little is known about these conditions in the mammalian embryo however. Olivo (1959) found apparently high concentrations of glutamic and aspartic acids in the brain of the fetal ox, but his results were not quantitative.

Very little systematic study has been made of the accumulation of lipoprotein constituents of the central nervous tissue during embryonic or early fetal stages. Brante (1949) showed that in rat and human fetuses the lipid content was relatively low prior to myelination, consisting mainly of lecithins and cephalins, and that there was then a dramatic increase in lipids during the myelination process. This phenomenon would repay further study.

d. Skin. Collagen apparently occurs in the skin of the fetal pig as a peptide precursor (Kobrle and Chvapil, 1961). The observations of Jackson and Smith (1957) on fetal osteoblasts in culture are referred to in Section III,D,5,f. Harkness and Harkness (1955) followed the collagen increase in whole fetuses of the rat.

e. Muscle: Myosin. Formerly myosin was identified by physicochemical methods (Nicholas, 1950) as well as by its ATPase activity (Herrmann and Nicholas, 1948). de Villafranca (1954) showed that two distinct ATPases, one magnesium-activated and one calcium-activated, both increased at the onset of contractility in rat embryonic muscle. Further analysis of myosin development in mammals must await the application of fluorescent antibody-labeling methods, such as were used on chick embryos by Holtzer *et al.* (1957).

f. Blood: Hemoglobin. The development of serum and plasma proteins is dealt with by Solomon in Chapter 7 of this volume. Kellehar and Villee (1962) and Wise *et al.* (1963) give further details about their appearance in the rat fetus, and Pantelouris and Hale (1962) describe plasma protein patterns in the fetal mouse. The hemoglobin of mammalian fetuses is of special interest because it differs electrophoretically as well as physiologically from that of the adult. Most is known about human hemoglobin types. Huehns *et al.* (1961) identified two new hemo-globin components (additional to the three types already known to exist) in 9-day human embryos. All of these disappear within 1 week, so that the 10-week embryo contains only the normal fetal hemoglobin. It would be interesting to know if this change at 10 weeks is connected with the fact that from the 28 mm (8½-week) stage onward, the spleen begins to take over hemopoiesis instead of the liver. In fetal mice, a critical change occurs at 12–16 days (Craig and Russell, 1964).

4. Conclusion

Much work has been omitted from this account because it was carried out not directly on the mammalian embryo but, in frustration as it were, on more accessible objects, such as the placenta, or on cultures of isolated tissues. There is no intention of belittling those findings, but they are bound to need verification from further study of the embryo itself, pref-erably *in situ*. There are enormous gaps in our information, and the ob-vious conclusion to be drawn is that more short-term biochemical work on living mammalian embryos at all stages of their development is very much needed.

IV. General Interpretations of the Biochemical Patterns

A. *Their Relevance to the Older Concepts of Experimental Embryology*

Investigations of biochemical patterns in vertebrate embryos received their initial impetus from the provocative results of tissue-grafting experi-ments in the 1920's and 1930's. As was pointed out at the beginning of this chapter, one particular hope of biochemical investigators was to re-veal the antecedents—perhaps interpretable as the causes—of cellular differentiation in the embryo, at the molecular level. So it is pertinent now to consider to what extent this hope has been realized and whether the biochemical findings have added to or elucidated the results obtained by more classic methods. In the past, attempts were made to explain these results by theories and concepts which, because they could not im-mediately be proved or disproved, have dominated the thinking of em-bryologists for several decades. The meaning of some of these long-stand-ing concepts should now be reassessed in the light of the recent studies of biochemical patterns.

B. *The Oldest of the Controversies: "Preformation" versus "Epigenesis"*

Although no one today believes, as did the original "preformationists," that the egg contains the adult organism in miniature, we still have to admit that eggs that are nutritionally independent of their environment (which *most are*) must contain precursors of all the future structures of the organism in some form. For any system to develop into an organism, two essentials must be present, viz., the raw materials and a system for controlling how these raw materials are converted into structure. It might seem obvious to assign the controlling function to the genes in the nucleus and to regard the cytoplasm as simply the store of raw materials. But, since Briggs and King (1957) and Gurdon (1962) showed that the nuclei of embryonic cells retain all the potentialities of the zygote nucleus even at late stages when the tissues are clearly differentiated, it has become essential to believe that the cytoplasm exerts some control over which genes act at what time. Recently, Bloch (1962) has suggested that histones, a major component of DNA, may act as gene regulators. These histones have been shown to change during the development of the snail *Helix aspersa* (Bloch and Hew, 1960), although they do not seem to be involved in cell differentiation in early embryos of *Rana* (Moore, 1963). Beerman (1963) has suggested that the appearance of "puffs" on giant chromosomes of insects, is connected with "repression" or "induction" of gene activity, according to Monod and Jacob's terminology. Monod and Jacob's scheme (1961) of how genes and cytoplasmic molecules which are enzyme inducers or repressors may interact is now familiar to most biologists and is discussed with relation to embryonic development by Waddington (1962). The evidence in support of Monod and Jacob's scheme comes only from work on bacteria, however, and one should not assume that similar mechanisms necessarily operate in embryonic tissues.

Having emphasized the necessity for breaking down the conventional boundary between the functions of nucleus and cytoplasm and for admitting that the two interact, one may now question whether it is correct to regard the cytoplasm as a mere store of raw material. In Section I,B it was emphasized that the original spatial layout of the storage reserves can profoundly influence the course of development. Raven (1961) has suggested that the materials themselves carry "information," being packaged and arranged in ways that provide instructions for future development. The findings in electron microscopy linked with enzymology appear to support Raven's view. Thus, one may perhaps regard the yolk platelet as equipped with the enzymes for its own breakdown (Panijel, 1950; Nass, 1962; Deuchar, 1958) and some of these enzymes may even be incorporated into its crystalline lattice structure (Karasaki and Komoda, 1958). In mitochondria the enzyme activities can now be recognized as belonging to particular subunits that are visible under the electron microscope (Green and Fleischer, 1962). Therefore, there are at least two abundant, "self-controlling" systems in the cytoplasm of embryonic cells. Not to be forgotten is the "cytoplasmic DNA" also; if it acts in the same way as nuclear DNA, it may regulate what proteins are formed. But most embryologists prefer to think of the cytoplasmic DNA-like material as "nutritional" rather than carrying any particular information. A further possibility is that its information is redundant, i.e., not needed because it is already present in nuclear DNA. Raven (1961) has suggested that there must be much redundant information in the egg contents in order to account for the adaptability of embryonic cells.

Summarizing the current viewpoints, then, it may be said that present-day "preformationists" think, in static terms, of cytoplasmic materials pre-arranged and packaged in certain ways that are informative, whereas the "epigeneticists" are concerned with the dynamics of how these informative packages interact with one another, both within the cytoplasm and between the nucleus and the cytoplasm, in each embryonic cell. The higher levels of interaction between cells and tissues will be considered in the next section.

C. Cell Interactions and Induction Phenomena

The induction phenomena revealed by Spemann and his followers have dominated embryological work and thinking for many years (see Tiedemann, Chapter 1 of Volume II). The techniques for measuring transfer of materials between adjacent tissues have only recently been perfected, however, and many of the experimental results are inconclusive so far. Niu and Twitty (1953) were the first to use a cell-culture method to test the effects on ectoderm of material that normally exuded from mesoderm. But in later work Niu (1958) has used chemical extracts rather than exudates. There is still a great need for investigations on the metabolites normally exchanged between pairs of tissues that lie in contact with each other during embryonic development.

The word "induction" is used by microbiologists to describe the appearance of enzyme activities in response to the addition of suitable substrates. The few claims that enzyme induction is demonstrable in embryonic cells (Gordon and Roder, 1953; Boell, 1949; Stearns and Kostellow, 1958) have not yet been confirmed. But one should take into serious consideration the possibility that small-molecule metabolites in embryonic cells may sometimes evoke or stimulate enzyme activities, which could in their turn set off chains of reactions leading far along certain courses of differentiation. It may be that the classic "induction" of neural plate by mesoderm is directly linked to some enzyme induction. Does the Monod-Jacob scheme (according to which the inducer inactivates a cytoplasmic "repressor" which is the product of a "regulator" gene) apply to embryonic induction too?

It is clear that these new concepts do not offer easy explanations of tissue interaction in embryos. But their existence demands that the older, more vague concepts should be reformulated, just as the existence of labeling techniques makes it imperative to extend work on chemical exchanges between cells.

D. The "Field" and "Gradient" Concepts

Perhaps it ought to have been the main theme of this chapter to show whether or not the biochemical patterns in vertebrate embryos give evidence of the existence of the "fields" or "gradients" that have so often been postulated in order to explain experimental results. It must, however, be pointed out that these are statistical concepts; they were originally introduced in an attempt to explain differences in the frequencies of a certain type of result. For example, the idea of a "limb field" arises from the fact that a certain quality—that of being able to form a limb— is possessed *more often* by cells from what is called the center of the field than by cells at its periphery. It is deduced that the central cells possess some material in greater *quantity* than peripheral cells. But this inference is not itself put to any experimental test, and the evidence for a quantitative difference rests entirely on those differences in frequency of the results obtained. Therefore, most of the postulated fields or gradients would be adequately illustrated by "fate maps," modified only by the addition of contour lines whose spacing indicated the degree of certainty that the tissue named would develop from that region.

All the biochemical patterns described or illustrated in the present account are several steps away in argument from these fields and gradients of former authors. We need not, therefore, be surprised if they do not agree well with them. Taking any of the patterns mentioned so far, e.g., those illustrated in Fig. 5, it would be possible to say that they represent some gradient in concentration, usually from anterior to posterior, or dorsal to ventral, of a constituent or an enzyme activity. But it is doubtful if, considered in this way, they have much meaning. The gradients may simply be manifestations of the number of cells present or of the ratio of soluble constituents to yolk—which, as was emphasized previously (Section I,B) arises from the original distribution of components in the egg. Besides, one must remember that patterns which an observer "snapshots" at an arbitrarily chosen stage are not static; they may be changing very rapidly. Finally, we face an insoluble quibble as to which came first, the biochemical gradient or the visible difference in the embryonic cells. The biochemist likes to think that he is finding the *earliest* changes, but can he really do so? His evidence of biochemical differences is often derived from analyses of embryonic regions, which he was able to recognize and isolate because they already *looked* different.

Reflecting on all these logical difficulties, it is not possible to say more from the biochemical evidence than that gradients certainly exist in embryos. We still do not know how, or for how long, they are maintained; or whether they have any far-reaching morphogenetic significance.

One field that should receive special mention because there have been further speculations about its existence recently (see Raven, 1961; Curtis, 1962) is the cortical field of the amphibian egg. Both the classic centrifugation and recent grafting experiments suggest very strongly that the cortex carries information controlling the future polarity of the embryo. It seems unlikely, however, that such properties exist in the cortex of much larger eggs (e.g., those of birds) in which the whole embryo develops in a very small sector. Electron microscopy may reveal more about this in the future.

E. Concluding Remarks

1. Bringing the Concepts up to Date

To bring the concepts "field, gradient, and induction" into line with current thinking they now need to be conceived on a much smaller scale, at the ultrastructural level. The ribosome seems a suitable candidate for the title of "organizer" (using Spemann's term) because it acts as a template on which proteins are shaped and given organization. But, if we think of induction as involving enzyme induction (see Section IV,C), this property might have nothing to do with the ribosomes unless, in certain cases, their state of aggregation is affected by the enzyme.

"Fields" envisaged that the ultrastructural level could include the zones around mitochondria in which their enzymes act, as well as the zones around templates on which replication was taking place. The replicated molecules themselves may form concentration "gradients." There are many other cytoplasmic constituents, visible with the electron microscope, which appear to be distributed in concentration gradients too.

2. The "Molecular Embryology" of the Future

The recent evidence about patterns of isozyme distribution in embryonic tissues and on the different forms of hemoglobin (see Section III,E,3,b,f) has brought to light the fact that proteins themselves "develop" during embryonic life. This finding opens up an entirely new field for research and one in which the biochemists will feel much more at home. The gradual differentiation of these molecules in the embryo can now become the focus of interest, and its relevance to variations in cells extrapolated later.

Experimental control over the type of proteins synthesized is also a foreseeable possibility; DNA or ribosomes from selected sources could be used as determinants either in cell-free systems or injected into the egg. Injections of such materials into amphibian eggs have been tried by Markert and Ursprung (1963) and by Newth and Billett (personal communication, 1963), but with uncertain results so far, judged by morphological and histological criteria. There is a more immediate need to look at the proteins of such treated eggs. In conclusion, it may be emphasized that the *amphibian egg* is the most conveniently large cell to use for trials of this kind, and biochemists wishing to study protein transformations in cells would do well to turn their attention to this material. The embryo is, in fact, the most efficient of all protein-transforming systems.

ACKNOWLEDGMENTS

The author would like to thank Professor E. M. Baldwin, Professor J. Z. Young, and Dr. F. Billett for criticism of this manuscript and for some helpful suggestions.

REFERENCES

Adams, C. E., Hay, M. F., and Lutwak-Mann, C. (1961). *J. Embryol. Exptl. Morphol.* **9**, 468.

Adams, C. W. M., and Davison, A. N. (1959). *J. Neurochem.* **4**, 282.

Aketa, K. (1954). *Embryologia* (*Nagoya*) **2**, 63.

Allenspach, A. L., and Hamilton, H. L. (1962). *J. Morphol.* **111**, 321.

Ambellan, E., and Webster, G. (1962). *Develop. Biol.* **5**, 452.

Anders, F., Vester, F., Klinke, K., and Schumacher, H. (1962). *Biol. Zentr.* **81**, 45.

Ansell, G. B., and Richter, D. (1954). *Biochem. J.* **57**, 70.

Arndt, E. A. (1956). *Protoplasma* **47**, 1.

Atlas, M., Bond, V. P., and Cronkite, E. P. (1960). *J. Histochem. Cytochem.* **8**, 171.

Austin, C. R. (1961). "The Mammalian Egg." Blackwell, Oxford.

Austin, C. R., and Bishop, M. W. H. (1959). *Exptl. Cell Res.* **17**, 35.

Baldwin, E. M. (1949). "An Introduction to Comparative Biochemistry," 3rd ed. Cambridge Univ. Press, London and New York.

Baltus, E., and Brachet, J. (1962). *Biochim. Biophys. Acta* **61**, 157.

Barth, L. G., and Barth, L. J. (1954). "The Energetics of Development." Columbia Univ. Press, New York.

Barth, L. G., and Sze, L. C. (1953). *Physiol. Zool.* **26**, 205.

Beerman, W. (1963). *Colloq. Ges. Physiol. Chem. 1962* **13**, 64-79.

Bellairs, R. (1963). *J. Embryol. Exptl. Morphol.* **11**, 201.

Bensted, J. P. M., Dobbing, J., Morgan, R. S., Reid, R. T. W., and Payling-Wright, G. (1957). *J. Embryol. Exptl. Morphol.* **5**, 428.

Berg, G. G., and Creaser, C. W. (1953). *Anat. Record* **117**, 614.

Berg, G. G., and Szekerczes, J. (1962). *J. Exptl. Zool.* **149**, 147.

Bieber, A. L., Cheldelin, V. H., and Newburgh, R. W. (1962). *Biochemistry* **1**, 533.

Billett, F. (1957). *Biochem. J.* **67**, 463.

Billett, F., and Mulerkhar, L. (1958). *J. Embryol. Exptl. Morphol.* **6**, 52.

Billett, F., and Perry, M. M. (1957). *Proc. Roy. Phys. Soc. Edinburgh* **26**, 15.

Bloch, D. P. (1962). *Proc. Natl. Acad. Sci. U. S.* **48**, 324.

Bloch, D. P., and Hew, H. Y. C. (1960). *J. Biophys. Biochem. Cytol.* **8**, 69.

Block, R. J., and Weiss, K. W. (1956). "Amino-acid Handbook." C. C Thomas, Springfield, Illinois.

Boell, E. J. (1949). *Anat. Record* **105**, 600.

Boell, E. J., and Weber, R. (1955). *Exptl. Cell Res.* **9**, 559.

Borger, G., and Peters, T. (1933). *Z. Physiol. Chem.* **214**, 91.

Brachet, J. (1949). "Chemical Embryology." Wiley (Interscience), New York.

Brachet, J. (1960). "The Biochemistry of Development." Pergamon, New York.

Brachet, J. (1963). *Develop. Biol.* **7**, 348.

Brachet, J., Decroly-Briers, M., and Hoyez, J. (1958). *Bull. Soc. Chim. Biol.* **40**, 2035.

Brand, L., and Mahler, H. R. (1959). *J. Biol. Chem.* **234**, 1615.

Brand, L., Dahl, C., and Mahler, H. R. (1960). *J. Biol. Chem.* **235**, 2456.

Brante, G. (1949). *Acta Physiol. Scand.* **18** (Suppl. 63).

Briggs, R., and King, T. J. (1957). *J. Morphol.* **100**, 269.

Bristow, D. A., and Deuchar, E. M. (1964). *Exptl. Cell Res.* **35**, 580.

Brown, D. D., and Caston, J. D. (1962). *Develop. Biol.* **5**, 435.

Brown, D. D., and Littna, E. (1964a). *J. Mol. Biol.* **8**, 669.

Brown, D. D., and Littna, E. (1964b). *J. Mol. Biol.* **8**, 688.

Butschak, G. (1960). *Acta Biol. Med. Ger.* **5**, 83.

Camerino, P. W., and Wright, L. D. (1962). *J. Lipid Res.* **3**, 416.

Caston, J. D. (1962). *Develop. Biol.* **5**, 468.

Catayée, G., and Bonhomme, C. (1961). *Compt. Rend. Soc. Biol.* **155**, 2411.

Ceas, M. P., and Naselli, A. (1958). *Acta Embryol. Exptl. Morphol.* **1**, 207.

Chaube, S., and Carter, C. E. (1961). *Biochem. Pharmacol.* **7**, 117.

Chen, P. S. (1956). *Exptl. Cell Res.* **10**, 675.

Chen, P. S. (1960). *Exptl. Cell Res.* **21**, 523.

Chèvremont, M., Bassleer, R., and Baeckeland, E. (1960). *Arch. Biol. (Liege)* **72**, 511.

Clavert, J. (1962). *Advan. Morphogenesis* **2**, 27-60.

Clayton, R. M. (1953). *J. Embryol. Exptl. Morphol.* **1**, 25.

Colas, J., and Devillers, C. (1962). *Compt. Rend.* **255**, 997.

Coleman, J. R. (1962). *Develop. Biol.* **5**, 232.

Colle-Vandevelde, A. (1961). *J. Embryol. Exptl. Morphol.* **9**, 68.

Consden, R., Gordon, A. H., and Martin, A. J. P. (1944). *Biochem. J.* **38**, 224.

Craig, M. L., and Russell, E. S. (1964). *Develop. Biol.* **10**, 191.

Curtis, A. S. G. (1957). *Proc. Roy. Phys. Soc. Edinburgh* **26**, 25.

Curtis, A. S. G. (1962). *J. Embryol. Exptl. Morphol.* **10**, 410.

Curtis, D. R., and Watkins, J. C. (1963). *J. Physiol. (London)* **166**, 1.

Dalcq, A. M. (1957). "Introduction to General Embryology." Oxford Univ. Press, London and New York.

Dalcq, A. M. (1960). *In* "Fundamental Aspects of Normal and Malignant Growth" (W. W. Nowinski, ed.), pp. 305-400. Elsevier, Amsterdam.

Dalcq, A. M., and Pasteels, J. (1938). *Acad. Roy. Med. Belg.* [3] **6**, 261.

Dalcq, A. M., and Pasteels, J. (1955). *Exptl. Cell Res. Suppl.* **3**, 72.

Davidson, J. N. (1961). "The Biochemistry of the Nucleic Acids." Methuen, London and Wiley, New York.

D'Amelio, V., and Ceas, M. P. (1957). *Experientia* **13**, 152.

D'Amelio, V., and Salvo, A. M. (1961). *Acta Embryol. Morphol. Exptl.* **4**, 250.

de Gennaro, L. D. (1959). *Growth* **23**, 235.

DeHaan, R. L. (1958). *In* "The Chemical Basis of Development" (W. D. McElroy and B. Glass, eds.), pp. 339-380. Johns Hopkins Press, Baltimore, Maryland.

Denis, H. (1961). *J. Embryol. Exptl. Morphol.* **9**, 422.

Detlaff, T. A. (1962). *J. Embryol. Exptl. Morphol.* **10**, 1.

Deuchar, E. M. (1956). *J. Embryol. Exptl. Morphol.* **4**, 327.
Deuchar, E. M. (1958). *J. Embryol. Exptl. Morphol.* **6**, 223.
Deuchar, E. M (1960a). *Develop. Biol.* **2**, 129.
Deuchar, E. M. (1960b). *J. Embryol. Exptl. Morphol.* **8**, 259.
Deuchar, E. M. (1961a). *Exptl. Cell Res.* **25**, 364; **26**, 568.
Deuchar, E. M. (1961b). *Nature* **191**, 1006.
Deuchar, E. M. (1962). *Biol. Rev. Cambridge Phil. Soc.* **37**, 378.
Deuchar, E. M. (1963a). *Acta Embryol. Exptl. Morphol.* **6**, 1.
Deuchar, E. M. (1963b). *Exptl. Cell Res.* **30**, 528.
Deuchar, E. M., and Herrmann, H. (1962). *Acta Embryol. Morphol. Exptl.* **5**, 161.
Deuchar, E. M., and Bristow, D. A. (1965). *Nature (London)* **205**, 1321.
de Villafranca, G. W. (1954). *J. Exptl. Zool.* **127**, 367.
Devillers, C. (1951). *Arch. Anat. Microscop.* **40**, 298.
Devillers, C. (1961). *Advan. Morphogenesis* **1**, 379-428.
Devillers, C., and Rosenberg, J. (1953). *Compt. Rend.* **237**, 1561.
Devillers, C., Colas, J., and Cantacuzène, A.-M. (1957). *Compt. Rend.* **245**, 1461.
Duspiva, F. (1939). *Protoplasma* **32**, 211.
Duspiva, F. (1963). *Colloq. Ges. Physiol. Chem. 1962* **13**, 205-234.
Eakin R. M., and Lehmann, F. E. (1957). *Arch. Entwicklungsmech. Organ.* **150**, 177.
Eakin, R. M., Kutsky, P. B., and Berg, W. E. (1951). *Proc. Soc. Exptl. Biol. Med.* **78**, 502.
Ebert, J. D. (1958). In "The Chemical Basis of Development" (W. D. McElroy and B. Glass, eds.), pp. 526-545. Johns Hopkins Press, Baltimore, Maryland.
Ebert, J. D., and Wilt, F. H. (1960). *Quart. Rev. Biol.* **35**, 261.
Ebert, P. S., and Prockop, D. J. (1962). *Biochem. Biophys. Res. Commun.* **8**, 305.
Emanuelsson, H. (1955). *Acta Physiol. Scand.* **34**, 124.
Emanuelsson, H. (1958). *Acta Physiol. Scand.* **44**, 336.
Emanuelsson, H. (1961a). *Acta Physiol. Scand.* **52**, 197.
Emanuelsson, H. (1961b). *Acta Physiol. Scand.* **53**, 46.
Eppenberger, H. M., Eppenberger, M., Richterich, R., and Aebi, H. (1964). *Develop. Biol.* **10**, 1.
Feldman, M., and Waddington, C. H. (1955). *J. Embryol. Exptl. Morphol.* **3**, 44.
Felix, K., Baumer, L., and Schörner, E. (1936). *Z. Physiol. Chem.* **243**, 43.
Fell, H. B. (1961). *Symp. Soc. Study Develop. Growth* **19**, 139-160.
Fell, H. B., Dingle, J. D., and Webb, M. (1962). *Biochem. J.* **83**, 63.
Ficq, A. (1954). *J. Embryol. Exptl. Morphol.* **2**, 194.
Finamore, F. J. (1955). *Exptl. Cell Res.* **8**, 533.
Finamore, F. J. (1962). *J. Cellular Comp. Physiol.* **60** (Suppl. 1), 14.
Finamore, F. J., and Volkin, E. (1958). *Exptl. Cell Res.* **15**, 405.
Fine, I. H., Kaplan, N. O., and Kuftiner, D. (1963). *Biochemistry* **2**, 116.
Fish, W. J., Boyd, J. E., and Stokes, W. M. (1962). *J. Biol. Chem.* **237**, 334.
Flexner, L. B., Belknap, E. L., and Flexner, J. B. (1953). *J. Cellular Comp. Physiol.* **42**, 151.
Flexner, L. B., Flexner, J. B., Roberts, R. B., and de la Haba, G. (1960). *Develop. Biol.* **2**, 288.
Flickinger, R. A. (1949). *J. Exptl. Zool.* **112**, 465.
Flickinger, R. A. (1956). *J. Exptl. Zool.* **131**, 307.
Flickinger, R. A. (1961). *Symp. Germ Cells Develop., Pallanza, 1960* pp. 29-48.
Flickinger, R. A., and Stone, G. (1960). *Exptl. Cell Res.* **21**, 541.
Flickinger, R. A., Hatton, E., and Rounds, D. E. (1959). *Exptl. Cell Res.* **17**, 30.

Friedberg, F., and Eakin, R. M. (1949). *J. Exptl. Zool.* **110**, 33.

Friedberg, F., Schulman, M. P., and Greenberg, D. M. (1948). *J. Biol. Chem.* **173**, 437.

Gahan, P. B., Chayen, J., and Silcox, A. A. (1962). *Nature* **195**, 1115.

Giudice, G. (1962). *Develop. Biol.* **5**, 402.

Glenister, T. W. (1961). *J. Anat.* **95**, 474.

Glucksmann, A. (1951). *Biol. Rev. Cambridge Phil. Soc.* **26**, 59.

Goldstein, B., and Gintsbourg, M. (1936). *Enzymologia* **1**, 369.

Goldstein, B., and Milgrom, E. J. (1935). *Ukrain. Biokhem. Zh.* **8**, 139.

Gordon, M. W., and Roder, M. (1953). *J. Biol. Chem.* **200**, 859.

Green, D. E., and Fleischer, S. (1962). *In* "Horizons in Biochemistry" (M. Kasha and B. Pullman, eds.), pp. 381-420. Academic Press, New York.

Green, N. M., and Lowther, D. A. (1959). *Biochem. J.* **71**, 55.

Gregg, J. R., and Ornstein, N. (1953). *Biol. Bull.* **105**, 466.

Grodzinski, Z. (1956). *Acta Biol. Exptl. (Lodz)* **17**, 41.

Gurdon, J. B. (1962). *Develop. Biol.* **4**, 256.

Hamburger, V., and Hamilton, H. L. (1951). *J. Morphol.* **88**, 49.

Hansson, E., and Garzo, T. (1961). *Experientia* **17**, 502.

Harkness, M. L., and Harkness, R. D. (1955). *J. Physiol. (London)* **128**, 225.

Harkness, R. D. (1961). *Biol. Rev. Cambridge Phil. Soc.* **37**, 399.

Hayes, F. R. (1949). *Quart. Rev. Biol.* **24**, 281.

Hell, A. (1964). *J. Embryol. Exptl. Morphol.* **12**, 609, 621.

Herrmann, H. (1953). *J. Embryol. Exptl. Morphol.* **1**, 291.

Herrmann, H. (1960). *Science* **132**, 529.

Herrmann, H., and Lebeau, P. L. (1962). *J. Cell Biol.* **13**, 465.

Herrmann, H., and Nicholas, J. S. (1948). *J. Exptl. Zool.* **107**, 177.

Herrmann, H., and Schultz, P. W. (1958). *Arch. Biochem.* **73**, 296.

Herrmann, H., Lerman, L., and White, P. W. (1958). *Biochim. Biophys. Acta* **27**, 161.

Hishida, T.-O., and Nakano, E. (1954). *Embryologia (Nagoya)* **2**, 67.

Hisoaka, K.-K., and Firlit, C. F. (1962). *J. Morphol.* **111**, 239.

Hisoaka, K.-K., and Hopper, A. F. (1957). *Anat. Record* **129**, 297.

Hoagland, M. B., Keller, E. B., and Zamecnik, P. C. (1956). *J. Biol. Chem.* **218**, 345.

Hoff-Jørgensen, E., and Zeuthen, E. (1951). *Nature* **169**, 245.

Holder, L. A., and Bellairs, A. d'A. (1962). *J. Herpetol.* **3**, 54.

Holtfreter, J. (1943). *J. Exptl. Zool.* **93**, 251.

Holtfreter, J., Koszalka, T. R., and Miller, L. L. (1950). *Exptl. Cell Res.* **1**, 453.

Holtzer, H. (1961). *Symp. Soc. Study Develop. Growth* **19**, 35-87.

Holtzer, H., Marshall, J. M., and Finck, H. (1957). *J. Biophys. Biochem. Cytol.* **3**, 705.

Hopsu, V. K., Ruponen, S., and Talanti, S. (1961). *Experientia* **17**, 271.

Huehns, E. R., and Dance, N. (1964). *Nature* **201**, 1095.

Huehns, E. R., Flynn, F. V., Butler, E. A., and Beaven, G. H. (1961). *Nature* **189**, 496.

Huggett, A. St. G. (1929). *J. Physiol. (London)* **47**, 360.

Ignat'eva, G. M. (1959). *Dokl. Biol. Sci. Sect. (English Transl.)* **128**, 774.

Inoue, K. (1961a). *Develop. Biol.* **3**, 657.

Inoue, K. (1961b). *J. Embryol. Exptl. Morphol.* **9**, 563.

Inoue, K. (1961c). *Acta Embryol. Exptl. Morphol.* **4**, 183.

Ito, Y. (1957). *Acta Embryol. Exptl. Morphol.* **1**, 118.

Jackson, S. F. (1956). *Proc. Roy. Soc.* **B144**, 556.

Jackson, S. F. (1958). *Federation Proc.* **17**, 78.

Jackson, S. F., and Smith, R. H. (1957). *J. Biophys. Biochem. Cytol.* **3**, 913.

Jaeger, L. (1945). *J. Cellular Comp. Physiol.* **25**, 97.

Jolley, R. L., and Labby, D. H. (1960). *Arch. Biochem. Biophys.* **90**, 122.

Kafer, E., and Pollak, J. K. (1961). *Exptl. Cell Res.* **22**, 120.

Kaighn, M. E. (1964). *Develop. Biol.* **9**, 56.

Karasaki, S. (1963). *J. Ultrastruct. Res.* **9**, 225.

Karasaki, S., and Komoda, T. (1958). *Nature* **181**, 407.

Kavanau, J. L. (1958). *In* "The Chemical Basis of Development" (W. D. McElroy and B. Glass, eds.), pp. 443-447. Johns Hopkins Press, Baltimore, Maryland.

Kellehar, P., and Villee, C. (1962). *Biochim. Biophys. Acta* **59**, 252.

Kenney, F. T., and Kletchmer, N. (1959). *J. Clin. Invest.* **38**, 2189.

Kivrikko, K. I. (1963). *Nature* **197**, 593.

Klein, N. W., McConnell, E., and Buckingham, B. J. (1962). *Develop. Biol.* **5**, 296.

Kobrle, V., and Chvapil, M. (1961). *Nature* **190**, 909.

Kohn, J. (1961). *Clin. Chim. Acta* **3**, 450.

Krammer, K. (1950). Dissertation, Rostock.

Kuiken, K. A., Norman, W. H., Lyman, C. M., Hale, F., and Blotter, L. (1943). *J. Biol. Chem.* **151**, 615.

Kusa, M. (1956). *Embryologia (Nagoya)* **3**, 105.

Kutsky, P. B., Eakin, R. M., Berg, W. E., and Kavanau, J. L. (1953). *J. Exptl. Zool.* **124**, 263.

Kuusi, T. (1958). *Arch. Soc. Zool. Botan. Fennicae "Vanamo"* **13**, 97.

Léderer, E., and Léderer, M. (1955). "Chromatography: A Review of Principles and Applications." Elsevier, Amsterdam.

Levy, B. M. (1962). *Cancer Res.* **22**, 441.

Linderstrøm-Lang, K., and Holter, H. (1933). *Compt. Rend. Trav. Lab. Carlsberg Ser. Chim.* **19**, 1.

Løvtrup, S. (1955). *Compt. Rend. Trav. Lab. Carlsberg Ser. Chim.* **29**, 262.

Løvtrup, S. (1958). *J. Embryol. Exptl. Morphol.* **6**, 15.

Løvtrup, S., and Pigon, A. (1958). *J. Embryol. Exptl. Morphol.* **6**, 486.

Lu, C. Y., and Finamore, F. J. (1963). *Comp. Biochem. Physiol.* **9**, 41.

Lucy, J. A. (1960). *Biol. Rev. Cambridge Phil. Soc.* **35**, 533.

Lucy, J. A., and Rinaldini, L. M. (1959). *Exptl. Cell Res.* **17**, 385.

Lutz, H., and Bernard, S. (1960). *Compt. Rend.* **250**, 192.

Maderson, P. F. A., and Bellairs, A. d'A. (1962). *Nature* **195**, 401.

Mahler, H. R., Wittenberger, M. H., and Brand, L. (1958). *J. Biol. Chem.* **233**, 770.

Manwell, C., Baker, C. M. A., Roslansky, J. D., and Foght, M. (1963a). *Proc. Natl. Acad. Sci. U. S.* **49**, 496.

Manwell, C., Baker, C., and Childers, W. (1963b). *Comp. Biochem. Physiol.* **10**, 103.

Markert, C. L., and Ursprung, H. (1962). *Develop. Biol.* **5**, 363.

Markert, C. L., and Ursprung, H. (1963). *Develop. Biol.* **7**, 560.

Marshall, M. E., and Deutsch, H. F. (1950). *J. Biol. Chem.* **185**, 155.

Mitoma, C., Smith, T. E., Friedberg, F., and Rayford, C. (1959). *J. Biol. Chem.* **234**, 78.

Monod, J., and Jacob, F. (1961). *Cold Spring Harbor Symp. Quant. Biol.* **26**, 389.

Monroy, A., Ishida, M., and Nakano, E. (1961). *Embryologia (Nagoya)* **6**, 151.

Mookerjee, S., Deuchar, E. M., and Waddington, C. H. (1953). *J. Embryol. Exptl. Morphol.* **1**, 399.

Moore, B. C. (1963). *Proc. Natl. Acad. Sci. U. S.* **50**, 1018.

Mulnard, J. (1960). *Symp. Germ Cells Develop., Pallanza, 1960* pp. 639-688.

Nace, G. W., and Schechtman, A. M. (1948). *J. Exptl. Zool.* **108**, 217.

Nace, G. W., and Schechtman, A. M. (1953). *J. Exptl. Zool.* **122**, 423.

Nakano, E. (1956). *Embryologia (Nagoya)* **3**, 89.

Nass, S. (1962). *Biol. Bull.* **122**, 232.

Needham, J. (1931). "Chemical Embryology," 3 vols. Cambridge Univ. Press, London and New York.

Needham, J. (1942). "Biochemistry and Morphogenesis." Cambridge Univ. Press, London and New York.

Neuberger, A., and Slack, H. G. B. (1953). *Biochem. J.* **53**, 47.

Neuberger, A., Perrone, J. C., and Slack, H. G. B. (1951). *Biochem. J.* **49**, 199.

Neuman, R. E. (1950). *Proc. Soc. Exptl. Biol. Med.* **75**, 37.

New, D. A. T. (1955). *J. Embryol. Exptl. Morphol.* **3**, 326.

New, D. A. T., and Stein, K. F. (1964). *J. Embryol. Exptl. Morphol.* **12**, 101.

Newburgh, R. W., Buckingham, B., and Herrmann, H. (1962). *Arch. Biochem. Biophys.* **97**, 94.

Nicholas, J. S. (1950). *Proc. Am. Phil. Soc.* **94**, 175.

Niu, M. C. (1958). *Proc. Natl. Acad. Sci. U. S.* **44**, 1264.

Niu, M. C., and Twitty, V. C. (1953). *Proc. Natl. Acad. Sci. U. S.* **39**, 985.

O'Brien, B. R. A. (1961a). *Stain Technol.* **36**, 57.

O'Brien, B. R. A. (1961b). *J. Embryol. Exptl. Morphol.* **9**, 202.

Ogawa, Y. (1960). *Nature* **186**, 77.

Ogawa, Y. (1961). *Biochim. Biophys. Acta* **54**, 397.

Ohi, Y. (1962). *Embryologia (Nagoya)* **7**, 208.

Olivo, F. (1959). *Boll. Soc. Ital. Biol. Sper.* **35**, 371.

Oppenheimer, J. (1958). *J. Exptl. Zool.* **140**, 247.

Owen, J. A., Silberman, H. J., and Got, C. (1958). *Nature* **182**, 1373.

Panijel, J. (1950). *Biochim. Biophys. Acta* **5**, 349.

Pantelouris, E. M., and Hale, P. A. (1962). *Nature* **195**, 79.

Pantelouris, E. M., and Mulerkhar, L. (1957). *J. Embryol. Exptl. Morphol.* **5**, 51.

Pasteels, J. (1940). *Arch. Biol. (Paris)* **51**, 335.

Pelc, S. R., Coombes, J. D., and Budd, G. C. (1961). *Exptl. Cell Res.* **24**, 192.

Persijn, J. P., Daems, W. T., de Man, J. C. H., and Meijer, A. E. F. H. (1961). *Histochemie* **2**, 372.

Peterson, E. R., and Murray, M. R. (1955). *Am. J. Anat.* **96**, 319.

Pfautsch, M.-E. (1960). *Embryologia (Nagoya)* **5**, 139.

Philip, J., and Vesell, E. S. (1962). *Proc. Soc. Exptl. Biol. Med.* **110**, 582.

Pickford, G. E. (1943). *J. Exptl. Zool.* **92**, 143.

Popp, R. A. (1958). *J. Exptl. Zool.* **138**, 1.

Prockop, D. J., Peterkofsky, B., and Udenfriend, S. (1962). *J. Biol. Chem.* **237**, 1581.

Proffit, W. R., and Edwards, L. E. (1962). *J. Exptl. Zool.* **151**, 53.

Radde, I., and McCance, R. A. (1959). *Nature* **183**, 115.

Ramon y Cajal, S. (1928). "Degeneration and Regeneration of the Nervous System." (R. M. May, transl. and ed.), Oxford Univ. Press, London and New York.

Raven, C. P. (1961). "Oögenesis: The Storage of Developmental Information." Pergamon, New York.
Rawles, M. E. (1936). *J. Exptl. Zool.* **72**, 271.
Rizzoli, C. (1957). *Boll. Soc. Ital. Biol. Sper.* **33**, 223.
Roberts, E., and Borges, P. R. F. (1955). *Cancer Res.* **15**, 697.
Roberts, E., Lowe, I. P., Chanin, M., and Jelinek, B. (1957). *J. Exptl. Zool.* **135**, 239.
Roosen-Runge, E. C. (1938). *Biol. Bull.* **75**, 119.
Rosenbaum, R. M. (1960). *Develop. Biol.* **2**, 427.
Rosenberg, E. E. (1960). *Acta Anat.* **41**, 300.
Rothfels, U. (1954). *J. Exptl. Zool.* **135**, 239.
Rudnick, D. (1959). *J. Exptl. Zool.* **142**, 643.
Rudnick, D. (1963). *Develop. Biol.* **7**, 94.
Rudnick, D., and Waelsch, H. (1955). *J. Exptl. Zool.* **129**, 309.
Rudnick, D., Mela, P., and Waelsch, H. (1953). *Nature* **172**, 253.
Sauer, M. E., and Chittenden, A. C. (1959). *Exptl. Cell Res.* **16**, 1.
Schechtman, A. M. (1948). *Proc. Soc. Exptl. Biol. Med.* **68**, 263.
Schultz, P. W., and Herrmann, H. (1958). *J. Embryol. Exptl. Morphol.* **6**, 262.
Shen, S. C., Greenfield, P., and Boell, E. J. (1955). *J. Comp. Neurol.* **102**, 717.
Shen, S. C., Greenfield, P., and Boell, E. J. (1956). *J. Comp. Neurol.* **106**, 433.
Singer, S. J., and Schick, A. F. (1961). *J. Biophys. Biochem. Cytol.* **9**, 519.
Sirlin, J. L., and Waddington, C. H. (1954). *Nature* **174**, 309.
Sirlin, J. L., and Waddington, C. H. (1956). *Exptl. Cell Res.* **11**, 197.
Sirlin, J. L., Brahma, S. K., and Waddington, C. H. (1956). *J. Embryol. Exptl. Morphol.* **4**, 248.
Smith, S. (1957). *In* "The Physiology of Fishes" (M. E. Brown, ed.), Vol. 1, pp. 323-359. Academic Press, New York.
Snedecor, J. G., and Henrikson, R. C. (1959). *Anat. Record* **134**, 641 (abstr.).
Solomon, J. B. (1957a). *Biochim. Biophys. Acta* **23**, 241.
Solomon, J. B. (1957b). *Biochim. Biophys. Acta* **24**, 584.
Spar, G. L. (1953). *J. Exptl. Zool.* **123**, 467.
Spek, J. (1942). *Protoplasma* **37**, 49.
Spiegel, M., and Frankel, D. L. (1961). *Science* **133**, 275.
Spratt, N. T. (1948). *J. Exptl. Zool.* **107**, 39.
Spratt, N. T. (1958). *In* "The Chemical Basis of Development" (W. D. McElroy and B. Glass, eds.), pp. 629-645. Johns Hopkins Press, Baltimore, Maryland.
Sriramulu, V. (1959a). *Proc. Indian Acad. Sci.* **B49**, 108.
Sriramulu, V. (1959b). *J. Animal Morphol. Physiol.* **6**, 109.
Stearns, R. N., and Kostellow, A. B. (1958). *In* "The Chemical Basis of Development" (W. D. McElroy and B. Glass, eds.), pp. 448-457. Johns Hopkins Press, Baltimore, Maryland.
Stegner, H.-E. (1960). *Z. Mikroskop. Anat. Forsch.* **66**, 489.
Stockdale, F. E., Abbott, J., Holtzer, S., and Holtzer, H. (1963). *Develop. Biol.* **7**, 293.
Stolk, A. (1959). *Nature* **183**, 763.
Stolk, A. (1961). *Koninkl. Ned. Akad. Wetenschap. Proc. Ser. C* **64**, 560.
Sze, L. C. (1953). *J. Exptl. Zool.* **122**, 577.
Tatarskaia, R. I., Kafiani, K. K., and Kanopkaite, S. J. (1958). *Biokhimiya* **23**, 494.
Tencer, R. (1961). *Exptl. Cell Res.* **23**, 418.

Thompson, R. G., and Ballou, J. E. (1956). *J. Biol. Chem.* **223**, 795.

Tooze, J., and Davies, H. G. (1963). *J. Cell Biol.* **16**, 501.

Trinkaus, J. P. (1949). *Proc. Natl. Acad. Sci. U. S.* **35**, 218.

Urbani, E. (1955). *Experientia* **11**, 209.

Vainio, T., Saxen, L., Toivönen, S., and Rapola, J. (1962). *Exptl. Cell Res.* **27**, 527.

Vakaet, L. (1955). *Arch. Biol. (Liege)* **66**, 1.

Van der Ghinst, M. (1935). *Bull. Histol.* **12**, 257.

von Hahn, H. P., and Herrmann, H. (1962). *Develop. Biol.* **5**, 309.

Vyazow, A. E. (1962). "Immunogenese Embryologia." USSR Acad. Sci. Publ., Moscow.

Waddington, C. H. (1932). *Phil. Trans. Roy. Soc.* **B221**, 179.

Waddington, C. H. (1956). "Principles of Embryology." Macmillan, New York.

Waddington, C. H. (1962). "New Patterns in Genetics and Development." Columbia Univ. Press, New York.

Waddington, C. H., and Mulerkhar, L. (1957). *Proc. Zool. Soc. Bengal (Mookerjee Mem. Vol.)* p. 141.

Waddington, C. H., and Perry, M. M. (1962). *Proc. Roy. Soc.* **B156**, 459.

Waddington, C. H., and Sirlin, J. L. (1954). *J. Embryol. Exptl. Morphol.* **2**, 340.

Waddington, C. H., Feldman, M., and Perry, M. M. (1955). *Exptl. Cell Res. Suppl.* **3**, 360.

Wallace, R. A. (1961). *Develop. Biol.* **3**, 486.

Walshe, J. W. (1953). *Lancet* i, 1075.

Walter, H., and Mahler, H. R. (1958). *J. Biol. Chem.* **230**, 241.

Warshawsky, H., and Droz, B. (1962). *Anat. Record* **142**, 289 (abstr.).

Watterson, R. L. (1949). *J. Morphol.* **85**, 337.

Watterson, R. L., Veneziano, R., and Brown, D. A. (1958). *Physiol. Zool.* **31**, 49.

Weber, R. (1962). *Symp. Intern. Soc. Cell Biol.* **1**, 393-409.

Weber, R., and Boell, E. J. (1962). *Develop. Biol.* **4**, 452.

Weil-Malherbe, H. (1953). *Naturwissenschaften* **40**, 545.

Wiggert, B. O., and Villee, C. A. (1964). *J. Biol. Chem.* **239**, 444.

Wilde, C. E. (1955). *J. Morphol.* **97**, 313.

Wilde, C. E. (1956). *J. Exptl. Zool.* **133**, 409.

Wilt, F. H. (1962). *Proc. Natl. Acad. Sci. U. S.* **48**, 1582.

Wise, R. W., Ballard, F. J., and Ezekiel, E. (1963). *Comp. Biochem. Physiol.* **9**, 23.

Woerdeman, M. W. (1933). *Proc. Koninkl. Akad. Wetenschap. Amsterdam* **36**, 477.

Yamamoto, T. (1954). *Exptl. Cell Res.* **6**, 56.

Yamamoto, T. (1956). *Exptl. Cell Res.* **10**, 387.

Yamamoto, T. (1962). *Embryologia (Nagoya)* **7**, 228.

Zeuthen, E. (1952). *Pubbl. Staz. Zool. Napoli* **23**, 47.

Zotin, A. I. (1958). *J. Embryol. Exptl. Morphol.* **6**, 564.

Part III

GENERAL BIOCHEMISTRY OF DEVELOPMENT

Chapter 6

ENZYME DEVELOPMENT IN RELATION TO FUNCTIONAL DIFFERENTIATION

FLORENCE MOOG

Department of Zoology
Washington University
St. Louis, Missouri

I. Introduction

Although less than 20 years have elapsed since Green (1946) observed that textbooks of biochemistry treat "enzymes much in the manner that feathers and scales are dealt with in textbooks of anatomy," the preenzymatic approach now seems to belong to the remote past. In recent years it has been recognized that the protein catalysts we call enzymes are of the quintessence of life. Enzymatic considerations loom large in physiology, immunology, endocrinology, even microanatomy. In biochemistry itself a preponderant part of research is currently devoted to enzyme synthesis, enzyme structure, and enzyme action.

To every general problem of enzymology, the study of enzymes in embryos adds a dimension. The problems of enzyme form and structure are in embryology extended into the area of differentiation at the molecular level, where one must inquire into the degree of resemblance between an enzyme molecule performing a given action in mature tissue, and its counterpart in earlier stages. The regulation of enzyme activity poses some acute questions in systems in which both enzymes and regulators are developing. The role of enzymes in the physiology of adult organs must be expanded in developmental stages into a study of the ontogeny of physiological processes, including not only matters like transport, synthesis, and contraction, but reaching also to the difficult problems, peculiar to the embryo, of induction and differentiation. At the level of gene action, investigations into enzyme development hold particular promise, for the appearance or disappearance of an enzyme at a given site may provide clues to the differential gene activities that must be basic to the larger patterns of embryogeny.

In the three decades since Needham (1931) served as "skillful obstetrician" to the science of chemical embryology, our knowledge of enzymes in development has grown lustily. In 1930 there were scarcely twenty useful papers in the field (and most of those on extracellular enzymes); now as many may appear in a month. The advances that have been made are, of course, uneven. Certainly the old romantic notion of an all but enzyme-free egg that only gradually acquires the biochemical complexity of its elders has long since perished under the weight of evidence, as studies on the sea urchin egg have shown with particular force (cf. Chapter 1 in this volume). That each enzyme increases at its own rate, according to its own pattern, is also fully established (cf. Moog, 1952; Boell, 1955). Figure 1 exemplifies the kinds of evidence from which these conclusions spring. It is clear too that embryogenesis has its reflection in the energetics and metabolism of development (Boell, 1955). The control of differentiation itself, however, the area in which the highest hopes were once centered, has yielded the severest disappointments. Although enzymes no doubt play a role, the agents that direct the process appear to lie at the still obscure level of dynamic cell structure.

This chapter will be concerned with enzymes *qua* enzymes. It will deal with enzymes primarily as objects of differentiation—as definable molecules that arise out of differentiative processes to become functional components of the cells in which they appear. The chapter will consider the patterns of enzyme growth and regression, and the functional conse-

quences of these patterns in the developmental continuum; it will examine the character of enzymes during the course of development and
the factors that affect enzyme activity and growth. Metabolic studies in
which enzyme action is inferred rather than specifically identified are
treated in Chapters 3–5 of this volume. This chapter will be largely concerned with vertebrates, since these animals have been the usual subjects

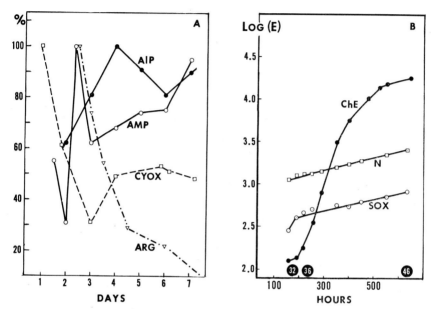

FIG. 1. Researches illustrating the enzymatic richness of early embryonic tissue
and the individuality of enzyme accumulation patterns.   A. Activities of four enzymes
of different types during the first week of development of the chick embryo. Activities
are plotted as percentages of the highest activity determined during the first week
of development. Of the four enzymes shown, only cytochrome oxidase attains a higher
level (130%) later in the period of incubation. AlP, alkaline phosphatase; AMP,
aminopeptidase; ARG, arginase; CYOX, cytochrome oxidase. Adapted from Moog,
(1952).   B. The increase of two enzymes in the brain of *Ambystoma punctatum*,
in relation to the growth of tissue nitrogen. Succinoxidase (SOX) parallels accumulation of general tissue nitrogen (N), but cholinesterase (ChE) follows an independent
pattern. Stage numbers are encircled in black (Boell *et al.*, 1955).

of investigations directed at the kind of problems to which this chapter
is addressed.

II. The Meaning of Enzyme Measurements

It is easy to assay an enzyme in a fragment of tissue or in two fragments separated by the dimension of time. Frequently, such assays reveal
that the specific activity of the enzyme has increased faster than the

tissue has grown, i.e., the activity per unit protein rises with time. What does such a change mean? It is not easy to interpret.

To be entirely valid, the interpretation ought to be based on a single cell type, not on an average of many cell types. The specific activity of an enzyme in an embryonic organ might rise because of faster growth of the enzyme itself, or of faster growth of a cell type rich in the enzyme. Partly to avoid this difficulty there has been a tendency to concentrate on organs, like liver and muscle, that are comparatively simple histologically. In complex organs, quantitative determinations of enzyme activity are made more meaningful if they are paralleled by histological or preferably histochemical analyses. Nilausen's demonstration (1958) that the increase of alkaline phosphatase in the human fetal retina is accounted for by the advance of vasoformative tissue is an example of the way in which localization studies obviate the misconceptions that might arise from simple determination of activity in a homogenate. Similar clarification can be attained by the microanalysis of small, identifiable masses of cells. An example is provided by the work of Smith and Kissane (1963), described in Section VII.

The interpretation of the functional significance of an enzyme depends also on knowledge of localization at the intracellular level. Clearly, an enzyme molecule attached to a membrane or particle may perform a different service from one not so bound. Shifts in localization may be considerable. In embryonic rat liver, for example, 55 % of alanine-glutamic acid transferase is bound to mitochondria, but only 20 % is so bound in mature tissue (Kafer and Pollak, 1961). The possibility that certain enzymes are liberated from their binding sites in the course of homogenization must also be taken into account. This precaution applies most acutely to those enzymes that in certain tissues, under certain physiological conditions, are sequestered in lysosomes (see Section V,A,2).

Granted that a valid increase in enzyme activity occurs in an interval of time, several explanations are possible. Two have been appreciated for many years: (1) The amount of apoenzyme has grown faster than the protein mass in which it occurs; (2) there has been a gain of dissociable activators, or a loss of dissociable inhibitors. Such dissociable factors may occur within the same cells as the enzyme itself, and thus be relevant to the problem of *in vivo* activity, or they may be irrelevant in the sense of being freed from other cells by the homogenization process. In the past it has been generally accepted that a linear relation between homogenate concentration and reaction rate under optimal conditions justified the conclusion that enzyme concentration is measured (cf. Boell, 1955). In addition, many workers routinely combine homogenates of high and low activity, or boiled and unboiled homogenates, to eliminate the possibility that observed activity differences are due to dissociable or heat-stable factors.

Recent research, however, has made it clear that an increase in enzyme activity, in the absence of dissociable activators or inhibitors, is no more than circumstantial evidence for differential synthesis of apoenzyme protein. Wright (1960) has demonstrated that the same enzyme may change in stability during the course of development, so that some stages may, under certain conditions, give false low values. Moreover, numerous enzymes are apparently able to undergo interconversions between active and inactive states under physiological conditions; such interconversions may entail alternate monomeric and polymeric states or they may reflect the occurrence of an inhibitor that is under some conditions firmly bound at the active site. These possibilities, as they apply to developmental problems, will be considered in Sections VI,B,1 and VII.

The actual significance of an apparent change in enzyme activity may vary with the investigator's point of view. If one is primarily interested in the enzyme as an object of differentiation, it is of first importance to know when it is being synthesized at a differential rate; whether it is synthesized in active or inactive form is secondary. Unless the timing of synthesis is known, it is obviously fruitless to attempt to interpret the result in terms of the differentiative mechanism controlling the genes responsible for the formation of the enzyme.

If, on the other hand, one is interested in the contribution that the enzyme makes to the functioning of the developing tissue, then it is the amount of active enzyme that is of primary concern. Further differences arise here, however, for the usual techniques for determining enzyme activity measure the maximum work which the enzyme can accomplish, not what it actually accomplishes under *in vivo* conditions. Within the intact cell a given enzyme may be limited by the rate at which other enzymes make its substrate available, or by the supply of ADP or DPN, and so on.[1] The evidence to be discussed in Sections IV and VI,A will provide ample reason for caution in attributing functional significance to ordinary enzyme measurements. It is possible, however, to gain some insight into the relation between enzyme growth or activation on the one hand, and functional maturation on the other, by focusing on enzymes which are related to some terminal product or process that can itself be measured.

---

[1] The following abbreviations are used in this paper. ADP, ATP(ase): adenosinedi(tri)phosphate(ase); AcPase, AlPase: acid, alkaline phosphatase; (A)ChE: (acetyl)cholinesterase; DPN, TPN: di(tri)phosphopyridine nucleotide; DNA, RNA: deoxyribo-, ribonucleic acid; G6P(ase): glucose-6-phosphate(ase); GDH, LDH, MDH, SDH: glutamic, lactic, malic, succinic dehydrogenase; TP: tryptophan pyrrolase.

III. Basic Differentiation and Functional Differentiation

The egg at fertilization contains, in addition to its genetic equipment, a variety of cytoplasmic proteins, including a large complement of enzymes. This is not surprising, since the egg is the product of a differentiated system having the capacity to endow the oogonium with whatever substances evolution has proved useful. In the sea urchin, enzymes are implicated in the events that follow immediately on the contact of egg and sperm (Monroy, 1957b). The cleaving amphibian egg has been shown to contain more than twenty enzymes (Boell, 1955; Løvtrup, 1955; Wallace, 1961). Although the earliest stages of the development of the chick embryo have attracted relatively little attention, it is clear that enzymes or other specific proteins are identifiable in the blastoderm (Moog, 1952; Zacks, 1954; Ebert et al., 1955; Billett and Mulherkar, 1958). On the basis of sensitive enzymatic (Løvtrup, 1955; Coleman, 1962) or immunological (Ebert et al., 1955; Holtzer et al., 1957) techniques, however, certain specific enzyme proteins apparently are absent at very early stages. Despite the fact that negative findings on this question sometimes have proved flagrantly unreliable in the past, the more recent reports are acceptable in general terms, since current concepts of protein synthesis no longer require a template molecule which would need to be part of the baggage of the ovum.

Probably the earliest stages of cytoplasmic development proceed on enzymes provided by the maternal system. It has long been known that initial respiratory rates in sea urchins and amphibians are far below the levels that the contained oxidative enzymes would permit; in both forms it now appears that oxygen uptake is limited by high ATP/ADP ratios (Immers and Runnström, 1960; Gregg, 1960). In amphibian eggs not only oxidative enzymes but others of all types increase little or not at all before the larval stage (Løvtrup, 1955; Wallace, 1961). Studies of ribosome turnover also indicate that there is no synthesis of new ribosomes or soluble proteins until the larva hatches (Brown and Caston, 1962).

In this early period the germ layers are formed and arranged in their proper relation to each other, and the embryo assumes the form of a generalized member of its phylum or class. The decisive events of this period we may subsume under the heading of *basic differentiation*, by which we therefore mean the specification of the major parts of the future organism out of previously indifferent material. The processes underlying these phenomena remain inscrutable, despite much analytical effort. Some possibilities have been negated, however. Whereas it was once thought that enzyme activities control the events of early differentiation by providing energy and substrates, it now appears that the events of early differentiation, by consuming energy and substrates, control the activities of enzymes (Immers and Runnström, 1960; Gregg, 1960)! As Holter (1949) foresaw, the true causative agencies of basic differentiation are more subtle than enzymes.

Development is, of course, a continuum in which separate phases are more distinct in the mind of the investigator than in the life of the embryo. To reduce the present problem to manageable proportions, however, one may say that functional differentiation begins with the visible delimitation of organ-forming material: liver diverticulum, nephrotome, retinal layer of optic cup, and so on. At this stage the cells of the future organ have received a set of instructions which, though they may be lost (Holtzer et al., 1960), can apparently not be replaced by others. It is the working out of this set of instructions that constitutes functional differentiation. The process encompasses the growth of the rudiment, the differentiation of new cell types, and the preparation for the function that the organ will perform. Since mature tissues differ strikingly in their enzyme profiles, it is obvious that enzymogenesis must be an important aspect of the total process.

A number of pertinent questions arise when one attempts to consider the development of enzymes in relation to the functional differentiation of the embryo. Some of the most important of these are the following:

1. When does a given enzyme first appear in detectable quantities? Does it occur in the same cell type on first appearance as later?

2. At what stages does the enzyme protein accumulate faster than other proteins? When does its accumulation simply keep pace with general protein synthesis? When does it fall behind?

3. What factors elicit the appearance and differential accumulation of the enzyme? Two kinds are of concern here: *intrinsic* factors, by which one means the over-all differentiation of the cell (or tissue) to the level at which accumulation of the given enzyme is possible, and *extrinsic* diffusable factors which promote the derepression (or repression) of the enzyme-forming mechanism.

4. What other events are necessarily correlated with the accumulation of an enzyme? This question probes into the nature of the intrinsic factors. Here one may ask, for example, whether the proliferation mechanism must be switched off before a specific protein can be rapidly synthesized, whether structural changes must attend the development of an enzyme, whether enzymes linked in a common pathway must accumulate according to the same pattern, whether functional activity is essential to the continued growth or maintenance of an enzyme.

5. What consequences follow from the differential accumulation of

an enzyme in a tissue? It is axiomatic that an enzyme-dependent step does not occur in the absence of the enzyme; but it is not clear that the converse is true. If an enzyme can "idle" in a developing tissue, we need to inquire into the factors that keep it in an inactive state. In sum, this question is concerned with the conditions that make mature functional activity possible.

6. Is a given enzymatic activity performed by the same kind of molecule throughout development? Although it has long been suspected that enzyme molecules may change during development (cf. Moog, 1952), positive evidence has begun to appear only recently for at least a few enzymes (see Section VII). So we can ask questions 1–5 over again, in terms of the individual molecular forms by which a single enzymatic activity is accomplished.

On some of the preceding questions we have substantial information, on others mere tantalizing wisps. Certainly no unified theory of functional differentiation is at hand yet. Real advances have been made, however, and from a few vantage points we seem to glimpse the most profitable directions for further exploration. These are the subjects considered in the following pages.

IV. Enzymes and Functional Differentiation: Some Case Histories

Changes in enzyme activity during development are least enigmatic in situations where correlated structural and/or functional events provide clues to the meaning of the activity change. This section will comprise a survey of five organs in which study of enzyme development has proved of heuristic value. Where enzyme "increase" is referred to, it may in many cases be provisionally accepted as indicating differential enzyme synthesis, since the influence of dissociable or heat-labile inhibitors or activators frequently has been ruled out. Nevertheless, the possibility that the activity increase results from freeing of a tightly bound inhibitor or from polymerization or some similar molecular change in most cases remains open. In almost all investigations cited, enzyme activity has been referred to a protein (or total nitrogen) basis.

A. Liver

The advantages of large size, ease of homogenization and extraction, and relative uniformity of structure, outweighing the drawbacks of complexity of function, have long made the liver a favorite object for studies of developmental metabolism in mammals and chick embryos. Aside from work on enzymatic changes in metamorphosis, however (see Volume II, Chapter 5), the enzymology of liver development in lower vertebrates has been largely ignored.

Although the early and distinctive origin of the liver as a diverticulum from the gut would seem to make the organ an ideal subject for histochemical studies of early differentiation, little attention has been paid to this aspect, aside from the observation that in the chick embryo the early diverticulum is rich in alkaline phosphatase (AlPase), as all tissues are in the earliest phases of differentiation. By the time the glycogen-accumulating function is assumed, the AlPase has disappeared, except in the vascular endothelium, and acid phosphatase (AcPase) begins to accumulate in the parenchyma (Moog, 1944). More recently, Weber and Boell (1962) have shown that the low cytochrome oxidase activity of *Xenopus* liver mitochondria is foreshadowed by almost identically low activity in the mitochondria from the endoderm at the stage when the liver diverticulum first appears.

In the chick embryo enzymes of what, in the absence of more specific information, may be called general metabolic function follow several different patterns. Peptidase increases sixteenfold between 5 and 7 days, but thereafter only slightly (Dumm and Levy, 1949). Proteinase activity is six times higher at 10 days than at $7\frac{1}{2}$ days, and continues rising slowly (Russo-Caia, 1960). Cytochrome oxidase and succinic dehydrogenase (SDH) activity rise steadily from 7 to 20 days (Davidson, 1957). Lactic (LDH), glutamic (GDH), and malic (MDH) dehydrogenases rise two- to threefold from 7 to 15 days, but then decline sharply (Solomon, 1959); the regression is marked by a shift of GDH, but not the other dehydrogenases, from supernate to mitochondria. Some enzymes do not change in activity at any time. Adenosine deaminase activity is constant from 7 days *in ovo* to adulthood (Solomon, 1960), and aldolase is constant in liver and other organs throughout the incubation period (Davidson, 1957).

The mammal on which we have had the most extensive information on development of liver enzymes for some time is the guinea pig. Using liver as a basis for comparison in their instructive series of studies on the functional differentiation of the cerebral cortex (Flexner, 1955a), Flexner and his co-workers have shown that enzymes in both organs change according to independent patterns (for early references, see Flexner, 1955b). From 35 days to term, cytochrome oxidase and AcPase activity of liver increase, whereas AlPase declines (Flexner *et al.*, 1956). Apyrase and SDH and apparently aldolase remain at the same level, though variable, with SDH alone rising sharply in the newborn animal.

In the rat, which is much less mature than the guinea pig at birth, cytochrome oxidase, SDH (Potter *et al.*, 1945), GDH, malic and isocitric dehydrogenases (Dawkins, 1959) increase rapidly after birth, reaching close to the adult level within 3 days. These increases and others in the same period (see below) are interesting in the light of the fact that the liver scarcely grows during the first 10 days after birth (Widdowson and McCance, 1960; Oliver et al., 1962). In contrast with other oxidative enzymes, DPNH-cytochrome c reductase does not reach the adult level before 28 days. This exception may be more apparent than real, however, for the greater part of the reductase activity, unlike that of other enzymes of the respiratory chain, is microsomal rather than mitochondrial (Dawkins, 1959). A similar situation may account for the gradual increase of apyrase to a maximum at 25 days (Potter et al., 1945).

LDH activity in mouse liver is constant during the first 3 weeks of life, falling slightly thereafter (Flexner et al., 1960). From late fetal life until adulthood, GDH undergoes little change in the rabbit liver (Stave, 1960); as in other animals AlPase activity declines and that of AcPase rises (Kawasaki, 1958).

In both birds and mammals much interest has centered on the development of the glycogen-storing function of the liver. It has been known for many years that glycogen appears in the liver of the chick embryo by day 7 (Dalton, 1937), when mitotic activity, previously rapid, has fallen to a low level (O'Connor, 1954; Lövlie, 1959). Phosphorylase could first be found histochemically on day 7 by Grillo (1961), although Lövlie claims to have demonstrated it at 3 days. According to Guha and Wegmann (1961), phosphorylase kinase does not appear until 12 or 13 days, the early embryonic liver, unlike that of the adult, being devoid of inactive phosphorylase. If liver fragments from 3-day chick embryos are cultured in vitro, they deposit glycogen within 24 hours (Lövlie, 1959), but the livers of explanted whole embryos do not do so. These interesting results show that the relatively late appearance of glycogen in vivo is not due to inability to produce essential enzymes, and Lövlie offers evidence militating against the idea that mitosis and glycogen deposition are necessarily antagonistic. The explanation may lie in the balance of carbohydrate distribution among liver, embryo, and yolk sac (cf. Willier, 1955). According to Beaumont (1954) and Bellec (1957), the livers of premetamorphic tadpoles also deposit glycogen in vitro, but not in vivo.

In the fetal guinea pig liver, glycogen is not detectable until 56 days (Hard et al., 1944). Shortly thereafter, it rises meteorically to term, falls almost to zero within a day and a half, and then accumulates again (Kornfeld and Brown, 1963). That this pattern is a result of factors within the liver, rather than in the hormonal milieu or in the relation between liver and placenta, is suggested by the fact that intestinal epithelium contains abundant glycogen as early as day 17 in utero (Peyrot, 1957; Moog and Ortiz, 1960). Uridine diphosphoglucose-glycogen glucosyltransferase, which participates in glycogen synthesis, does rise from about 58 days to term, when it reaches its adult value, but it shows about two-thirds or its adult activity as early as 46 days; UDP-glucose-pyro-phosphorylase also rises in the same pattern at the same time, and phosphorylase increases about fivefold from 64 days to 2 days after birth, thereafter declining (Kornfeld and Brown, 1963). In contrast to these enzymes, glucose-6-phosphatase (G6Pase) is barely detectable at 64 days, thereafter rising to a maximum at birth that is twice the adult level (Nemeth, 1954). Rat liver also contains phosphorylase, phosphoglucomutase, and phosphohexoisomerase in fetal stages, but G6Pase appears only at

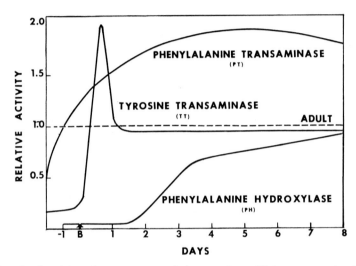

FIG. 2. Activities of components of the tyrosine-oxidizing system in the liver of the rat before and after birth. These enzymes catalyze the following reactions: PT, phenylpyruvate $\rightleftharpoons$ phenylalanine; PH, phenylalanine $\rightarrow$ tyrosine; TT, tyrosine $\rightleftharpoons$ p-hydroxyphenylpyruvate (Kretchmer, 1959); B, birth.

birth (Bot et al., 1960; Weber and Cantero, 1957). A kind of glycogen storage disease is thus a normal fetal condition in mammals that are born in both mature and immature states. The fetal human liver, however, appears to contain G6Pase by week 22 (Auricchio and Rigillo, 1960) or possibly earlier (Villee, 1954).

The human infant oxidizes phenylalanine and tyrosine at birth, but the premature infant is unable to do so (Kretchmer, 1959). The same inability seems to exist in fetal rats, rabbits, pigs (Kenney and Kretchmer, 1959), and guinea pigs (Goswami and Knox, 1961). The defect is a complex one (Fig. 2). The conversion of phenylalanine to tyrosine fails in fetal stages because one component of the two-step phenylalanine hydroxylase system is missing from fetal liver; in the rat the full system is

complete by 4 days (Kenney *et al.*, 1958). Tyrosine itself cannot be converted to *p*-hydroxyphenylpyruvate because of a lack of tyrosine-α-ketoglutarate transaminase (Kretchmer *et al.*, 1956; Auerbach and Waisman,
1959). As might be expected, however, the fetal liver is not generally deficient in transaminases (Stave, 1960; Kafer and Pollak, 1961). One more
component of the tyrosine-oxidizing system is *p*-hydroxyphenylpyruvate
oxidase, which converts its substrate to homogentisate. This enzyme is
present, but in inactive form which can be made active by ascorbic acid
or dichlorophenolindophenol (Kretchmer, 1959; Goswami and Knox,
1961). After birth spontaneous activity rises abruptly in the guinea pig,
but remains low in the rat until the age of 2 weeks (Goswami and Knox,
1961). In about 1 % of human infants spontaneous activity increases relatively late, with the result that the baby shows a hydroxyphenyluria that
corrects itself suddenly (Bloxam *et al.*, 1960).

The normal human newborn presents a self-limiting jaundice owing
to the failure of the liver to conjugate bilirubin. Brown and Zuelzer
(1958) have shown that in the fetal guinea pig liver a similar inability
to conjugate bilirubin is caused by a lack of both the transferase which
catalyzes the reaction: uridine diphosphate glucuronic acid (UDPGA)
+ bilirubin → UDP + bilirubin glucuronide; and of the dehydrogenase
which converts UDPG to UDPGA. Enzyme activity and, consequently,
capacity for glucuronide synthesis reach adult levels within 7 to 10 days
after birth. Dutton (1959) confirmed these results and extended them to
the mouse and man. A similar situation seems to occur in the rat liver, in
which synthesis of bilirubin glucuronide is first detected before birth; at
birth it has reached half the adult level, and then climbs steadily to a
maximum at 5 or 6 weeks (Grodsky *et al.*, 1958). In the mouse liver also
the glucuronide-synthesizing system develops after birth, but β-glucuronidase, a rather ubiquitous enzyme, is very high in the infant animal
(Karunairatnam *et al.*, 1949; Paigen, 1961b).

One other system that has been studied in the developing liver is that
of tryptophan peroxidase (pyrrolase). Since the factors controlling the
development of this system have been extensively explored, it will be
considered later (Section VI,A and B,3).

B. *Retina*

In contrast to the liver, the retina is a small organ devoted principally
to a single function. Correlated enzymatic and structural changes in the
developing retina of the chick embryo have been previously reviewed
(Moog, 1958).

Since visual function matures rapidly (the pupillary reflex to light
being established at 17 days in the chick embryo), attention has centered

on enzymatic events associated with the onset of function. Glutamotrans-ferase, which is barely detectable at 17 days, rises fiftyfold within 48 hours, and continues rising to a maximum attained some time after hatching (Rudnick and Waelsch, 1955; Moscona and Hubby, 1963). Enzyme increase seems to occur equally in all cell layers (Rudnick, 1963). At 15 days, when the rods and cones first become distinguishable, Mg^{++}-activated apyrase undergoes a sharp increase to a maximum level attained before the pupillary reflex sets in (Coulombre, 1955). Cholinesterase also increases at this time, but rather gradually, in a pattern not obviously associated with the critical events of the 15–17 day period (Lindemann, 1947). However, histochemical studies indicate that the increase of the latter enzyme around the time of onset of functional capacity is the result of accumulation at the cholinergic terminals of the inner plexiform layer (Shen et al., 1956).

The visual function of the mature rabbit retina is highly dependent on glycolysis, being extraordinarily sensitive to iodoacetic acid, whereas anoxia has little effect (Noell, 1951). In an extensive study of the glucose catabolism of whole retina in vitro, Cohen and Noell (1960) have revealed striking differences between the retina of the 5- to-7-day-old rabbit, after cell division has ceased but before the visual function begins, and that of the adult. Both form lactate by the Embden-Meyerhof pathway, but the oxygen uptake of the adult organ is more strongly affected by iodoacetic acid. The young retina shows a stronger Pasteur effect and a marked Crabtree effect (i.e., inhibition of respiration by added glucose). The rate of oxygen uptake is low up to 7 days, but shortly thereafter begins rising to reach the adult level by 20 days; this shift is clearly correlated with the beginning of visual activity at 9 days. The infant retina is deficient in Krebs' cycle enzymes (Schimke, 1959). Since the mitochondria of the visual cells are concentrated in the inner segments of the rods and cones, Cohen and Noell (1960) advance the interesting speculation that electron transport in the metabolic chain may be involved in the primary excitation of visual events. The actual occurrence of function is not essential to oxidative enzyme development, however, for GDH, LDH, isocitric, malic, and G6P dehydrogenases accumulate close to the normal 26-day level in rabbits raised in total darkness (Schimke, 1959). In the retina of the infant rat, both aerobic and anaerobic glycolysis are lower than in that of the adult, with a marked increase occurring at 12 to 13 days, when the eyes open (Graymore, 1959); again, the increase is not light-dependent.

Pigment formation in the pigmented epithelium of the retina in the chick embryo is completed by 10 days; at this time, tyrosinase has reached its maximum level, from which it drops steadily to zero at 14 days (Miyamoto and Fitzpatrick, 1957). In the fish retina phenol oxidase is similarly correlated with pigmentation (Tomita and Hishida, 1961). Little attention has otherwise been paid to the pigmented layer, although Coulombre (1955) has demonstrated that a Ca^{++}- or Mg^{++}-activated apyrase in this layer rises and falls in parallel with a Mg^{++}-activated apyrase in the neural epithelium.

C. Kidney

Although the metanephros, and to a lesser extent the mesonephros, have attracted considerable attention, study of the functional differentiation of the excretory organs presents some serious difficulties. In many amniotes, both kidneys function in fetal stages, the activity of the first kidney overlapping that of the second to an undefined extent. The metanephros particularly is a mixture of functional and differentiating nephrons, usually for a long time after birth. There are regional differences in the functional capacity of nephrons, and these may change from stage to stage—as is indicated, for example, by the occurrence of AlPase in the ascending and descending limbs of Henle's loop in the fetal but not the adult human kidney (Ivemark, 1958). In the unborn animal excretory function may also be shared by extraembryonic membranes. The mesonephros, metanephros, amnion, and chorioallantois of the 46-day pig fetus have the same level of glutaminase activity, which is equal to that of the kidney of the adult sow (Radde and McCance, 1960).

The nature of kidney organization had led to a histochemical approach to its embryogenesis more often than with other organs. The pioneer studies of Gersh (1937) on the kidneys of chick embryos and fetal rat, cat, opossum, and pig clearly established a relation between histological differentiation and the capacity for tubular elimination of phenol red. The same is true for the pronephros in the frog tadpole (Jaffee, 1954). Flexner (1939) employed the Nadi technique to demonstrate the presence of highly active cytochrome oxidase in nephrons that had arrived at the functional stage in the metanephros of the fetal pig; presecretory structures, stroma, and collecting ducts gave no reaction. Subsequent studies have shown that AlPase, AcPase, G6Pase, 5-nucleotidase, SDH, LDH, and β-glucuronidase are all localized in nephrons in the chick embryo and numerous mammals at the time when function begins (Moog, 1944; Junquiera, 1952; Rossi et al., 1954; Ogawa, 1958; Ivemark, 1958, 1959; Fisher and Gruhn, 1959; Vacek, 1960; Smith and Kissane, 1963). As pointed out before, however, not all segments of a tubule acquire their adult distribution of enzymes simultaneously (Ivemark, 1958; Fisher and Gruhn, 1959).

Despite the presence of numerous enzymes in definitive localizations, the kidney at birth is in most species deficient in functional capacity. Although certain deficiencies, particularly those relating to inability to maintain homeostasis, may have a hormonal basis (Heller, 1962), the over-all picture suggests enzymatic immaturity. This point has been explored most fully in the rat, in which the metanephros as late as 3 days before birth consists largely of stellate mesenchyme in which a few scattered tubules may be found. Nephrogenesis is actively proceeding at birth, but is not completed until 28 days of age. By histochemical means Fisher and Gruhn (1959) showed that cytochrome oxidase and SDH, although present at birth, achieved normal distribution and maximal staining intensity only at 39 days. Glutaminase and carbonic anhydrase, which may be important in acid–base balance, are low at birth and remain low during the first 2 weeks; then an upturn begins that is still underway, especially in females, at 56 days (Wacker et al., 1961). AlPase activity is also low at birth and falls significantly during the first 14 days, the climb toward adult levels not beginning until 21 days. General protein concentration, by contrast, rises rapidly during the first 7 days, and only very slowly thereafter (Wacker et al., 1961). The flavin-containing enzyme D-amino acid oxidase is similarly below the adult level for the first 14 days, then begins a fivefold increase; the flavoprotein xanthine oxidase, which is barely detectable in the newborn kidney, begins increasing at 9 days (Burch et al., 1958). It is interesting that all these enzymes are in short supply during the period of dependent infancy, but are accumulating actively at the time (about 16 days in the rat) when the young animal is capable of being weaned and of maintaining an independent life.

D. Heart

As an object for studies of functional differentiation, the heart has two important advantages: a measurable function that is visible to the eye, and an essential protein that is relatively easy to identify. This second characteristic has been brilliantly exploited by Ebert (1953), who used immunochemical means to determine when cardiac myosin first appears. Using an antiserum to purified myosin from the heart of the adult chicken, Ebert demonstrated that a cross-reactive substance is diffusely distributed in the epiblast at stage 3 (early primitive streak), becoming limited to the presumptive heart-forming areas by the time the head process appears. Actin, however, is not found before the head-process stage, when it is already localized in the heart-forming areas (Ebert et al., 1955). It would be interesting to know whether myosin, on first appearance, is enzymatically competent or whether the enzymatic site differentiates independently of the antigenic site. Using a moderately sensitive method, Klein (1961) was unable to detect myosin-associated ATPase activity until $2\frac{1}{2}$ days after the heart had begun to pulsate.

Working with explanted chick blastoderms, Spratt (1950) showed that heart develops in 2×10^{-5} M iodoacetic acid, in which central nervous system degenerates, but the reverse is true in 5×10^{-3} M fluoride. This interesting indication of enzymatic differences in early differentiation has not been effectively followed up. AlPase is the only enzyme that has been localized in the heart primordia, from which it disappears as soon as contractile tissue has differentiated (Moog, 1944). In a careful study employing a number of substrates and inhibitors Zacks (1954) failed to find esterase activity before 68 hours, although George and Iype (1959), using the Gomori "Tween" method, which they believed to demonstrate lipase but which probably demonstrates aliesterase (Nachlas and Seligman, 1949), found activity in 40-hour heart muscle. Continuing their study by a quantitative method from 7 days on, George and Iype reported that "lipase" activity of the ventricle approximately doubles between 7 and 12 days, levels off, then rises slightly between 16 and 18 days; after hatching there is a sharp rise that was followed for only 1 day. Dipeptidase rises from 4 days to a maximum at 16 days that is higher than the activity of the adult heart (Russo-Caia, 1958). Proteinase activity rises only slightly (Russo-Caia, 1960).

The high work output of the heart has attracted considerable attention to enzymes involved in the liberation of energy. Succinoxidase activity is present in the ventricle of the chick embryo at 24 hours, but does not begin to increase until 48 hours; it rises then to 5 days, levels off to 9 days, and then climbs again gradually but steadily until hatching, with a suggestion of a plateau between 15 and 18 days (Sippel, 1954). Cytochrome oxidase and SDH also rise after 4 or 5 days (Davidson, 1957). Lactic and malic dehydrogenases increase slightly from 7 days to hatching, with the latter exhibiting a slight upsurge at 14 days (Solomon, 1958). Although other enzymes have not been determined sequentially in the heart of the chick embryo, several enzymes of the citric acid cycle, in addition to those already mentioned, have been demonstrated in the 10-day heart (Mahler et al., 1958; Cahn et al., 1962).

Growth of succinoxidase in the heart of the rat embryo is remarkably similar to that in the chick, being characterized by a sharp increase at the onset of function (about $9\frac{1}{2}$ days), followed by a plateau for 3 days; the activity then doubles between 16 and 18 days to assume a constant level unaffected by birth or postnatal development (Sippel, 1954). According to Cooper (1955), however, ventricular SDH grows rapidly immediately after birth, not attaining the adult level for about 20 days; atrial activity rises less, so that the ratio of SDH activity in the right ventricle to that in the atria changes from 1.4 at birth to 2.4 in adult-hood. Sippel (1954), by comparing the pattern of succinoxidase activity with the growth of wet weight and nitrogen in the hearts of the chick embryo and fetal rat, has given convincing reason for concluding that the increase of succinoxidase activity is "probably less related to total synthetic processes than it is to other aspects of cardiac differentiation." In the chick embryo succinoxidase activity roughly parallels cardiac efficiency (i.e., percentage work output per unit work equivalent of oxygen consumed; cf. Hughes, 1949). This parameter, which is strongly influenced by the fact that the respiratory rate of developing heart falls up to 6 days (Warburg and Kubowitz, 1927), turns upward at the same time that succinoxidase emerges from its first phase of constancy (6–8 days). In the ventricle of the pig fetus, succinoxidase activity is progressively higher at 60, 80, and 110 days of gestation, just as in smaller animals (Shirley et al., 1957).

The ventricle of the 2-day chick embryo is rich in intracellular Na^+, which drops to a low level at 7 days; intracellular K^+ meanwhile increases, but more gradually (Klein, 1960). These facts bespeak a sodium pump which Klein (1961) has identified as a Mg^{++}-activated ATPase (the influence of Na^+ and K^+ on the ATPase was not tested). This Mg^{++}-ATPase surges up more than 400 %, in close parallel with the work output of the heart, between 4 and 8 days, after which it grows more gradually to the adult level reached soon after hatching. Ca^{++}-ATPase, which is found in the expected association with the myosin fraction, was barely detectable at 4 days, and then rose steadily to a maximum just after hatching.

An enzyme known to play a quite specific role in impulse conduction is acetylcholinesterase (AChE) (see Section V,C). The view that the enzyme may also have a more general metabolic function (its substrate being present in protozoa, spleen, and placenta) is supported by Zack's identification (1954) of AChE in chick embryo heart by 68 hours, 2 days before vagal innervation is established in the myocardium. In the salamander heart, in which no nonspecific cholinesterase (ChE) is found, AChE begins accumulating in the heart shortly after contractions start, and reaches one-third of its maximum level by the time the vagus nerve arrives (Sippel, 1955). In the same study Sippel showed that in the rat, in which specific activities are four to five times higher than in amphibians, AChE activity rises abruptly to a maximum at 12 days in utero that is higher than the adult level. In the atrium, which contains the intracardiac elements of the vagus, AChE activity increases a little later and a little more slowly, attaining at 16 days (2 days after the vagus nerves enter the heart) a maximum about 60 % higher than that of the ventricle.

Nonspecific ChE activity is in each chamber only about 25 % of that of the specific enzyme and rises slightly in a pattern showing no particular relation to innervation. These data seem to imply that AChE anticipates its specific function, but possibly acts in some less specific capacity as well.

E. *Intestine*

Although there have been occasional papers on the enzymogenesis of the stomach and other parts of the digestive tract, most attention has centered on the small intestine. This organ is, of course, a complex one histologically, but the absorptive epithelium is sharply delimited and has lent itself well to correlated studies of structure, enzymology, and function.

The small intestine, like other parts of the gastrointestinal tract, begins full-scale functional activity rather suddenly, at birth or hatching. Some absorption, however, does seem to occur in prenatal stages. The fetal mammal swallows amniotic fluid, and the chick embryo ingests some of the albumen, for the apparent digestion of which the stomach is provided with HCl and pepsin on day 12 of incubation (Pokorna *et al.*, 1955). That such precocious activity is not essential for continued differentiation, however, is indicated by the fact that in the fetal dog and rabbit (Davletova, 1961), as well as in the duck embryo (Ragozina, 1955), gastrointestinal development proceeds normally when the oral opening is blocked by deformity or experimental intervention.

The growth and distribution of β-galactosidase (lactase) is of obvious interest in animals that live on milk in infancy. In the whole small intestine of the rat, β-galactosidase activity undergoes a tenfold rise from 18 days, when it is first measurable, to birth at 22 days; thereafter, activity falls off, reaching the low adult level by 28 days, when normally the animals have been weaned (Alvarez and Sas, 1961; Doell and Kretchmer, 1962). The rabbit shows a similar pattern, although the prenatal rise is more gradual (Doell and Kretchmer, 1962). In both animals, as well as in the human infant, there appear to be two β-galactosidases, of which the predominant one is specific for lactose and is particulate; the other, a soluble enzyme, hydrolyzes both lactose and *o*-nitro-β-galactoside (Doell and Kretchmer, 1962).

Since the particulate fraction of intestine is made up partly of fragments of the striated border of the epithelial cells, these results suggested that β-galactosidase, like AlPase, is localized in the microvilli; and Doell and Kretchmer (1963) have now shown that the two enzymes are associated in the same fraction in the intestine of the infant rat. This association is interesting because the accumulation pattern of the lactose-splitting enzyme in the fetal rat is virtually identical with that of AlPase in the mouse (cf. Moog, 1959, 1962a) and also in the rat, as far as one can judge from histochemical examination (Cohen, 1957); both enzymes rise steeply in the last 3 days before birth to a high level which promptly falls. That alkaline phosphatase is localized in the striated border is well known (see Section V,A,3). Unlike β-galactosidase, however, AlPase undergoes a second steep rise from 15 to 18 days after birth in the mouse (cf. Moog, 1959, 1962a), and slightly later in the rat (Halliday, 1959). At this time the animals are able to be weaned. In both animals the second upsurge represents a new molecular form, characterized by high activity on phenylphosphatase relative to β-glycerophosphate (Moog, 1962b; Moog et al., 1963).

In the duodenum of the chick embryo, AlPase increases about fifty-fold between 17 days in ovo and the day after hatching; it then drops off somewhat (cf. Moog, 1959, 1962a). Histochemical examination makes it clear that the accumulation of phosphatase is entirely concomitant with the differentiation of the striated border, the small activity detectable before 17 days being localized in the mesenchyme. As in the weanling mouse, the increase involves the differentiation of a phenylphosphate-preferring enzyme (Kato, 1959). Since the young chick does not shift from milk to solid food, as mammals do, it is not surprising that there is no second rise of phosphatase activity (cf. Moog, 1959, 1962a). There is no second rise either in the guinea pig, which is sufficiently mature at birth to eat the food supplied to the adults (Moog and Ortiz, 1960). This animal is especially interesting in that the increase of AlPase, although confined to a short period, does not immediately precede birth, but anticipates birth by about 4 weeks, during which time a high phosphatase level is maintained in the microvilli with little variation.

Nonspecific esterase (Richardson et al., 1955), adenosine deaminase (Fisher et al., 1962), and SDH (Nunnally, 1962) have also been examined in the duodenum of the chick embryo. They reveal two different patterns of growth. Esterase, which is localized in the epithelium, including the brush border, increases in a pattern virtually identical to that of AlPase, although the magnitude of the change is less. SDH, which is also in the epithelium, and adenosine deaminase, do not shoot up until the day of hatching. The activity of the former then rises about sixfold to a maximum above the adult level, at 4 days; the latter rises fortyfold to a maximum at 12 days. A particularly interesting finding is that at the time when the rise of activity is underway, the epithelial cells covering a single villus may vary greatly in their apparent SDH content (Nunnally, 1962).

AlPase has been studied histochemically in the developing digestive tracts of Oryzias latipes (Ikeda, 1959) and the steelhead trout (Prakash,

1961). In the early stages of both fishes, phosphatase is localized in mesenchyme and undifferentiated endoderm, in patterns quite reminiscent of those shown in the young chick embryo (Moog, 1944). With the appearance of the striated border, phosphatase is found in it. When the yolk sac of the trout is absorbed and the young fry emerges, phosphatase is concentrated in the brush border exactly as in birds and mammals (Prakash, 1961).

The developing digestive tract of *Bufo vulgaris* has recently been the subject of an intriguing series of studies by Bondi. If tailbud embryos are immobilized by the insertion of a glass thread (hair or nylon thread have no effect), or by immersion in Chloretone, the intestine becomes shorter and wider than that of normal tadpoles, with little coiling (Bondi, 1959, 1962). Such abnormal intestines are deficient in dipeptidase, amylase, lipase, and alkaline proteinase, although they have more acid proteinase than control intestines (Bondi and Bellini, 1960). RNA and DNA contents are also below normal (Bondi and Bellini, 1962). AlPase, examined by the Gomori technique, is localized in the brush border in apparently equal quantities (incubation times are not stated) in the anterior regions of normal and abnormal intestines. In the posterior part, however, the enzyme is abundant also in the supranuclear cytoplasm in the anomalous organs only, and on the contrary it appears to be absent from the abnormal large intestine (Bondi, 1962). When the experimental animals undergo metamorphosis, lipase, amylase, and proteinase content, as well as RNA and DNA, rise to or above normal levels (Bondi and Bellini, 1960, 1962).

F. *General Conclusions*

Examination of the patterns of enzyme change cited in this section supports two general conclusions:

1. Within the same tissue or organ, enzymes tend to increase or decrease in activity independently of each other. Certainly, there are parallel changes, and these may be of considerable significance (see Section IX). It is often observed, however, that two enzymes which both show an increasing trend will rise at different rates and reach their maxima at different times.

2. The patterns of change for individual enzymes are frequently multiphasic. An enzyme that has been accumulating rapidly may shift to maintaining a constant level of activity for some time, or even regress, and later increase again.

These conclusions are not new (cf. Moog, 1952; Boell, 1955) and will not be discussed further. The factors underlying these phenomena will be explored in subsequent sections.

About the relation between shifting patterns of enzyme activity and the development of functional capacity in the tissue concerned, it is still not possible to draw firm conclusions. It is, of course, well established that enzymes begin to accumulate in anticipation of the function they subserve. This is especially clear in those cases in which the dependent function can be accurately specified, as with the β-galactosidase of the rat intestine (Doell and Kretchmer, 1962); but it is also evident in cases in which the significance of the enzyme must be inferred from its high level of activity in the mature tissue, as with the glutamotransferase of the chick retina (Rudnick and Waelsch, 1955). Both these enzymes accumulate shortly before birth or hatching. Not infrequently, however, enzyme activities rise with no immediate reference to their related functions at all. The guinea pig, with its protracted gestation period, furnishes some striking examples. Phosphorylase and other enzymes involved in glycogen deposition are found in the liver, at substantial though submaximal levels of activity, several weeks before glycogen itself appears (Nemeth et al., 1954; Kornfeld and Brown, 1963). AlPase accumulates to the adult level, in a differentiated striated border, a month before birth (Moog and Ortiz, 1960).

The investigations of guinea pig liver just cited revealed that the activity of the glycogen-forming enzymes rises concomitantly with the deposition of glycogen. Do rising levels of enzyme activity generally reflect enhanced intensity of functional activity? This is a difficult question, partly because it is often not readily possible to measure function with any accuracy. The evidence now available, however, does not encourage one to conclude more than that all essential enzymes must be raised to a critical level before the dependent function can begin. This relationship is apparent in the Flexner studies, which demonstrated that the responsiveness of the cerebral cortex to stimulation sets in soon after several enzyme activities have begun to grow (Flexner, 1955a). In the duodenum of the chick, the rate of glucose absorption in vitro is close to its maximum by 2 days after hatching (Bogner and Haines, 1961). By this time, AlPase, which is probably involved in the transport mechanism, has also reached its highest level (cf. Moog, 1959, 1962a); however, SDH, which no doubt takes part in supplying energy for transport, continues to increase in activity for about 2 days more (Nunnally, 1962). In the young rat, glucose absorptive capacity is progressively higher at 10, 20, and 30 days (Koldovsky et al., 1962), but the degree of parallelism between this change and the elevation of AlPase (Halliday, 1959; Moog, 1962a) or other enzymes has not been explored.

A striking disparity between enzyme level and functional capacity is illustrated by the transport-associated Mg^{++}-ATPase of the heart of the chick embryo. This enzyme increases 450 % between 4 and 7 days, in parallel with a severe loss of Na^+ content; although some of this loss is caused by disappearance of cardiac jelly, a large part results from extrusion (Klein, 1961). But the enzyme activity is scarcely altered at all between 7 and 14 days, when the Na^+ efflux rate and the percentage intracellular Na–K exchangeability both increase sharply (Klein, 1960). Interestingly enough, the myosin-associated Ca^{++}-ATPase, which is directly related to contractility, rises steadily, though at a declining rate, throughout the embryonic period (Klein, 1961). Its pattern is thus quite unlike that of succinoxidase (see Section IV,D), which is involved in supplying energy for contraction (Sippel, 1954).

These few examples, and others like them, indicate that the activity of an enzyme as determined in a homogenate does not necessarily reveal the functional contribution of the enzyme *in vivo*. This conclusion is not unexpected. Biochemists recognize that "the enzyme activity of composite systems may not always be demonstrated as the sum of the activities of the individual enzymes contained therein" (Green and Jarnefeldt, 1959). A full appreciation of the functional significance of a given enzyme, as well as a key to its developmental pattern in many cases, is to be sought in its structural relations. This problem will be considered in the following section.

V. The Structural Basis of Enzyme Development

Waddington (1962) insists that "cellular differentiation does face us with problems that are essentially morphological in nature." The fact that differentiation is a morphological problem helps us to understand why measured changes in enzyme activity are generally not directly interpretable in terms of growth or function. Differentiation involves not simply the synthesis of new proteins, but also the organization of such proteins into functionally significant structures. Hence, it is reasonable to assume that structural development, from the macromolecular to the histological level, will play a role in limiting or promoting the growth, or regulating the activity, of integral enzymes.

A. *Enzymes and Organelles*

1. MITOCHONDRIA

The demonstration that mitochondria are organizations of enzymes and cofactors is one of the major advances of the past two decades. The recognition of the importance of mitochondria presents several problems to the student of development: Are mitochondria present in early stages? Do they accumulate at varying rates in different tissues? Do they undergo differentiation? The last question is of particular interest in the present context, because it brings forward the possibility of alterations in enzymatic composition. There is also the consideration, of practical as well as theoretical importance, that the mitochondria of early stages might be smaller, more fragile, or more likely to release enzymes or cofactors than those of mature tissues (cf. Solomon, 1959).

Recent studies with the electron microscope have left no doubt that mitochondria are part of the basic equipment with which the egg is provided by the maternal system. Bodies having the typical double membrane and internal cristae have been discovered in the unfertilized eggs of sea urchins (Gross et al., 1960; Berg et al., 1962) and Tubifex (Weber, 1958). Although doubts have been raised in the past about the enzymatic competence of these young mitochondria it now seems clear, on the basis of studies employing both cytochemical and isolation methods, that the mitochondria of sea urchins, ctenophores, the clam Spisula, and Tubifex are rich in ATPase, several cytochromes, SDH, cytochrome oxidase, and several related enzymes (Monroy, 1957a; Reverberi, 1957; Weber, 1958; Maggio and Ghiretti-Magaldi, 1958; Strittmatter and Strittmatter, 1961). Cytochrome oxidase is also present on mitochondria in the ovarian eggs of Rana pipiens (Recknagel, 1950) and Xenopus (Boell and Weber, 1955).

That mitochondria must differentiate structurally is apparent from the variations that classic cytology discovered in the size and shape of these bodies. Some of the steps in this differentiation are clearly illustrated in the elegant work of Eakin and Lehmann (1957), who report that the mitochondria, irregular globs in the early gastrular ectoderm of Xenopus, become long and slender in the neural cells of the tailbud embryo and short and swollen in the epidermis.

The enzymatic differentiation of mitochondria in amphibian tissue has been extensively studied by Weber and Boell (1955, 1962). Working with mitochondria isolated from developing Xenopus embryos, Weber and Boell showed that there is more than a threefold difference in the specific cytochrome oxidase activity of these organelles from the dorsal (mesodermal) and ventral (endodermal) halves of the tailbud embryo. Interestingly enough, the activities established so early are carried over unchanged in the late larval stages to the muscle and liver derivatives, the former having three times the cytochrome oxidase activity of the latter (Table I). ATPase activities, however, rose, achieving a higher level in liver than in muscle mitochondria. Acid phosphatase and cathepsin activities also reached much higher levels in liver, but the possibility was not ruled out that these enzymes are really associated with lysosomes. Weber and Boell (1962) suggest that the striking differences attained by mitochondria in liver and skeletal muscle may be related to form differences, the mitochondria of muscle being densely packed with cristae, whereas those from liver have a larger volume of internal ground substance.

The most extensive studies on mitochondria of the early chick embryo were made by Carey and Greville (1959a, b). Mitochondria isolated from whole 5-day embryos exhibited succinoxidase and ATPase activity; the strong activation of the latter by 2,4-dinitrophenol, as with mitochondria from adult tissues, indicates that fractionation causes no serious damage. The organelles contained a normal complement of cytochromes, as Brand

TABLE I

ENZYMATIC DIFFERENTIATION OF MITOCHONDRIA FROM EMBRYONIC AND LARVAL TISSUES OF Xenopus[a]

Source of mitochondria	Cytochrome oxidase[b]		ATPase[b]	
	SA	R	SA	R
Tailbud embryo	1038	1.0	4.55	1.0
Dorsal half of embryo "mesoderm"	2493	2.4	8.86	1.9
Larval tail muscle	2030	2.0	18.5	4.1
Ventral half of embryo "endoderm"	768	0.7	5.52	1.2
Larval liver	649	0.6	32.3	7.1

[a] Weber and Boell (1962).

[b] SA, specific activity (units per microgram total nitrogen); R, ratio of activity compared with tailbud embryo.

et al. (1960) have also reported. The 5-day mitochondria effectively utilized several intermediates of the tricarboxylic acid cycle, with little difference being evident between those from whole embryos and those from isolated head, trunk, or nerve cord + somites (Carey and Greville, 1959b). A probable shift in mitochondrial competence, however, has been reported by Walter and Mahler (1958), who found that the mitochondrial fraction is less active than the nuclear fraction in incorporating labeled proteins, peptides, and amino acids on day 5, but more active on day 9.

The finding that the mitochondria of the young embryos are furnished with standard equipment does not preclude later change. Sippel's (1954) intriguing suggestion that the increasing efficiency of embryonic heart muscle may be the result, in part, of an increasingly closer packing of succinoxidase particles in the mitochondria has not been followed up. Brand et al. (1960) have shown however that the mitochondria of the 14-day chick embryo heart contain coenzyme Q and also a series of cytochromes in the same absolute concentrations as in actively respiring adult tissues; the same is true of 14-day liver mitochondria. Nevertheless, a striking change in liver mitochondria was demonstrated by Solomon (1959), who found a 60 % increase in mitochondrial GDH between 12 and 16 days, concomitant with an approximately 80 % decrease of the same enzyme in the supernate. There seemed to be no change in the tightness of binding of GDH to the mitochondria from stage to stage.

The possibility that enzyme increases may be associated with relative growth of the mitochondrial population was convincingly shown by Gustafson and Hasselberg (1951), who found that during development of the sea urchin egg to the pluteus stage a number of enzymes known to occur in mitochondria increased according to a common pattern between 10 and 30 hours, whereas another group that are not bound to mitochondria did not change in specific activity. LiCl blocked both mitochondrial multiplication and increase of enzyme activities. A similar phenomenon occurs in rat liver. Dawkins (1959) has shown that a much larger proportion of total nitrogen of rat liver is found in the mitochondrial fraction in adults than in fetuses the day before birth. Subfractionation indicated no difference in size distribution of mitochondrial particles between the two stages. These considerations indicate that the brisk elevations of enzymes of the respiratory chain during the first 3 days after birth are related to increase in numbers of mitochondria. Differentiation also does take place, however, since the respiratory activity of fetal mitochondria is strongly stimulated by DNP and is rapidly lost on aging, whereas the respiration of adult mitochondria is not much affected by these factors; probably there is a change in permeability.

A striking example of enzymatic differentiation is that of the accumulation of cytochrome oxidase and succinoxidase in skeletal muscle of rats. Shen (1955) showed that these enzymes increase in parallel, at a constant rate, in the mitochondrial fraction of muscles from day 15 *in utero* to day 12 after birth. In a study extending up to adulthood, Kiesseling (1962) has found that in unfortified media mitochondria of muscles from the period between birth and 18 days have a respiratory rate less than one-tenth of that of mitochondria from 4-month-old rats. Since addition of DPN, cytochrome c, and coenzyme A (to which the adult organelles are only slightly sensitive) raised the level in the infant preparation to no more than one-third the adult level, Kiesseling concluded that the difference must be caused partly by "incomplete development of enzyme systems" in the mitochondria of the infant muscle.

2. LYSOSOMES

The brilliant work of de Duve and his collaborators (cf. de Duve, 1959) has established the existence of a class of particles called lysosomes.

These are of the size of small mitochondria, are surrounded by an apparently single membrane of lipoprotein nature, lack oxidative activity, but contain a battery of hydrolytic enzymes active under acid conditions. In adult tissues they clearly appear to play a role in necrotic processes, and it has also been suggested that the controlled release of lysosomal enzymes may affect the turnover of cellular constituents (cf. Novikoff, 1960).

Since lysosomes are ruptured by ordinary homogenization methods, it is essential that developmental studies of all enzymes associated with lysosomes be carried out under conditions that will distinguish between "free" and "bound" enzyme; otherwise, misleading conclusions may be drawn. This precaution appears to be necessary even in early embryonic stages, for bound hydrolases have been reported as early as the 48-hour stage of the chick embryo, although they apparently do not occur in prehatching stages in amphibians (Brachet et al., 1958). The presence of cathepsin, acid phosphatase, and other hydrolases does not necessarily mean that lysosomes are present, as Weber and Niehus (1961) have shown for the tadpole tail and Doell and Kretchmer (1962) for the infant rat intestine. Nevertheless, studies that have been carried out under controlled conditions suggest that lysosomes are instrumental in at least some of the degenerative processes that are part of the totality of development.

In the chick embryo, Scheib-Pfleger and Wattiaux (1962) have shown that between 8 and 9 days there is a loss of protein from the Mullerian ducts of male embryos, but not of females. The lysosomal enzymes acid phophatase, acid RNase, β-glucuronidase, and cathepsin at the same time increase slightly per unit wet weight, with the result that their specific activity is significantly elevated in male ducts. At 8 days, only about 20 % of acid phosphatase activity is in the free form (i.e., not sedimentable at 125,000 g), but at 9 days 55 % is free, the other hydrolases undergoing similar shifts. No comparable changes occur in female ducts; but Brachet et al. (1958), who found a similar liberation of enzymatic activity in the male, showed that hydrolase activity is also released in the right duct of females at 11–12 days, the free activity in the future oviduct (left) meanwhile remaining unchanged.

The possibility that lysosomes may participate in normal growth and differentiation is raised by the work of Fell and her colleagues on the influence of excess vitamin A on chick embryo limb cartilage in vitro. When the vitamin A content of the medium is raised, the cartilage matrix disintegrates with consequent change in size and shape of the rudiment (Dingle et al., 1961). It now seems that this result can be attributed to a release of acid proteases from lysosomes under the influence of the vitamin (Fell and Dingle, 1963).

3. MICROVILLI

Extensive investigations with the electron microscope have left no doubt that the microvilli of the small intestine, kidney tubule cells, and other sites are true organelles of distinctive structure. Those of the small intestine, for example, have a double membrane covering a fibrous core which extends into the apical cytoplasm of the epithelial cells (Zetterquist, 1956). Although the enzymology of intestinal microvilli is not well known, it is clear that they are rich in AlPase. This localization, regarded with strident skepticism when it was based only on the Gomori technique, has now been demonstrated quantitatively in isolated microvilli (Holt and Miller, 1962), and also with the electron microscope (Clark, 1961), the latter demonstration making it clear that the enzyme occurs in the membranes covering the microvilli.

The first period of accumulation of phosphatase is concomitant with the development of microvilli in the fetal mouse, fetal guinea pig, and chick embryo (cf. Moog, 1962a). In the latter animal the development of phosphatase activity and of the striated border are accelerated in parallel by cortisone (Moog and Richardson, 1955) and retarded in parallel by thyroid inhibition (Moog, 1961b). The differentiation seems to have a decisive effect on the development of the enzyme, for phosphatase does not accumulate, even under the influence of adrenocorticoids, in intestinal epithelium allowed to spread as sheets of squamous tissue in culture (Lasfargues and Di Fine, 1951); but fragments of intestine maintained under organ culture conditions do produce elevated phosphatase activity in microvilli (Hancox, 1954; Moog and Kirsch, 1955). Clark's electron micrographs (1961) suggest that in the mouse the size and density of the microvilli do not change significantly after birth, but enzymatic differentiation does occur. At the beginning of the third postnatal week in both mice and rats a new and highly active phosphatase appears in the duodenum, where it is also localized in the striated border, but not in the jejunum (Moog, 1961a, 1962b; Moog et al., 1963).

β-Galactosidase accumulates in the rat intestine before birth in a pattern similar to that of AlPase (Doell and Kretchmer, 1962) and is subsequently found in the same fraction as the latter (Doell and Kretchmer, 1963). If these indications that β-galactosidase is also a component of microvilli are reliable, differentiation must occur in respect to this enzyme too, for β-galactosidase begins to decline rapidly soon after birth (Alvarez and Sas, 1961; Doell and Kretchmer, 1962).

4. Other Structural Components

An important aspect of differentiation at the ultrastructural level is the formation of endoplasmic reticulum appropriate to the cell type. Ova are generally poor in endoplasmic reticulum, and Brachet (1960) points out that the "development of a typical ergastoplasm occurs at a rather late stage of development, as a result of a high order of structural, physiological, and biochemical differentiation." One might add that the differentiation of ergastoplasm may itself be the basis for further differentiation. Thus, Waddington and Perry (1962) have described in the urodele notochord two types of ergastoplasm arising in succession, one type being implicated in the formation of the distended cells and the other in the formation of the later-arising sheath. Despite occasional references to the localization of enzymes in microsomes, it is not yet possible to deal with enzyme development in terms of association with endoplasmic reticulum. In the future, however, the elucidation of such association may contribute significantly to our understanding of functional differentiation.

B. *Muscle, Myosin, and ATPase*

The peculiar properties of myosin, enabling it to serve as structure, contractile element, and enzyme, make the development of this substance a matter of special interest. In the present context, four questions present themselves: When does myosin first make its appearance? At what rate does it accumulate in different situations? Is Ca^{++}-activated ATPase an invariable property of myosin? What is the relation of myosin accumulation to contractility and muscular capacity?

The occurrence of cardiac myosin on the blastoderm of the chick embryo during primitive streak formation has already been mentioned (Section IV,D). Ca^{++}-activated ATPase activity has not been reported in the heart before 4 days (Klein, 1961), but one suspects that a more sensitive technical approach will reveal activity at an earlier stage. Studies on skeletal muscle myosin, which seems to appear later than the cardiac variety, present a clearer picture. Using fluorescent antibody to adult chicken skeletal muscle myosin, Holtzer *et al.* (1957) demonstrated the presence of myosin in brachial somites of the embryo at stage 16 (about 52 hours). The antibody was clearly localized on myofibrils, which are thus shown to be present about half a day earlier than they can be seen with iron-hematoxylin staining. Contraction on addition of ATP to glycerinated myoblasts was not observed before stage 21. More recently, Deuchar (1960a), in a beautifully simple study, has shown that Ca^{++}-ATPase activity is present in homogenates of both somites and unsegmented mesoderm of the 13-somite embryo (stage 11), being about

36 % higher in the segmented material. Mg^{++}-ATPase activity, which was equal in segmented and unsegmented mesoderm, was partly removed by glycerol extraction, but the activity of Ca^{++}-ATPase per unit nitrogen was increased. Although the activity demonstrated by Deuchar may represent a precursor molecule in which the antigenic properties of myosin have not differentiated, it seems likely that the disparity between these results and those of Holtzer's group simply reflect the intrinsically greater sensitivity of enzymatic methods. On the other hand, immuno-chemical analysis might also reveal myosin at an earlier stage, if a microprecipitin test were employed, as in the identification of cardiac myosin (Ebert, 1953). Ogawa (1962a) failed to find actin before 3 days or myosin before 4 days, but he might have obtained different results had he used homogenates of muscle-forming regions, as Deuchar did, rather than whole embryos.

In both *Rana pipiens* and *Triturus* (Ogawa, 1962b) a material re-acting with antiserum to adult myosin or actomyosin can be demonstrated in tailbud stages shortly before movement begins. The occurrence of ATPase activity in salt extracts of *Rana pipiens* larvae of the stage when the first movements are seen was reported by Barth and Barth (1951). Nass (1962) has gone on to provide an admirably thorough demonstra-tion of molecular differentiation in developing actomyosin, the unique feature of the study being that ATPase activity was assayed in material precipitated by antibodies to adult actomyosin, so that enzymatic dif-ferences were examined in molecules that are alike antigenically. The actomyosin thus isolated from larvae showed the following differences from that of adults: (1) strong activation by both Mg^{++} and Ca^{++} at both high and low KCl concentrations, whereas adult actomyosin was affected only at low salt concentration; (2) in the presence of Ca^{++}, a pH opti-mum between 7 and 8, with adult actomyosin having its optimum be-tween 9 and 10; (3) adenylpyrophosphatase activity, as opposed to strict ATPase activity of the adult form. At the free-swimming tadpole stage, the specific activity is almost three times that of adult actomyosin. In-terestingly enough, the shift to adult characteristics occurs before meta-morphosis.

In stages well after the establishment of muscle function, myosin and actomyosin accumulate rapidly in the chick embryo, rising from less than 10 mg per gram of leg muscle at 10 days to about 25 mg at hatch-ing; the adult maximum of 60 mg per gram is attained gradually (Csapo and Herrmann, 1951; see also Herrmann, 1963). The myofibrillar fraction of breast muscle undergoes an increase of the same magnitude in the first month after hatching (Robinson, 1952a). The Ca^{++}-ATPase activity of the myofibrillar fraction, however, rises from 36.7 units at 13 days to

55.8 units near hatching and declines in the growing bird (Robinson, 1952b). But it appears that the ATPase activity per gram of total muscle protein increases gradually after hatching.

It is tempting to correlate the achievement of maximal ATPase activity in myosin at the end of the embryonic life of the chick with the muscular effort required in the hatching process. In the rat, the only mammal extensively investigated, the specific ATPase activity of the myosin fraction increases steadily from prenatal stages until after the attainment of sexual maturity. This was shown by de Villafranca (1954) in a study which carefully distinguished between Mg^{++}-ATPase, also abundant in muscle, and Ca^{++}-ATPase. Although Herrmann et al. (1949) reported the occurrence of myosin with weak ATPase activity as early as 14 days, de Villafranca was unable to isolate a myosin fraction at 15 days, within a day of the time that contraction begins. At 19 days myosin was readily detected. The specific ATPase activity of the myosin fraction rose rapidly from day 19 in utero to 20 days after birth, after which it continued to climb at a slower rate. Myosin itself continues to accumulate, relative to whole muscle growth, until adulthood (Herrmann and Nicholas, 1948).

The foregoing considerations show decisively that the growth of the Ca^{++}-activated ATPase of skeletal muscle is correlated with, but not parallel to, the accumulation of myosin. There is clearly a differentiation of myosin with respect to both the level and the characteristics of its ATPase activity. This differentiation may simply represent, as Nass (1962) points out, "slight changes at the active centers, perhaps only related to minor differences in protein folding." The possibility that a more substantial change is involved, however, arises from the finding of Robinson (1952c) that water extracts of chick leg muscle, even in late embryonic stages, have an ATPase with characteristics like those of the ATPase associated with the salt-extractable (myofibrillar) fraction. As the typical myosin-ATPase activity rises, the water-soluble activity falls. Robinson (1952c) suggests that "possibly the elaboration of the adult myofibril may proceed by some form of aggregation of protofibrillar structure." At the cytochemical level it appears that material reacting with fluorescent antimyosin is at first spread diffusely throughout the myofibril, but soon assumes a banded pattern in which only the A bands react (Holtzer et al., 1957; Engel and Horvath, 1960). The further elucidation of these phenomena affords a favorable opportunity for enlarging our understanding of development at the level of molecular organization and differentiation.

Although the means of identifying the myosin molecule are not yet sure enough to establish with certainty the time when it first appears,

Deuchar's work (1960a) does suggest that in skeletal muscle, just as in the heart (Ebert, 1953), chemical differentiation precedes visible differentiation. Possibly, myosin-ATPase is actually involved in some of the early steps in morphogenesis. This interesting possibility is supported by Deuchar's finding (1960b) that segmentation and Ca^{++}-ATPase increase in the chick embryo are both inhibited by ω-bromoallylglycine and are both released from the inhibition by leucine; moreover, ATP accelerates somite formation, at the same time enhancing ATPase activity, in the chick embryo and in *Xenopus* as well (Deuchar, 1960b, 1961).

C. Cholinesterase and the Myoneural Junction

Because of its essential role in activity and behavior, acetylcholinesterase (AChE) has been of interest to students of development since Nachmansohn (1939) first measured its increase in the brains of chick embryos and several fetal mammals. The pioneer studies of Sawyer in the 1940's clearly established a relationship between enzyme level and swimming ability in salamander larvae (cf. Sawyer, 1955). In one of the numerous investigations that have followed on Nachmansohn's observations, Kavaler and Kimel (1952) showed that AChE rises rapidly before neurophysiological reactivity begins. The development of the enzyme in the heart has already been mentioned (Section IV,D).

Histochemical study of AChE has made it possible to show that the enzyme is characteristically, though not exclusively, localized at synaptic terminals.[2] For example, this is nicely shown in the development of the retina (Section IV,B). In the optic lobes of the frog ChE appears to increase rapidly at the time when optic fibers are penetrating into them; if one eye is removed in the larval stage, the optic tectum of the contralateral side subsequently shows a ChE deficit demonstrable by both histochemical and quantitative methods (Boell *et al.*, 1955). Although this study did not establish the localization of the enzyme with great precision, it appears to be postjunctional, for Hess (1961) found that removing an eye in the adult stage caused no visible loss of ChE in the corresponding tectal area; in this case, other active connections probably maintained the ChE after the degeneration of the optic fibers. In newborn mammals eye removal lowers ChE in the superior colliculus, but has no effect at the adult stage (Hess, 1960).

At the myoneural junction, the positioning of ChE is now known with exactness, thanks to the application of the electron microscope to this

---

[2] AChE is only relatively specific, its substrate preferences overlapping those of nonspecific (pseudo)ChE. The two enzymes (each of which may include a spectrum of types) have many properties in common. In histochemical preparations they can be only partially distinguished from each other (Chessick, 1954; Engel, 1961).

cytochemical problem. Barrnett (1962) has demonstrated elegantly that the enzyme occurs on both sides of the synaptic gap, in the nerve terminals, and also in apparently high concentration on the junctional folds of the muscle itself. In the course of the development of the fetal rat (Kupfer and Koelle, 1951), goat (Beckett and Bourne, 1958), and chick embryo (Mumenthaler and Engel, 1961), ChE can be found in developing muscle before motor fibers arrive. In all cases the accumulation of massive quantities at the myoneural junction follows the arrival of nerve fibers and occurs concomitantly with the elaboration of the motor end plate. Extrajunctional ChE declines as junctional ChE increases (Mumenthaler and Engel, 1961). Quite possibly these are different molecular forms. When thigh muscle of 13-day chick embryos is maintained in culture, the general cytoplasmic activity persists and becomes localized at the Z lines, as it does in mature fibers, but end plates and the heavy concentrations of ChE associated with them do not appear (Engel, 1961).

VI. Factors Affecting Enzyme Levels during Development

Functional differentiation entails the accumulation of specific enzymes in appropriate spatial configurations. To the extent that this development is a matter of synthesis of specific proteins, it is stimulating to examine it in the light that emanates from a quarter century of productive research into enzymogenesis in microorganisms. The challenging theory of Jacob and Monod (1961, 1963), which has become the unifying principle of studies on protein synthesis, is reviewed in Chapter 8 of this volume. Suffice it to say here that in microorganisms the formation of a given enzyme may be prevented or elicited by the switching off and on of genes following the addition of specific substances to the medium. Although it at first seemed that only substrates are effective in inducing the specific enzymes that act on them, it is now clear that a variety of substances act by releasing the synthesis of an enzyme from a normally repressed state (Vogel, 1961).

Although attempts have been made to apply the Jacob-Monod scheme to the stable transformations of basic differentiation (e.g., Moore, 1962), there are difficulties in focusing simultaneously on *Escherichia coli* and early embryos, as Holtzer (1963) has pointed out with wit and cogency. At later stages as well, the important differences between bacteria and embryos must not be lost sight of. First, in dealing with embryos, we are faced not with a shift from virtual nonproduction to production of an enzyme in many instances, but rather with a change in rate of production that is small in comparison with the many thousandfold rate changes observed in bacteria; hence, it seems to be the activity of modifier genes rather than of the primary gene that is ordinarily the target of the controlling mechanisms. Second, as pointed out in the preceding section, the growth of an enzyme in an embryo often involves the integrated differentiation of structure in which numerous enzymes are concomitantly implicated. Nevertheless, functional differentiation does offer some parallels to induction in microorganisms. In particular, much of functional differentiation, though not fully reversible, is subject to modulation (cf. Weiss, 1939), i.e., the elaborated characteristics of the tissue go into eclipse in the absence of factors required to maintain the definitive state. This phenomenon resembles what happens to an enzyme in a bacterium placed in a medium devoid of inducer.

A. Synthesis or Activation?

Before it becomes profitable to deal with enzyme changes in terms of control of gene action in any sense, it is necessary to determine conclusively when an enzyme is actually being synthesized at a differential rate. The variety of interpretations that can be put on changes of enzyme activity as measured in homogenates has been discussed in Section II. The purpose of the present section is to examine the evidence that has permitted us to decide whether, in particular instances, an enzyme is altered in actual concentration during an interval of time or is being differentially activated (or restrained) without concentration change. The evidence for activation will be considered first.

The practice of combining homogenates of high and low activity or of dialyzing a small volume of one homogenate against a large volume of the other (Paigen, 1961b) has ruled out the possibility that dissociable cofactors are commonly involved in alterations of activity. Such factors are not often encountered in microorganisms either (Fincham, 1960). Nevertheless, enzymes may be present without being active. This is illustrated by the tyrosine-oxidizing system of the mammalian liver (Fig. 2, Section IV,A) of which at least three components pass from an inactive state at or soon after birth. As pointed out before, the phenylalanine hydroxylase system lacks a labile component at birth (Kenney et al., 1958). Immunochemical and isotopic studies indicate that the sharp rise in activity of tyrosine transaminase at birth in the rat is not the result of de novo synthesis (Kenney, 1960). p-Hydroxyphenylpyruvate oxidase is low in fetal rat and guinea pig livers, but can be raised to the postnatal level by incubation with dichlorophenol-indophenol (Table II); as development proceeds, the enzyme gradually shifts from the activatable to the spontaneously active form (Goswami and Knox, 1961). Since these enzymes act in sequence, it is interesting that tyrosine transaminase should become spontaneously active at birth in the rat, but p-hydroxy-phenylpyruvate oxidase not until the age of 2 weeks.

Beginning in 1938, Bodine and his students described in grasshopper eggs a protyrosinase which is activated by several chemical agents and also by heating to 80°C (cf. Bodine et al., 1944). More recently, it has been shown that heat activation is a not uncommon phenomenon in microorganisms, in which it results from the coincidence of heat-labile inhibitor and heat-stable enzyme (Swartz et al., 1958). In developmental

TABLE II

THE GROWTH OF p-HYDROXYPHENYLPYRUVATE OXIDASE ACTIVITY AND ITS CONVERSION FROM ACTIVATABLE TO SPONTANEOUSLY ACTIVE FORM IN THE LIVER OF THE RAT AND GUINEA PIG[a, b]

	p-Hydroxyphenylpyruvate oxidase activity		
Animal, age	Basal[c]	Total	Activatable (%)
Rat, prenatal:			
14–16 Day	0.26	1.2	78
18–20 Day	1.7	4.5	62
Rat, postnatal:			
1 Week	1.6	4.3	62
2 Weeks	4.6	7.4	37
2 Months	6.8	7.6	10
Guinea pig:			
50-Day fetus	0.3	2.6	88
Newborn (1 day)	7.0	7.6	8
Weanling	14.5	16.7	13
Adult	9.0	9.1	1

[a] The enzyme oxidizes p-hydroxyphenylpyruvate to homogentisate.

[b] Adapted from Goswami and Knox (1961).

[c] *Basal*, activity of homogenate without pretreatment; *total*, activity of homogenate after 15 minutes incubation with glutathione and dichlorophenol-indophenol; *activatable*, total activity — basal activity/total activity × 100.

studies the practice of boiling homogenates generally causes complete inactivation, but this result does not rule out the existence of heat-labile (protein) inhibitors, which might in some cases account for apparently low enzyme activity at certain stages. But there is little positive evidence. Ceska and Fisher (1959) ascribed the well-known decrease in arginase in the young chick embryo to a high molecular weight inhibitor, probably ribonucleoprotein. Eliasson (1962) showed, however, that the putative inhibitor acts merely by nonspecific binding of divalent ions. Nevertheless, growing realization of the importance of allosteric inhibition (Jacob and Monod, 1963) suggests that substances quite unrelated to the substrate may be effective in suppressing enzyme activity in developing systems.

The role of substrate itself in controlling both enzyme activity and enzyme stability is illustrated clearly by the work of Wright and her colleagues on the slime mold. Between the beginning of differentiation (early aggregation) and preculmination, the specific activities of isocitric dehydrogenase, GDH, G6P dehydrogenase, and alanine-α-ketoglutaric acid transaminase undergo no change, but the first two are unstable in extracts unless protected by added substrate (Wright, 1960). Reasoning from these results that the activity of enzymes in slime mold differentiation may be controlled by the rate at which endogenous substrate becomes available, Wright proceeded to show that the *in vivo* activity of GDH, which is a bridge for the entry of amino acids into the citric acid cycle, parallels the intracellular concentration of glutamate (Wright and Bard, 1963; Brühmüller and Wright, 1963). Although these results add an important new dimension to our understanding of enzyme control in differentiation, it remains to be seen how far they can be generalized; differentiation in the slime mold is somewhat special in that it occurs in a period of starvation.

The evidence that changes in enzyme activity in development actually represent differential synthesis is still largely indirect, resting to some extent on many failures to demonstrate any other type of control. There is however some direct evidence. Of course, myosin, measured as myofibrillar fraction, can be shown to increase faster than other muscle proteins in the chick embryo (Robinson, 1952c). An intensive immunochemical study has proved that the increase of carbamyl phosphate synthetase activity in the liver of the tadpole metamorphosing under the influence of thyroxine represents *de novo* synthesis (Metzenberg *et al.*, 1961; see Volume II, Chapter 5). The fact that two related enzymes that seem to increase rapidly at birth in the mammalian liver are in reality converted from an inactive to an active form, as pointed out earlier in this section, does not establish a general rule, even for liver. That rapid increase is compatible with synthesis is shown by tryptophan pyrrolase (TP), which is virtually absent from fetal liver but surges up to adult values within a few hours after birth in the guinea pig or at 15 days in the rat (Nemeth, 1959). The normal increase is completely blocked in a newborn guinea pig treated with puromycin, an inhibitor of protein synthesis, or with 5-fluorouracil, an inhibitor of RNA synthesis (Nemeth and de la Haba, 1962; Nemeth, 1962). In adult liver TP activity is elevated by tryptophan or cortisone, but this increase is only partly inhibited by puromycin or 5-fluorouracil. Feigelson and Greengard (1962) have shown that the TP apoenzyme is inactive in the absence of its co-factor hematin; tryptophan exerts its inductive effect by influencing the partitioning of hematin between apoTP and other heme-binding proteins. With tyrosine transaminase the situation is reversed, for this enzyme, which is converted from an inactive to an active form at birth in the rat, in adult life responds to substrate administration by *de novo* synthesis (Kenney, 1960, 1962a, b). Evolution has apparently selected a variety of mechanisms for making enzymes adaptable during the course of animal life.

One more evidence for synthesis of an enzyme in development comes from the work of Moscona and collaborators on cultured chick embryo retinas. In culture the retina accumulates glutamine transferase (now identified as a glutamine synthetase; Kirk and Moscona, 1963) several days earlier than *in vivo* (Moscona and Hubby, 1963). Puromycin stops the growth of enzyme activity reversibly, and actinomycin D, an inhibitor of DNA-dependent RNA synthesis, blocks it irreversibly (Kirk and Moscona, 1963). The amount of enzyme existing before inhibition remained stable.

B. *The Adaptability of Enzymes in Developing Systems*

1. Substrate Induction and Product Repression

That enzymes can be induced by substrate injection in mature animals is well-established (cf. Knox *et al.*, 1956). Attempts to demonstrate the same phenomenon in developing systems however have not had a happy history. The first positive finding to be published in full was that of Gordon and Roder (1953), who reported obtaining large increases in adenosine deaminase activity in the liver of the chick embryo by administration of adenosine. Neither Solomon (1960) nor Fisher *et al.* (1962) were able to repeat this result. An even more exciting claim that tryptophan peroxidase can be induced in dissociated cells of amphibian gastrulae (Stearns and Kostellow, 1958), from which it is normally absent, was subsequently refuted by Kato (cf. Ebert, 1960) and Spiegel and Frankel (1961). Roeder (1957) showed that the administration of arginine to chick embryos of 5 days or later transiently raised the level of activity of arginase without affecting its rate of decline. According to Eliasson, however, injected arginine has a strong but still transitory effect only at 24 hours, and no effect at all between 3 and 6 days. Thus far, the only uncontested demonstration of substrate induction appears to be that of Kato (1959), who was able, in a carefully controlled study, to produce increases in AlPase activity in the liver, duodenum, mesonephros, and metanephros in chick embryos between 14- and 19-days' incubation by injections of phenylphosphate. Four other substrates proved ineffective as inducers. Of particular interest was the fact that AcPase activity was not affected at all by any substrate. That AlPase is an adaptive and AcPase a constitutive enzyme has been suggested on the basis of the variability of the one and the constancy of the other in a variety of situations (Moog, 1959).

A negative case that is especially instructive is that of tryptophan pyrrolase (TP) in the fetal liver. In the adult rat, rabbit, and guinea pig, this enzyme is readily inducible by its substrate (cf. Knox et al., 1956; Nemeth, 1959). Although the enzyme rises abruptly at birth in the guinea pig and at 16 days in the rat, it cannot be raised to mature levels by administration of tryptophan to fetus or infant (Auerbach and Waisman, 1959; Nemeth, 1959). Yet, as soon as the enzyme begins its "spontaneous" upsurge, it becomes inducible. Here the induction is plainly a consequence of differentiation, not the cause of it. The relevant change in this case may be the appearance of heme-binding proteins which can inhibit TP by taking up the hematin on which the activity of the apoenzyme depends (Feigelson and Greengard, 1962; see Section VI,A).

Under *in vitro* conditions, Kato (1959) was able to elevate AlPase activity in fragments of chick embryo duodenum about 50 % by addition of phenylphosphate to the medium. Working also with intestine, Jones et al. (1956) were able to prevent loss of cholinesterase by addition of acetylcholine, whether the explants were growing or not. A much more striking case is that of Cox and Pontecorvo (1961), who proceeded from the assumption that, since AlPase is present in all cells in early stages of differentiation (Moog, 1944), it must be repressed in mature cells in which it appears absent. By addition of phenylphosphate to long-established strains of human fibroblasts, these authors succeeded in raising the enzyme to a high level of activity in cells in which it had been previously undetectable.

In intact embryos one positive and one negative case of product repression have been reported. Walker and Walker (1962) claim that arginine-glycine transaminase is reduced to 8 % of its normal 11-day value in chick embryo liver by administration of creatine on day 6. The authors suggest that the normal decline of the enzyme before birth may be caused by endogenous synthesis of creatine. In younger embryos, Eliasson (1963) was unable to repress arginase activity by injecting urea. The precocious increase of glutamine synthetase in chick embryo retina *in vitro*, already noted (Section IV,B), is an apparent instance of derepression resulting from the removal of an organ from its normal environment (Moscona and Hubby, 1963). The addition of glutamine to the medium inhibited the increase by less than 20 %, although glutamate inhibited it by 60 % (Kirk and Moscona, 1963). These findings are in contrast to the opposite effects of glutamine and glutamate in HeLa and

L cells, in which the former substance depresses but the latter elevates glutamotransferase activity (DeMars, 1958; Paul and Fottrell, 1963).

2. HORMONAL EFFECTS

The attempts to demonstrate that differential enzyme growth may be controlled by substances directly related to enzyme action have thus far met with only limited success. Current concepts of control of protein synthesis, however, have considerably broadened the range of substances that may induce or repress enzyme production (Jacob and Monod, 1961, 1963). There are two possibilities: an extrinsic molecule may itself act on the regulator-operator system controlling the action of a structural gene, or it may act on the cell (or the organism) in such a way as to produce or liberate an inducer or repressor. In two cases of apparent substrate-induced enzyme formation in rat liver, it has been found that the substrate has no effect in adrenalectomized animals (Lin and Knox, 1957; Civen and Knox, 1959).

The literature of endocrinology overflows with instances of alterations in enzyme activity brought about by change in hormonal status (cf. Knox et al., 1956). Although hormones generally do not influence enzymes in homogenates, Villee and co-workers have demonstrated a direct effect of estrogen in cell-free preparations of human placenta (Villee, 1960). The steroid appears to influence the rate of action of a transhydrogenase that catalyzes the reaction

$$\text{TPNH} + \text{DPN} \rightleftharpoons \text{TPN}^+ + \text{DPNH}$$

thus, key enzymes in the Krebs cycle and hexose monophosphate shunt are stimulated by the increased supply of oxidized TPN. In the rat uterus, however, estrogen promptly accelerates protein synthesis, apparently without the intervention of a steroid-sensitive transhydrogenase (Mueller et al., 1961). This de novo synthesis is the probable basis of previously demonstrated increases in enzyme activity (Mueller et al., 1958).

A convincing demonstration that hormones can stimulate enzyme synthesis comes from the elegant work of Kenney (1962a, b) on tyrosine-α-ketoglutarate transaminase (TKGT) in rat liver, an enzyme that is inducible by tyrosine only in the presence of adrenocorticoids (Lin and Knox, 1957). By preparing an antiserum to highly purified TKGT, Kenney (1962a) was able to show that administration of hydrocortisone resulted in an increase of enzyme antigen; moreover, there was no cross-reactive precursor found in any subcellular fraction. Further studies with C^{14}-leucine indicated that hydrocortisone stimulates TKGT synthesis in adrenalectomized rats without affecting the degradation rate (Kenney,

1962b). For tryptophan pyrrolase the evidence strongly suggests that corticoids raise the rate of formation of apoenzyme, which may then be activated by the influence of substrate on the availability of hematin (Feigelson *et al.*, 1962; Lee and Baltz, 1962).

These positive cases do not, of course, establish a rule that hormones act by affecting enzyme synthesis. There is, for example, evidence that steroids may affect the structural integrity of an enzyme molecule (Yielding and Tomkins, 1962). The vexed question of mechanism of hormone action is far from settled (cf. Hechter, 1955; Jenkin, 1962). In one case, however, we do have decisive evidence that a hormone can affect specific chromosomal loci. This is Clever's series of studies (1962, 1963) demonstrating that in *Chironomus* larvae ecdysone, the insect molting hormone, promotes puffing at two loci in physiological doses; one locus appears more sensitive than the other. During the normal pupal molt the same two loci undergo puffing, the more sensitive one reacting first, when the endogenous hormone titer is low. These results apparently indicate a direct effect on a gene, which responds by producing RNA (the puff), which, in turn, stimulates the synthesis of some specific protein.

Although hormones begin to exert differentiative effects, probably on a local rather than a systemic scale at first, as early as the time of sexual divergence of the gonads (cf. Burns, 1961), there has been surprisingly little interest in the effect of endocrine factors on enzymes in development. The only unequivocal case of hormone-induced enzyme synthesis in development is the previously mentioned study of carbamyl phosphate synthetase in the metamorphosing tadpole (Section VI,A). In the regression of the oviducts of the male chick embryo, the androgen seems to exert its effect by liberating several catabolic enzymes from a sequestered state (Scheib-Pfleger, 1955; Brachet *et al.*, 1958; Scheib-Pfleger and Wattiaux, 1962). Early pituitary removal alters the carbohydrate metabolism of the liver of the chick embryo (Konigsberg, 1954) and of the rat (Jacquot, 1955), and thyroid inhibition retards protein accumulation in the skeletal muscles (Konigsberg, 1958); although these effects bespeak an enzymatic basis, none has been sought. Nemeth (1959), however, has shown that the low level of tryptophan pyrrolase in the liver of the fetal rat cannot be elevated by cortisone, which is an effective inducer in older animals; this result, which might be predicted in view of the fact that the fetal adrenal cortex secretes actively before birth (Kitchell and Wells, 1952), again indicates that responsiveness to an inducer itself depends on prior differentiation.

The only enzyme in amniote development that has been studied intensively from the point of view of endocrine control is the AlPase of the intestinal epithelium (Section IV,E). In the chick embryo, the normal fiftyfold increase that begins at about day 18 *in ovo* can be advanced 3 or 4 days by the administration of cortisone or ACTH (cf. Moog, 1959, 1962a) or prevented by pituitary ablation (Watterson *et al.*, 1959). The normal increase fails to occur and cannot be elicited by cortisone, if thyroid hormone is not available (Moog, 1961b). Similar dependence on corticoids exists in the infant mouse, in which correlated study of adrenal development suggests that the normal upsurge of duodenal phosphatase between 15 and 18 days depends on prior enhanced activity of the adrenal cortices (cf. Moog, 1958).

How corticoids exert their effect on phosphatase is, however, unknown. Isolated duodenum in a synthetic medium responds to hydrocortisone by increase of AlPase (Moog and Kirsch, 1955), even though some formation of enzyme seems to occur in the absence of the hormone (Hancox, 1954). *In vivo* the effect of exogenous hormone is quite slow, requiring in the chick embryo from 1 to 5 days (depending on age at injection) to produce a significant increase of AlPase. Histochemical and histological studies reveal that the effect of the hormone is to accelerate an elaborate series of differentiative events, with phosphatase beginning to be elevated only when the microvilli in which it occurs have begun to develop (Moog, 1959). In the infant mouse, the correlated structural effects, though less obvious, are still far-reaching. In both mouse (Clark, 1959) and rat (Halliday, 1959), exogenous cortisone suppresses the protein-absorbing capacity of the infant epithelium at the same time that it brings about a rise of phosphatase activity.

The influence of thyroprivia on the brain of the infant rat has been studied by Hamburgh and Flexner (1957). If thyroid function is destroyed at birth by I^{131}, cytochrome oxidase and aldolase activities are unaffected and ChE is somewhat lowered; but SDH is severely repressed after the age of 10 days, when cortical neuroblasts begin to assume the characteristics of mature neurons. In the light of the fact that hormone therapy is variably effective in alleviating the mental retardation of cretinism, it is interesting that the authors were able to restore SDH levels to normal only if treatment was started at day 10, not if it was delayed to day 15. SDH increase is also repressed in the duodenum of the chick embryo by lack of thyroid hormone (Nunnally, 1962).

3. OTHER FACTORS AFFECTING ENZYME DEVELOPMENT

The evidence that patterns of enzyme development are controlled by such readily identifiable factors as substrates, products, and hormones is apparently scarce. Although more evidence will unquestionably be forthcoming, it seems reasonable to assume that other categories of factors will be implicated by future research. It is not unlikely that tissue-specific agents like the nerve growth factor extensively investigated by Levi-Montalcini and collaborators (cf. Levi-Montalcini and Angeletti, 1961), the skin factor isolated by Cohen (1962), and the inducer of vertebral cartilage described by Lash *et al.* (1962) are effective in altering patterns of enzyme development in the tissues they influence.

The possibility of enzymatic response to relatively unspecific factors, on the other hand, is suggested by the studies of Fell (1954) and Moscona (1959) on atypical differentiation of the chorioallantoic membrane of the chick embryo. The former author showed that the 4-day allantoic sac will produce tall, columnar epithelial cells with secretory goblet cells if cultured intact, or without goblet cells if everted on a stiff clot. Moscona found that the chorionic epithelium will keratinize simply in response to the opening of the egg. Probably both cases will be found to involve the formation of enzymes normally repressed in the chorioallantois.

Various negative results also point to the intervention of unidentified factors in enzyme development. Nemeth (1959), for example, could not hasten the normal postnatal upsurge of TP in the guinea pig or rabbit liver by tryptophan or cortisone or retard it by hypoxia; yet he did demonstrate that the increase promptly followed birth, whether premature, postmature, or normal. In the rabbit retina, failure of function to be carried on scarcely interfered with normal enzyme increase (Schimke, 1959). Similar independence is shown by the retina of the chick embryo, which cannot maintain its ganglion cell layer if placed in an ectopic position, yet begins to accumulate glutamotransferase at the same time as a normal retina *in situ*, despite the lack of normal nerve connections (Rudnick, 1959). That enzyme increase is delayed until the normal time is interesting in the light of the fact that glutamotransferase activity rises much earlier in retinas in organ culture than in those *in situ* (Moscona and Hubby, 1963). Retinas from 10-day embryos, however, respond to culture conditions more promptly than those from 7-day embryos, suggesting that a level of competence must be differentiated before the inducing situation can elicit a reaction; but morphogenesis was not accelerated in parallel with glutamotransferase increase. A need for the differentiation of a responsive condition is also suggested by the failure of rat cerebrum and spinal cord to undergo the elevations of oxidative enzyme activity characteristic of reactive gliosis in animals less than 10 days old (Osterberg and Wattenberg, 1963).

One of the oldest generalizations in causal morphology is that there is an antagonism between growth and differentiation. Certainly, many cells undergo their specific (including enzymatic) differentiation after they have ceased to divide. This is true both for the nervous system, in which cell division ceases early, and for the intestine, in which continuing divisions in the crypts feed out the cells that assume the form, the enzymology, and the transport capacity that characterizes their brief journey over the surface of the villus. In the intact organism a shift from proliferation to differentiation might result simply from differential partitioning of simple nutrients among the tissues of the increasingly complex organism (cf. Balinsky, 1960). Maximal exposure to nutrient may explain the tendency of embryonic cells cultured in monolayers to divide rapidly and fail to accumulate characteristic enzymes, as is true for retina (Moscona and Hubby, 1963) or intestinal epithelium (Lasfargues and Di Fine, 1951), or fail to produce a specific product, as is true for chondrocytes (Stockdale et al., 1963). That other factors may be also involved, however, is indicated by Stockdale and Holtzer's (1961) interesting demonstration that myoblasts within the same culture appear to synthesize either DNA or myosin, but not both.

VII. Enzyme Form and Structure

The accumulation of evidence showing that isodynamic enzymes may differ in molecular form holds great promise for the biochemistry of development. Although the idea that the "same" enzyme may not always be the same in structure dates back to Desreaux and Herriot's observations on pepsin in 1939, it was not until two decades later that this problem began to move forward rapidly. It is now well established that enzymes that perform the same catalytic act in the same organ in different species or in different organs in the same species may differ among themselves. This has been shown with special clarity by Schlamowitz (1958; Schlamowitz and Bodansky, 1959), who used immunochemical techniques to demonstrate differences among AlPases. By histochemical means Allen (1961) has shown that LDH's differing in substrate specificity are regionally distributed in several tissues of the mouse. Probably such differences occur even within single cells, for it seems likely that isodynamic enzymes will vary in structure according to their subcellular localization, as Thorne (1960) has shown for malic dehydrogenase.

There is now abundant evidence that molecules performing the same enzymatic function may be validly distinguished on the basis of kinetic properties and may be physically separable from each other by electrophoresis, column chromatography, and serological techniques. Usually isozymes differ from each other in several characteristics, but there are enigmatic exceptions.[3] For example, highly purified E. coli AlPase, ap-

---

[3] It is not always obvious what the word "isozyme" should signify. Quite distinct

pearing to be a unitary substance by Tiselius electrophoresis, sedimentation, and chromatography, yields four bands in starch-gel electrophoresis (Bach et al., 1961). This case is particularly striking, for all four bands are products of a single gene and, therefore, if current views of protein formation are correct, ought to be identical in primary, secondary, and tertiary structure. What the actual nature of the differences among individual members of a series of isozymes is, can only be determined by intensive physicochemical studies, such as have been vigorously carried forward by Markert and his associates (cf. Markert, 1963a).

LDH, a soluble and ubiquitous enzyme, has lent itself more fruitfully than any other to isozyme analysis. This enzyme occurs in a minimum of five forms separable by starch-gel electrophoresis (Markert and Moller, 1959). The proportions of these isozymic forms vary from organ to organ and also within the same organ in the course of its development (Markert and Ursprung, 1962), although embryonic heart, liver, and muscle tend to drift toward a common isozymic pattern in tissue culture (Phillip and Vessell, 1962). The probable explanation of some of the shifts in isozyme composition that have been observed during development recently has been put forward by Smith and Kissane (1963). By microanalysis of tiny sections of developing kidney, these authors have shown with admirable clarity that the glomeruli, proximal tubules, and collecting ducts retain the same predominant form of LDH throughout development, the apparent change in the organ as a whole (Markert and Ursprung, 1962) being due to an increase in the relative amount of proximal tubule tissue.

The possible physiological significance of the LDH forms has been the subject of a series of intriguing studies by Nathan Kaplan and his colleagues. In the chicken they find a single isozyme, designated "H," in the heart, and a different isozyme (M) in breast muscle. These two forms differ in amino acid composition (cf. Markert, 1963a). The former is markedly inhibited by increasing concentration of pyruvate and, hence, is adapted to aerobic conditions; the latter is unaffected by quite high concentrations of pyruvate. By immunochemical analysis Cahn et al. (1962) have shown that the breast muscle of the 6-day embryo contains mostly H type, but shifts gradually to M type. Birds that are powerful fliers, however, have H-type LDH in their breast muscles (Wilson et al., 1963). The rat heart at 9 days in utero contains predominantly M type, perhaps reflecting a relatively anaerobic environment; subsequently there is a shift toward the H form (Fine et al., 1963). Since heart, muscle, and

---

proteins which happen to work on the same substrates (e.g., DNase I and II, AcPase and AlPase) are not isozymes. The term apparently should be used to denote related molecules that are isodynamic in action and show minor physicochemical differences of systematic nature.

also liver (Fine *et al.*, 1963) are relatively homogeneous, and thus unlike kidney, these studies seem to reveal genuine differentiation at the molecular level.

LDH can be dissociated into four inactive subunits (Appella and Markert, 1961). Cahn *et al.* (1962) and Markert (1963a) have proposed that the subunits are of two sorts, H and M, each produced by a corresponding gene, the five active LDH's thus being tetramers composed of four H-units (H type), four M-units (M type) or any combination of the two. The correctness of this hypothesis is indicated by the fact that recombining monomers dissociated from the four H- and 4 M-isozymes yields five isozymes in the expected proportions (Markert, 1963b). Moreover, the character of each subunit appears to be inherited independently (Shaw and Barto, 1963).

Isozymes are found in the unfertilized egg, with some forms being apparently carried over from the maternal system and unable to maintain themselves as development proceeds (Moore and Villee, 1963; Goldberg and Cather, 1963). Neither in early embryogenesis nor in functional differentiation, however, has much interest yet been shown in any but the LDH isozymes, despite the fact that many enzymes are known to occur in multiple forms. In the intestine of the mouse a single AlPase seems to be present during the first 2 weeks after birth. Under the influence of adrenocorticoids the infant enzyme in the duodenum is then abruptly converted to a new phosphatase differing from its predecessor in catalytic, electrophoretic, and chromatographic behavior (Moog, 1961a; Moog *et al.*, 1963). As a consequence of this change the duodenal and jejunal phosphatases of the mature intestine differ from each other to the extent that they do not cross-react in immunochemical tests (Moog and Angeletti, 1962). A negative case has been reported by Nemeth (1961), who finds that the small amount of TP in the liver of the 5-day rat is chromatographically identical with that found in greater abundance in the adult liver. Phosphorylase, which is found in adult tissues as an enzymatically active monomer and an inactive dimer, occurs in its active form in the liver of the chick embryo before the inactive form, or the related kinase, appear (Guha and Wegmann, 1961).

VIII. The Genetic Basis of Enzyme Development

That enzyme production is controlled by genes, although a broadly established fact to the microbial geneticist, is not much more than an article of faith to the embryologist. Although chemical differentiation is widely discussed in genetic terms, the demonstrations that patterns of enzyme growth can actually be traced to a genetic basis are scarce. There is, however, one case showing decisively the early intervention of genes in enzyme production. In a cross involving eggs of a sea urchin, in which AlPase activity is low, and sperm of the sand dollar, in which phosphatase activity is high, Flickinger (1957) showed that the level of activity of the hybrids at 3 days was significantly above that of the maternal species at the same age.

At present, clinical studies of "inborn errors of metabolism" furnish the most extensive evidence we have that enzyme production in higher animals is controlled by Mendelian genes (cf. Strauss, 1960). Phenylketonuria provides a clear example. In this disorder, which appears to involve a single recessive gene, there is a failure to produce one of the two fractions of the phenylalanine hydroxylase system necessary for the transformation of phenylalanine to tyrosine (see Section IV,A). Heterozygotes seem to be deficient, but not lacking, in the affected enzyme. Since the affected fraction normally begins to appear shortly after birth (Kenney et al., 1958), it may be inferred that the mutant gene is unable to respond to derepressive factors operating in the perinatal period.

The numerous instances cited in this chapter in which an enzyme is undetectable until a late stage indicate that many genes are held in a repressed state throughout much of development. Some of these cases may, of course, be based on conversion of an inactive to an active form, but in others de novo synthesis can be demonstrated, as in the accumulation of TP in the infant liver (Nemeth and de la Haba, 1962; Nemeth, 1962). In such cases the search for a derepressive mechanism acting directly on the operon responsible for the formation of the enzyme may be a fruitful one. As Fincham (1960) points out, however, "where an enzyme is inducible or formed only under rather special conditions, one would expect its production to be susceptible at many points to genetic changes, whereas enzymes which are essential for growth and are more or less constitutive in growing cells may on the whole be subject only to rather direct and specific effects of mutations." It is, in fact, remarkable how few enzymes show constitutive characteristics in developing systems. Hence, the search for controlling mechanisms may be expected sometimes to lead through rather complex series of modifier genes.

Paigen's instructive study (1961a, b) of β-glucuronidase accumulation in the young mouse, however, does indicate that the structure of an enzyme and the time of its accumulation may be under the control of the same chromosomal region. β-Glucuronidase is present in much higher quantity in DBA/2 (GG) mice than in C3H/Ha (gg); the difference is maintained at all stages in liver, spleen, thymus, kidney, and heart (Fig. 3). In both strains the enzyme is partly lysosomal and partly microsomal, apparently having the same form at both sites. In the mutant (gg) the activity is lowered at both sites, though to a greater degree in microsomes (Paigen, 1961a). Backcrosses of heterozygotes ($GG \times gg$) to the gg strain yielded no dissociation between quantity and localization, indicating that the genes controlling these parameters are closely linked or identical.

The accumulation patterns, however, are different for each organ, and show individual differences between the two strains in each organ (Paigen, 1961b). Representative patterns are shown in Fig. 3. On the basis of

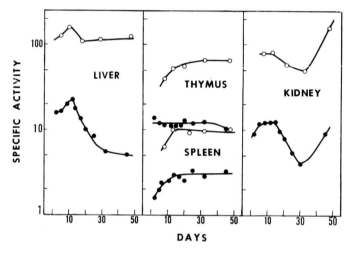

Fɪɢ. 3. The specific activity of β-glucuronidase in four organs of young DBA mice (open circles) and C3H mice (closed circles). Each organ has an individual accumulation pattern with divergences between wild type and mutant strain occurring at different times in the various organs. Adapted from Paigen (1961b).

these results, the author suggests that three factors may interact to promote enzymatic differentiation: "the locus which determines the structure of the enzyme; the diffusible specific inducers and repressors of enzyme synthesis; and the 'controlling elements' which might act to determine when during development the structural genes become sensitive to the local diffusible factors" (Paigen, 1961b). The possibility that the "controlling elements" may be genetic is supported by McClintock's (1956) classic work on *Zea mays*. Whether the timing factors act by direct interplay among operons, as proposed by Jacob and Monod (1963), or whether they act indirectly, as, for example, through alterations in the ability of the cell surface to facilitate or bar the entrance of diffusible factors, remains problematical.

IX. Summary and Perspective

The enzymology of functional differentiation is a subject on which facts are abundant, generalizations scarce. Beyond the well-established rule that developing tissues have distinctive enzyme complements varying according to patterns peculiar to the individual tissue, no further conclusions of equal firmness can yet be drawn. It appears that the timing of enzyme changes is usually intelligible from a teleonomic point of view, although there are conspicuous exceptions. From a causal point of view, the patterns of enzyme growth in embryos remain obscure. The small amount of evidence now available suggests that enzyme activity and growth in developing tissues are controlled by a diversity of mechanisms.

If new generalizations are not at hand, it is nevertheless clear that within recent years the study of enzymes in embryos has entered upon a new phase of great promise, the emphasis having shifted from the descriptive to the analytical area. Thanks to the application both of new concepts and of new techniques, we are acquiring insights and information that begin to illuminate the obscurities of earlier investigations. The achievements of the immediate past enable us to foresee the direction in which important advances can be looked for in the near future.

In the first place, it is clearly necessary in studying the development of an enzyme activity to determine whether it is carried out by one or more molecular forms. The interpretation of both formation of the enzyme and its functional significance depends on recognition at the molecular level. Investigations of physical, kinetic, and antigenic properties have already proved their value in this area. Although it is possible that recent preoccupation with LDH (Section VII) has given a misleading importance to change of molecular form in development, it is nonetheless essential now to examine the possible multiple nature of every enzyme under study.

Future work must also concern itself more closely than that of the past with the actual meaning of alterations of enzyme activity. The assumption that enzyme activity in homogenates does, under appropriately controlled conditions, reflect enzyme concentration, is hardly tenable in the face of some of the findings described in Section VI. To determine the presence of inactive enzyme is relatively simple in cases in which the antigenic site becomes available before the enzymatic (Kenney, 1960). The presence of an enzyme precursor with both sites masked would be more difficult to detect; but the use of inhibitors of protein synthesis (provided their use proves feasible in vivo; cf. Nemeth, 1962) may be expected to reveal those situations in which an inactive form is to be sought. In addition, the possibility of sequential differences in enzyme stability must also be taken into account (Wright, 1960).

The need to determine the localization of enzymes, not only on a cellular but also on an intracellular level, is of obvious utility from both a structural and a functional point of view. Extensive studies involving differential centrifugation of mature tissues have contributed substantially to our understanding of intracellular metabolism. Many workers have already applied differential centrifugation to problems of developmental enzymology with promising results (Sections IV and V,A). To an important extent, however, the student of development needs in this area to venture outside of the guidelines of biochemistry, for some of the secrets of functional differentiation are no doubt hidden in that difficult period that precedes the manifestation of recognizable form. Chemogenesis frequently precedes morphogenesis or histogenesis. An extreme example is provided by the thyroid of the chick embryo, which is able to trap iodide on day 5 (Trunnel and Wade, 1955), even before the appearance of the fenestrated epithelial plates from which the follicles arise; other steps leading to the synthesis of the thyroid homone are added one by one over the next 4 days. What enables an apparently undifferentiated cell (or group) to execute a differentiated function? Electron microscopy and immunohistochemistry will probably be of use in dealing with this question; but the answer probably lies in the still unapproachable area of the *in vivo* dynamics of fine structure. Although the exploration of this area is also fundamental to our understanding of the physiology of mature cells, in differentiating cells it entails the additional problem that structure must be increasing in complexity as new enzymes and new processes appear.

When the status of an enzyme at various times in development is well understood, the problem of its control, whether of activity or formation, may be approached with some confidence. This problem must, of course, be dealt with at several levels, the first being the organismic. Certainly enzyme development is influenced by extrinsic factors that may diffuse from neighboring tissues or be transported by the blood stream. A strong hint as to the importance of such factors comes from the existence of critical periods, in which numerous enzymes in different organs are simultaneously affected. Surely it is not mere coincidence that a variety of enzymes in the brain (Flexner, 1955a, b), the intestine (Moog and Ortiz, 1960), and the lungs (Sorokin *et al.*, 1959) should all increase at the beginning of the sixth week of gestation in the guinea pig. Similar critical periods can be delineated in every animal whose development has been extensively studied, probably the most fully documented being the first half of the third postnatal week in the mouse and rat, when growth slackens and numerous enzymes of brain, retina, liver, intestine, and other organs abruptly increase. The adrenal cortex has been implicated in some of these events (Moog, 1959), but other glands no doubt are involved as well.

The second level at which the control of enzyme development must be dealt with is the cellular. Ultimately, it is the individual cell that forms the enzyme, in response to intrinsic or extrinsic factors impinging on the chromosomal apparatus. Although the intact organism may supply clues, the isolation of parts under study, in organ culture or under other conditions that permit synthesis of specific proteins, now seems necessary for a closer approach to the problem in hand. The still unexploited potentialities of culture methods in the study of differentiation recently have been illustrated vividly by Konigsberg's remarkable achievement (1963) in raising large and well-differentiated muscle colonies from a single muscle cell *in vitro*. If culture studies are to yield valuable information about the substances that directly or indirectly induce or repress enzyme formation, however, the wider use of synthetic media is clearly indicated. The time-honored place of serum in tissue culture research does not cancel out the fact that serum contains variable amounts of hormones, nutrients, and even enzymes (cf. Rossi *et al.*, 1959); embryo extract is an even less desirable ingredient, for it not only contains some of the same substances as serum, but may be rich in the very unknown that the research is designed to identify. The impressive studies of Wolff and collaborators on organ culture in chemically defined media demonstrate that different organs may have quite individual requirements that could not be delineated in undefined media (e.g., Wolff *et al.*, 1960).

The last and most challenging level of study of control of enzyme development is the intracellular. It has been pointed out several times in this chapter that the new or enhanced production of an enzyme, although it represents a step in the total differentiation of the cell, itself depends on the state of differentiation of the cell. Many enzymes are indifferent to the critical periods that strongly influence others; a change in one enzyme does not necessarily affect even others in the same pathway (e.g., Nemeth, 1961). Here we are brought sharply face to face with an inescapable distinction between the embryo and the bacterium. In the developing embryo, it again appears that all nuclei are equal in their genic equipment (Gurdon, 1963); but they are decidedly unequal in their capacity to respond to the extrinsic situation. It is not to be thought that studies of enzyme development, however penetrating, will alone elucidate the nature of the intrinsic differentiation that determines the response to extrinsic influences. Nevertheless, the continued acquisition of precise information about the normal and experimental conditions under which enzyme formation may be elicited or repressed in developing tissues may aid in illuminating the physical and conceptual recesses in which the intimate nature of differentiation resides.

One final point deserving mention concerns the relation of the study of enzymogenesis to clinical practice. Prematurity and the perinatal period are still fraught with disorders for which there is not yet any fully effective therapy. Observations of these disorders, however, have yielded numerous clues to patterns of enzymogenesis (cf. Driscoll and Hsia, 1958; Kretchmer, 1959), as this chapter has pointed out. Conversely, investigations into the timing of enzyme formation or activation and their dependence on conditions operating within the organism are likely to contribute importantly to the rational management of the disorders that beset the first days of postnatal life. In this area, the fostering of mutual interests between the laboratory and the clinic may be expected to lead to mutual advantage.

REFERENCES

Allen, J. M. (1961). Ann. N. Y. Acad. Sci. 94, 937.
Alvarez, A., and Sas, J. (1961). Nature 190, 826.
Appella, E., and Markert, C. L. (1961). Biochem. Biophys. Res. Commun. 6, 171.
Auerbach, V. H., and Waisman, H. A. (1959). J. Biol. Chem. 234, 304.
Auricchio, S., and Rigillo, N. (1960). Biol. Neonatorum 2, 146.
Bach, M. L., Signer, E. R., Levinthal, C., and Sizer, I. W. (1961). Federation Proc. 20, 255.
Balinsky, B. I. (1960). "An Introduction to Embryology." Saunders, Philadelphia, Pennsylvania.
Barrnett, R. J. (1962). J. Cell Biol. 12, 247.
Barth, L. G., and Barth, L. J. (1951). J. Exptl. Zool. 116, 99.
Beaumont, A. (1954). Compt. Rend. Soc. Biol. 148, 29.
Beckett, E. B., and Bourne, G. H. (1958). Acta Anat. 35, 226.
Bellec, A. (1957). Compt. Rend. Soc. Biol. 151, 1353.
Berg, W. E., Taylor, D. E., and Humphreys, W. J. (1962). Develop. Biol. 4, 165.
Billett, F., and Mulherkar, L. (1958). J. Embryol. Exptl. Morphol. 6, 52.
Bloxam, H. R., Day, M. G., Gibbs, N. K., and Woolf, L. I. (1960). Biochem. J. 77, 320.
Bodine, J. H., Tahmisian, T. N., and Hill, D. L. (1944). Arch. Biochem. 4, 403.
Boell, E. J. (1955). In "Analysis of Development" (B. H. Willier, P. Weiss, V. Hamburger, eds.), pp. 520-555. Saunders, Philadelphia, Pennsylvania.
Boell, E. J., and Weber, R. (1955). Exptl. Cell Res. 9, 559.
Boell, E. J., Greenfield, P., and Shen, S. C. (1955). J. Exptl. Zool. 129, 415.
Bogner, P. H., and Haines, I. A. (1961). Proc. Soc. Exptl. Biol. Med. 107, 265.
Bondi, C. (1959). Riv. Biol. (Perugia) 51, 469.
Bondi, C. (1962). Riv. Biol. (Perugia) 55, 59.
Bondi, C., and Bellini, L. (1960). Riv. Biol. (Perugia) 53, 449.
Bondi, C., and Bellini, L. (1962). Riv. Biol. (Perugia) 55, 89.
Bot, G., Andrassy, K. O., and Kovacs, D. F. (1960). Acta Physiol. Acad. Sci. Hung. 17, 377.

Brachet, J. (1960). "The Biochemistry of Development." Pergamon, New York.

Brachet, J., Decroly-Briers, M., and Hoyez, J. (1958). *Bull. Soc. Chim. Biol.* **40**, 2039.

Brand, L., Dahl, C., and Mahler, H. R. (1960). *J. Biol. Chem.* **235**, 2456.

Brown, A. K., and Zuelzer, W. W. (1958). *J. Clin. Invest.* **37**, 332.

Brown, D. D., and Caston, J. D. (1962). *Develop. Biol.* **5**, 412.

Brühmüller, M., and Wright, B. E. (1963). *Biochim. Biophys. Acta* **71**, 50.

Burch, H. B., Lowry, O. H., deGubareff, T., and Lowry, S. R. (1958). *J. Cellular Comp. Physiol.* **52**, 503.

Burns, R. K. (1961). *In* "Sex and Internal Secretions" (W. C. Young, ed.), Vol. I, pp. 76-160. Saunders, Philadelphia, Pennsylvania.

Cahn, R., Kaplan, N. O., Levine, L., and Zwilling, E. (1962). *Science* **136**, 962.

Carey, N. H., and Greville, G. D. (1959a). *Biochem. J.* **71**, 159.

Carey, N. H., and Greville, G. D. (1959b). *Biochem. J.* **71**, 166.

Ceska, M., and Fisher, J. R. (1959). *Biol. Bull.* **117**, 611.

Chessick, R. D. (1954). *J. Histochem. Cytochem.* **2**, 258.

Civen, M., and Knox, W. E. (1959). *Science* **129**, 1672.

Clark, S. L. (1959). *J. Biophys. Biochem. Cytol.* **5**, 41.

Clark, S. L. (1961). *Am. J. Anat.* **109**, 57.

Clever, U. (1962). *J. Insect Physiol.* **8**, 357.

Clever, U. (1963). *Develop. Biol.* **6**, 73.

Cohen, A. (1957). *Compt. Rend. Soc. Biol.* **151**, 918.

Cohen, L. H., and Noell, W. K. (1960). *J. Neurochem.* **5**, 253.

Cohen, S. (1962). *J. Biol. Chem.* **237**, 1555.

Coleman, J. R. (1962). *Develop. Biol.* **5**, 232.

Cooper, W. G. (1955). *Anat. Record* **123**, 103.

Coulombre, A. J. (1955). *Am. J. Anat.* **96**, 153.

Cox, R. P., and Pontecorvo, G. (1961). *Proc. Natl. Acad. Sci. U. S.* **47**, 839.

Csapo, A., and Herrmann, H. (1951). *Am. J. Physiol.* **165**, 701.

Dalton, A. J. (1937). *Anat. Record* **68**, 393.

Davidson, J. (1957). *Growth* **21**, 287.

Davletova, L. V. K. (1961). *Zh. Obshch. Biol.* **22**, 201; *Ref. Zh. Biol.* No. 2M50 (1962).

Dawkins, M. J. R. (1959). *Proc. Roy. Soc.* **B150**, 284.

de Duve, C. (1959). *In* "Subcellular Particles" (T. Hayashi, ed.), pp. 128-159. Ronald, New York.

DeMars, R. (1958). *Biochim. Biophys. Acta* **27**, 435.

Desreaux, V., and Herriot, M. R. (1939). *Nature* **144**, 287.

Deuchar, E. M. (1960a). *J. Embryol. Exptl. Morphol.* **8**, 251.

Deuchar, E. M. (1960b). *J. Embryol. Exptl. Morphol.* **8**, 259.

Deuchar, E. M. (1961). *Exptl. Cell Res.* **23**, 21.

de Villafranca, G. W. (1954). *J. Exptl. Zool.* **127**, 367.

Dingle, J. T., Lucy, J. S., and Fell, H. B. (1961). *Biochem. J.* **79**, 497.

Doell, R. G., and Kretchmer, N. (1962). *Biochim. Biophys. Acta* **62**, 353.

Doell, R. G., and Kretchmer, N. (1963). *Biochim. Biophys. Acta* **67**, 516.

Driscoll, S. G., and Hsia, D. Y. (1958). *Pediatrics* **22**, 785.

Dumm, M. E., and Levy, M. (1949). *J. Cellular Comp. Physiol.* **33**, 373.

Dutton, G. J. (1959). *Biochem. J.* **71**, 141.

Eakin, R. M., and Lehmann, F. E. (1957). *Arch. Entwicklungsmech. Organ.* **150**, 177.

Ebert, J. D. (1953). *Proc. Natl. Acad. Sci. U. S.* **39**, 333.

Ebert, J. D. (1960). *Carnegie Inst. Wash. Year Book* **59**, 389.

Ebert, J. D., Tolman, R. A., Mun, A. M., and Albright, J. F. (1955). *Ann. N. Y. Acad. Sci.* **60**, 968.

Eliasson, E. (1962). *Exptl. Cell Res.* **26**, 175.

Eliasson, E. (1963). *Exptl. Cell Res.* **30**, 74.

Engel, W. K. (1961). *J. Histochem. Cytochem.* **9**, 66.

Engel, W. K., and Horvath, B. (1960). *J. Exptl. Zool.* **144**, 209.

Feigelson, P., and Greengard, O. (1962). *J. Biol. Chem.* **237**, 1908.

Feigelson, P., Feigelson, M., and Greengard, O. (1962). *Recent Progr. Hormone Res.* **18**, 491.

Fell, H. B. (1954). *J. Embryol. Exptl. Morphol.* **2**, 348.

Fell, H. B., and Dingle, J. T. (1963). *Biochem. J.* **87**, 403.

Fincham, J. R. S. (1960). *Advan. Enzymol.* **22**, 1.

Fine, I. H., Kaplan, N. O., and Kuftiner, D. (1963). *Biochemistry* **2**, 116.

Fisher, E. R., and Gruhn, J. (1959). *Proc. Soc. Exptl. Biol. Med.* **101**, 781.

Fisher, J. R., Chilson, O. P., and Chan, S. K. (1962). *Biochim. Biophys. Acta* **58**, 371.

Flexner, J. B., Greenblatt, C. L., Cooperband, S. R., and Flexner, L. B. (1956). *Am. J. Anat.* **98**, 129.

Flexner, L. B. (1939). *J. Biol. Chem.* **131**, 703.

Flexner, L. B. (1955a). *In* "Biochemistry of the Developing Nervous System" (H. Waelsch, ed.), pp. 281-300. Academic Press, New York.

Flexner, L. B. (1955b). *Ann. N. Y. Acad. Sci.* **60**, 986.

Flexner, L. B., Flexner, J. B., Roberts, R. B., and de la Haba, G. (1960). *Develop. Biol.* **2**, 313.

Flickinger, R. A. (1957). *Biol. Bull.* **112**, 21.

George, J. C., and Iype, P. T. (1959). *J. Exptl. Zool.* **141**, 291.

Gersh, I. (1937). *Contrib. Embryol. Carnegie Inst. Wash.* **26**, 34.

Goldberg, E., and Cather, J. N. (1963). *J. Cellular Comp. Physiol.* **61**, 31.

Gordon, M. W., and Roder, M. (1953). *J. Biol. Chem.* **200**, 859.

Goswami, M. N. D., and Knox, W. E. (1961). *Biochim. Biophys. Acta* **50**, 35.

Graymore, C. N. (1959). *Brit. J. Ophthalmol.* **43**, 34.

Green, D. E. (ed.) (1946) *In* "Currents in Biochemical Research," pp. 149-164. Wiley (Interscience), New York.

Green, D. E., and Jarnefeldt, J. (1959). *Perspectives Biol. Med.* **2**, 163.

Gregg, J. R. (1960). *Biol. Bull.* **119**, 428.

Grillo, T. I. A. (1961). *J. Histochem. Cytochem.* **9**, 386.

Grodsky, G. M., Carbone, J., and Franska, R. (1958). *Proc. Soc. Exptl. Biol. Med.* **97**, 291.

Gross, P. R., Philpott, D. E., and Nass, S. (1960). *J. Biophys. Biochem. Cytol.* **7**, 135.

Guha, S., and Wegmann, R. (1961). *J. Histochem. Cytochem.* **9**, 454.

Gurdon, J. B. (1963). *Quart. Rev. Biol.* **38**, 54.

Gustafson, T., and Hasselberg, I. (1951). *Exptl. Cell. Res.* **2**, 642.

Halliday, R. (1959). *J. Endocrinol.* **18**, 56.

Hamburgh, M., and Flexner, L. B. (1957). *J. Neurochem.* **1**, 279.

Hancox, N. M. (1954). *Acta Anat.* **21**, 18.

Hard, W. L., Reynolds, O., and Winbury, M. (1944). *J. Exptl. Zool.* **96**, 189.

Hechter, O. (1955). *Vitamins Hormones* **13**, 293.

Heller, H. (1962). *In* "The Development of Homeostasis" (E. F. Adolph, ed.), pp. 77-90. Academic Press, New York.

Herrmann, H. (1963). In "Cytodifferentiation and Macromolecular Synthesis" (M. Locke, ed.), pp. 85-118. Academic Press, New York.

Herrmann, H., and Nicholas, J. S. (1948). J. Exptl. Zool. 107, 165.

Herrmann, H., Nicholas, J. S., and Vosgian, M. E. (1949). Proc. Soc. Exptl. Biol. Med. 72, 455.

Hess, A. (1960). J. Exptl. Zool. 144, 11.

Hess, A. (1961). Anat. Record 140, 295.

Holt, J. H., and Miller, D. (1962). Biochim. Biophys. Acta 58, 239.

Holter, H. (1949). Pubbl. Staz. Zool. Napoli 21 (Suppl.), 60.

Holtzer, H. (1963). Colloq. Ges. Physiol. Chem. 13, 127.

Holtzer, H., Marshall, J. M., and Finck, H. (1957). J. Biochem. Biophys. Cytol. 3, 705.

Holtzer, H., Abbott, J., Lash, J., and Holtzer, S. (1960). Proc. Natl. Acad. Sci. U. S. 46, 1533.

Hughes, A. W. (1949). J. Royal Microscop. Soc. 69, 145.

Ikeda, A. (1959). Hiroshima J. Med. Sci. 8, 71.

Immers, J., and Runnström, J. (1960). Develop. Biol. 2, 90.

Ivemark, B. I. (1958). J. Anat. 92, 98.

Ivemark, B. I. (1959). Acta Pathol. Microbiol. Scand. 45, 1.

Jacob, F., and Monod, J. (1961). J. Mol. Biol. 3, 318.

Jacob, F., and Monod, J. (1963). In "Cytodifferentiation and Macromolecular Synthesis" (M. Locke, ed.), pp. 30-64. Academic Press, New York.

Jacquot, R. (1955). J. Physiol. (Paris) 47, 857.

Jaffee, O. C. (1954). J. Cellular Comp. Physiol. 44, 347.

Jenkin, P. M. (1962). "Animal Hormones," Pt. I. Pergamon, New York.

Jones, M., Featherstone, R. M., and Bonting, S. L. (1956). J. Pharmacol. Exptl. Therap. 116, 114.

Junquiera, L. C. U. (1952). Quart. J. Microscop. Sci. 93, 247.

Kafer, E., and Pollak, J. K. (1961). Exptl. Cell Res. 22, 120.

Karunairatnam, M. C., Kerr, L. M., and Levvy, G. A. (1949). Biochem. J. 45, 496.

Kato, Y. (1959). Develop. Biol. 1, 477.

Kavaler, F., and Kimel, V. M. (1952). J. Comp. Neurol. 96, 113.

Kawasaki, K. (1958). Acta Med. Biol. (Niigata) 6, 29.

Kenney, F. T. (1960). Biochem. Biophys. Res. Commun. 2, 333.

Kenney, F. T. (1962a). J. Biol. Chem. 237, 1610.

Kenney, F. T. (1962b). J. Biol. Chem. 237, 3495.

Kenney, F. T., and Kretchmer, N. (1959). J. Clin. Invest. 38, 2189.

Kenney, F. T., Reem, G. H., and Kretchmer, N. (1958). Science 127, 86.

Kiesseling, K. H. (1962). Exptl. Cell Res. 28, 145.

Kirk, D. L., and Moscona, A. A. (1963). Develop. Biol. 8, 341.

Kitchell, R., and Wells, L. J. (1952). Endocrinology 50, 83.

Klein, R. L. (1960). Am. J. Physiol. 199, 613.

Klein, R. L. (1961). Am. J. Physiol. 201, 858.

Knox, W. E., Auerbach, V. H., and Lin, E. C. C. (1956). Physiol. Rev. 36, 164.

Koldovsky, O., Faltova, E., Hahn, P., and Vacek, Z. (1962). In "The Development of Homeostasis" (E. F. Adolph, ed.), pp. 155-164. Academic Press, New York.

Konigsberg, I. R. (1954). J. Exptl. Zool. 125, 151.

Konigsberg, I. R. (1958). J. Cellular Comp. Physiol. 52, 13.

Konigsberg, I. R. (1963). Science 140, 1273.

Kornfeld, R., and Brown, D. H. (1963). J. Biol. Chem. 238, 1604.

Kretchmer, N. (1959). *Pediatrics* **23**, 606.

Kretchmer, N., Levine, S., McNamara, H., and Barnett, H. L. (1956). *J. Clin. Invest.* **35**, 236.

Kupfer, C., and Koelle, G. B. (1951). *J. Exptl. Zool.* **116**, 397.

Lasfargues, E., and Di Fine, J. (1951). *J. Cellular Comp. Physiol.* **37**, 175.

Lash, J. W., Hommes, F. A., and Zilliken, F. (1962). *Biochim. Biophys. Acta* **56**, 313.

Lee, J. D., and Baltz, B. E. (1962). *Endocrinology* **70**, 84.

Levi-Montalcini, R., and Angeletti, P. U. (1961). *Quart. Rev. Biol.* **36**, 99.

Lin, E. C. C., and Knox, W. E. (1957). *Biochim. Biophys. Acta* **26**, 85.

Lindemann, V. F. (1947). *Am. J. Physiol.* **148**, 40.

Lövlie, A. M. (1959). *Nytt Mag. Zool.* **8**, 5.

Løvtrup, S. (1955). *Compt. Rend. Trav. Lab. Carlsberg Ser. Chim.* **29**, 261.

McClintock, B. (1956). *Cold Spring Harbor Symp. Quant. Biol.* **21**, 197.

Maggio, R., and Ghiretti-Magaldi, A. (1958). *Exptl. Cell Res.* **15**, 95.

Mahler, H. R., Wittenberger, M. H., and Brand, L. (1958). *J. Biol. Chem.* **233**, 770.

Markert, C. L. (1963a). *In* "Cytodifferentiation and Macromolecular Synthesis" (M. Locke, ed.), pp. 65-84. Academic Press, New York.

Markert, C. L. (1963b). *Science* **140**, 1329.

Markert, C. L., and Moller, F. (1959). *Proc. Natl. Acad. Sci. U. S.* **45**, 753.

Markert, C. L., and Ursprung, H. (1962). *Develop. Biol.* **5**, 363.

Metzenberg, R. L., Marshall, M., Paik, W. K., and Cohn, P. P. (1961). *J. Biol. Chem.* **236**, 162.

Miyamoto, M., and Fitzpatrick, T. (1957). *Science* **126**, 449.

Monroy, A. (1957a). *J. Cellular Comp. Physiol.* **50**, 73.

Monroy, A. (1957b). *Intern. Rev. Cytol.* **6**, 107.

Moog, F. (1944). *Biol. Bull.* **86**, 51.

Moog, F. (1952). *Ann. N. Y. Acad. Sci.* **55**, 57.

Moog, F. (1958). *In* "Embryonic Nutrition" (D. Rudnick, ed.), pp. 87-92. Univ. Chicago Press, Chicago, Illinois.

Moog, F. (1959). *In* "Cell, Organism and Milieu" (D. Rudnick, ed.), pp. 121-155. Ronald, New York.

Moog, F. (1961a). *Develop. Biol.* **3**, 153.

Moog, F. (1961b). *Gen. Comp. Endocrinol.* **1**, 416.

Moog, F. (1962a). *Federation Proc.* **21**, 51.

Moog, F. (1962b). *In* "Biological Interactions in Normal and Neoplastic Growth" (W. J. Brennan and W. L. Simpson, eds.), pp. 439-454, Little, Brown, Boston, Massachusetts.

Moog, F., and Angeletti, P. U. (1962). *Biochim. Biophys. Acta* **60**, 440.

Moog, F., and Kirsch, M. H. (1955). *Nature* **175**, 722.

Moog, F., and Ortiz, E. (1960). *J. Embryol. Exptl. Morphol.* **8**, 182.

Moog, F., and Richardson, D. (1955). *J. Exptl. Zool.* **130**, 29.

Moog, F., Vire, H. R., and Grey, R. D. (1963). *Proc. 16th Intern. Congr. Zool. Washington, D. C., 1963* **2**, 301.

Moore, J. (1962). *J. Cellular Comp. Physiol.* **60** (Suppl. 1), 19.

Moore, R. O., and Villee, C. A. (1963). *Comp. Biochem. Physiol.* **9**, 81.

Moscona, A. (1959). *Develop. Biol.* **1**, 1.

Moscona, A., and Hubby, J. L. (1963). *Develop. Biol.* **7**, 192.

Mueller, G. C., Herranen, A. M., and Jervell, K. F. (1958). *Recent Progr. Hormone Res.* **14**, 95.

Mueller, G. C., Gorski, J., and Aizawa, Y. (1961). *Proc. Natl. Acad. Sci. U. S.* **47**, 164.

Mumenthaler, M., and Engel, W. K. (1961). *Acta Anat.* **47**, 274.
Nachlas, M. M., and Seligman, A. M. (1949). *Anat. Record* **105**, 677.
Nachmansohn, D. (1939). *Bull. Soc. Chim. Biol.* **21**, 761.
Nass, M. K. (1962). *Develop. Biol.* **4**, 289.
Needham, J. (1931). "Chemical Embryology." Cambridge Univ. Press, London and New York.
Nemeth, A. M. (1954). *J. Biol. Chem.* **208**, 773.
Nemeth, A. M. (1959). *J. Biol. Chem.* **234**, 2921.
Nemeth, A. M. (1961). *Biochim. Biophys. Acta* **48**, 189.
Nemeth, A. M. (1962). *J. Biol. Chem.* **237**, 3703.
Nemeth, A. M., and de la Haba, G. (1962). *J. Biol. Chem.* **237**, 1190.
Nemeth, A. M., Insull, W., and Flexner, L. B. (1954). *J. Biol. Chem.* **208**, 765.
Nilausen, K. (1958). *Acta Ophthalmol.* **36**, 65.
Noell, W. K. (1951). *J. Cellular Comp. Physiol.* **37**, 283.
Novikoff, A. B. (1960). In "Developing Cell Systems and their Control" (D. Rudnick, ed.), pp. 167-204. Ronald, New York.
Nunnally, D. A. (1962). *J. Exptl. Zool.* **149**, 103.
O'Connor, R. J. (1954). *J. Embryol. Exptl. Morphol.* **2**, 26.
Ogawa, K. (1958). *J. Japan. Obstet. Gynecol. Soc.* **9**, 32.
Ogawa, Y. (1962a). *Exptl. Cell Res.* **26**, 269.
Ogawa, Y. (1962b). *Exptl. Cell Res.* **26**, 526.
Oliver, I. T., Ballard, F., Shield, J., and Bentley, P. (1962). *Develop. Biol.* **4**, 108.
Osterberg, K. A., and Wattenberg, L. W. (1963). *Proc. Soc. Exptl. Biol. Med.* **113**, 145.
Paigen, K. (1961a). *Exptl. Cell Res.* **25**, 286.
Paigen, K. (1961b). *Proc. Natl. Acad. Sci. U. S.* **47**, 1641.
Paul, J., and Fottrell, P. F. (1963). *Biochim. Biophys. Acta* **67**, 334.
Peyrot, A. (1957). *Monit. Zool. Ital.* **64**, 107.
Phillip, J., and Vessell, E. S. (1962). *Proc. Soc. Exptl. Biol. Med.* **110**, 582.
Pokorna, Z., Hašková, V., and Hinzova, E. (1955). *Cesk. Biol.* **4**, 138. *Ref. Zh. Biol.* No. 25824 (1957).
Potter, V. R., Schneider, W. C., and Liebl, G. J. (1945). *Cancer Res.* **5**, 21.
Prakash, A. (1961). *J. Exptl. Zool.* **146**, 237.
Radde, I. C., and McCance, R. A. (1960). *Nature* **183**, 115.
Ragozina, M. N. (1955). *Tr. Inst. Morfol. Zhivot. Akad. Nauk. SSSR* **14**, 250; *Ref. Zh. Biol.* No. 77177 (1956).
Recknagel, R. (1950). *J. Cellular Comp. Physiol.* **35**, 111.
Reverberi, G. (1957). *Acta Embryol. Morphol. Exptl.* **1**, 134.
Richardson, D., Berkowitz, S., and Moog, F. (1955). *J. Exptl. Zool.* **130**, 57.
Robinson, D. S. (1952a). *Biochem. J.* **52**, 621.
Robinson, D. S. (1952b). *Biochem. J.* **52**, 628.
Robinson, D. S. (1952c). *Biochem. J.* **52**, 633.
Roeder, M. (1957). *J. Cellular Comp. Physiol.* **50**, 241.
Rossi, F., Pescetto, G., and Reale, E. (1954). *Compt. Rend. Assoc. Anat.* **41**, 1.
Rossi, F., Bonsignore, A., Reale, E., Vivori, E., and Luzzatto, L. (1959). *J. Histochem. Cytochem.* **7**, 17.
Rudnick, D. (1959). *J. Exptl. Zool.* **142**, 643.
Rudnick, D. (1963). *Develop. Biol.* **7**, 94.
Rudnick, D., and Waelsch, H. (1955). *J. Exptl. Zool.* **129**, 309.
Russo-Caia, S. (1958). *Ric. Sci.* **28**, 1886.

Russo-Caia, S. (1960). *Ric. Sci.* **30**, 148.

Sawyer, C. H. (1955). *J. Exptl. Zool.* **129**, 561.

Scheib-Pfleger, D. (1955). *Bull. Biol. France Belg.* **89**, 404.

Scheib-Pfleger, D., and Wattiaux, R. (1962). *Develop. Biol.* **5**, 205.

Schimke, R. T. (1959). *J. Biol. Chem.* **234**, 700.

Schlamowitz, M. (1958). *Ann. N. Y. Acad. Sci.* **75**, 373.

Schlamowitz, M., and Bodansky, O. (1959). *J. Biol. Chem.* **234**, 1433.

Shaw, C. R., and Barto, E. (1963). *Proc. Natl. Acad. Sci. U. S.* **50**, 211.

Shen, S. C. (1955). *In* "Biological Specificity and Growth" (E. G. Butler, ed.), pp. 73-92. Princeton Univ. Press, Princeton, New Jersey.

Shen, S. C., Greenfield, P., and Boell, E. J. (1956). *J. Comp. Neurol.* **106**, 433.

Shirley, R. L., Fitzwater, R. N., Newland, H. W., and Davis, G. K. (1957). *Proc. Soc. Exptl. Biol. Med.* **96**, 238.

Sippel, T. O. (1954). *J. Exptl. Zool.* **126**, 205.

Sippel, T. O. (1955). *J. Exptl. Zool.* **128**, 165.

Smith, C. H., and Kissane, J. M. (1963). *Develop. Biol.* **8**, 151.

Solomon, J. B. (1958). *Biochem. J.* **70**, 529.

Solomon, J. B. (1959). *Develop. Biol.* **1**, 182.

Solomon, J. B. (1960). *Biochem. J.* **75**, 278.

Sorokin, S., Padykula, H. A., and Hermann, E. (1959). *Develop. Biol.* **1**, 125.

Spiegel, M., and Frankel, D. L. (1961). *Science* **133**, 275.

Spratt, N. T. (1950). *Biol. Bull.* **99**, 120.

Stave, U. (1960). *Biol. Neonatorum* **2**, 68.

Stearns, R. N., and Kostellow, A. (1958). *In* "The Chemical Basis of Development" (W. D. McElroy and B. Glass, eds.), pp. 448-453. Johns Hopkins Press, Baltimore, Maryland.

Stockdale, F. E., and Holtzer, H. (1961). *Exptl. Cell Res.* **24**, 508.

Stockdale, F. E., Abbott, J., Holtzer, S., and Holtzer, H. (1963). *Develop. Biol.* **7**, 293.

Strauss, B. S. (1960). "An Outline of Chemical Genetics." Saunders, Philadelphia, Pennsylvania.

Strittmatter, P., and Strittmatter, C. F. (1961). *J. Cellular Comp. Physiol.* **57**, 87.

Swartz, M. N., Kaplan, N. O., and Lamberg, M. F. (1958). *J. Biol. Chem.* **232**, 1051.

Thorne, C. J. R. (1960). *Biochim. Biophys. Acta* **42**, 175.

Tomita, H., and Hishida, T. (1961). *Embryologia (Nagoya)* **5**, 423.

Trunnel, J. B., and Wade, P. (1955). *J. Clin. Endocrinol. Metab.* **15**, 107.

Vacek, Z. (1960). *Cesk. Morfol.* **8**, 123.

Villee, C. A. (1954). *Cold Spring Harbor Symp. Quant. Biol.* **19**, 186.

Villee, C. A. (1960). *In* "Developing Cell Systems and their Control" (D. Rudnick, ed.), pp. 93-113. Ronald, New York.

Vogel, H. J. (1961). *In* "Control Mechanisms in Cellular Processes" (D. M. Bonner, ed.), pp. 23-66. Ronald, New York.

Wacker, G. R., Zarkowsky, H. S., and Burch, H. B. (1961). *Am. J. Physiol.* **200**, 367.

Waddington, C. H. (1962). *J. Cellular Comp. Physiol.* **60** (Suppl. 1), 93.

Waddington, C. H., and Perry, M.M. (1962). *Proc. Roy. Soc.* **B156**, 459.

Walker, M. S., and Walker, J. B. (1962). *J. Biol. Chem.* **237**, 473.

Wallace, R. A. (1961). *Develop. Biol.* **3**, 486.

Walter, H., and Mahler, H. R. (1958). *J. Biol. Chem.* **230**, 241.

Warburg, O., and Kubowitz, F. (1927). *Biochem. Z.* **189**, 242.

Watterson, R. L., Brown, D. A., and Bartha, A. (1959). *Anat. Record* **133**, 347.

Weber, G., and Cantero, A. (1957). *Cancer Res.* **17**, 995.
Weber, R. (1958). *Arch. Entwicklungsmech. Organ.* **150**, 542.
Weber, R., and Boell, E. J. (1955). *Rev. Suisse Zool.* **62**, 260.
Weber, R., and Boell, E. J. (1962). *Develop. Biol.* **4**, 452.
Weber, R., and Niehus, B. (1961). *Helv. Physiol. Pharmacol. Acta* **19**, 103.
Weiss, P. (1939). "Principles of Development." Holt, New York.
Widdowson, E. M., and McCance, R. A. (1960). *Proc. Roy. Soc.* **B152**, 188.
Willier, B. H. (1955). In "Analysis of Development" (B. H. Willier, P. Weiss, and
    V. Hamburger, eds.), pp. 574-619. Saunders, Philadelphia, Pennsylvania.
Wilson, A. C., Cahn, R. D., and Kaplan, N. O. (1963). *Nature* **197**, 331.
Wolff, E., Haffen, K., and Dieterlen, F. (1960). *Ann. Nutr. Aliment.* **14**, 11.
Wright, B. E. (1960). *Proc. Natl. Acad. Sci. U. S.* **46**, 798.
Wright, B. E., and Bard, S. (1963). *Biochim. Biophys. Acta* **71**, 45.
Yielding, K. L., and Tomkins, G. M. (1962). *Recent Progr. Hormone Res.* **18**, 467.
Zacks, S. I. (1954). *Anat. Record* **118**, 509.
Zetterquist, H. (1956). "The Ultrastructural Organization of the Columnar Absorb-
    ing Cells of the Mouse Jejunum." Godvil, Stockholm.

Addendum

Since this chapter was completed, a number of important studies on enzyme development have appeared. The purpose of this addendum is to call attention to a few of these studies that seem particularly pertinent to the problems that have been discussed in this chapter.

Work on multiple forms of enzymes continues to increase the precision of our understanding of the nature of enzyme differentiation. Creatine kinase, a specialized enzyme found only in nervous and muscular tissues, occurs in three forms that appear in sequential order in correlation with rising activity levels. Only form I is present in brain and skeletal muscle of the 11-day fetal rat; in the brain, in which activity remains constant throughout development, form I persists, but in skeletal muscle activity increases 20–40 times above the 11-day level as form I is replaced by II and then by III (Eppenberger *et al.*, 1964). Although this study and others like it have employed starch-gel electrophoresis, Walker (1963) has used kinetic analysis to resolve the glucokinase of rat and guinea pig liver into two forms, only one of which is present in fetal life. The theory of lactic dehydrogenase structure meanwhile has grown more complex, as increasing numbers of subbands of the principal isozymes are discovered (Fritz and Jacobson, 1965). In the brain, liver, and spleen of the chick embryo Nebel and Conklin (1964) have found a sixth isozyme not readily accounted for in terms of the model of a tetramer composed of two types of subunits combining at random. A series of "X" bands appearing during the sexual maturation of the pigeon testes has been attributed to the action of a third gene (Blanco *et al.*, 1964); this gene seems to control the synthesis of a polypeptide that can combine with the subunit produced by one of the other two LDH-controlling loci.

Some useful light has been shed on the control of LDH differentiation by Cahn's intriguing investigation (1964) of changes in cultures of dissociated heart cells of the 6- to 8-day chick embryo. In such cultures the normal heart-type subunits, which are implicated in oxidative metabolism, tend to be replaced by muscle-type subunits; but this abnormal shift can be retarded by citrate cycle intermediates, coenzyme A, and especially high oxygen tension. In the newborn rat Bonavita *et al.* (1964) have found that anoxia can shift aspartate aminotransferase reversibly from the normally predominant pyridoxal form to the pyridoxamine form.

Attempts to account for the developmental patterns of (apparently) unitary enzymes also continue to multiply. Klein (1963) has produced evidence indicating that the transfer ATPase of the heart of the young chick embryo is actually induced by the high concentration of sodium ions that it extrudes. Koldovsky and Chytil (1965) have found that both adrenalectomy and feeding of lactose delay the decrease of lactase activity in the intestine of the 2-week-old rat, but do not prevent it. The control of development of the hippuric acid-synthesizing system in rat liver has proved more elusive, for the normal increase between 15 and 30 days proceeds unaltered in the face of a variety of experimental treatments (Brandt, 1964).

The question whether the genetic control of sequentially acting enzymes is coordinate (in the microbial sense) has been explored by Barrett (1964), who has shown that in various organs of the frog tadpole xanthine dehydrogenase and uricase rise and fall according to patterns that are similar, but not strictly parallel. The timing of genetic control has been the subject of a valuable study by Wessels (1964) demonstrating that the capacity of exocrine cells of the rat fetal pancreas in culture to produce zymogen granules, and presumably amylase (Rutter *et al.*, 1964), becomes resistant to actinomycin D after 3 days, as if a system capable of forming zymogen has been stabilized. In the intestinal mucosa of the young mouse, the paradoxical effect of actinomycin D and also puromycin in enhancing alkaline phosphatase activity has suggested that the control of a pattern of enzyme increase may be exerted on the synthesis of an inhibitor rather than of the enzyme itself (Moog, 1965). The possibility that a hormone may participate quite directly in the synthesis of an enzyme has been strengthened by continued studies on ecdysone, which now appears to promote production of DNA-dependent RNA (Clever, 1964). According to Shaaya and Sekeris (1965), the ecdysone titer of blowfly larvae at the onset of pupation parallels the activity of DOPA-decarboxylase, an enzyme apparently involved in the hardening and darkening of the pupal case.

ADDENDUM REFERENCES

Barrett, D. (1964). *Develop. Biol.* **10**, 289.
Blanco, A., Zinkham, W. H., and Kupchyk, L. (1964). *J. Exptl. Zool.* **156**, 137.
Bonavita, V., Guarneri, R., and Scardi, V. (1964). *Life Sci.* **3**, 889.
Brandt, I. K. (1964). *Develop. Biol.* **10**, 202.
Cahn, R. D. (1964). *Develop. Biol.* **9**, 327.
Clever, U. (1964). *Science* **146**, 794.
Eppenberger, H. M., Eppenberger, M., Richterich, R., and Aebi, H. (1964). *Develop. Biol.* **10**, 1.
Fritz, P. J., and Jacobson, K. B. (1965). *Biochemistry* **4**, 282.
Klein, R. L. (1963). *Biochim. Biophys. Acta* **73**, 488.
Koldovsky, W., and Chytil, F. (1965). *Biochem. J.* **94**, 266.
Moog, F. (1965). *Advan. Enzyme Regulation* **3**, 221.
Nebel, E. J., and Conklin, J. L. (1964). *Proc. Soc. Exptl. Biol. Med.* **115**, 532.
Rutter, W. J., Wessels, N. K., and Grobstein, C. (1964). *J. Natl. Cancer Inst.* Suppl. **13**, 51.
Shaaya, E., and Sekeris, C. E. (1965). *Gen. Comp. Endocrinol.* **5**, 35.
Walker, D. G. (1963). *Biochim. Biophys. Acta* **77**, 209.
Wessels, N. K. (1964). *Develop. Biol.* **9**, 92.

Chapter 7

DEVELOPMENT OF NONENZYMATIC PROTEINS IN RELATION TO FUNCTIONAL DIFFERENTIATION

J. B. SOLOMON

Chester Beatty Research Institute
London, England

Quae visa, vera; quae non, veriora!

I. General Introduction

The appearance of specific proteins in embryonic development may either be the final product of complex biochemical patterns of synthesis by the embryo itself or it may be the result of the incorporation of proteins of maternal origin into the embryo. Both mechanisms are governed by complex genetic control, the study of which is now becoming possible for proteins such as hemoglobin whose amino acid structure is completely known. The appearance of proteins in embryonic development can be detected by both immunological and electrophoretic techniques. It must be stressed that immunological methods only detect the antigenic determinants on a protein molecule,[1] and in some cases it is possible that positive immunological reactions are obtained from antigenic determinants on protein subunits at a stage in the synthesis of a protein before final conjugation and tertiary folding have been completed. Only after these complex processes have occurred and a sufficient quantity of the protein molecule has accumulated can differentiation be observed at a morphological level. This may be neatly summarized in the quotation at the head of this chapter—"What you see is true; but what you do not see is more true!"

Only a few examples of work on organ-specific proteins are included here. More emphasis has been placed on those few proteins which are obtainable in pure form such as α-crystallin and hemoglobin, together with one of the most fascinating examples of highly specific protein synthesis—antibody formation.

II. Methods for the Separation of Proteins

The first methods used to separate proteins involved their precipitation with salts or other specific reagents. The discoveries of chromatography and electrophoresis in more recent years have provided a wide variety of methods for the separation of proteins. Many of the separations of serum proteins referred to in this chapter were made on the Tiselius electrophoresis apparatus which utilizes the principle of free-boundary electrophoresis (see Longsworth, 1959). The protein solution in a buffer of suitable pH is covered by carefully layering a buffer solution of the same concentration and pH in a U-tube. A direct current is passed through these solutions, and the movement of the protein boundary is observed by utilizing the high refractivity of protein solutions and the schlieren phenomenon. By this means a shadow indicating the position

---

[1] *Determinant or determinant groups:* the part of the structure of the antigenic molecule that is involved in the combination with antibody specific for this antigen.

of the boundary is thrown on a photographic plate. At pH 8.6 serum proteins are anionic and, hence, all migrate toward the anode. Serum albumin migrates most rapidly followed by the α-, β- and γ-globulins in order of decreasing velocity (e.g., see Fig. 13). This method is of limited application, however, because only the fastest and slowest protein components are separated from the other components.

Chromatographic separation of proteins on ion-exchange columns is widely used, but because some proteins denature when absorbed on synthetic resins, weakly acidic or basic cellulose columns offer certain advantanges in this respect. Adsorption chromatography on columns of calcium phosphate gel has been superseded largely by the use of cellulose in conjunction with stepwise elution procedures.

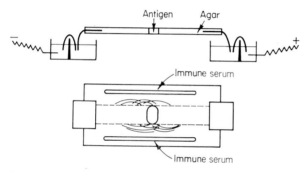

FIG. 1.   Sketch of apparatus for immunoelectrophoresis. After Wunderly (1960).

Proteins separated by simple diffusion through an agar gel in tubes may be identified by downward diffusion of antigen that will mark each protein capable of reacting with it by precipitation lines (Oudin method). A similar method credited to Ouchterlony (1948) gives better resolution. A petri dish containing agar gel has wells punched in it, so that the proteins diffusing from one well can meet the antigen diffusing from another. This method is particularly useful in identifying a common protein antigen among several fractions.

Zone electrophoresis on paper is only of use when a rapid preliminary examination of a protein mixture is required and does not give any better resolution than the Tiselius method. For preparative work and fine separation, paper has been superseded by other supporting media, such as granular starch, powdered cellulose, or resin beads. Starch gel has a remarkable resolving power for serum proteins (see Smithies, 1959) this may be caused by the molecular size of the various proteins partly governing their migration rates in starch gel. When electrophoresis in agar gel is combined with serological precipitation (Grabar and Williams,

1953), a very high resolution of serum proteins is obtained. This method is called immunoelectrophoresis. After a normal electrophoretic run antiserum is added to a groove running along the length of the agar gel (Fig. 1) and then the antiserum is allowed to diffuse laterally to meet the zones of fractionated proteins. Each protein component reacting with the antiserum is marked by its precipitation with antibody (Fig. 2). This method is much more sensitive than those previously described because only 5 µg globulin can be detected and up to twenty-two protein components of serum can be separated qualitatively. Variation of concentration of both the antigenic mixture of proteins as well as the antiserum

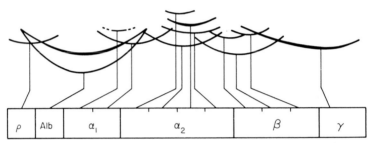

FIG. 2. Immunoelectrophoresis of blood serum prealbumin, ρ; albumin, Alb; α-, α_1-, α_2-, β-, and γ-globulins. After Martin and Scheidegger (1957).

are necessary to give the optimum conditions for the appearance of precipitation lines. Paper electrophoresis, however, has the advantage over immunoelectrophoresis in that elution and densitometric evaluation of the various protein bands are possible. For full details of the above methods the reader is referred to Bailey (1962) and Wunderly (1960).

III. Ontogeny of Certain Tissue-Specific Proteins

A. Introduction

Some sets of tissue antigens, such as the histocompatibility antigens (Section V,A,9), which are involved in tissue transplantation reactions, are probably present on the surfaces of all cells in the body.[2] Such antigens may differ in their location and their amount in different tissues (Tyler, 1946) and are "individual-specific" in that they are genetically determined for the species and individuals of each species. The appearance of organ-specific proteins or tissue-specific proteins with their various antigenic determinants during differentiation may be detected by immunological methods. One protein may have several antigenic

---

[2] *Histocompatibility antigens:* the antigenic components of cells of a graft that are involved in transplantation reactions.

determinants; so inevitably, many antigenic determinants of the same or different proteins are shared by different organs. This makes the preparation of an organ-specific antiserum very difficult as careful absorption of each of the cross-reacting components is necessary before the antiserum can be considered at all organ-specific. Such absorption considerably reduces the potency of the antisera and this makes the early detection of organ-specific antigens more difficult. Another hazard is that saline extracts of organs may not extract all the antigenic proteins and the efficiency of extraction of any one antigenic protein may vary considerably as the structure of a particular tissue becomes more complex during differentiation (Tyler, 1957). There are still too few carefully controlled experiments illustrating the appearance of organ-specific antigens. Only one or two examples will be given here; details of other experiments concerning the detection of adult antigens and the effect of organ-specific antiserum on embryonic development are given in a review by Flickinger (1962).

B. Some Organ-Specific Proteins of the Chicken Embryo

1. SPLEEN, HEART, AND BRAIN

Ebert (1951) has studied the appearance of adult antigens in the spleen, heart, and brain of the developing chick embryo. Saline extracts of these organs from adult chicken were injected into rabbits to obtain antisera to the antigens of the adult organs. In addition, antisera to saline extracts of spleen, heart, and brain from 9-, 12-, and 18-day-old embryos were similarly obtained. Complement in such antisera was inactivated, and the antisera were then absorbed with whole chicken blood.[3] As both the control and the antiorgan sera cross-reacted with heterologous organ antigens at low dilution, each organ antiserum was separately absorbed with each test antigen.[4]

When saline extracts of these organs from 9-, 12-, and 18-day-old embryos and adult chicken were precipitin-tested with these antisera the following antigens were revealed (Fig. 3). There was no change in heart antigens during development and, of the two adult heart antigens, one was also present in brain extracts from 18 days of incubation. There was also only one adult antigen specific for the brain throughout development; but the two additional antigenic components, common to the

---

[3] *Complement:* cofactors present in normal serum that are essential for full antibody activity, such as hemolytic or bactericidal activity.

[4] *Heterologous:* derived from animals of other species. *Homologous:* derived from animals of the same species but of different genetic constitution. *Isologous:* derived from animals of the same genetic constitution.

spleen and heart at all the ages studied, did not appear in the brain until 18 days of incubation. One adult spleen antigen (S_1) was present in the spleen throughout development together with the common spleen–brain antigen previously mentioned. A second spleen-specific antigen (S_2) was found in 18-day-old and adult spleen. This was confirmed by recip- rocal absorption tests, e.g., absorption with only 9- or 12-day-old embryo spleen antigens only removed the capacity to react with 9- or 12-day-old spleen extracts and such sera still reacted with 18-day-old and adult

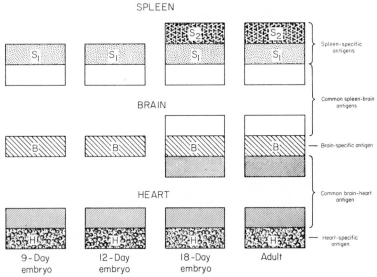

Fig. 3.   Saline-soluble organ antigens of the chick embryo. After Ebert (1951).

spleen extracts. It is possible to detect at least seven antigens in adult chicken spleen by the Ouchterlony method (Wyttenbach, 1960).

2. Liver

Croisille (1960) has studied the ontogeny of liver antigens in the chick embryo by immunoelectrophoresis (Grabar and Williams, 1953). Of the fourteen antigens detected in adult chicken liver one was present in liver extracts of the 5-day-old embryo, six in the 6½-day-old embryo, seven in the 8- to 9-day embryo, nine in the 17- to 18-day embryo, and eleven of the fourteen adult antigens were present in extracts of 5-day- old chick liver.

3. Duodenum

Antisera against adult chicken duodenum were tested with saline extracts of 11- to 21-day-old chick embryo duodena by the Ouchterlony

(1948) plate method (van Alten, 1959). Of the nine antigens present in adult duodenum, two were present in extracts of duodena from 11- to 13-day-old embryos and four in 15- to 17-day embryos; however, only three were detected in 18- to 20-day-old embryos, although four were again detected in extracts of duodena from hatching chicks (21 days of incubation).

C. Collagen

1. PHYSIOLOGICAL FUNCTION

Compared to other proteins, collagen is relatively inert under normal metabolic conditions. Collagen is essentially a structural protein and provides a mechanical structure for the soft tissues of nearly all animals. In the vertebrates, the amount of collagen in the various tissues of the body varies from 0.01 % in the vitreous humor to 30 % in tendon (in which 90 % of the total protein is collagen). Collagen is relatively inextensible and has a high tensile strength which is in part caused by associated substances such as acid mucopolysaccharides, and, in bone, with calcium hydroxyapatites (Harkness, 1961). Under certain conditions, e.g., during parturition, the collagen of the cervix can be rapidly broken down and resorbed resulting in greater flexibility of the tissue.

2. METHODS OF DETECTION

Collagen may be detected in tissues by its distinctive X-ray diffraction pattern, by its characteristic cross-banded fiber structure under the electron microscope and by its high hydroxyproline content (up to 20 %) which is a specific component. Hydroxylysine (2 %) is also a specific amino acid and about one-third of collagen consists of glycine.

3. VARIOUS FORMS OF COLLAGEN

There are three forms of collagen identifiable by their different solubilities. One is extractable by dilute organic acids (acid-soluble collagen) and represents newly formed collagen fibrils; this fraction has the highest concentration in young growing tissues but decreases during postnatal life. It has the same appearance, X-ray diffraction, and amino acid composition as insoluble collagen. The third fraction is termed "neutral saltsoluble" and is extractable by neutral or weakly alkaline salt solutions; this fraction ("procollagen") is the precursor of collagen fibers (Harkness et al., 1954) and its amount is related to the rate of collagen production.

A monomer termed "tropocollagen" is believed to be the basic building unit and to consist of rods 2000–3000 Å long and less than 50 Å in diameter (Schmitt et al., 1953). This monomer then aggregates to form collagen fibrils which are cylindrical bundles of molecules 500–1000 Å in diameter and of very great length. The intermediate forms constitute the acid- and neutral salt-soluble collagens.

4. Changes in Total Collagen during Development

An increase in tissue content of collagen may take place either by an increase in the size of the fibrils or in the production of more fibrils. A good example of the ontogenesis of the collagen fibril is seen in the chick embryo using the electron microscope. Jackson (1956) showed that the first collagen fibrils (about 80 Å in diameter) appeared in parallel bundles in the metatarsal tendons of the 8-day-old chick embryo. Two days later, intercellular spaces became visible and the fibrils were situated both intracytoplasmically and intercellularly. From 11 days of incubation onward the intercellular groups of fibrils increased in diameter to 120 Å and interfibrillary material was deposited. After 14 days the fibrils had cross-striations characteristic of immature collagen and had again increased in diameter to 210 Å and were now definitely outside the cytoplasm. The diameter of the fibers increased progressively with age, an especially rapid phase being at 12–18 days of incubation. At hatching, the fibril diameter was 400 Å and increased to 750 Å in the adult. Collagen fibers have also been found to increase in diameter during the embryonic growth of rat skin (Gross, 1950) and human skin (Linke, 1955); further increases in both diameter and length of the fibrils occur after birth (Banfield, 1955).

The content of collagen (usually measured by the content of hydroxyproline) increases during the development of (1) the chick embryo, where greater accumulation of collagen occurs in the heart, skin, and skeletal muscle than in the liver (Neuman, 1950; Herrmann and Barry, 1955; Rosenberg, 1960); (2) the frog, hydroxyproline first appeared between Shumway stages 21 and 22 and increased linearly to 5 μg per embryo at stage 25^{+11} (Edds, 1958), after which fibrils accumulated rapidly in the body basement lamella (Edds and Sweeny, 1961); (3) the rat, fetal collagen increased from 0.07 % at 13–15 days of gestation to 0.42 % body weight at 20–22 days of gestation (Harkness and Harkness, 1955) and also increased in rat lung, liver, kidney, and skin during postnatal development (Chvapil, 1956, 1957; Chvapil and Kobrle, 1961); (4) calfskin where the hydroxyproline content increased at the same rate as the diameter of the fibrils increased (Gebhardt, 1960); collagen also increases in cattle tendon and sclera during fetal development and in cattleskin during both fetal and postnatal development (Smits, 1957); and in (5) the human femur, collagen rose to maximum level at 25–28 days of gestation (Dickerson, 1962) and there was a steady increase in human liver during postnatal life (Hutterer *et al.*, 1959). In all mammals as the liver increases in size so the proportion of collagen becomes greater; this adaptation is the result of the greater mechanical structure required in the larger-sized organs. For example, the collagen content of fetal rat liver is only 0.01 %, whereas that of the elephant is 10 % of the wet weight (Harkness and Harkness, 1955).

In many organs collagen only increases during embryonic life and after birth may even decrease. Such organs are chicken skeletal muscle, which halves its collagen content during the first 27 weeks of postnatal life (Dickerson, 1960); chicken cornea and heart muscle (Chvapil, 1957); rat femur (Chvapil and Kobrle, 1961); and guinea pig spleen and skeletal muscle (Elster and Lowry, 1950).

5. Changes in the Soluble Collagen Content of Tissues

Early work on rabbits, cattle, and man showed that there was a higher proportion of acid-soluble collagen in the young than in the adult (Nageotte and Guyon, 1934). This has also been found in guinea pigs by Gross (1958) who suggests that the rate of production of collagen monomers (tropocollagen) exceeds its rate of polymerization into fibrils.

Generally, the proportion of soluble collagen decreases during growth (Banfield, 1952; Kobrle and Chvapil, 1958). For example, in skin from the bovine embryo neutral salt-soluble collagen decreased in proportion throughout development, but the acid-soluble fraction increased twenty-fold until birth and then decreased during the next 2 years (Orekhovitch, 1950; Gebhardt, 1960). In human skin, the acid-soluble collagen decreased from birth (100 %) to a minimum of 37 % at 30–40 years, but then increased to 80 % at 70–80 years of age (Banfield, 1959).

D. *Erythrocyte Antigens*

The blood-group antigens are associated with the erythrocytes. In the chicken embryo the erythrocytes bear some of the adult antigens before 4 days of incubation (Burke *et al.*, 1944; Briles *et al.*, 1948). Several blood groups are also known to be present on erythrocytes of 29-somite dove embryos (Miller, 1953). Certain antigens appear on the chicken erythrocyte during development; Briles *et al.* (1948) found only one of the D group at 3 days of incubation, but three more of this allele appeared 24 days later on erythrocytes of 6-day-old chicks. Similar acquisition of further antigens by erythrocytes soon after birth has been noted in sheep (Yčas, 1949) and cattle (Stormont, 1949). The erythrocyte antigens A, B, M, N, and Rh+ have been detected in human embryos as early as 6 weeks (Bornstein and Israel, 1942) or 11 weeks of gestation

(Stratton, 1943). Erythrocyte antigens in the man are usually only weakly antigenic during early fetal development, but can be readily typed in a newborn child and continue to become more strongly antigenic until about 20 years of age.

E. Ontogeny of Proteins of the Lens

1. INTRODUCTION

Most of the water-soluble lens proteins consist of α- and β-crystallins (globulins) and an albumin type called γ-crystallin (Woods and Burky, 1927). α-Crystallin has been obtained in a highly purified state, so that highly specific antisera can be obtained. The two other lens proteins, β-crystallin and γ-crystallin, have not yet been purified so completely, and preparations of these latter two crystallins are, particularly in the case of γ-crystallin, electrophoretically very heterogeneous. The high degree of organ specificity of lens protein means that absorption of lens antiserum with other tissue extracts is less necessary, and so the lens antiserum may be utilized at maximum titer.

A detailed description of the morphological development of the lens of the chicken is given by McKeehan (1951) and Coulombre (1961).

2. ONTOGENY OF LENS PROTEINS IN VARIOUS SPECIES

a. Appearance of Adult Lens Antigens during Embryonic Development. The first detailed analysis of the appearance of lens antigens in the course of embryonic development was carried out by Burke et al. (1944). Utilizing the relatively insensitive method of complement fixation, it was demonstrated that adult lens antigen appeared in the chick embryo at 6 days of incubation. At this time of development adult lens antisera exerted a specific effect upon the lens in ovo.

By means of precipitin reactions in capillary tubes Ten Cate and van Doorenmaalen (1950) were able to demonstrate that lens antigens characteristic for the adult are present in extracts of lens primordia from 60-hour chick embryos. At this time of development the invaginating lens placode is still open to the surface and lens fibers have not been formed yet. Unfortunately, the presence of adult lens antigens at this early stage was not confirmed by obtaining negative results after absorption of the adult lens antisera with 60-hour lens homogenate (as in Ebert, 1951).

Beloff (1959), using an antiserum prepared against the lightly centrifuged supernatant of adult chicken lens, found by means of the Oudin technique that the adult lens contains four different antigenic fractions. One of these antigens was detectable in the embryonic lens after 4½ to 6½ days of incubation, a second one could be detected after

15 days, a third one was found after 18 days of incubation, while the last one appeared 1 day after hatching. The relative concentrations of these antigens in lens extracts of the embryos were markedly different from those of the adult. Considering the relative insensitivity of the Oudin method it may be possible that the adult antigens are, in fact, present at earlier stages of development as suggested by the work of Ten Cate and van Doorenmaalen (1950). In further studies, Beloff tried to correlate the appearance of a particular antigen with the histological development of the lens. The appearance of the first lens antigen at $4\frac{1}{2}$ days of development coincided with the formation of the early lenticular cells destined to become the nucleus or core of the lens. The second lens antigen appeared after 8 days of incubation which is the time when the marginal lens fibers begin to surround those of the nucleus. Beloff (1959) observed that an antiserum prepared against bovine α-crystallin produced no precipitation when tested with extracts of lens from 72-hour chick embryos; one precipitin zone, however, became visible with extracts from 8- to 14-day-old chick embryos and two precipitin zones with adult chick lens extracts. It is possible, in view of later findings, that the antiserum prepared against adult lens had only a low content of lens antibodies, since lens antigens and particularly α-crystallin have been detected by other workers at a considerably earlier stage of development.

Langman (1959a) used the Ouchterlony double-diffusion technique in conjunction with adult lens antiserum. By means of this technique it was found that the first adult lens antigen appears at the lens placode stage (50 hours, 19–24 somites) and that its appearance is followed by that of three other antigens during the formation of the lens vesicle and the development of the first lens fibers. A fifth lens antigen appears after 96 hours of incubation (42–45 somites) as the lens fibers begin to develop in the marginal zone. A sixth antigen appeared after 10 days of incubation and a seventh at hatching. Similar results were also obtained by Konyukhov and Lishtvan (1959) who detected one adult lens antigen in the lens placode (23–25 somites), three antigens in the lens vesicle of the 3-day-old embryo, six antigens in the 4-day-old lens, and seven in lenses from later embryonic stages as well as in the adult lens.

b. *The Crystallins in Lens Development.* More recently, Maisel and Langman (1961) have succeeded in isolating the main components of α-, β-, and γ-crystallin and have attempted to correlate the appearance of the precipitin bands during development with the various crystallins. α-Crystallin was found to appear after about 60 hours of development and β-crystallin (characterized by four closely related bands) after 72 hours of incubation (Fig. 4). γ-Crystallin appeared after 10 days of incubation.

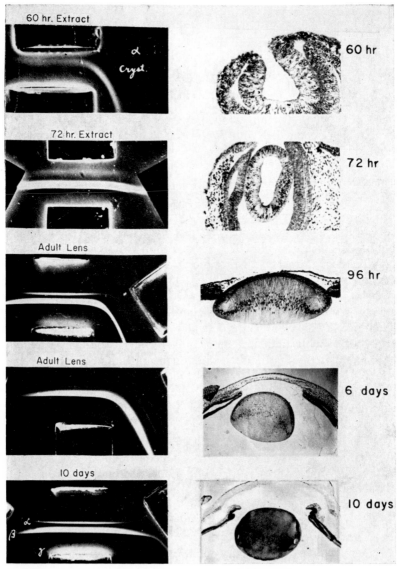

FIG. 4. Formation of α-, β-, and γ-crystallins during development of the chick embryo. Note coalescence bands for α-crystallin in 60-hour lens, for α- and β-crystallin in 96-hour lens and with α-, β-, and γ-crystallin in 10-day lens. The plates on the right-hand side illustrate the histological development of the lens. After Maisel and Langman (1961).

c. Localization of Adult Lens Antigens by the Fluorescent Antibody Technique. When a fluorescein-labeled antiserum to adult chicken lens was used to stain sections of embryonic chick lenses, a positive reaction was seen only in lens from 5 days of incubation onward. The lens epithelium of the marginal zone and particularly the protoplasm around the nucleus were the most fluorescent (van Doorenmaalen, 1958).

In a similar study, Clarke and Fowler (1960) stained sections of normal embryos (from 7-somite to 5 days of incubation) with a similar fluorescent antibody preparation. Fluorescence was strongest in the optic vesicle prior to the inductive period, then became of equal intensity in the optic vesicle and lens ectoderm during the induction period (9–21 somites), and finally intensified in the lens after induction.

d. Effect of Adult Lens Antiserum on Lens Development. In this type of study it must be remembered that the specificity of the antibody effect on the embryo is dependent on both the concentration of antibodies in the antiserum (Ebert, 1950) and on the presence of a certain amount of antigen before cytotoxic effects of antibody are observed.

Langman *et al.* (1957) cultured optic vesicles and their overlying ectoderm, derived from 5- to 20-somite embryos, in normal media and in media containing adult lens antiserum. The explants cultured in the normal media continued their development and formed normal lenses; those cultured in lens antiserum, however, showed degeneration of the cells of the presumptive lens ectoderm if obtained from embryos younger than 18-somites. This effect was specific because adjacent head ectoderm survived the treatment with lens antiserum. Further work by Langman (1959b) in studying the effect of lens antiserum on the presumptive lens ectoderm without the associated eyecup indicated that degeneration occurred only when the ectoderm was obtained from 11- to 17-somite embryos. Langman suggested that the first lens antigen was formed at the 11-somite stage, i.e., shortly after contact between the optic cup and presumptive lens ectoderm has been established and shortly before loss of vacuolization, nuclear orientation, and the palisade phenomenon appear (McKeehan, 1951). These findings have been confirmed by Fowler and Clarke (1960), who applied adult lens antiserum to the chick embryo *in ovo.* Abnormalities of the forebrain and eyecup only developed when the embryos were treated prior to the 10-somite stage. Application of antiserum at the 11- to 19-somite stages produced eyecup defects and the absence, or reduction in size, of the lens. Treatment at the 20- to 25-somite stages produced only minor defects. In further experiments (Langman, 1963), chick embryos of 32 hours of incubation were treated with antibodies prepared against isolated α-, β-, and γ-crystallin. It was found that α-crystallin antibodies exerted a cytotoxic effect on the optic vesicle and the overlying ectoderm, but that the β- and γ-crystallin anti-bodies were unable to interfere with normal development. This suggests that α-crystallin is present in the cells of the optic vesicle as well as in those of the presumptive lens ectoderm.

3. Ontogeny of Lens Proteins in Other Species

a. Frog. Ten Cate and van Doorenmaalen (1950) detected adult lens antigens in frog embryos (*Rana esculenta*) at Shumway stages 19 and 20 when only the lens bud is present. Flickinger (1958) has found positive reactions of antigenic preparations from the head and trunk of hatched frog larvae against antifrog and anticattle lens serum absorbed with frog brain extracts. Adult lens antigens were also detected with such antisera in immature frog oocytes, neurulas, the tails of late-stage feeding larvae, the pigmented retina-iris, and the aqueous humor of adult eyes (Flickinger and Stone, 1960). At Shumway stage 16, the optic cup, optic vesicle, and oral sucker all showed the presence of adult lens antigen. Eight adult lens antigens were detected by the Ouchterlony method with unabsorbed antiserum to adult frog lens; one was probably present in early and late-stage feeding larvae and the aqueous humor, two lens antigens were common to two brain antigens, and another adult lens antigen, which was common to both lens and brain, was also found in immature oocytes (Flickinger, 1962).

b. Mouse. The action of adult lens antisera labeled with various fluorescent dyes on sections of embryonic mouse lens (1-week-old) showed diffuse cross-reactions with brain and a somewhat stronger re-action with the eyecup and lens vesicle; most of the fluorescence sur-rounded the cavity of the lens vesicle (Clayton, 1954). In the eye of the 1-week-old mouse most of I^{131}-labeled adult lens antisera were taken up differentially by different layers of the retina (Clayton and Feldman, 1955).

c. Cattle. Four α-crystallins have been isolated from adult bovine lens by column chromatography and one of these occurred as a dimer. Two of these α-crystallins were found in lens of the fetal calf at the third month of gestation and a third α-crystallin appeared 2 months later (Ebert, 1960). All four α-crystallins were present in the lens of the newborn calf. Progressively smaller amounts of γ-crystallin were present in the cortical fibers of the developing lens, but γ-crystallin was re-tained in the nuclear fibers.

F. *Summary*

The great difficulties in the detection of organ-specific antigens and the considerable technical care required before any claims for organ specificity can be made, are well illustrated by the classic work of Ebert (1951). Immunoelectrophoresis should help expand this field of research in which much remains to be investigated. Immunological cross-reactions owing to common antigenic determinants in various organs of the body, species-specific antigens, and individual-specific antigens (histocompatibility and erythrocyte antigens) confront the investigator with a formidable array of potential immune reactions which need the utmost care in selection for specificity for purposes of experimentation. Only when pure proteins, e.g., α-crystallin, are used for the preparation of antisera can really reliable results be obtained. Nevertheless, the appearance of new antigenic determinants and, hence, possibly new protein structures during development is now well established at least for the spleen, liver, duodenum, lens, and erythrocytes. On the other hand, it appears that histocompatibility antigens which are involved in transplantation reactions are fully manifest in very early embryonic life.

IV. Changes in Serum Proteins during Development

A. Introduction

The functional differentiation of the liver will be examined now by following the changes in the various serum protein fractions. Whereas albumin, fibrinogen, and most of the α- and β-globulins are synthesized by liver cells (e.g., Miller and Bale, 1954; Dancis et al., 1957), antibodies which are generally associated with the γ-globulin fraction are produced by the plasma cells of lymphoid origin.

The distinction between albumins and globulins was originally based on their different solubilities, the albumins being more soluble than the globulins.

Albumin constitutes the major component of the serum of adult mammals, is the most soluble of serum proteins, and has a relatively low molecular weight (e.g., 66,000 for human serum albumin). Because albumin has the greatest molecular concentration in adult serum its function has generally been attributed to maintaining the water balance of the serum. In the serum of the rat, horse, and man two albumin components have been demonstrated (see Moore, 1959). In certain human families it has been found that almost no albumin is present in the serum. In these individuals the colloid-osmotic pressure of the analbuminemic serum was about one-half of normal showing that serum albumin is not exclusively responsible for maintaining the osmotic pressure of human serum. The serum globulins are proteins with lower mobility than albumin in the Tiselius electrophoresis apparatus. They were arbitrarily designated α-, β-, and γ-globulins in order of decreasing mobility. The α- and β-globulins contain proteins conjugated with polysaccharides (glycoproteins or mucoproteins) or lipoid substances (lipoproteins). Typical α-glycoproteins of great interest in the development of several animals are fetuin and haptoglobin; however, there is little known about any changes in levels of such glycoproteins as transferrin and ceruloplasmin (β-globulins) during development. Studies on another globulin, fibrinogen, during fetal development are still somewhat fragmentary. Most of the γ-globulins have a molecular weight of about 160,000, but some γ-globulins have a molecular weight of 1,000,000. Although antibodies are generally associated with the γ-globulin fraction they may also be β_{2A}- and β_{2M}-globulins (Heremans, 1959; see Section V,A,8).

It must be remembered that each main protein fraction comprises several proteins; it is still extremely difficult even with modern methods of separation to detect the appearance of one protein of one major group during the concomitant disappearance of another protein of the same group. In developmental studies not only relative but absolute concentrations should be considered. Unfortunately, only relative concentrations are usually given, but as there is a general increase in total serum protein during fetal development and immediate postnatal development the relative concentration usually parallels the absolute concentration. This means that although there may be a decrease in relative (percent) concentration of a given fraction the absolute concentration (milligrams per 100 ml serum) may remain constant or even rise during development. Because of the impossibility of relating the electrophoretograms of one worker to another without mutual marker proteins, the changes of serum protein during development will be described in a somewhat broad sense to endeavor to present a coherent serum protein pattern during the development of each animal.

There are several protein fractions in embryonic serum which defy accurate classification at present. These include the fastest migrating components, the "prealbumins" (which are so described, not because they are in any way precursors of albumin, but because of their greater anodic mobility than the main albumin group), various proteins which have similar mobilities to adult plasma proteins and fetuin. Fetuin, an acid glycoprotein migrating between albumin and α-globulin on electrophoretograms, has not yet been isolated from species other than cattle and, where evidence suggests its presence, it is referred to as "fetuin-like."

The active synthesis of γ-globulins coincides with the appearance of plasma cells in the young animal (Engle and Woods, 1960). The onset of synthesis of γ-globulin is obscured by the transfer of maternal γ-globulin which has a profound effect upon the pattern of the serum proteins near the time of birth. Antibodies of maternal origin are transmitted from the yolk sac in the chick both before, and just after, hatching; from the placental circulation of the mother to the fetus in the guinea pig, rabbit, monkey, and human; and both before and after birth in the mouse and rat. In the ungulates, maternal antibody is transmitted only after birth by the ingestion of the immune lactoglobulins present at high concentration in the colostrum. The times of transmission of passive immunity and, hence, of the immunoglobulins (Section V,A,8) is summarized in Table III (Section V,A,6). Maternal γ-globulin is transferred much more readily than albumin, but maternal α- and β-globulins are not transferred to the young animal (e.g., Bangham *et al.*, 1958). For further reading see the reviews of Kekwick (1959) and Engle and Woods (1960).

B. Serum Protein Patterns during the Development of Various Species

1. LAMPREY

A recent examination of the changes of serum proteins in a primitive vertebrate the lamprey *Petromyzon marinus dosatus* by Rall *et al.* (1961),

TABLE I
CHANGES OF SERUM PROTEINS OF THE DEVELOPING LAMPREY[a]

Stage of development	Globulins as % total serum proteins			
	α_1	α_2	β	γ
Larva		70	8	22
Young adult	6	71	10	13
Mature adult	37	45	10	8

[a] After Rall *et al.* (1961).

using paper electrophoresis, indicated that in the larval lamprey 70 % of the serum protein is an α_1-globulin; in the young adult, two α-globulins can be distinguished, the α_1 type composed 6 % and the α_2-globulin constituted 71 % of the total protein. In the mature adult α_1- and α_2-globulin were present in about equal concentrations and the "γ-globulin" declined from 22 % in the larval form to 8 % in the mature adult (Table I).

2. FROG

There is little or no albumin present in the serum of tadpoles of *Rana catesbeiana* (Fig. 5) (Frieden *et al.*, 1957) or *Rana heckscheri* (Herner and Frieden, 1960). In the Ranidae metamorphosis is accompanied by marked increases in the slower and faster moving components at the expense of the proteins of intermediate mobility, and as soon as metamorphosis ceases the pattern of serum proteins remains unchanged.

In *Xenopus laevis,* however, the total serum protein concentration as well as the albumin/globulin ratio continues to increase during the growth of the frog.

3. Chick Embryo

a. Egg Yolk and Egg White Proteins. The work of Schechtman (1947) and Nace and Schechtman (1948) suggests that the serum

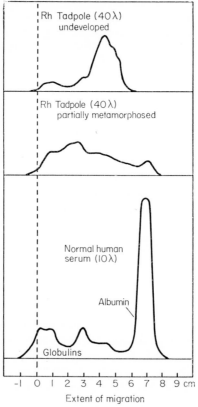

Fig. 5. Comparison of tadpole and human serum proteins by electrophoresis. After Frieden *et al.* (1957).

proteins of the early embryo are derived from the yolk and egg white (cf. Williams, Volume I, Chapter 7). Further evidence to support this is provided by Kaminski and Durieux (1956) who showed that sera from embryos and adults all contained conalbumin which is immunologically identical with that of egg white (also Marshall and Deutsch, 1951). At 11 days of incubation ovalbumin appeared in the embryonic sera, but only traces of this protein were observed in 2-day-old chick sera. Ovomucoid appeared in the sera only at about 17 days of incubation.

b. *Embryonic Types of Serum Protein.* In the serum of 5- and 6-day-old chick embryos four protein components have been determined (Weller and Schechtman, 1962); these are an α_1-albumin continuum

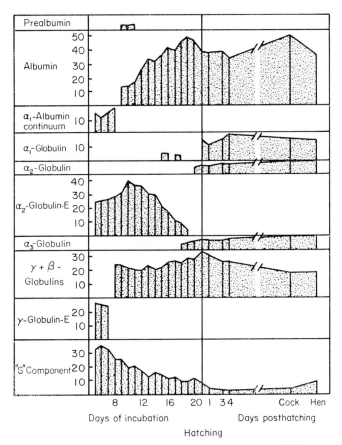

FIG. 6. Ontogeny of serum proteins in the chicken. After Weller and Schechtman (1962).

(15 %), an "S" component (slow migrating) which declined from 34 to 9 % at hatching (Fig. 6) and embryonic types of α_2- and γ-globulins designated α_2-globulin-E (25 %) and γ-globulin-E (30 %). The γ-globulin-E in 5- and 6-day-old embryos was associated with the β-globulin fractions in later development as the γ-globulin even in adult serums migrated slightly faster than human γ-globulin which was used as a marker. Specific embryonic types of α-globulins had been detected pre-

viously in the chick embryo by Kaminski and Durieux (1956) using immunoelectrophoresis. These workers found an α_1-globulin-E from 8 days of incubation which persisted until at least 2 days after hatching. An α_2-globulin-E which appeared at 7–8 days (Weller and Schechtman, 1962) or 11 days of incubation (Kaminski and Durieux, 1956) was replaced by an adult type α_2-globulin in 2-day-old chick serum (Fig. 6).

    c. α-Globulins. Weller and Schechtman (1962) found little or no consistent appearance of α_1-globulin until hatching and then it remained at adult level (15%). At 18 days of incubation these authors reported the appearance of an α_3-globulin which reached the adult level (9%) soon after hatching.

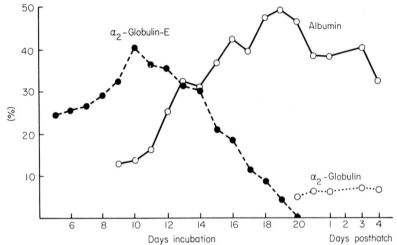

Fig. 7. Changes of albumin and α-globulin in the development of the chick. After Weller and Schechtman (1962).

    d. Albumin. Nace (1953) detected a substance with the antigenicity of chicken serum albumin at 5 days of incubation; but this may be an antigenic determinant of a smaller molecule because albumin does not appear as a distinct electrophoretic component until 9–11 days (Weller and Schechtman, 1962; Kaminski and Durieux, 1956). Albumin may be derived from the α_2-globulin-E as this latter fraction increased from 5–10 days of incubation and then decreased from 14–20 days of development during the time when albumin appeared. Serum albumin increased from 13% total protein at 9 days up to 50% at 19 days of incubation and then showed a slight decrease at hatching (Fig. 7) (Weller and Schechtman, 1962), but increased steadily from 0.58 to 1.35 mg/100 ml during the first 10 weeks of age (Vanstone *et al.*, 1955).

e. Prealbumins. As many as three prealbumins, which are rich in phospholipid, have been detected in chick embryos by velocity sedimentation analysis (Marshall and Deutsch, 1950) and serological techniques (Brandt *et al.*, 1951). These prealbumins decreased in relative amount during embryonic development until they disappeared at 3 days after hatching (also Vanstone *et al.*, 1955). In contrast to this early work more recent results show that only one prealbumin is usually seen throughout embryonic development (Kaminski and Durieux, 1956; Yesair *et al.*, 1959) but is absent from the serums of the adult cockerel; it has a greater mobility in the chick embryo than the adult hen, but its immunological specificity is the same (Kaminski and Durieux, 1956). In contrast to all these findings Weller and Schechtman (1962) only detected prealbumin (3 % of total protein) at 9–11 days of incubation.

f. γ-Globulin. Adult type γ-globulin has been detected in the serum of chick embryos on day 10 (Heim and Schechtman, 1954), on day 11 by electrophoretic separation (Borsos and Kent, 1958), and on day 10–12 by serological techniques (Brandt *et al.*, 1951; Nace, 1953). This γ-globulin is probably antibody of maternal origin as antibodies are known to be transferred from the yolk sac after 10 days of incubation (Section V,B,2,*a*). This antibody may migrate near or with the β-globulin fraction under certain conditions of electrophoresis (e.g., Weller and Schechtman, 1962). The work of Marshall and Deutsch (1950) suggested that γ-globulin increased 3- to 4-fold from 18 days of incubation to soon after hatching; this is consistent with the absorption of antibody from the yolk sac known to occur at this time (also Hradec and Lemež, 1954). γ-Globulin declined in relative amount to about 20 % of the adult level by 4 weeks after hatching (Borsos and Kent, 1958). The half-life of γ-globulin in newly hatched chicks has been calculated to be about 3 days (Patterson *et al.*, 1962). On this basis, only 0.1 % of the original transferred maternal γ-globulin would remain in the chick after 1 month. This accounts for the rate of decline of antibodies of maternal origin (see Section V,B,2,*a*).

g. Fibrinogen. Fibrinogen is a globulin of molecular weight 300,000 to 700,000 (according to the species) and is acted upon by the proteolytic action of thrombin to form fibrin clots. The development of the blood-clotting capacity of the chick embryo was investigated by Boll as early as 1870. Although plasma was produced on day 2 of incubation, the blood would not clot until day 12. At 13–14 days of incubation fibrinogen and prothrombin appeared (also Pickering and Gladstone, 1925).

h. Lipoproteins. From 8–11 days of incubation chick embryo serum consists mainly of lipoprotein of low mobility (Hradec and Lemež, 1954).

β-Lipoproteins reach a maximal level at 18 days of age and the amount of β-lipoprotein is much greater than the α-type at all ages (Yesair *et al.*, 1959). Large lipoprotein molecules were present in relatively low concentration until 16 days of incubation when their density decreased and their concentration rapidly increased severalfold. Similarly, total serum glycoprotein and seromucoid showed a marked increase at hatching and

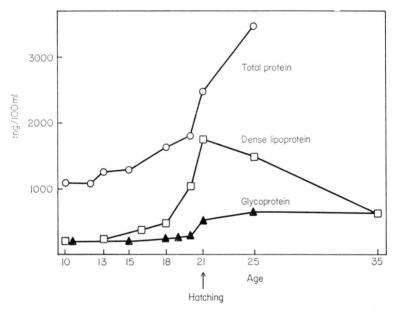

Fig. 8.   Changes of lipoprotein and glycoprotein in the chicken. After Schjeide and Ragan (1957).

further increases occurred 4 days after hatching (Fig. 8) (Schjeide, 1956; Schjeide and Ragan, 1957).

4. Rat

a. Albumin and Prealbumin. The total serum proteins are at a very low level in the newborn rat and increase rapidly to 78 % of the adult level within 3 weeks (Yoshino, 1960a). The albumin fraction increases rapidly from 34 to 52 % during the day before birth and 1 day after birth (Heim, 1961). A prealbumin (20 % of the total protein) in rat serums at 17–18 days of gestation (Gurvich and Karsaevskaya, 1956; Heim, 1961) probably becomes merged with the albumin group at 19 days of gestation as the albumin fraction then shows a corresponding rise (34-41 %) at this time (Heim, 1961). Prealbumin declined after birth from 7 % at 13 days to 3 % at 30 days of age and has been detected in adult rat sera (Deutsch and Goodloe, 1945; Halliday and Kekwick, 1957).

b. γ-Globulin. The young rat absorbs maternal antibodies from the colostrum via the gut for 20 days after birth (Culbertson, 1938). At birth the level of γ-globulin is only 2 %, and in germ-free rats suckled from germ-free mothers the γ-globulin remained at this low level for at least 18 months (Wostmann, 1961). γ-Globulin of maternal origin decreased from 11 % at 18 days to 2 % at 24 days of age and then rose slightly to 6 % by 40 days (Halliday and Kekwick, 1957); this increase may be associated with the active synthesis of γ-globulin (or naturally acquired antibody, see Section V,A,7). γ-Globulin comprised 15–20 % of adult serum proteins (Heim, 1961).

c. Lipoprotein. The β- to α-lipoprotein ratio of the serum proteins was very high (3.62) in the newborn rat and fell rapidly to half this value within 5 days; then it slowly decreased to the adult ratio (0.81) by 1–2 months (Yoshino, 1960b).

5. RABBIT

a. α- and β-Globulins. At 24 days of gestation fetal rabbit sera contain a high proportion of a β-globulin "complex" (44 % of total serum protein) and albumin (42 %) (Brambell *et al.*, 1953). This β-globulin complex consisted mainly of $α_2$-globulin (32 %) and only 8 % $β_2$-globulin (Shmerling and Uspenskaya, 1955; Myant and Osorio, 1958). $α_2$-Globulin decreased from 14 days of gestation to birth (Myant and Osorio, 1958), but was still twice as high at 1 day before birth as in the adult; a "fetuin-like" component (Section IV,B,11,*b*) may be present in this fraction (Iványi *et al.*, 1960a).

b. Albumin. At birth the total serum proteins are only about 60 % of the adult level. Newborn rabbits only synthesize about one-eighth of the albumin of adults; and the half-life of albumin in neonates is twice that of adults, but reaches the adult value at 2–3 months of age (Deich-miller and Dixon, 1960).

c. γ-Globulin. Albumin and γ-globulin of maternal origin are transferred from the yolk sac to fetal serum at 24 days of gestation (Brambell *et al.*, 1953; Sternberg and Dagenais-Perusse, 1956), and by birth γ-globulin had reached a higher level (17 %) than in the maternal serum. As there is no colostral transfer, the γ-globulin declines during the first 30 days of life (Thorbecke and Keuning, 1956) and in germ-free rabbits remains constant at about 0–2 % (Wostmann, 1961). In the normal rabbit γ-globulin increases from 30–60 days. Tissues from newborn rabbits show little if any γ-globulin production, 1-week-old rabbits showed slight γ-globulin production in the appendix, and at 3 weeks of age γ-globulin was also produced by the spleen and thymus (Thorbecke, 1960).

d. Haptoglobin. This protein, which can bind with hemoglobin (see Section IV,B,13,g), is sometimes present in low concentration (15 mg/100 ml) in newborn rabbits, but the haptoglobin level is markedly increased after wounding the skin (Iványi et al., 1960b). Haptoglobin was always found in the serum of normal adult rabbits at a level of 34 mg/100 ml.

6. Guinea Pig

α-Globulin declined rapidly from 11 % at birth to about 5 % after 1 month of age. Neither albumin nor γ-globulin showed much change in concentration during postnatal development (Wehmeyer, 1954).

7. Dog

Tiselius electrophoresis showed that the γ-globulin fraction increased (absolute concentration) from weaning until 17 weeks of age, and from 10–21 weeks the albumin also showed an absolute increase. Fibrinogen increased steadily in absolute concentration from 6 to 27 weeks of age (Lewis, 1946).

8. Pig

a. A "Fetuin-like" Component(?). Moore et al. (1945) report that a "fetuin-like" component (Section IV,B,11,b), migrating on electro-phoretograms near the α-globulins, decreased from 50–30 % during fetal development. Rook et al. (1951) showed that this component was present in newborn pigs and by 5 days of age had nearly disappeared. This component was not observed in pig embryos by Rutqvist (1958) nor in newborn pigs by other workers.

b. Albumin. The pig has been more extensively studied during its postnatal life. The serum of the newborn pig is unusual in that it has a very low proportion of albumin (2 %) (Šterzl et al., 1960; Lecce et al., 1961), which is one-sixth that of the newborn calf, goat, and sheep. Serum albumin rises rapidly in the suckled piglet and reaches maximal values (61 %) at 4 weeks of age (Rutqvist, 1958), but is only about 32 % of total protein in the adult. Serum proteins from the newborn piglet were not precipitable with trichloroacetic acid in contrast to those of the adult (Lecce et al., 1961). Comparison of the serum proteins of the adult and newborn pigs (Table II) show that as much as 64 % of the serum from newborn piglets was α_2-globulin (Šterzl et al., 1960).

c. γ-Globulin. Many workers have reported that the serum of the newborn pig has no γ-globulin (e.g., Earle, 1935; Barrick et al., 1954), but by concentrating such serum by chemical and immunochemical methods Šterzl et al. (1960) have measured 10–40 µg γ-globulin/100 ml. This γ-globulin, although it had antigenic determinants in common with adult γ-globulin, was not immunochemically identical, and also had a lower sedimentation coefficient (Franěk et al., 1961). As soon as suckling begins there is a tremendous and rapid increase (from 10 % rising to as high as 65 %) in γ-globulins within 9 hours after birth owing to the ingestion of colostral proteins via the gut (Havassy and Slanina, 1956). Polarographic and electrophoretic analyses showed that the γ-globulin then declined steadily to 7 % at 12 days and remained at this level for another 2 weeks. This was compensated for by an increase in β-globulin. After this, γ-globulin increased steadily to adult level at 2–6 months of age (Miller et al., 1961).

TABLE II

SERUM PROTEINS OF THE NEWBORN AND ADULT PIG[a]

| Pig | Albumin | Globulins (%) | | | |
		α_1	α_2	β	γ
Newborn	1.8	5.2	63.7	29.3	0–0.1
Adult	32.1	1.4	18.6	23.4	24.4

[a] After Šterzl et al. (1960).

When newborn pigs were deprived of colostrum, Bauriedel et al. (1954) could not detect any γ-globulin by electrophoresis for at least 6 weeks, but Staub and Boguth (1956) found that colostrum-deprived pigs began to synthesize γ-globulin at 2 weeks of age and by 8 weeks of age the levels of serum γ-globulin of such pigs were the same as those suckled normally. This latter finding coincided with the earliest reported synthesis of antibody at 2 weeks of age after injection of Brucella suis antigen at 1 week before birth (Šterzl et al., 1960).

9. GOATS

No γ-globulin was found in fetal goat serum (Fig. 9) by paper electrophoresis from 46–135 days of gestation (Barboriak et al., 1958a). During this period of development the proportion of albumin increased from 6–45 %. A "fetuin-like" component (Section IV,B,11,b) which migrated between the albumin and α_1-globulin fractions increased from 27 % at 46 days to 40 % at 60 days and then declined rapidly to 18 % by 90 days of gestation after which it decreased slowly.

10. SHEEP

A "fetuin-like" component (Section IV,B,11,b) which migrated between albumin and α_1-globulin decreased from 13 to 6 % during 49–138 days of gestation. During this time albumin increased from 20 to 40 % and the β-globulin fraction from 10 to 24 % of the total protein (Barboriak *et al.*, 1958b). Little, if any, γ-globulin could be detected in the serum of fetal or newborn lambs (Fig. 9), but after the ingestion of colostrum the serum γ-globulin rose to about 30 % during the first few days after birth at the expense of the α_2-globulin (Charlwood and Thompson, 1948; Smith and Holm, 1948; Dalgarno *et al.*, 1950). The

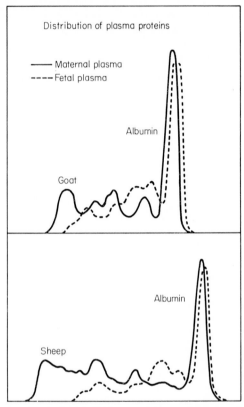

Fig. 9. Comparison of electrophoretic patterns of maternal and fetal serum proteins of a goat fetus (125 days old) and a sheep fetus (128 days old) with that of their mothers. After Barboriak *et al.* (1958b).

proportion of γ-globulin decreased rapidly during 5–10 days of age and continued to decrease (to 12 %) during the next 5–6 weeks.

11. Cattle

Serum proteins have not yet been studied in the fetal calf. Serum of the newborn calf contains only a small proportion (6 %) of β-globulin but large amounts of α-globulin (37 %) and albumin (57 %).

a. γ-Globulin. Before ingestion of colostrum the γ-globulin of the newborn calf was only 0–4 % of total protein (Jameson *et al.*, 1942;

San Clemente and Huddleson, 1943; Pierce, 1955a). After suckling there was a rapid rise in the γ-globulin level which reached 42 % at 36 hours after birth with compensating decreases in the albumin and α-globulin. This γ-globulin level was maintained until at least 5 days after birth (Jameson et al., 1942).

When calves were deprived of colostrum for 24 hours after birth, this sudden rise in serum γ-globulin did not occur (Hansen and Phillips, 1947), and γ-globulin showed a linear increase during the first 10 weeks after birth. Ten days after birth two γ-globulins could be resolved; γ_1-globulin (β_{2M}-) had the same mobility as that of maternal serum and γ_2-globulin (γ-) had a lower mobility. At 30 days of age the amount of γ_2-globulin exceeded that of γ_1-globulin (β_{2M}-globulin). Small amounts of a third γ-globulin with even lower mobility than γ_2-globulin could be distinguished later in development (Pierce, 1955a).

b. Fetuin. Fetuin was first discovered by Pedersen (1945) who isolated this protein from the serum of newborn calves, and Deutsch (1954) showed that about 45 % of the protein migrating in the α-globulin region was fetuin. This protein is an acid glycoprotein containing mannose and glucosamine; it is difficult to separate from albumin by ultracentrifugation and has an electrophoretic mobility similar to α-glycoproteins. The molecular weight is about 45,000. There is a high concentration of fetuin in newborn calf sera, but little in adult sera. In both colostrum-fed and colostrum-deprived calves the α-globulin, which largely consists of fetuin, reaches minimal values by 30 days of postnatal life (Hansen and Phillips, 1947).

12. HORSE

In the newborn unsuckled foal Polson (1943) used Tiselius electrophoresis to show that albumin (65 %) and α-globulin (32 %) accounted for most of the serum proteins and that there was no γ-globulin. Vitt et al. (1959) reported that γ-globulin appeared within 2 hours after the first suckling and 9–16 hours later it amounted to 20–25 % of the total serum protein; after only 1 day the relative and absolute amount of γ-globulin fell. By 5 days after birth Polson (1943) found only 2 % γ-globulin and this fall was compensated for by an increase in β-globulin which rose to 25 %. During the next 8 months γ-globulin gradually increased to 28 % of the total protein.

13. HUMAN

Thirty or more protein fractions have been distinguished in human serum, but only those which are known to change during development are mentioned here.

a. Prealbumin and Embryonic Serum Proteins. A prealbumin is the major component of serum from 10-week-old embryos (Malmnäs and Nihlén, 1950; Halbrecht and Klibanski, 1956). Four other distinct protein fractions reacting with antisera to adult serum were also present and three of these were fetal proteins because they disappeared at birth (Scheidegger *et al.*, 1956).

Bergstrand and Czar (1957) observed an embryonic serum protein component in 9-week-old fetuses which was not present in adult sera (Fig. 10). The proportion of this protein decreased from 19 to 6 % during the next 10 weeks of development. This "fetuin-like" component (Section IV,B,11,b) was absent from serum of older fetuses or newborn infants (Halbrecht *et al.*, 1958). Bergstrand and Czar (1957), however, showed that this embryonic component did not migrate at the same rate

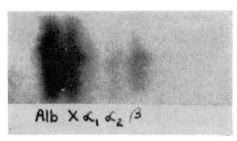

Fig. 10. Electrophoretic patterns of serum proteins of a 10-week-old human embryo. After Halbrecht *et al.* (1958).

as calf fetuin, and Bodman (1959) was unable to obtain a reaction with antiserum to calf fetuin. These latter two findings suggest that if this component is indeed fetuin, there are, nevertheless, species differences in the constitution of fetuin.

b. α- and β-Globulins. α- and β-Globulins have been detected by electrophoresis in 10-week-old embryo serum and by 14 weeks of gestation can be detected by serological reaction with antisera to adult serum (Scheidegger *et al.*, 1956).

c. Albumin. Ewerbeck and Levens (1950) showed that the rise in albumin during gestation is absolute and not relative. There was a relative decrease from about 90 % at 4 months to 60–65 % at 10 months (Fig. 11), but the absolute amount of albumin increased (Moore *et al.*, 1949) because there was more than a threefold rise in total protein during this period. The mean value for albumin reached adult level (50–60 %) within 3 months after birth.

d. γ-Globulin. γ-Globulin which is probably of maternal origin has been detected in the human fetus as early as 9 weeks of gestation and remained at about 5 % for the next 10 weeks (Bergstrand and Czar,

1957). During the last 6 months of gestation there was a rise in the γ-globulin fraction owing to increased placental transmission of maternal antibody (Moore *et al.*, 1949). Pfau (1954) found that γ-globulin rose from 5–7 % during 4–5 months of gestation to 21 % at birth (Fig. 11). After birth the γ-globulin (of maternal origin) in the newborn child then declined rapidly as there was no postnatal transfer via the colostrum. Dif-

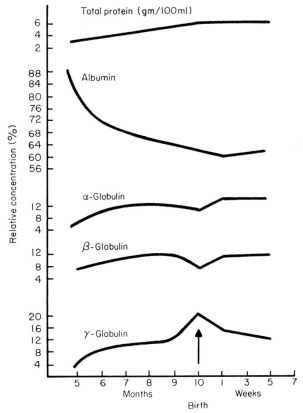

Fig. 11. Changes in serum proteins during human fetal development. After Pfau (1954).

fering rates of this decline in γ-globulin have been reported. Moore *et al.* (1949) found a rapid decrease during 1–2 months and a minimum level of 5 % was reached at about 6 months of age; others (Orlandini *et al.*, 1955; Panchenko, 1960) found only 5 % at 3 months and Knapp and Routh (1949) found that γ-globulin fell from 5 to 1 % during 6 weeks to 10 months after birth. γ-Globulin decreased gradually to its lowest values at 3–4 months of age and then slowly rose to near adult level at 7–11 months, and the mean value reached adult level at 3–5 years (Oberman *et al.*, 1956) or somewhat later (Knapp and Routh, 1949) (Fig. 12). Although 19S and 7S γ-globulins were present in maternal sera only 7S γ-globulins were detected in human umbilical cord sera (Slater, 1954). It thus appears that 19S γ-globulins are not transmitted to the fetus by the mother.

e. *Fibrinogen.* The newborn infant has as much plasma fibrinogen as the normal adult and even by 15–20 weeks of gestation has sufficient to produce clotting (Vahlquist *et al.*, 1953). Fibrinogen does not appear to be transmitted from the mother, although a similar decrease in the proportion of fibrinogen to that of maternal γ-globulin appears to occur after birth (Knapp and Routh, 1949). Some indications that fetal human fi-

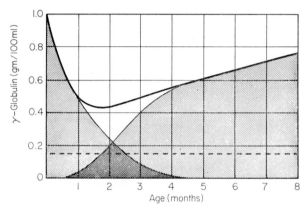

Fig. 12.   Levels of γ-globulin in the first months of postnatal life of the human. After Schultze (1959).

brinogen may be slightly different qualitatively are given by Burstein *et al.* (1954) who found that plasma clots of blood from newborn infants were more transparent and less compressible than those of the adult and, in the case of fetal blood clots, these properties were more sensitive to pH changes.

f. *Lipoprotein and Glycoprotein.* Cord blood has less β-lipoprotein and β-glycoprotein than adult blood but more nonmigrating lipoprotein and α_2-glycoprotein (Sohar *et al.*, 1956).

g. *Haptoglobin.* Haptoglobin is a protein of the α_2-globulin group in human serum which is capable of binding with hemoglobin (Jayle *et al.*, 1952). Three common types of haptoglobin have been differentiated by Smithies (1955) by starch-gel electrophoresis and have been designated Hp 1–1, Hp 2–1, and Hp 2–2 in order of their mobility (Smithies and Walker, 1956). Up to 7 or 8 haptoglobins may be detected in a single person. The genetics of the haptoglobins, as well as other serum proteins in man have been reviewed by Gitlin and Janeway (1960) and Ingram (1963). The physiological function of haptoglobin appears to be the removal of free hemoglobin from solution in the serum as a hemoglobin-haptoglobin complex. This is indicated by the absence of haptoglobin after a hemolytic crisis. As some African Negroes appear to lack haptoglobin, however, it may not be an essential serum component.

No haptoglobin could be found in fetal sera from human fetuses of 16–26-cm length or in samples of cord blood sera (Bergstrand et al., 1961). In some 17- to 30-week-old fetal sera, however, haptoglobins have been detected by starch-gel electrophoresis (Rausen et al., 1961; Hirschfeld and Lunell, 1962), although Galatius-Jensen (1958) could only type sera from 10 % of newborn infants for haptoglobin. Even when haptoglobin is present in sera of newborn infants it has no hemoglobin-binding capacity (Tuttle, 1955), but this begins to appear during the first weeks of postnatal life. Fine et al. (1961), using immunological techniques, identified a protein with the antigenicity of adult haptoglobin in cord blood. The binding capacity of this haptoglobin rose from 3 % in cord blood to 46 % after 1 month, was 70 % after 2 months, and reached adult level (100 %) within 2–4 months of age. The fetus can have a haptoglobin of a different genotype to the mother which indicates that haptoglobin is synthesized by the fetus (Galatius-Jensen, 1958; Rausen et al., 1961).

h. Gm Groups. The *Gm* groups of human sera (Grubb and Laurell, 1956) are divided into *Gm* (*a*+) types, which inhibit the agglutination of human Rh-positive group O erythrocytes when coated with incomplete anti-Rh antibodies, and *Gm* (*a*—) types which do not. The phenotype of the infant at birth is the same as that of the mother; but when the majority of maternal γ-globulin has disappeared at about 4 months of age its genotype becomes *Gm* (*a*—), and then as the infant synthesizes larger amounts of its own γ-globulin the permanent *Gm* genotype is expressed (Brønnestam and Nilsson, 1957; Moullec et al., 1956).

i. Ceruloplasmin. In the newborn human the concentration of ceruloplasmin, which is a blue α-globulin containing eight copper atoms per molecule, is only 7 mg/100 ml and this rises to adult level (30 mg/100 ml) by about 3–6 months of age (Sternlieb and Scheinberg, 1961).

C. Summary

Several examples are given here of proteins occurring in the serum during embryonic development which are characteristic for embryonic life. The most well-defined example of these is calf fetuin and it appears probable that similar, if not identical, proteins exist in other species. Even in the adult animal there are still many proteins with no known physiological function, and it is not surprising that the role of many embryonic proteins in a characteristically embryonic metabolism is, as yet, unknown. These embryonic proteins may be precursors of adult serum proteins or even organ-specific proteins. The best example of the epigenesis of serum proteins is Weller and Schechtman's work (1962) on the chick embryo. Here the differentiation of serum proteins from embryonic to characteristic adult types can clearly be seen and this is probably a direct result of functional differentiation of the liver cells in their increasing ability to synthesize adult proteins. Weller and Schechtman (1962) point out that there is a similarity between the serum of the young chick embryo and that of the young alligator (Baril *et al.*, 1961) and lamprey (Rall *et al.*, 1961), where α-globulins constitute 70–80 % of the total serum proteins.

In most species there is a steady increase of total plasma proteins in early development which is paralleled by an increase in albumin. The relative levels of α- and β-globulins often only change owing to their temporary replacement by the absorption of antibodies of maternal origin and later, in postnatal life, by the active synthesis of antibodies by the plasma cells.

Although the synthesis of each serum protein (other than the immunoglobulins) is probably related to gene activity controlling the functional differentiation of liver cells, there is some evidence for a type of feedback control of the production of serum proteins by the level of proteins in the serum. Certainly, during regeneration of the rat liver after partial hepatectomy Glinos (1958) found that regeneration was accelerated by artificial depletion of the serum proteins, whereas increasing the level of serum proteins by fluid restriction served to retard liver regeneration.

V. The Onset of Immune Reactions in Young Animals

A. *Introduction*

1. Cellular Components of the Immune System

The development of mechanisms involved in immune reactions during ontogeny has been outlined by Šterzl (1962). Even very young embryos possess macrophages and similar cell types capable of phagocytosis. Bacteria and other foreign particulate matter as well as antigen–antibody complexes are removed from the circulation by these phagocytes in the liver and spleen, where they are digested and metabolized. Another mechanism of the immune response is the cellular reaction of homograft response which is probably mediated by lymphocytes or stem cells. This reaction is primarily a cellular response, although it is possible that antibodies to the foreign graft may also be formed in the later stages of the homograft reaction. The delayed-type hypersensitivity reaction which will be referred to here is probably identical in its cellular mechanism to that of the homograft reaction (Medawar, 1959). Antibodies are produced by plasma cells which are derived from cells of lymphoid origin. When foreign material (antigen) is introduced into the body these plasma cells actively synthesize specific antibody which combines with the antigen to form a macromolecular complex. This complex is removed from the circulation by the phagocytes.

2. ROLE OF THE THYMUS

The thymus is the chief source of lymphocytes in mammals and is probably supplemented by the Bursa of Fabricius in birds. Surgical removal of the thymus or Bursa during early postnatal life greatly reduces not only subsequent antibody responses, but also impairs homograft immunity in mammals (Mueller et al., 1960; Miller, 1961; Archer and Pierce, 1961).

3. THE HOMOGRAFT REACTION

The nature of the homograft reaction is complex and its immune nature is probably based upon the action of cell-bound antibodies of lymphocytes (Brent, 1958; Medawar, 1958). This type of reaction is believed by many to be the first immune reaction to appear in ontogeny and the only immune reaction to be possessed by lower animals such as the invertebrates which display sensitization and cellular responses but cannot form antibodies (e.g., Triplett and Cushing, 1958).[5] This may be because the immunological attack in a transplantation reaction is directed against a relatively large portion of the cell surface (histocompatibility antigens) when compared to the antigenic determinants on a protein molecule. For this reason transplantation reactions (see Brent, 1958; Hašek et al., 1961) generally furnish a more sensitive means for detecting the onset of immunity in the young animal for they may be observed in many animals long before antibodies can be detected by serological methods.

4. PRIMARY AND SECONDARY ANTIBODY RESPONSES

The first injection of antigen into an adult animal usually elicits only a weak antibody response (primary response), but the animal becomes sensitized and on second injection of antigen large amounts of antibody are produced (secondary response). The intensity of antibody

---

[5] *Sensitization: see footnote 7 on transplantation immunity* (p. 405).

production depends, in large part, upon the strength (antigenicity) of the antigen used, e.g., particulate antigens elicit vigorous primary responses of greater magnitude than the secondary response to soluble protein antigens.

5. Sensitivity of Techniques for Measurement of Antibody

Generally, the sensitivity of methods for measuring antibodies decreases in this order: labeled antigen elimination, passive hemagglutination, agglutination, complement fixation, and precipitation. Most of the work on the earliest appearance of antibody in young animals has been carried out with conventional serological techniques. Recently, micromethods for the detection of antibody and the study of the immune elimination of labeled antigen have revealed that antibody formation occurs earlier in development than previously supposed.

6. Transmission of Maternal Antibody

It is important to know the origin of the antibody measured. In the serum of newborn animals there are large amounts of antibody of

TABLE III
Transmission of Passive Immunity[a]

Species	Transmission of passive immunity	
	Prenatal	Postnatal
Chick	+	++
Ox, goat, sheep	0	+++ (36 Hours)
Pig, horse	0	+++ (36 Hours)
Dog	0	++ (10 Days)
Mouse	+	++ (16 Days)
Rat	+	++ (20 Days)
Guinea pig, rabbit	+++	0
Monkey, man	+++	0

[a] After Brambell (1958).

maternal origin (passive antibody), the relative quantities being a reflection of the immunological history of the mother in her exposure to antigens prior to parturition (Grasset, 1929). As previously seen in Section IV the transmission of immunoglobulins has a profound effect upon the pattern of serum proteins near the time of birth. The time of transmission of antibodies in various species is indicated in Table III. Prenatal transfer via the placenta only occurs in those mammals in which the fetal and maternal circulation are separated by a single cell wall; in animals, such as the ruminants, with a more complex placental wall antibodies are absorbed via the colostrum (Ehrlich, 1892; Kutner and Ratner, 1923; Brambell, 1958).

After birth the passively acquired antibodies then diminish owing to increase in blood volume with age, catabolism, etc., and during this time the ability of young animals to form antibodies increases as a result of extensive lymphocytopoiesis and the formation of plasma cells. Exposure to antigen soon after birth will lead to removal of antigen with antibody of maternal origin to form a complex removed by the macrophages and then, if antigen is still in excess, the lymphocytes will be stimulated to differentiate into plasma cells and to actively synthesize antibody.

7. Naturally Acquired Antibody

Measurements of the amount of antibody formation in young animals is complicated not only by the presence of maternal antibodies but by the appearance of "natural antibodies" in the circulation within a few weeks or months after birth. Whether the "natural antibody" is supplied spontaneously by the immunologically competent cells of the organism by genetic predetermination (Jerne, 1955; Talmage, 1957; Burnet, 1959) in the same manner in which other proteins are normally synthesized is not yet known.[6] It is perhaps more probable that antibodies are never synthesized in the absence of antigenic stimulation (Wiener, 1951a). Natural antibody (naturally acquired) would then be synthesized in response to antigenic stimulation owing to intake of foreign proteins, antigens in vegetable foods, low-grade bacterial infection, or "normal" bacterial flora of the intestine. This has been strongly suggested by work with germ-free animals in which the γ-globulin and antibody levels are always much lower than normal or are even absent (Fig. 13). However, even germ-free animals may acquire experience of antigenic determinants which are common to plants, animals, and microorganisms from the sterile diet. For example, agglutinins to coliform bacteria (which are constituents of the intestinal flora) are absent in germ-free chicks, whereas in normal chicks the antibody response increases from negative titers at 10–15 days of age to full response at 22 weeks (Wagner, 1955, 1959). A similar difference of antibody response with age was also found in normal and germ-free chicks and rats injected with heterologous erythrocytes (Springer et al., 1959; Wagner, 1959). Lymphoid tissue is well developed in germ-free chicks, but there are fewer plasma cells and less γ-globulins than normal (Thorbecke et al., 1957).

Of great interest is the discovery of proteins in many mammals that are not antibodies, but yet are able to combine with certain particulate substances, such as phage, bacteria, protozoa, heterologous erythrocytes, and certain viruses. These proteins are not transferred from the maternal

---

[6] *Immunologically competent cells:* cells with immunological capacity to react in delayed-type hypersensitivity and homograft reactions.

circulation but are synthesized by the fetus. They coat the foreign particle with protein and this complex is then instantaneously removed by the macrophages in a similar manner to an antigen–antibody complex. In this fashion their action can be confused with that of naturally acquired antibodies. Some examples are properdin (Pillemer, 1956), conglutinin (Coombs *et al.*, 1961), and interferon (Isaacs and Lindemann, 1957).

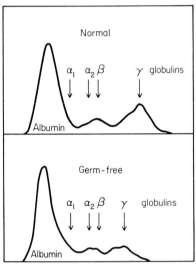

Fig. 13. Electrophoretic patterns of serum proteins of 11-week-old normal and germ-free chickens. After Wostmann (1959).

8. Different Types of Immunoglobulin

The question whether all γ-globulin is antibody with combining capacity to one antigen or another as suggested by Grabar (1947) remains open (see Porter, 1958). It is probable that antibody from adults is γ-globulin folded into specific shapes suitable for combining with antigen (Pauling, 1940). Because most of the antibody produced by adults resides in the γ-globulin fraction (Tiselius and Kabat, 1939), modern methods of electrophoresis have required an immunoglobulin concept (Heremans, 1959) to account for the heterogeneity of the "γ-globulin" fraction (see also Fahey, 1962). The γ-globulin fraction is 7S (sedimentation constant) and has a mobility on paper which extends far into the β_1-regions (Fig. 14) (Grabar and Williams, 1953). The γ-globulin fraction contains only 3 % carbohydrate in contrast with the β_{2A}- and β_{2M}-globulins (10 % carbohydrate). The β_{2A}-globulins are a smaller fraction which also contains antibodies and has a sedimentation constant of 7S, but have the same mobility as β_2-globulin on paper.

A third fraction is the β_{2M}-globulins (sometimes referred to as γ_{1M}-globulins), which is 19S and is probably composed of six protein units of the size of 7S γ-globulin polymerized via the disulfide bonds. This fraction is associated with cold agglutinins, isoagglutinins, and hemagglutinins.

Some antigens elicit chiefly 19S (macroglobulin) antibody; others elicit 7S antibody. Whereas the 7S γ-globulin is the chief product of an immune response of an adult, the 19S macroglobulin may be a characteristic response of immature plasma cells. This 19S antibody has perhaps a greater capacity for combining with antigen ("avidity") than 7S antibody. 19S Antibody has been detected as the initial response of young rabbits (Říha, 1962), sheep (Silverstein et al., 1963), and probably rats

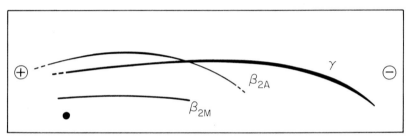

Fig. 14. Schematic representation of β_2- and γ-proteins. After Heremans (1959).

(Halliday, 1957) and as the only response of newborn and premature infants to various vaccines (Smith, 1960a). 19S Antibody precedes the appearance of 7S antibodies in adult rabbits after a single injection of antigen (Bauer and Stavitsky, 1961).

9. IMMUNOLOGICAL TOLERANCE

The phenomenon of immunological tolerance was first illustrated by Owen (1945) who found that dizygotic cattle twins were red-cell chimeras at birth and were tolerant of each other's red blood cells. This led Burnet and Fenner (1949) to suggest their "self-marker" hypothesis in which the embryo was thought to be unable to distinguish foreign cells ("nonself") and thus regarded them as "self," when such cells were introduced before the onset of immunological ability of the embryo. The classic work of Billingham et al. (1956) confirmed that there was indeed a phase during early development in which tolerance could be induced with moderate doses of antigen. Foreign cells introduced during this period were not rapidly rejected (shown by the prolonged retention of skin homografts) as the immunological competence of the embryo or neonate was too weak or even entirely absent. This phase of development, here referred to as the "perinatal phase," ends as soon as the onset of immunity occurs in the young animal which is then undergoing vigorous lymphocytopoiesis. Tolerance, once induced, may only be maintained while antigen is still present; once the chimeric state is lost, the skin homografts are rejected. Generally, tolerance becomes more difficult to induce in animals shortly after birth. The ease of induction of tolerance in the embryo compared with the adult is probably largely the result of the relative state of immunological competence which is based on the number of lymphoid cells of the recipients at these different ages of development. The perinatal phase only refers to a period of develop-

TABLE IV

The End of the "Perinatal Phase" with Respect to Moderate Doses of Lymphoid Cells[a, b]

Species	Gestation or in-cubation period (days)	End of "perinatal phase"
Cattle	283	Before birth
Man	280	Before birth
Sheep	150	50 Days before birth
Rabbit	32	10 Days before birth
Guinea pig	60	3 Days before birth
Mouse	21	2 Days after birth
Rat	22	3–14 Days after birth
Dog	63	7 Days after birth
Chicken	21	2 Days after hatching
Duck	28	13 Days after hatching

[a] The end of the perinatal phase is dependent to some extent upon the dose of lymphoid cells used to induce tolerance.
[b] Adapted from Billingham (1958).

ment before the onset of detectable immunity (Table IV). For the weaker antigens, such as soluble protein antigens, the onset of immunity occurs later in development than for particulate antigens and, consequently, the perinatal phase for such antigens is considerably prolonged.

It is still not known how the mother remains immunologically tolerant toward the fetus which contains transplantation antigens derived from the father. Transplantation antigens are known to be present early in the development—in the 4-day-old embryo of the chicken (Terasaki, 1959) and the mouse (Tyan and Cole, 1962). It is possible that in mammals the cells of the trophoblast act as an immunological barrier between mother and fetus.

In the following examination of the present knowledge of the onset of immunity in young animals of various species, each animal is dealt with approximately in the order of increasing antigenic stimulus, e.g., the first sign of antibody formation to soluble protein antigens is followed by that to the particulate antigens (bacteria and erythrocytes). Next, studies on the induction of tolerance, or partial tolerance, to such antigens are considered, as the end of the perinatal phase of development, after which no tolerance can be produced, coincides with the onset of antibody production. Finally, transplantation immunity and the induction of tolerance to skin homografts are considered.[7] In most species transplantation studies have been the most sensitive in marking the end of the perinatal phase of immunological development which is rapidly followed by immunological competence.

Immunological tolerance can be further studied in reviews on tolerance to cells (Hašek et al., 1961) and nonliving antigens (Smith, 1961). Certain aspects of immunology mentioned here are discussed more fully by Cushing and Campbell (1957).

B. The Onset of Immunity in Various Species

1. FROG

Skin homografts exchanged reciprocally between frogs (Rana catesbeiana) induce tolerance when grafted before 68 days of age (Shumway stage 25), but are generally rejected if grafted later. This onset of transplantation immunity coincides with the appearance of large numbers of small lymphocytes (Hildemann and Haas, 1959, 1961).

2. CHICKEN

a. Onset of Antibody Formation Measured by Serological Techniques. Early attempts to induce antibody formation by injection of a wide variety of antigens into the chick embryo were unsuccessful, e.g., diphtheria toxoid (Grasset, 1929), B. sporogenes (Weinberg and Guelin, 1936), bacteriophage or influenza virus (Beveridge and Burnet, 1946), and human erythrocytes (Burnet et al., 1950). In all these experiments serological estimations were made several weeks after the first injection of antigen into the embryo. It was concluded by these workers that the embryo could not produce antibodies. The induction of both active immunity and tolerance to heterologous antigens in embryos is complicated by the presence of antibodies of maternal origin. These begin to enter the circulation of the embryo from 10 days of incubation (Brandly et al., 1946; Buxton, 1952; Ryle, 1957; Mitchison, 1962a), increase in concentration at day 17–18 (Schechtman, 1947), and reach a maximum level just after hatching (Brambell, 1958). In hatched chicks, however,

---

[7] Transplantation immunity: a state of immunity (sensitization) manifest by accelerated graft rejection owing to prior contact with graft antigens.

the maturation of antibody response can be followed. One-day-old chicks and 1- to 12-week-old chicks were given three alternate daily injections of bovine serum and then challenged at 6 and 9 days after the last injection (Wolfe and Dilkes, 1948). The chicks initially injected at 1 day of age (and which were about 2 weeks old at challenge) showed a weak precipitin titer (ring test) and this increased steadily to a maximum level at 5 weeks of age (Table V). However, when a purified protein preparation, bovine serum albumin (BSA), was used as antigen in chicks from 5 weeks to 8 years of age, no antibody could be measured at 4 weeks of age, but the ability to produce antibody increased from 5 to 20 weeks of age (Wolfe et al., 1957a). Similarly, when Salmonella

TABLE V

MATURATION OF ANTIBODY FORMATION TO BOVINE SERUM IN YOUNG CHICKEN[a]

Age in weeks	Average titer (as tube numbers)
1 (day)	1.0
1	3.0
2	5.5
3	6.2
4	7.7
5	11.1
12	12.2

[a] After Wolfe and Dilkes (1948).

pullorum was used as antigen, maximum antibody production did not occur until 14 weeks after hatching (Buxton, 1954). Agglutinins to heterologous erythrocytes could not be detected by serological methods before 2 weeks after hatching (Bailey, 1923; Simonsen, 1955; but cf. Beckitt, 1958).

b. The Induction of Tolerance. Early attempts to induce tolerance to a wide variety of antigens in 11- to 14-day-old chick embryos were unsuccessful (Burnet et al., 1950; Cohn, 1956) probably owing to insufficient dosage of antigen or nonimmune elimination of the antigen and consequent loss of tolerance before serological testing. However, immunological tolerance was first demonstrated in chicken by Hašek (1953), who found depressed hemagglutinin formation in chicks several weeks after they had been previously parabiosed with the blood donor during embryonic life.

Partial tolerance to BSA may be induced in newborn chicks, and the degree of suppression of the antibody response 6 weeks later is antigen-specific and proportional to the dose of antigen (Wolfe et al., 1957b). Complete tolerance to BSA may be induced in chicks up to 12 days of age (Tempelis et al., 1958) provided that massive doses of antigen are used. The interesting experiments of Buxton (1954) were one of the earliest of the few examples concerning the induction of tolerance to bacterial antigen. Chick embryos were inoculated intravenously with heat-killed *Salmonella pullorum* at 15 days, or at 15 and 20 days, or at 20 days of incubation. The agglutinating and nonagglutinating responses were measured at 8 weeks after hatching by oral vaccination. The group only injected at 20 days of incubation showed higher antibody titers (10- to 100-fold) than the other two groups. These results indicate that tolerance was induced provided that the embryos were injected at 15 days of incubation, but not when embryos were only exposed to antigen for the first time as late as 20 days of incubation.

c. *Tolerance and the Onset of Antibody Formation to Erythrocytes Measured by Immune Elimination of Antigen.* The immune elimination of Cr^{51}-labeled erythrocytes reveals the presence of minute amounts of antibody and is thus eminently suitable for ontogenic studies. Beckitt (1958) showed that, while tolerance to turkey erythrocytes could be induced in 17-day-old chick embryos, the immune response appeared at 2 days after hatching and in 2-week-old chicks was as rapid as that of the adult. A large proportion of the turkey erythrocytes were immediately removed from the circulation owing to circulating hemagglutinin of maternal origin. Solomon and Tucker (1963a) have detected the onset of immunity to homologous erythrocytes at 2 days of age using Cr^{51}-labeled chicken erythrocytes as antigen. Tolerance can no longer be induced with moderate doses after 3 days of age (Solomon and Tucker, 1963a), but may be induced with massive doses of homologous erythrocytes in 8-day-old chicks (Mitchison, 1962a). The young chick can be sensitized between 1–4 days of age as shown by vigorous secondary responses when challenged at 7 days of age.

Immunological tolerance to erythrocytes can only be maintained while the antigen persists (Mitchison, 1959). The interval between the disappearance of erythrocytes and the second injection necessary to maintain tolerance, increases with the age of the bird. In young chicks, the interval is quite short, and the time needed for tolerance to be lost increases with age (Mitchison, 1962b). This could be caused by the more rapid turnover of the lymphocyte population in younger chicken in which lymphocytes tolerant to the antigen will have a shorter life-span than those of the adult.

d. *Complement.* The hemolysis of erythrocytes requires complement which appears in the serum of embryos during 17-21 days of incubation (Rywosch, 1907; Sherman, 1919; Polk *et al.*, 1938) well before the measurable onset of antibody formation.

e. *Onset of Transplantation Immunity and Lymphocytopoiesis.* Kalmutz (1962) has suggested from his studies with labeled bacteriophage antigen in opossum embryos that as soon as lymphocytes can be identified histologically they are sufficiently mature to participate in immune reactions. This also appears to be the case in the chicken. Lymphocytes from the thymus appear in the spleen of the chick embryo from 12 days of incubation when this organ becomes well vascularized. By 15 days of incubation the spleen contains a considerable number of lymphocytes (Sandreuter, 1951) which continue to increase during the next few weeks of development. Chick embryos may be sensitized to foreign cells at 15 days of incubation, so that the embryo later offers immunological resistance either to a second dose of foreign cells, which therefore proliferate less readily in its spleen, or to a skin homograft which shows accelerated rejection (Solomon, 1963a). Such sensitization could not be produced before 15 days of incubation, but is pronounced in the 19-day-old embryo or newly hatched chick. The suggestion that the unsensitized chick embryo was capable of weak homograft rejection (Murphy, 1914) has been confirmed by Isacson (1959) and Solomon and Tucker (1963b) who showed that the proliferation of foreign cells in the spleen of the embryo (splenomegaly) was maximal at 13–15 days of incubation, but was less in older embryos and absent at 2 days after hatching. The higher lymphocyte content of certain tissues of the chicken after hatching effectively impedes the induction of tolerance to foreign cells as shown by the retention of skin homografts (Billingham et al., 1956; Solomon, 1963b) and to foreign erythrocytes (Beckitt, 1958; Solomon and Tucker, 1963a). Soon after this perinatal phase in the immunological development of the chick its lymphoid cells are sufficient in number to produce splenomegaly when injected into a homologous embryo (Simonsen, 1957; Solomon, 1961). The chick is then said to be "immunologically competent."

3. Duck

When newly hatched ducklings were injected with bacterial antigens (*Brucella suis*) antibody formation commenced on 12–15 days of age (Šterzl, 1959). In ducks tolerance may be induced readily from 6–13 days after hatching, and Hašková (1957) obtained complete inhibition of the formation of heteroagglutinins to goose or chicken erythrocytes when such whole blood was injected during this period (probably owing to the persistence of lymphocytes).

4. Mouse

a. Induction of Immunity. When fetal mice were injected with bovine γ-globulin (BGG) or heat-killed tubercle bacilli on day 15–17 of gestation and then challenged at 5–6 weeks after birth, they exhibited quite as good an antibody response as adults (Rees and Garbutt, 1961). Nevertheless, this does not prove that sensitization occurred immediately after injection and, provided that the antigen persisted, sensitization may have occurred after birth. The maturation of antibody production in

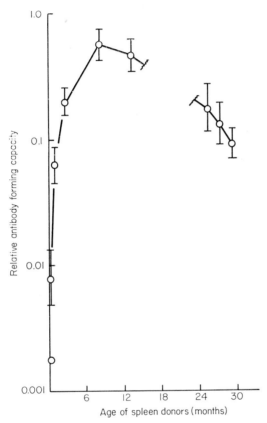

FIG. 15.   Relative antibody-forming capacity of 76 × 10⁶ spleen cells as a function of age. After Makinodan and Peterson (1962).

mouse spleen cells has been studied by Makinodan and Peterson (1962) who transferred spleen cells from mice (preimmunized with sheep erythrocytes) to irradiated (immunologically neutral) mice. Antibody production was not maximal until spleen cells were taken from mice of 8 months of age (Fig. 15), but antibody production was very rapid from 1 week to 1 month of postnatal life.

b. *Induction of Tolerance.* Transplantation immunity or tolerance may be induced in newborn mice according to the dose of spleen cells

(Howard and Michie, 1962). Tolerance to bovine serum albumin (BSA) (Terres and Hughes, 1959; Thorbecke et al., 1961) or to skin homografts (Billingham and Brent, 1957) can be induced in newborn mice with large doses of BSA or spleen cells, respectively. The induction of tolerance to skin homografts with single doses of spleen cells in young mice becomes increasingly difficult with increasing age and can not be produced at all in 13-day-old mice (Brent and Gowland, 1962). Successful induction of tolerance in adult F_1 mice by parabiotic union has been reported (Rubin, 1959). Whereas low doses of pneumococcal polysaccharide induce immunity in both newborn and adult mice (Siskind, 1962), large doses of this antigen induce tolerance in adults (Felton and Ottinger, 1942; Felton, 1949); also, Dresser (1962) has induced tolerance to protein antigen in adult mice.

5. RAT

Ten-day-old rats injected with S. pullorum produce antibody by 18 days of age, and this response is not affected by depriving the newborn rat of colostrum (Halliday, 1957). Electrophoresis of the serum showed that most of this antibody was associated with the β_{2M}-globulin fraction, whereas adult rat antibody is γ-globulin. Tolerance to erythrocytes can be induced in newborn rats (Simonsen, 1956; Nossal, 1958). Tolerance to rat skin homografts may be induced during the first 2 weeks of life in certain breeds (Woodruff and Simpson, 1955), but in other breeds, homograft rejection is as vigorous as the adult by day 3 of postnatal life (Steinmuller, 1961).

6. RABBIT

The rabbit and guinea pig resemble the monkey and man in that the young are born with full passive immunity. In the rabbit, as in the chick, antibodies are transmitted by the cells lining the yolk sac.

a. Soluble Protein Antigens. Early work by Freund (1930) and Baumgartner (1934) had indicated that the antibody response of young rabbits was weaker than that of adults. The onset of antibody formation varies with the antigen used. Rabbits younger than 2 weeks of age did not produce antibodies to a single injection of BSA (Eitzman and Smith, 1959). During 3–15 days of age the lymphocyte status of the rabbit is such that a given dose of heterologous protein can induce either tolerance or immunity. Before this period tolerance is induced and afterward only immunity (Smith and Bridges, 1956). Antibody to alum-precipitated BGG, however, was subsequently produced when rabbits were injected at 3–5 days of age (Harris et al., 1961).

b. Bacterial Antigens. When 5-day-old rabbits were injected intra-peritoneally with large doses of *S. paratyphi B.*, antibodies could be detected as early as 9 days of age and more generally by 13 days of age (Šterzl and Trnka, 1957). The excess antigen appeared to accelerate antibody production rather than inhibiting it, whereas smaller doses (as generally used for immunizing adult rabbits) did not produce antibodies until 20–29 days of age. Near-lethal doses, however, induced partial tolerance when given within the first few days of postnatal life. When T_2 phage was injected into newborn rabbits 19S antibody appeared 4–5 days later (Pernis *et al.*, 1963).

c. Erythrocyte Antigens. When heterologous erythrocytes were injected into newborn rabbits, after an initial removal of antierythrocyte antibody of maternal origin, antibodies were actively synthesized by the young rabbit and were serologically detectable 5 days later (Říha, 1961). There is good correlation between the appearance of plasma cells and the synthesis of antibodies and γ-globulin in the serum of young rabbits (Thorbecke and Keuning, 1956).

d. Tolerance and Transplantation Immunity. Fetal rabbits are capable of rejecting homografts at 1–3 days before birth (Egdahl, 1957). In fact, tolerance to homologous cells cannot readily be induced even as early at 20–22 days of gestation (Billingham *et al.*, 1956), and after this time neither tolerance to skin homografts nor runting was produced (Porter, 1960). The onset of immunological competence to homologous cells thus appears earlier than antibody synthesis to protein antigens.

7. GUINEA PIG

a. Immunity to Soluble and Particulate Antigens. It is well known that young guinea pigs are less readily sensitized against a variety of antigens than adults (e.g., Freund, 1929; Kliger and Olitzki, 1929). When 1-day-old guinea pigs were injected with BGG, antibody appeared 9 days later (Bishop and Gump, 1961), although the rate of antibody production was less than that of adults similarly injected. Tolerance to BSA or human γ-globulin (HGG) can be induced in newborn guinea pigs (Turk and Humphrey, 1961). Recent work has shown that guinea pigs may be sensitized *in utero*. This was indicated by Weiss (1958) who only induced a rather limited degree of actively acquired tolerance to tuberculoprotein or phenolized tubercle bacilli *in utero*. When guinea pigs were injected *in utero* at 1–2 weeks before delivery with various protein antigens in complete Freund's adjuvant and then challenged at birth, delayed-type hypersensitive reactions were elicited in about one-third of the animals so treated (Uhr, 1960). Newborn guinea pigs are able to produce heat-stable antibodies to phage antigen (Uhr *et al.*,

1962b). It is of interest that plasma cells have been observed histologically in the lymph nodes during late fetal development and in
neonates (Gyllensten, 1950).

b. *Transplantation Immunity.* Loeb, as early as 1930, showed that
10-day-old guinea pigs reject thyroid homografts less vigorously than
adults; Egdahl (1957) has found that guinea pigs can reject homografts
as early as 1–3 days before birth.

8. Pigs

Hoerlein (1957) found no vigorous production of antibody when
colostrum-deprived pigs (sensitized during the first few weeks of life to
a variety of antigens) were challenged, until at least 8 weeks of age.
However, Šterzl *et al.* (1960) detected antibody formation to *Brucella
suis* antigen 3 weeks after injection of piglets removed by caesarian section at 1 week before normal term. When 1-month-old pigs were injected with this antigen, antibody could be detected only 7 days later.
Heteroagglutinins to rabbit erythrocytes could be detected after 6 weeks
of life in normally suckled pigs and after 8 weeks in artificially fed piglets. The amount of complement increased steadily during the first 3
weeks of postnatal life (Šterzl *et al.*, 1961). Fetal pigs when immunized
with various particulate antigens at 1 month before birth produced
detectable amounts of antibody to phage, poliomyelitis virus and erythrocytes as early as 3 days after birth, and to bacterial antigens at 7–10
days after birth (Šterzl, 1963). This is an interesting example of
differing responses elicited by these various particulate antigens.

9. Sheep

Like the pig, the fetal sheep receives no maternal antibody before
colostrum is ingested (McCarthy and McDougall, 1953), but unlike the
pig, the fetal sheep possesses active immunity in the latter half of
gestation. Bacteriophage φX elicits the earliest antibody response in fetal
sheep as antibody (19S) to phage was produced 10 days after injection
of this antigen at 66–70 days of gestation. Antibody to ferritin in
Freund's adjuvant appeared slightly later than that to phage, and antibody to ovalbumin in Freund's adjuvant first appeared, some 4 weeks
after injection, at 120 days of gestation (Silverstein *et al.*, 1963). The
differing "antigenicities" of these various antigens is further illustrated
by the failure of the fetal lamb to produce antibodies to *Salmonella
typhosa* or BCG (Bacille-Calmette-Guérin) even near the end of gestation, and antibodies are not produced to these latter antigens until well
after birth (Barr *et al.*, 1953). The histological appearance of skin homografts showed incompatibility at 100–117 days of gestation within 2

weeks of grafting—a reaction as rapid as that of adult sheep (Schinckel and Ferguson, 1953).

10. CATTLE

When three calves were immunized at 41–47 days before birth with *Leptospira saxkoebing*, Fennestad and Borg-Petersen (1957) showed that they developed immunologically active γ-globulin *in utero*, and at birth the agglutinin–lysin titers of precolostral sera from the calves were much greater than those of the dams (which had previously been passively immunized). The onset of transplantation immunity probably occurs well before birth as newborn calves can reject skin homografts (Billingham and Lampkin, 1957). It is somewhat peculiar that intramuscular injection of *Trichomonas foetus B* antigen in calves up to 4 weeks old induced no formation of agglutinin and large amounts of this antigen given to 1-year-old calves depressed antibody formation (Kerr and Robertson, 1954; Pierce, 1955b). While this may appear to be an example of induction of tolerance in calves, others have failed to repeat these results, and the immunological picture with this antigen remains confusing and perplexing.

11. HUMAN

Delayed-type hypersensitivity can be induced in premature neonatal humans, and one premature infant of only 30-weeks gestation has shown such a reaction 3 weeks later (Uhr *et al.*, 1960). The premature neonate can also form antibody to phage antigen (Uhr *et al.*, 1962a). The newborn child has the capacity to produce antibody to flagella of coliforms which are present in the human at birth (Smith, 1960b), but has only half the amount of complement found in maternal serum (Traub, 1943). Early postnatal immunization (e.g., with diphtheria toxoid) usually results in poorer antibody responses; this is probably because antibodies of maternal origin effectively remove most of the antigen and insufficient is left to stimulate vigorous antibody formation (e.g., di Sant' Agnese, 1949). The antibodies of maternal origin decline slowly in the human infant during the first 3 months of postnatal life and have a half-life of 4–5 weeks (Barr *et al.*, 1949; Wiener, 1951b). Then there is an increase of γ-globulin owing to active synthesis of antibody (Norton *et al.*, 1952). When 2-week-old infants were immunized with diphtheria toxoid, antibody did not appear until 4–8 weeks later. Infants 2–6 months of age produce antibody to tetanus toxoid more rapidly and vigorously than younger infants (Osborn *et al.*, 1952). In humans the onset of active immunity is best seen in children born of agammaglobulinemic mothers. Good and Varco (1955) found that there was no antibody response to typhoid–paratyphoid A and B vaccine or to diphtheria–pertussis vaccine in such an infant during the first 2 months of postnatal life. No plasma cells were observed for the first 3 months (Bridges *et al.*, 1957), but γ-globulins, agglutinins, and toxins to the above antigens simultaneously appeared during 2–4 months of age. The γ-globulin concentration continued to increase until adult level was reached at 10 months of age.

C. *Summary*

The onset of immunity in the animals mentioned is crudely summarized in Table VI. The onset of immunity is taken as the earliest evidence for the presence of lymphocytes or cells which are capable of

TABLE VI

ONSET OF IMMUNOLOGICAL ABILITY IN YOUNG ANIMALS

Species	Onset of any form of immunity	Onset of antibody formation
Chicken	15 Days of incubation	3 Days post hatching
Duck	?	12–15 Days post hatching
Mice	Before birth?	A few weeks after birth
Rat	Birth	18 Days after birth
Rabbit	22 Days of gestation	5 Days after birth
Guinea pig	Before birth	10 Days after birth
Pig	?	3 Days after birth
Sheep	100 Days of gestation	80 Days of gestation
Cattle	Before birth	Birth
Human	Before birth	2 Months after birth

becoming sensitized to antigen. For some antigens sensitization can occur during the perinatal phase, but this by no means has been proven for all antigens. The differing antigenic stimulus offered by various types of antigen (according to the number of antigenic determinants, particle size, etc.) plays a large part in determining the intensity of the immune response. Even different particulate antigens evoke antibody formation at different times of development; this has been well illustrated in young pigs by Šterzl *et al.* (1963).

Again, the extent of the perinatal phase during which tolerance is readily induced can vary considerably according to the antigen used. In a similar manner, in transplantation reactions tolerance can be readily induced to cells which are only very weakly antigenic to the recipient quite late in the postnatal period; whereas cells which are strongly histoincompatible evoke vigorous immunity unless given in massive doses. Immunological competence arises shortly after the perinatal phase of development, and in some animals the appearance of immunological competence (for transplantation reactions) may also coincide with the earliest appearance of antibody formation (e.g., chicken and sheep).

The absorption of maternal antibodies by the young animal, in many cases, makes the detection of the onset of immunity to certain antigens more difficult—for example, when the antigen is given to the young animal it is sometimes removed by antibodies of maternal origin before immunity can be induced. Generally, the newborn animal has some form of active immunity, but the ability to produce antibodies does not mature until long after birth. The onset of immunity is dependent not only upon the lymphoid status of the young animal but also upon the "antigenicity" of the antigen. Transplantation reactions, involving the cellular histo-compatibility antigens are some of the most early detectable immune reactions in development probably because of the strong antigenic stimulus furnished by the transplantation of tissue. In contrast, many soluble proteins have only relatively weak antigenicity and the earliest production of antibody cannot be detected until considerably later in development.

The significance of the production of 19S antibody during the immune response of certain young animals is not yet clear. Generally, 19S antibody is the first type to appear after a single injection of antigen in the adult and 7S antibody production follows later. Young animals have a higher proportion of immature antibody-producing cells and relatively few plasma cells so that the primary response and even the secondary response are of the 19S type for a considerable time after birth.

VI. The Ontogeny of Hemoglobin

A. *Introduction*

Hemoglobin is really an enzymatic protein with oxygen as its substrate. Mammalian hemoglobin consists of four heme prosthetic groups combined with four polypeptide chains. The heme is a ferrous iron porphyrin and is common to all types of hemoglobin and myoglobin.

The phylogenetic differences in adult hemoglobins and the differences between embryonic, fetal, and adult forms within one species are all the result of changes in the amino acid composition of the globin moiety.

Methods of separation are only mentioned here, they are adequately reviewed by Gratzer and Allison (1960) and Baglioni (1963). In this chapter the hemoglobin of normal adult blood is referred to as Hb-A, of fetal blood as Hb-F, and those hemoglobins which are characteristic only of early embryonic development are referred to as "embryonic hemoglobins."

B. *Hemoglobins in the Developing Chick Embryo*

1. ALKALI DENATURATION

In the chicken, Hugounenq and Morel (1905) found that hemoglobin from young chick embryos was not as stable to alkali as adult hemoglobin, but in contrast Saha (1956) has found that hemoglobin from the 7-day-old chick embryo is slightly more alkali-resistant than Hb-A. If the more recent result is confirmed it means that chicken Hb-F resembles human and monkey Hb-F in this respect.

2. OXYGEN AFFINITY

a. The Chick Embryo. Hall (1934a) found that blood from chick embryos had a greater oxygen affinity than that from the mature fowl, and there was a progressive decrease in oxygen affinity of embryonic blood from 9 days of incubation until the early posthatching period.

b. General Remarks. It must be remembered that this type of early experiment on whole blood only indicates the presence of a fetal form of hemoglobin. However it has since been found that all mammalian Hb-F's have a higher oxygen affinity *in fetal blood* than their respective Hb-A's. In mammals this obviously facilitates the placental transfer of oxygen from the mother to the young.

The oxygen-dissociation curves (% saturation versus oxygen pressure) for all vertebrates are sigmoid in shape and this was thought to indicate heme-heme interactions; however, the four heme groups are now known to be too widely separated for this to be possible. The primitive vertebrates and the invertebrates have hemoglobin consisting of only one heme group in a low molecular weight (17,000) protein and, as for myoglobin, the oxygen-dissociation curve of such hemoglobins is hyperbolic. The Bohr effect, which is a decrease of oxygen affinity with increasing pH, assists the liberation of oxygen from oxyhemoglobin to the tissues. The nature of the oxygen-dissociation curve and the magnitude of the Bohr effect depend upon the number of cysteine residues per molecule of hemoglobin (Riggs, 1959). In the chick embryo, the Bohr effect is much less pronounced than for adult hemoglobin (Manwell *et al.*, 1963).

3. FIRST APPEARANCE OF HEMOGLOBIN

Hemoglobin is rapidly synthesized at about the 8-somite stage (Beard, 1958; O'Brien, 1961; Wilt, 1962) chiefly in the blood islands which gradually disintegrate to form blood cells. Two distinct globins have been detected by immunological methods in the unincubated chick blastoderm and the relative rates of incorporation of $Fe^{59}Cl_3$ and H^3-leucine (Wilt, 1962) indicate that heme is not bound to the globin component to any great extent before the 8-somite stage. One of the hemoglobins is probably Hb-F and the other component which disappears at 36–48 hours of incubation may be an "embryonic" type of hemoglobin also found in some other species. When this embryonic hemoglobin disappears it is replaced by what is probably Hb-A (Wilt, 1962).

4. Ontogeny of Embryonic, Fetal, and Adult Hemoglobins

In 48- and 72-hour blastoderms there are two hemoglobins which are immunologically and immunoelectrophoretically identical with those in adult blood (Wilt, 1962) and these have also been found by D'Amelio and Salvo (1959a) in 6-day-old embryos. D'Amelio and Salvo (1961) using starch and agar electrophoresis and immunological techniques also found that these two hemoglobin components are present at 60 hours of development, but by 85 hours these authors detected three hemoglobins which are identical with the three which they found in adult blood. By 11 days of incubation there were only traces of the two "embryonic" types of hemoglobin present. The presence of an early embryonic type of hemoglobin has been confirmed by Manwell *et al.* (1963) by paper electrophoresis. These authors and D'Amelio and Salvo (1961) differ from Wilt (1962) in that they found that embryonic hemoglobins were present up to 5 days of incubation and had virtually disappeared by 11 days of incubation; whereas Wilt (1962) found only one embryonic type which disappeared at 36–48 hours of incubation. By the use of electrophoresis and chromatography Fraser (1961) found that Hb-F constitutes 84 % of the hemoglobin at 5 days of incubation, and the proportion of Hb-F declined so that Hb-F reached its lowest level (28 %) at hatching and then remained at this level in the adult. The time in development when workers have found that there are equal amounts of Hb-F and Hb-A in the embryo appear to vary considerably; Johnson and Dunlap (1955) found as much as 70 % Hb-F at 13 days of incubation, Fraser (1961) noticed 50 % Hb-F at 11 days, and Manwell *et al.* (1963) measured 50 % Hb-F as early as 7 days of incubation. Most workers find that adult chicken blood contains about 80 % Hb-A and 20 % Hb-F (Johnson and Dunlap, 1955; van der Helm and Huisman, 1958; D'Amelio and Salvo, 1959a). Three hemoglobins have been separated from adult chicken blood by Rodnan and Ebaugh (1956) and D'Amelio and Salvo (1959b) and this has been confirmed by Manwell *et al.* (1963) who isolated them by continuous-flow curtain electrophoresis. "Fingerprinting" (paper electrophoresis of the peptides after hydrolysis) of these fractions showed some differences in the peptide constitution of the three adult hemoglobins.

5. POSSIBLE ASSOCIATION OF HB-F WITH PRIMITIVE ERYTHROCYTES OR
   CHANGING SITES OF HEMOPOIESIS

Although it is possible to correlate the decreasing amounts of early embryonic hemoglobin with a decrease in transitory forms of primitive erythrocytes in the blood it is very difficult to correlate the diminishing amount of Hb-F during embryonic development with either primitive erythrocytes or with a change in the predominance of one hemopoietic site over another (e.g., bone marrow over yolk sac). The supposition that Hb-F is exclusive to the primitive erythrocyte is untenable as the primitive erythrocyte begins to disappear from the circulation at 5 days of incubation and the definitive erythrocytes predominate in embryonic blood as early as 7 days of incubation; all the primitive erythrocytes have completely disappeared by 15 days (Dawson, 1936; O'Connor, 1952). Neither can the proposition that Hb-F is synthesized exclusively by one hemopoietic site such as the yolk sac be supported, even though the yolk sac is the predominant site of hemopoiesis in the young embryo when the proportion of Hb-F is high; at about 14 days of incubation hemopoiesis is localized mainly in the bone marrow (Dawson, 1936; Sandreuter, 1951). The continued production of Hb-F during postnatal life is also not compatible with such a proposition.

C. Embryonic and Fetal Hemoglobins in the Human

1. ALKALI DENATURATION

The hemoglobin of fetal and cord blood is more alkali resistant than placental hemoglobin (Körber, 1866). In fact, Hb-F is more alkali resistant than any of the several human adult hemoglobins, so that this reaction may be conveniently used both to identify and measure Hb-F in a mixture of other forms of hemoglobin. This higher resistance to alkali has been attributed to the γ-chains of Hb-F, but it may be due to the difference in the chemical bonds between the α- and γ-chains of Hb-F compared to the bonds between the α- and β-chains of Hb-A. Blood from newborn infants contains as much as 80 % of the alkali resistant Hb-F (Haurowitz, 1929). The different alkali-denaturation rates of normal adult and cord blood are shown in Fig. 16.

2. OXYGEN AFFINITY

Barcroft (1947) found that fetal blood had a higher oxygen affinity than adult blood, and Jonxis (1949) has correlated the different oxygen affinities with alkali-denaturation rates. The higher oxygen loading of fetal human blood may not be a property of the Hb-F component, because Allen et al. (1953) found that when solutions of Hb-A and Hb-F were dialyzed against the same buffer solution they both had the same oxygen affinity. Therefore, intrinsically the two hemoglobins have the same oxygen equilibrium characteristics, but as the environmental pH differs, Hb-A and Hb-F appear to behave differently with respect to oxygen loading. In the case of the human this is probably related to the

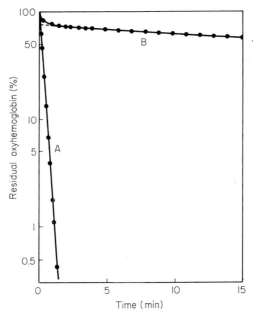

FIG. 16.   Alkali-denaturation rates of adult and cord blood. A, Normal adult; B, cord blood (76 % Hb-F). After White and Beaven (1959).

Bohr effect of Hb-F at approximately neutral pH values (see Manwell, 1960).

3. CRYSTAL FORMS AND SOLUBILITIES

Distinct crystal forms for Hb-A and Hb-F are well established (Haurowitz, 1935; Jope and O'Brien, 1949). The latter authors observed differences between adult and fetal hemoglobins in the temperature-solubility curves of the carbon monoxide hemoglobin, methemoglobin, and oxyhemoglobin derivatives.

4. TRYPTOPHAN ABSORPTION

Human Hb-F can also be distinguished from Hb-A by its more pronounced tryptophan absorption band in the ultraviolet spectra at 289 mμ (Jope, 1949; White and Beaven, 1959). The only other species known to display this property is the monkey.

5. ANTIGENICITY

The differing antigenicities of Hb-A and Hb-F have been demonstrated using rabbit or guinea pig antisera (Chernoff, 1953; Goodman and Campbell, 1953; Diacono and Castay, 1956). Both Hb-A and Hb-F can be detected immunologically in the newborn infant, but no Hb-F could be detected in adult blood (Darrow et al., 1940).

6. STRUCTURE

The difference between Hb-A and Hb-F lies in differences in amino acid composition in the globin molecule. There are four isoleucine residues per half-molecule of Hb-F (Stein et al., 1957), but there is no isoleucine in adult hemoglobin (Ingram, 1961). The "fingerprinting" technique of Ingram (1958) enables the peptides of hemoglobin to be studied after their release by tryptic digestion and separation by paper chromatography. This method was used by Hunt (1959) to compare Hb-A and Hb-F; peptides were derived from α- and β-chains in Hb-A and from the α- and γ-chains in Hb-F. Fingerprinting of the peptides confirmed the earlier findings of Schroeder and Matsuda (1958) that the α-chains of both forms were identical and had the N-terminal sequence valine-leucine. The β-chains of Hb-A are N-terminal in valine-histidine-leucine and differ from the γ-chains of Hb-F, which are N-terminal in glycine-histidine-phenylalanine, so that the difference between Hb-F and Hb-A resides in one of the two polypeptide chains. The simplified formula for Hb-A can thus be written $\alpha_2\beta_2$ and for Hb-F $\alpha_2\gamma_2$. The composition of the peptides obtained by tryptic digestion of Hb-A have been determined by Konigsberg et al. (1961) and Braunitzer et al. (1961). The sequence of the α-chains of both Hb-A and Hb-F is common, but the difference between the β_2- and γ_2-polypeptide chains is caused by the different arrangement of forty-two amino acids in one polypeptide chain (Schroeder et al., 1962).

7. AN EMBRYONIC HEMOGLOBIN IN EARLY DEVELOPMENT

The alkali-denaturation rate of hemoglobin from a 7- to 12-week-old human fetus was determined by adding sodium hydroxide electrophotometrically (Drescher and Künzer, 1954). This hemoglobin had an alkali-denaturation rate between that previously found for Hb-F and Hb-A and is probably another embryonic type of hemoglobin. Drescher and Künzer (1954) suggested that this embryonic hemoglobin could be associated with the primitive erythrocytes which are replaced at about 10–12 weeks of fetal life. Confirmation of their work by Butler et al. (1960) using electrophoresis and alkali denaturation showed that no embryonic type of hemoglobin was present in any fetus older than 9 weeks of age. Further work has indicated that this embryonic hemoglobin also appears with erythroblastosis which is the result of an upset of gene control (Halbrecht et al., 1959). It is possible that two embryonic hemoglobins exist in very young embryos (Huehns et al., 1961).

8. DECLINE OF HB-F DURING DEVELOPMENT

Halbrecht and Klibanski (1956) showed that 10-week-old embryos contained 83 % of an alkali-resistant hemoglobin (Hb-F) which decreased to 52 % by 20 weeks of gestation. Earlier work (Haurowitz, 1929) had indicated that newborn infant blood contained as much as 80 % of the more alkali-resistant Hb-F. The proportion of Hb-F remains fairly constant from week 24–32 of gestation and then falls at a rate of 2.5–4 % per week (Cook et al., 1957), so that it has virtually been completely replaced by Hb-A by the end of 1 year (Fig. 15) (Jonxis, 1949, White and Beaven, 1959). Minute amounts of Hb-F may persist in normal adult blood as up to 0–5 % Hb-F has been detected by the serological ring-test technique (Chernoff, 1953) and amino acid analysis (Huisman et al., 1955).

9. INCREASE IN HB-A DURING DEVELOPMENT

Using the alkali-denaturation method Walker and Turnbull (1955) found that Hb-A first appears (1–2 %) in the fetus at 13 weeks and rises to 10 % by 23 weeks of gestation; Hb-A remains at this level until 38 weeks, after which it continues to rise to 30 % of the total hemoglobin at 42 weeks of gestation. If the oxygen supply to the fetus becomes deficient, the extra hemoglobin produced is almost entirely Hb-F (Walker, 1954).

10. GENETIC CONTROL OF HB-F SYNTHESIS

There is good genetic evidence that the α-chains of both Hb-F and Hb-A are under the control of the same gene and are chemically identical. In the change from synthesis of Hb-F to synthesis of Hb-A only the synthesis of γ-peptide chains under the control of the γ-genes is discontinued and the β-gene actively commences the synthesis of the β-peptide chain of Hb-A. In pathological conditions, such as sickle cell anemia and thalassemia, from 40–100 % of the total hemoglobin may be Hb-F (Itano, 1953). Humans with common types of thalassemia suffer a genetic interference with the normal synthesis of the β-polypeptide chains of Hb-A which results in Hb-F (which has no β-chains) being formed in excess.

11. Possible Association of Embryonic and Fetal Hemoglobin with Different Types of Erythrocyte

Although Künzer (1957) has suggested that the existence of the three hemoglobins in the human embryo corresponds with the mesoblastic, hepatic, and medullary periods of hemopoiesis, the switch from synthesis of Hb-F to Hb-A cannot be correlated with these periods, and some workers believe that some cells may contain both Hb-A and Hb-F (e.g., Betke, 1959). So far, it appears that the embryonic hemoglobin may well be associated with a primitive (nucleated) erythrocyte because it disappears so early in development. Hb-F may be associated with the large fetal erythrocytes. Walker (1954) has correlated the disappearance of the larger fetal type of erythrocyte with the disappearance of Hb-F when these cells are replaced by smaller mature erythrocytes containing Hb-A. By 6 weeks after birth these fetal cells can no longer be detected (Walker, 1954).

12. Summary of the Ontogeny of Human Hemoglobins

The ontogeny of the three types of hemoglobin in the human seems to consist of the appearance and early disappearance by 9–10 weeks of gestation of embryonic types of hemoglobin. Hb-F in the young embryo is only slowly replaced by Hb-A. This replacement does not begin until 13 weeks of gestation, and Hb-A represents only 10 % of the total hemoglobin at 8 months of gestation. This is the time when enucleated cells are first seen and there is then an increase of 20 % in Hb-A so that the newborn infant has about 30 % Hb-A. The major hemoglobin component of the blood is still Hb-F during 1–3 weeks after birth. The large fetal-type cells which disappear completely from the blood about 6 weeks after birth may contain the major proportion of Hb-F.

D. Fetal Hemoglobins in Other Species

Fetal types of hemoglobin have been detected in a wide variety of animals ranging from the lamprey to the human. Phylogenetically, the most noticeable change in the evolutionary series is in the oxygen capacity of the blood which increases 10- to 20-fold from invertebrates to fish and mammals (Redfield, 1933).

1. Lamprey

The blood hemoglobin of the sea lamprey *Petromyzon marinus* has been shown by Wald and Riggs (1951) to have a mixture of primitive and highly specialized properties. Lamprey hemoglobin has a molecular weight of 17,000, contains only a single heme, and has an isoelectric point typical of invertebrate hemoglobin. The hemoglobin of higher vertebrates consists of four such units (molecular weight 64,500). The lamprey is also of great interest in that it is the only adult vertebrate with an oxygen-dissociation curve which is a rectangular hyperbola. Although lamprey hemoglobin has only one heme it differs from myoglobin in that it is an efficient oxygen transporter because of its relatively low oxygen affinity and very large Bohr effect owing to one free sulfhydryl group per molecule. In 1958, Adinolfi and Chieffi compared larval and adult hemoglobins of the cyclostome *Petromyzon planeri* by starch-gel electrophoresis and found that the two larval hemoglobins migrated more rapidly than the two adult hemoglobins.

2. DOGFISH, RAY, AND SKATE

In the ovoviviparous spiny dogfish *Squalus suckleyi*, which has one of the longest gestation periods of any living vertebrate (23 months), fetal hemoglobin is present throughout most, if not all, of prenatal life (Manwell, 1958a). Hb-A and Hb-F of the dogfish differ in their oxygen-equilibrium curves and alkali-denaturation rates. The fetal blood has a greater oxygen affinity than adult blood (like other mammals), but both hemoglobins have a small Bohr effect. The Californian smooth dogfish *Mustelus californicus* also has Hb-F and Hb-A and in contrast to *Squalus suckleyi* has true viviparity and a placenta (Manwell, 1960). There are no, or only slight, differences in the hemoglobins of adult and fetal viviparous rays (McCutcheon, 1936) and skates (Manwell, 1958b).

3. OTHER FISH

The presence of Hb-F during the early postlarval development of the teleost fish *Scorpaenichthys marmoratus* is indicated by an alkali-labile component which denatures more rapidly than Hb-A (Manwell, 1957). There is also fetal hemoglobin in the surf perch *Embiotoca lateralis* which is viviparous (Manwell, 1957). The function of Hb-F in these fishes is obscure, as oxygen tensions for both adult fishes and their pelagic young are similar.

4. FROG

McCutcheon in 1936 showed that there were probably changes in hemoglobin during the metamorphosis of the bullfrog *Rana catesbeiana* as the oxygen affinity of frog blood decreased during development. The Bohr effect with adult frog hemoglobin (Fig. 17) was much more pronounced than with hemoglobin obtained before metamorphosis (McCutcheon, 1936; Riggs, 1951). Hemoglobins of larval and adult *Rana esculenta* also exhibit different electrophoretic mobilities (Dessauer

et al., 1957; Chieffi *et al.*, 1960). In frogs there may be a correlation between the type of hemoglobin synthesized and a particular site of erythropoiesis; for instance, after splenectomy of bullfrogs, McCutcheon (1938)

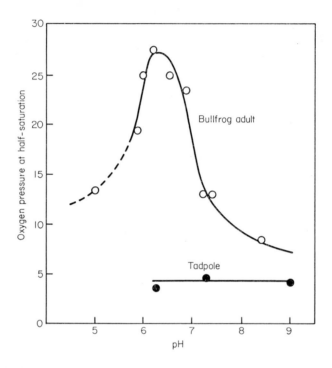

Fig. 17. Variation with pH of the oxygen pressure at half-saturation of tadpole
and adult bullfrog hemoglobin. After Riggs (1951).

showed that the hemoglobin synthesized by the bone marrow had a
lower oxygen affinity than that from the spleen. In the tadpole hemoglobin is synthesized in the mesonephros.

5. Terrapin

The blood of the terrapin embryo *Malaclemys centrata* also has a
higher oxygen affinity than that of the adult (McCutcheon, 1947). This
animal is unique in that the oxygen affinity remains constant until
hatching and then progressively decreases during the first year of life.
The adult type of hemoglobin is not completely established until the
second year. Terrapin Hb-A has a lower loading but higher unloading
capacity for oxygen than Hb-F.

6. Mouse

Barrowman and Roberts (1961) showed that both adult and fetal mouse hemoglobin are denatured by alkali and oxidized to methemoglobin at the same rate. When hemoglobins from fetal mice were converted to the stable cyanmethemoglobins and separated by electrophoresis in starch gel, the hemoglobin from fetuses at 12–15 days of gestation showed a different pattern to those from fetuses of 16 days and onward. Hemoglobin from newborn mice was identical with that from the adult. At 12 days of gestation fetal mouse blood contained three hemoglobins. The predominant, slowest moving component began to decline in amount at 14 days of gestation and had completely disappeared 1 day later. At 16 days another component disappeared, so that after this time there was only the most rapidly migrating hemoglobin left (Barrowman and Craig, 1961). These transitions in hemoglobin patterns occur at the same time as a decrease in the proportion of large nucleated erythrocytes in the fetal circulation owing to the cessation of erythropoiesis in the yolk sac. During 14–16 days nucleated erythrocytes fall from 21 to 1 %, so that the two fetal types of hemoglobin may have been present in the nucleated erythrocytes manufactured by the yolk sac. Hb-A is associated with the second and third generation of nonnucleated erythrocytes derived from the liver and bone marrow, respectively.

7. Rabbit

In rabbits fetal hemoglobin has a greater oxygen affinity than that of the adult (Hall, 1934b), this is highest at 24 days of gestation (Barron and Battaglia, 1956). The oxygen-dissociation curves of blood from the 24-day-old rabbit fetus are hyperbolic and rapidly become sigmoidal until they fall in the adult range at birth (30 days). This explains why the hemoglobin from adult and newborn rabbits reacted identically with adult hemoglobin antiserum (Westendorp Boerma et al., 1960).

8. Goat

Fetal goat blood has a higher oxygen affinity that that of the mother (Hall, 1934b; Barcroft et al., 1935). In the newborn goat there is no Hb-A and the faster moving fetal hemoglobins consist of two components. One fetal hemoglobin (Hb-F_2) is more alkali-resistant than the other (Hb-F_1). Hb-F_2 behaves like the adult component with respect to alkali resistance and like fetal hemoglobin in its electrophoretic and chromatographic mobility. Hb-F_2 disappears at 3 weeks after birth and may be associated with a type of erythrocyte only produced in the fetus (van der Helm et al., 1958). The Hb-F component which is not so alkali-resistant constitutes 60 % of the total hemoglobin in newborn goats and soon disappears so that only 12 % is left after 5 weeks, and there is none apparent in adult blood (Fig. 18). Incorporation of radioactive iron and glycine indicates that fetal hemoglobin continues to be synthesized for some time after birth (Visser *et al.*, 1957).

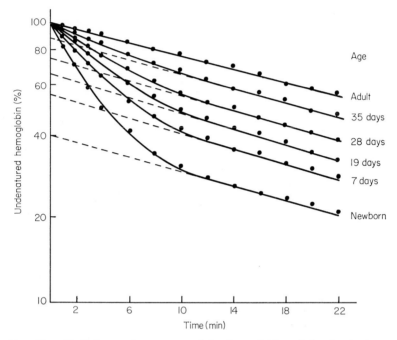

Fig. 18. Alkali-denaturation curves of the hemoglobins of the developing goat. After van der Helm *et al.* (1958).

9. Sheep

Fetal sheep hemoglobin has a higher oxygen affinity and only attains the degree of inflection in the oxygen-dissociation curve typical of an adult at 40 days after birth (Hill and Wolvekamp, 1936). The "variable solvent" and "constant solvent" methods used by Karvonen (1949) showed that at pH 7.2 the adult hemoglobin was about twenty times more soluble than the fetal type which indicated that the Hb-F differed from Hb-A. A third type of hemoglobin was detected in young lambs. The amount of Hb-F changed during development. At 120 days of gestation hemoglobin was 100 % fetal type and at birth Hb-F was 50 % of the total; the transition from fetal to adult form was complete at 2–3 months of postnatal life. Sheep hemoglobins from adult and fetal sheep are antigenically different (Westendorp Boerma *et al.*, 1960) and have been separated by electrophoresis (Cabannes and Serain, 1957) and chromatography (Boardman and Partridge, 1955). Adult sheep can have either one or two Hb-A's (e.g., Harris and Warren, 1955; see Gratzer and Allison, 1960).

10. CATTLE

In newborn calves, Grimes *et al.* (1958) found that Hb-F constitutes 41–100 % of the total hemoglobin. Hb-F disappeared rapidly from the blood of the developing calf and by 65–97 days of age was entirely replaced by Hb-A. This coincided with the disappearance of a hemoglobin fraction which was very rapidly denatured by alkali (Bangham, 1957). In some calves the disappearance of Hb-F was obscured by the simultaneous appearance of a second adult type of hemoglobin (Hb-B) which had the same electrophoretic mobility. Many breeds of cattle have two adult types of hemoglobin (polymorphism). Some differences in amino acid composition have been found between the fetal and adult hemoglobins of cattle. Hb-F has more isoleucine and less methionine and histidine than adult hemoglobin; also in strong phosphate buffer Hb-F is six times more soluble than Hb-A (Wyman, 1948). Further work with a Moore and Stein column has indicated that Hb-F also differs from the adult form in its serine, alanine, isoleucine, histidine, and lysine content (Timmer *et al.*, 1957).

11. HORSE

At present no difference between horse fetal and adult hemoglobins has been found by oxygen-dissociation curves, chromatography, alkali denaturation, fingerprinting, or X-ray crystallography (Stockell *et al.*, 1961).

12. MONKEY

Hb-A and Hb-F of monkeys have been separated by electrophoresis in agar (Beaven and Gratzer, 1959). The alkali-denaturation method showed that blood of newborn monkeys contained 40–60 % alkali-resistant hemoglobin (Hb-F), and during 9–13 weeks of age the Hb-F fell to 1–6 % which is the normal adult level (Sen *et al.*, 1960). For further studies the reader is referred to the reviews of McCarthy (1954), White and Beaven (1959), Gratzer and Allison (1960), and Ingram (1961).

E. *Possible Fetal Forms of Myoglobin*

The chief function of myoglobin is the storage of oxygen in the muscle. Myoglobin has only one heme in each molecule and only a single chain polypeptide as the protein component. Jonxis and Wadman (1952) first noticed that there was a slight difference between human fetal and adult myoglobin in their resistance to alkali denaturation and the fetal myoglobin (Mb-F) was less soluble in ammonium sulfate at pH 7.4. Slight differences in the ultraviolet absorption curves at the tryptophan band suggested differences between the carbon monoxide compounds of Mb-A and Mb-F in cows and humans (Rossi-Fanelli *et al.*, 1954). These suggestive results were confirmed in humans by Singer *et al.* (1955) when both adult and fetal metmyoglobin were distinguished by spectroscopic and paper electrophoretic techniques. Mb-F was the only type in premature and newborn infants, and replacement of Mb-F and Mb-A took place during the first 6 months of life in much the same manner as hemoglobin. Cow Mb-A and Mb-F have also been separated by paper electrophoresis by Timmer *et al.* (1957); but as these workers found that a Moore and Stein amino acid analysis showed no difference between Mb-A and Mb-F the existence of a fetal myoglobin in cows remains uncertain.

F. *Summary*

Fetal forms of hemoglobin in nearly all species exhibit a greater oxygen capacity *in the fetal circulation* which gives the embryo a respiratory advantage while in the egg or uterus. Birds appear to be unique in retaining fetal hemoglobin during adult life, a condition also found only in man during abnormal gene activity. If the changing types of oxygen-dissociation curves of terrapin blood during development can be equated with the disappearance of a fetal hemoglobin then this animal is one of the slowest to lose fetal forms of hemoglobin. Fetal hemoglobin only disappears relatively slowly after birth in goats, sheep, cattle, monkeys, and man, although it is difficult to comprehend a physiological requirement of such a compound in postnatal life. On the other hand, the newborn rabbit has no fetal hemoglobin and in the hatching chick fetal hemoglobin has also declined to its adult level. Fetal forms of hemoglobin have not been observed in the cat (Brinkman and Jonxis, 1936), pig, and horse, and there is only slight evidence for fetal hemoglobin in viviparous rays and skates.

Characteristic embryonic types of hemoglobin have been found during the early stages of embryonic development in chickens, mice, and man and may be associated with the primitive erythrocytes. The definite identity of such embryonic hemoglobins, however, needs to be firmly established by chemical investigation. Goats, and possibly sheep, have two types of fetal hemoglobin at birth and one disappears more rapidly than the other. While it is possible that one type of fetal hemoglobin in mice and goats is associated with nucleated erythrocytes, the definite association of fetal hemoglobin with a cell type or hemopoietic site is not general.

VII. Conclusions

There is a vast amount of research work remaining to be done to investigate the ontogeny of other proteins and also to complete many of the studies mentioned above. It will remain for the next few decades with, it is to be hoped, an increasing number of biochemists working on these problems of development to plot the patterns of protein synthesis in man and in at least the more common of the domestic animals.

Generally, the approach of the chemical embryologist has been to detect in the developing embryo the earliest appearance of proteins (or their antigenic determinants) typical of the adult. Only occasionally is it possible to study the synthesis of small protein molecules and their subsequent assembly to form the large molecules characteristic of the adult protein. This is beautifully illustrated by the work on collagen which has been accomplished in the case of this protein only because physical methods such as X-ray diffraction and electron microscopy could be used.

Exciting new work on the immunology of young animals is suggested by those immune mechanisms against particulate antigens that involve proteins capable of combining with foreign particles, but, unlike antibodies, are not produced by the plasma cells. As such proteins are actively synthesized by the fetus and young animal they offer a completely new field of research that is, as yet, almost unexplored. There are few proteins which appear to be characteristic only of embryonic life. It is possible that there are relatively few such proteins and that many of them only appear during development because a storage of the precursors of adult proteins occurs before the final steps in modification of the protein molecule to the adult type are made. No such transitory proteins appear during the development of the lens, but some embryonic types of globulin have been reported in chick embryo serum during early development. These globulins appear to be precursors of adult globulins as they disappear when the adult types become established in the serum. There are many reports of embryonic types of hemoglobin (other than Hb-F) which still require chemical confirmation and it is not known whether they are precursors of Hb-F or Hb-A. The two most well-defined protein types characteristic of fetal life are fetuin, whose physiological role is as yet unknown, and fetal hemoglobins. Both types of protein have been isolated and in the case of human Hb-F the complete structure is known. The recent elucidation of the structures of human Hb-A and Hb-F is a tremendous step forward for developmental biochemistry as it is undoubtedly the most dramatic example of molecular differentiation. It is now possible to compare the differences between a molecule especially synthesized by the embryo for the conditions of embryonic life with that of the adult type. The switch from synthesis of Hb-F to that of Hb-A owing to the switch of different gene activities is one of the most fascinating epigenetic models of functional differentiation of proteins at the present time. The methods by which this genetic control of hemoglobin synthesis operates is now open to speculation (see Ingram, 1963) which will provide the stimulus for further research on the mechanisms of the genetic regulation of the functional differentiation of proteins during development.

REFERENCES

Adinolfi, M., and Chieffi, G. (1958). *Nature* **182**, 730.

Allen, D. W., Wyman, J., and Smith, C. A. (1953). *J. Biol. Chem.* **203**, 81.

Archer, O., and Pierce, J. C. (1961). *Federation Proc.* **20**, Pt. 2, 26.

Baglioni, C. (1963). In "Molecular Genetics" (J. H. Taylor, ed.), Pt. 2, p. 405. Academic Press, New York.

Bailey, C. E. (1923). *Am. J. Hyg.* **3**, 370.

Bailey, J. L. (1962). "Techniques on Protein Chemistry." Elsevier, Amsterdam.

Banfield, W. G. (1952). *Proc. Soc. Exptl. Biol. Med.* **81**, 658.

Banfield, W. G. (1955). *J. Gerontol.* **10**, 13.

Banfield, W. G. (1959). *A.M.A. Arch. Pathol.* **68**, 680.

Bangham, A. D. (1957). *Nature* **179**, 467.

Bangham, D. R., Hobbs, K. R., and Terry, R. J. (1958). *Lancet* **II**, 351.

Barboriak, J. J., de Bella, G., Setnikar, I., and Krehl, W. A. (1958a). *Am. J. Physiol.* **193**, 89.

Barboriak, J. J., Meschia, G., Barron, D. H., and Cowgill, G. R. (1958b). *Proc. Soc. Exptl. Biol. Med.* **98**, 635.

Barcroft, J. (1947). "Researches in Prenatal Life." Blackwell, Oxford, England.

Barcroft, J., Flexner, L. B., Herkel, W., McCarthy, E. F., and McClurkin, T. (1935). *J. Physiol. (London)* **83**, 192.

Baril, E. F., Palmer, J. L., and Bartel, A. H. (1961). *Science* **133**, 278.

Barr, M., Glenny, A. T., and Randall, K. J. (1949). *Lancet* **II**, 324.

Barr, M., Glenny, A. T., and Howie, J. W. (1953). *J. Pathol. Bacteriol.* **65**, 155.

Barrick, E. R., Matrone, G., and Osborne, J. C. (1954). *Proc. Soc. Exptl. Biol. Med.* **87**, 92.

Barron, D. H., and Battaglia, F. C. (1956). *Obstet. Gynecol. Surv.* **11**, 465.

Barrowman, J., and Craig, M. (1961). *Nature* **190**, 818.

Barrowman, J., and Roberts, K. B. (1961). *Nature* **189**, 409.

Bauer, D. C., and Stavitsky, A. B. (1961). *Proc. Natl. Acad. Sci. U. S.* **47**, 1667.

Baumgartner, L. (1934). *J. Immunol.* **27**, 407.

Bauriedel, W. R., Hoerlein, A. B., Picken, J. C., and Underkofler, L. A. (1954). *J. Agr. Food Chem.* **2**, 468.

Beard, R. G. (1958). *Ann. Rept. Carnegie Inst. Wash. Dept. Embryol.* **57**, 336.

Beaven, G. H., and Gratzer, W. B. (1959). *Nature* **184**, 1730.

Beckitt, A. M. (1958). B.Sc. thesis, Edinburgh University.

Beloff, R. H. (1959). *J. Exptl. Zool.* **140**, 493.

Bergstrand, C. G., and Czar, B. (1957). *Scand. J. Clin. Lab. Invest.* **9**, 277.

Bergstrand, C. G., Czar, B., and Tarukoski, P. H. (1961). *Scand. J. Clin. Lab. Invest.* **13**, 576.

Betke, K. (1959). *Folia Haematol.* **76**, 292.

Beveridge, W. I. B., and Burnet, F. M. (1946). *Med. Res. Council (Brit.) Spec. Rept. Ser.* **256**.

Billingham, R. E. (1958). *In* "Chemical Basis of Development" (W. D. McElroy and B. Glass, eds.), pp. 575-591. Johns Hopkins Press, Baltimore, Maryland.

Billingham, R. E., and Brent, L. (1957). *Transplant. Bull.* **4**, 67.

Billingham, R. E., and Lampkin, G. H. (1957). *J. Embryol. Exptl. Morphol.* **5**, 351.

Billingham, R. E., Brent, L., and Medawar, P. B. (1956). *Phil. Trans. Roy. Soc. London* **B239**, 357.

Bishop, D. W., and Gump, D. (1961). *Proc. Soc. Exptl. Biol. Med.* **106**, 24.

Boardman, N. K., and Partridge, S. M. (1955). *Biochem. J.* **59**, 543.

Bodman, J. (1959). *Clin. Chim. Acta* **4**, 103.

Boll, F. (1870). *Arch. Anat. Physiol. Wiss. Med.* p. 718.

Bornstein, S., and Israel, M. (1942). *Proc. Soc. Exptl. Biol. Med.* **49**, 718.

Borsos, T., and Kent, H. N. (1958). *Proc. Soc. Exptl. Biol. Med.* **99**, 105.

Brambell, F. W. R. (1958). *Biol. Rev. Cambridge Phil. Soc.* **33**, 488.

Brambell, F. W. R., Hemmings, W. A., Henderson, M., and Kekwick, R. A. (1953). *Proc. Roy. Soc.* **B141**, 300.

Brandly, C. A., Moses, H. E., and Jungherr, E. L. (1946). *Am. J. Vet. Res.* **7**, 333.

Brandt, L. W., Clegg, R. E., and Andrews, A. C. (1951). *J. Biol. Chem.* **191**, 105.

Braunitzer, G., Gehring-Müller, R., Hilschmann, N., Hilse, K., Hobom, G., Rudloff, V., and Wittman-Liebold, B. (1961). *Z. Physiol. Chem.* **325**, 283.

Brent, L. (1958). *Progr. Allergy* **5**, 271.

Brent, L., and Gowland, G. (1962). *Nature* **196**, 1298.

Bridges, R. A., Condie, R. M., Zak, S. J., and Good, R. A. (1957). *Federation Proc.* **16**, 352.

Briles, W. E., McGibbon, W. H., and Irwin, M. R. (1948). *Genetics* **33**, 97.

Brinkman, R., and Jonxis, J. H. P. (1936). *J. Physiol. (London)* **88**, 162.

Brønnestam, R., and Nilsson, S-. B. (1957). *Vox Sanguinis* **2**, 316.

Burke, V., Sullivan, N. P., Petersen, H., and Weed, R. (1944). *J. Infect. Diseases* **74**, 225.

Burnet, F. M. (1959). "The Clonal Selection Theory of Acquired Immunity." Cambridge Univ. Press, London and New York.

Burnet, F. M., and Fenner, F. (1949). "The Production of Antibodies." Macmillan, New York.

Burnet, F. M., Stone, J. D., and Edney, M. (1950). *Australian J. Exptl. Biol. Med. Sci.* **28**, 291.

Burstein, M., Lewi, S., and Walter, P. (1954). *Sang* **25**, 102.

Butler, E. A., Flynn, F. V., and Huehns, E. R. (1960). *Clin. Chim. Acta* **5**, 571.

Buxton, A. (1952). *J. Gen. Microbiol.* **7**, 268.

Buxton, A. (1954). *J. Gen. Microbiol.* **10**, 398.

Cabannes, R., and Serain, C. (1957). *Compt. Rend. Soc. Biol.* **151**, 87.

Charlwood, P. A., and Thompson, A. (1948). *Nature* **161**, 59.

Chernoff, A. I. (1953). *Blood* **8**, 413.

Chieffi, G., Siniscalco, M., and Adinolfi, M. (1960). *Atti Accad. Nazl. Lincei, Rend. Classe Sci. Fis. Mat. Nat.* **28**, 233.

Chvapil, M. (1956). *Physiol. Bohemoslov.* **5**, 421.

Chvapil, M. (1957). *Cesk. Fysiol.* **6**, 102.

Chvapil, M., and Kobrle, V. (1961). *Experientia* **17**, 226.

Clarke, W. M., and Fowler, I. (1960). *Develop. Biol.* **2**, 155.

Clayton, R. M. (1954). *Nature* **174**, 1059.

Clayton, R. M., and Feldman, M. (1955). *Experientia* **11**, 29.

Cohn, M. (1956). *Transplant. Bull.* **3**, 70.

Cook, C. D., Brodie, H. R., and Allen, D. W. (1957). *Pediatrics* **20**, 272.

Coombs, R. R. A., Coombs, A. M., and Ingram, D. G. (1961). "The Serology of Conglutination and its Relation to Disease." Blackwell, Oxford, England.

Coulombre, A. J. (1961). *Intern. Rev. Cytol.* **11**, 161.

Croisille, V. (1960). *J. Embryol. Exptl. Morphol.* **8**, 216.

Culbertson, J. T. (1938). *J. Parasitol.* **24**, 65.

Cushing, J. E., and Campbell, D. H. (1957). "Principles of Immunology." McGraw-Hill, New York.

Dalgarno, A., Godden, W., and McCarthy, E. F. (1950). *Biochem. J.* **46**, 162.

D'Amelio, V., and Salvo, A. M. (1959a). *Acta Embryol. Morphol. Exptl.* **2**, 118.

D'Amelio, V., and Salvo, A. M. (1959b). *Z. Naturforsch.* **14B**, 455.

D'Amelio, V., and Salvo, A. M. (1961). *Acta Embryol. Morphol. Exptl.* **4**, 250.

Dancis, J., Braverman, N., and Lind, J. (1957). *J. Clin. Invest.* **36**, 398.

Darrow, R. R., Nowakovsky, S., and Austin, M. H. (1940). *Arch. Pathol.* **30**, 873.

Dawson, A. B. (1936). *Z. Zellforsch. Mikroskop. Anat.* **24**, 256.

Deichmiller, M. P., and Dixon, F. J. (1960). *J. Gen. Physiol.* **43**, 1047.

Dessauer, H. C., Fox, W., and Ramirez, J. R. (1957). *Arch. Biochem. Biophys.* **71**, 11.

Deutsch, H. F. (1954). *J. Biol. Chem.* **208**, 669.

Deutsch, H. F., and Goodloe, M. B. (1945). *J. Biol. Chem.* **161**, 1.

Diacono, H., and Castay, M. (1956). *Compt. Rend. Soc. Biol.* **150**, 669.

Dickerson, J. W. T. (1960). *Biochem. J.* **75**, 33.

Dickerson, J. W. T. (1962). *Biochem. J.* **82**, 56.

di Sant'Agnese, P. A. (1949). *Pediatrics* **3**, 333.

Drescher, H., and Künzer, W. (1954). *Klin. Wochschr.* **32**, 92.

Dresser, D. W. (1962). *Immunology* **5**, 378.

Earle, I. P. J. (1935). *J. Agr. Res.* **51**, 479.

Ebert, J. D. (1950). *J. Exptl. Zool.* **115**, 351.

Ebert, J. D. (1951). *Physiol. Zool.* **24**, 20.

Ebert, J. D. (1960). *Ann. Rept. Carnegie Inst. Wash. Dept. Embryol.* **59**, 386.

Edds, M. V. (1958). *Proc. Natl. Acad. Sci. U. S.* **44**, 296.

Edds, M. V., and Sweeny, P. R. (1961). *In* "Synthesis of Molecular and Cellular Structure" (D. Rudnick, ed.), pp. 111-138, Ronald Press, New York.

Egdahl, R. H. (1957). Ph.D. thesis, University of Minnesota, Minneapolis, Minnesota.

Ehrlich, P. (1892). *Z. Hyg. Infektionskrankh.* **12**, 183.

Eitzman, D. V., and Smith, R. T. (1959). *Proc. Soc. Exptl. Biol. Med.* **102**, 529.

Elster, S. K., and Lowry, E. L. (1950). *Proc. Soc. Exptl. Biol. Med.* **75**, 127.

Engle, R. L., and Woods K. R. (1960). *In* "The Plasma Proteins" (F. W. Putnam, ed.), Vol. 2, p. 183. Academic Press, New York.

Ewerbeck, H., and Levens, H. E. (1950). *Monatsschr. Kinderheilk.* **98**, 436.

Fahey, J. L. (1962). *Advan. Immunol.* **2**, 41.

Felton, L. D. (1949). *J. Immunol.* **61**, 107.

Felton, L. D., and Ottinger, B. (1942). *J. Bacteriol.* **43**, 94.

Fennestad, K. L., and Borg-Petersen, C. (1957). *Nature* **180**, 1210.

Fine, J. M., Imperato, C., Battistini, A., and Moretti, J. (1961). *Nouvelle Rev. Franc. Hematol.* **1**, 72.

Flickinger, R. A. (1958). *Biol. Bull.* **115**, 201.

Flickinger, R. A. (1962). *Advan. Immunol.* **2**, 309.

Flickinger, R. A., and Stone, G. (1960). *Exptl. Cell Res.* **21**, 541.

Fowler, I., and Clarke, W. M. (1960). *Anat. Record* **136**, 194.

Franěk, F., Říha, I., and Šterzl, J. (1961). *Nature* **189**, 1020.

Fraser, R. C. (1961). *Exptl. Cell Res.* **25**, 418.

Freund, J. (1929). *J. Immunol.* **17**, 465.

Freund, J. (1930). *J. Immunol.* **18**, 315.

Frieden, E., Herner, A. E., Fish, L., and Lewis, E. J. C. (1957). *Science* **126**, 559.

Galatius-Jensen, F. (1958). *Acta Genet. Statist. Med.* **8**, 248.

Gebhardt, D. O. E. (1960). A biochemical study on the development of collagen. Thesis. Amsterdam University.

Gitlin, D., and Janeway, C. A. (1960). *In* "The Plasma Proteins" (F. W. Putnam, ed.), Vol. 2, p. 407. Academic Press, New York.

Glinos, A. D. (1958). *In* "Chemical Basis of Development" (W. D. McElroy and B. Glass, eds.), pp. 813-842. Johns Hopkins Press, Baltimore, Maryland.

Good, R. A., and Varco, R. L. (1955). *J. Lancet* **75**, 245.

Goodman, M., and Campbell, D. H. (1953). *Blood* **8**, 422.

Grabar, P. (1947). "Les Globulines du Serum Sanguin." Desoer, Liège.

Grabar, P., and Williams, S. A. (1953). *Biochim. Biophys. Acta* **10**, 193.

Grasset, E. (1929). *S. African Inst. Med. Res. Publ.* **4**, 171.

Gratzer, W. B., and Allison, A. C. (1960). *Biol. Rev. Cambridge Phil. Soc.* **35**, 459.

Grimes, R. M., Duncan, C. W., and Lassiter, C. A. (1958). *J. Dairy Sci.* **41**, 1527.

Gross, J. (1950). *Am. J. Pathol.* **26**, 708.

Gross, J. (1958). *J. Exptl. Med.* **107**, 265.

Grubb, R., and Laurell, A-.B. (1956). *Acta Pathol. Microbiol. Scand.* **39**, 390.

Gurvich, A. E., and Karsaevskaya, N. G. (1956). *Biochemistry* (*USSR*) (Engl. Transl.) **21**, 771.

Gyllensten, L. (1950). *Acta Anat.* **10**, 130.

Halbrecht, I., and Klibanski, C. (1956). *Nature* **178**, 794.

Halbrecht, I., Klibanski, C., Brzoza, H., and Lahav, M. (1958). *Am. J. Clin. Pathol.* **29**, 340.

Halbrecht, I., Klibanski, C., and Bar Ilan, F. (1959). *Nature* **183**, 327.

Hall, F. G. (1934a). *J. Physiol.* (*London*) **83**, 222.

Hall, F. G. (1934b). *J. Physiol.* (*London*) **82**, 33.

Halliday, R. (1957). *Proc. Roy. Soc.* **B147**, 140.

Halliday, R., and Kekwick, R. A. (1957). *Proc. Roy. Soc.* **B146**, 431.

Hansen, R. G., and Phillips, P. H. (1947). *J. Biol. Chem.* **171**, 223.
Harkness, M. L. R., and Harkness, R. D. (1955). *J. Physiol.* (*London*) **128**, 225.
Harkness, R. D. (1961). *Biol. Rev. Cambridge Phil. Soc.* **36**, 399.
Harkness, R. D., Marko, A. M., Muir, H. M., and Neuberger, A. (1954). *Biochem. J.* **56**, 558.
Harris, H., and Warren, F. L. (1955). *Biochem. J.* **60**, xxix.
Harris, S., Harris, T. N., Ogburn, C. A., and Farber, M. B. (1961). *Federation Proc.* **20**, 27.
Hašek, M. (1953). *Cesk. Biol.* **2**, 265.
Hašek, M., Lengerová, A., and Hraba, T. (1961). *Advan. Immunol.* **1**, 1.
Hašková, V. (1957). *Folia Biol.* (*Prague*) **3**, 129.
Haurowitz, F. (1929). *Z. Physiol. Chem.* **183**, 78.
Haurowitz, F. (1935). *Z. Physiol. Chem.* **232**, 124.
Havassy, J., and Slanina, L. (1956). *Vet. Casopis* **5**, 31.
Heim, W. G. (1961). *J. Embryol. Exptl. Morphol.* **9**, 53.
Heim, W. G., and Schechtman, A. M. (1954). *J. Biol. Chem.* **209**, 241.
Heremans, J. F. (1959). *Clin. Chim. Acta* **4**, 639.
Herner, A. E., and Frieden, E. (1960). *J. Biol. Chem.* **235**, 2845.
Herrmann, H., and Barry, S. R. (1955). *Arch. Biochem. Biophys.* **55**, 526.
Hildemann, W. H., and Haas, R. (1959). *J. Immunol.* **83**, 478.
Hildemann, W. H., and Haas, R. (1961). *Folia Biol.* (*Prague*) **7**, 422.
Hill, R., and Wolvekamp, H. P. (1936). *Proc. Roy. Soc.* **B120**, 484.
Hirschfeld, J., and Lunell, N-.O. (1962). *Nature* **196**, 1220.
Hoerlein, A. B. (1957). *J. Immunol.* **78**, 112.
Howard, J. G., and Michie, D. (1962). *Transplant. Bull.* **29**, 1.
Hradec, J., and Lemež, L. (1954). *Cesk. Morfol.* **2**, 260.
Huehns, E. R., Flynn, F. V., Butler, E. A., and Beaven, G. H. (1961). *Nature* **189**, 496.
Hugounenq, L., and Morel, A. (1905). *Compt. Rend.* **141**, 848.
Huisman, T. H. J., Jonxis, J. H. P., and Dozy, A. (1955). *Biochim. Biophys. Acta* **18**, 576.
Hunt, J. A. (1959). *Nature* **183**, 1373.
Hutterer, F., Rubin, E., Singer, J., and Popper, H. (1959). *Proc. Soc. Exptl. Biol. Med.* **102**, 534.
Ingram, V. M. (1958). *Biochim. Biophys. Acta* **28**, 539.
Ingram, V. M. (1961). "Hemoglobin and Its Abnormalities." Thomas, Springfield, Illinois.
Ingram, V. M. (1963). "The Hemoglobins in Genetics and Evolution." Columbia Univ. Press, New York.
Isaacs, A., and Lindemann, J. (1957). *Proc. Roy. Soc.* **B147**, 258.
Isacson, P. (1959). *Yale J. Biol. Med.* **32**, 209.
Itano, H. A. (1953). *Science* **117**, 89.
Iványi, J., Iványi, P., Soukupová, M., and Czambelová, A. (1960a). *Folia Biol.* (*Prague*) **6**, 108.
Iványi, P., Iványi, J., and Ujhelyiová, M. (1960b). *Folia Biol.* (*Prague*) **6**, 445.
Jackson, S. F. (1956). *Proc. Roy. Soc.* **B144**, 556.
Jameson, E., Alvarez-Tostado, C., and Sortor, H. H. (1942). *Proc. Soc. Exptl. Biol. Med.* **51**, 163.

Jayle, M. F., Boussier, G., and Badin, J. (1952). *Bull. Soc. Chim. Biol.* **34**, 1063.

Jerne, N. K. (1955). *Proc. Natl. Acad. Sci. U. S.* **41**, 849.

Johnson, V. L., and Dunlap, J. S. (1955). *Science* **122**, 1186.

Jonxis, J. H. P. (1949). In "Hemoglobin" (F. J. W. Roughton and J. C. Kendrew, eds.), 1st ed., pp. 261-267. Butterworths, London.

Jonxis, J. H. P., and Wadman, S. K. (1952). *Nature* **169**, 884.

Jope, E. M. (1949). In "Hemoglobin" (F. J. W. Roughton and J. C. Kendrew, eds.), 1st ed., pp. 205-219. Butterworths, London.

Jope, E. M., and O'Brien, J. R. P. (1949). In "Hemoglobin" (F. J. W. Roughton and J. C. Kendrew, eds.), 1st ed., pp. 269-278. Butterworths, London.

Kalmutz, S. E. (1962). *Nature* **193**, 851.

Kaminski, M., and Durieux, J. (1956). *Exptl. Cell Res.* **10**, 590.

Karvonen, M. J. (1949). In "Hemoglobin" (F. J. W. Roughton and J. C. Kendrew, eds.), 1st ed., pp. 279-287. Butterworths, London.

Kekwick, R. A. (1959). *Advan. Protein Chem.* **14**, 231.

Kerr, W. R., and Robertson, M. (1954). *J. Hyg.* **52**, 253.

Kliger, I. J., and Olitzki, L. (1929). *Z. Hyg. Infektionskrankh.* **110**, 459.

Knapp, E. L., and Routh, J. I. (1949). *Pediatrics* **4**, 509.

Kobrle, V., and Chvapil, M. (1958). *Arch. Gewerbepathol. Gewerbehyg.* **16**, 526.

Körber, E. (1866). Inaugural dissertation, Dorpat; cited by Bischoff, H. (1926). *Z. Ges. Exptl. Med.* **48**, 472.

Konigsberg, W., Guidotti, G., and Hill, R. J. (1961). *J. Biol. Chem.* **236**, PC 55.

Konyukhov, B. V., and Lishtvan, L. L. (1959). *Arch. Anat.* (*Strasbourg*) **8**, 32.

Künzer, W. (1957). *Nature* **179**, 477.

Kutner, A., and Ratner, B. (1923). *Am. J. Diseases Children* **25**, 413.

Langman, J. (1959a). *J. Embryol. Exptl. Morphol.* **7**, 193.

Langman, J. (1959b). *J. Embryol. Exptl. Morphol.* **7**, 264.

Langman, J. (1963). *Proc. Can. Cancer Res. Conf. 1962* Vol. 5, pp. 349-362. Academic Press, New York.

Langman, J., Schalekamp, M. A. D. H., Kuyken, M. P. A., and Veen, R. (1957). *Acta Morphol. Neerl.-Scand.* **1**, 142.

Lecce, J. G., Matrone, G., and Morgan, D. O. (1961). *Ann. N. Y. Acad. Sci.* **94**, 250.

Lewis, L. A. (1946). *J. Biol. Chem.* **162**, 473.

Linke, K. W. (1955). *Z. Zellforsch. Mikroskop. Anat.* **42**, 331.

Loeb, L. (1930). *Physiol. Rev.* **10**, 547.

Longsworth, L. G. (1959). In "Electrophoresis" (M. Bier, ed.), pp. 137-177. Academic Press, New York.

McCarthy, E. F. (1954). *Cold Spring Harbor Symp. Quant. Biol.* **19**, 133.

McCarthy, E. F., and McDougall, E. I. (1953). *Biochem. J.* **55**, 177.

McCutcheon, F. H. (1936). *J. Cellular Comp. Physiol.* **8**, 63.

McCutcheon, F. H. (1938). *J. Exptl. Biol.* **15**, 431.

McCutcheon, F. H. (1947). *J. Cellular Comp. Physiol.* **29**, 333.

McKeehan, M. S. (1951). *J. Exptl. Zool.* **117**, 31.

Maisel, H., and Langman, J. (1961). *J. Embryol. Exptl. Morphol.* **9**, 191.

Makinodan, T., and Peterson, W. J. (1962). *Proc. Natl. Acad. Sci. U. S.* **48**, 234.

Malmnäs, C., and Nihlén, H. (1950). *Nord. Med.* **44**, 1255.

Manwell, C. (1957). *Science* **126**, 1175.

Manwell, C. (1958a). *Physiol. Zool.* **31**, 93.

Manwell, C. (1958b). *Science* **128**, 419.

Manwell, C. (1960). *Ann. Rev. Physiol.* **22**, 191.

Manwell, C., Baker, C. M. A., Roslansky, J. D., and Foght, M. (1963). *Proc. Natl. Acad. Sci. U. S.* **49**, 496.

Marshall, M. E., and Deutsch, H. F. (1950). *J. Biol. Chem.* **185**, 155.

Marshall, M. E., and Deutsch, H. F. (1951). *J. Biol. Chem.* **189**, 1.

Martin, E., and Scheidegger, J. J. (1957). *Schweiz. Med. Wochschr.* **87**, 286.

Medawar, P. B. (1958). *Proc. Roy. Soc.* **B148**, 145.

Medawar, P. B. (1959). *In* "Cellular and Humoral Aspects of Hypersensitive States" (H. S. Lawrence, ed.), pp. 504-534, Cassell, London.

Miller, E. R., Ullrey, D. E., Ackerman, I., Schmidt, D. A., Hoefer, J. A., and Luecke, R. W. (1961). *J. Animal Sci.* **20**, 31.

Miller, J. F. A. P. (1961). *Lancet* **II**, 748.

Miller, L. L., and Bale, W. F. (1954). *J. Exptl. Med.* **99**, 125.

Miller, W. J. (1953). *Physiol. Zool.* **26**, 124.

Mitchison, N. A. (1959). *In* "Biological Problems of Grafting" (F. Albert and G. Lejeune-Ledant, eds.), pp. 239-259. Blackwell, Oxford, England.

Mitchison, N. A. (1962a). *Immunology* **5**, 341.

Mitchison, N. A. (1962b). *Immunology* **5**, 359.

Moore, D. H. (1959). *In* "Electrophoresis" (M. Bier, ed.), pp. 370-426. Academic Press, New York.

Moore, D. H., Shen, S. C., and Alexander, C. S. (1945). *Proc. Soc. Exptl. Biol. Med.* **58**, 307.

Moore, D. H., DuPan, R. M., and Buxton, C. L. (1949). *Am. J. Obstet. Gynecol.* **57**, 312.

Moullec, J., Kherumian, R., Sutton, E., and Espagnon, P. (1956). *Rev. Hematol.* **11**, 512.

Mueller, A. P., Wolfe, H. R., and Meyer, R. K. (1960). *J. Immunol.* **85**, 172.

Murphy, J. B. (1914). *J. Exptl. Med.* **19**, 181.

Myant, N. B., and Osorio, C. (1958). *Nature* **182**, 866.

Nace, G. W. (1953). *J. Exptl. Zool.* **122**, 423.

Nace, G. W., and Schechtman, A. M. (1948). *J. Exptl. Zool.* **108**, 217.

Nageotte, J., and Guyon, L. (1934). *Comp. Rend. Assoc. Anat.* **29**, 408.

Neuman, R. E. (1950). *Proc. Soc. Exptl. Biol. Med.* **75**, 37.

Norton, P. M., Kunz, H. W., and Pratt, E. L. (1952). *Pediatrics* **10**, 527.

Nossal, G. J. V. (1958). *Australian J. Exptl. Biol. Med. Sci.* **36**, 235.

Oberman, J. W., Gregory, K. O., Burke, F. G., Ross, S., and Rice, E. C. (1956). *New Engl. J. Med.* **255**, 743.

O'Brien, B. R. A. (1961). *J. Embryol. Exptl. Morphol.* **9**, 202.

O'Connor, R. J. (1952). *J. Anat.* **86**, 320.

Orekhovitch, K. D. (1950). *Dokl. Akad. Nauk SSSR* **71**, 521.

Orlandini, T. O., Sass-Kortsak, A., and Ebbs, J. H. (1955). *Pediatrics* **16**, 575.

Osborn, J. J., Dancis, J., and Julia, J. F. (1952). *Pediatrics* **9**, 736.

Ouchterlony, Ö. (1948). *Arkiv. Kemi Mineral. Geol.* **26B**, 1.

Owen, R. D. (1945). *Science* **102**, 400.

Panchenko, M. D. (1960). *Pediatriya* **38**, 20.

Patterson, R., Younger, J. S., Weigle, W. O., and Dixon, F. J. (1962). *J. Gen. Physiol.* **45**, 501.

Pauling, L. (1940). *J. Am. Chem. Soc.* **62**, 2643.
Pedersen, K. O. (1945). *Nature* **154**, 575.
Pernis, B., Ghezi, I., and Turri, M. (1963). *Nature* **197**, 807.
Pfau, P. (1954). *Arch. Gynaekol.* **185**, 208.
Pickering, J. W., and Gladstone, R. J. (1925). *Proc. Roy. Soc.* **B98**, 516.
Pierce, A. E. (1955a). *J. Hyg.* **53**, 247.
Pierce, A. E. (1955b). *J. Hyg.* **53**, 261.
Pillemer, L. (1956). *Ann. N. Y. Acad. Sci.* **66**, 233.
Polk, A., Buddingh, G. J., and Goodpasture, E. W. (1938). *Am. J. Pathol.* **14**, 71.
Polson, A. (1943). *Nature* **152**, 419.
Porter, K. A. (1960). *Nature* **185**, 789.
Porter, R. R. (1958). *Nature* **182**, 670.
Rall, D. P., Schwab, P., and Zubrod, C. G. (1961). *Science* **133**, 279.
Rausen, A. R., Gerald, P. S., and Diamond, L. K. (1961). *Nature* **191**, 77.
Redfield, A. C. (1933). *Quart. Rev. Biol.* **8**, 31.
Rees, R. J. W., and Garbutt, E. W. (1961). *Immunology* **4**, 88.
Riggs, A. (1951). *J. Gen. Physiol.* **35**, 23.
Riggs, A. (1959). *Nature* **183**, 1037.
Říha, I. (1961). *Folia Microbiol. (Prague)* **6**, 355.
Říha, I. (1962). In "Mechanisms of Immunological Tolerance" (M. Hašek, A. Lengerová, and M. Vojtíšková, eds.), pp. 103-106. Publ. House Czech. Acad., Prague.
Rodnan, G. P., and Ebaugh, F. G. (1956). *Federation Proc.* **15**, 155.
Rook, J. A., Moustgaard, J., and Jakobsen, P. E. (1951). *Kgl. Vet. Højsk Aarsskr.* p. 81.
Rosenberg, E. E. (1960). *Acta Anat.* **41**, 300.
Rossi-Fanelli, A., Cavallini, D., and de Marco, C. (1954). *Arch. Biochem. Biophys.* **50**, 496.
Rubin, B. A. (1959). *Nature* **184**, 205.
Rutqvist, L. (1958). *Am. J. Vet. Res.* **19**, 25.
Ryle, M. R. (1957). *J. Exptl. Biol.* **34**, 365.
Rywosch, M. (1907). *Zentr. Bakteriol. Parasitenk. Abt. I. Orig.* **44**, 468.
Saha, A. K. (1956). *Indian J. Physiol. Allied Sci.* **10**, 87.
San Clemente, C. L., and Huddleson, I. F. (1943). *Mich. State Univ. Agr. Expt. Sta. Tech. Bull.* **182**, 3.
Sandreuter, A. (1951). *Acta Anat.* **11**, Suppl. 14, 1.
Schechtman, A. M. (1947). *J. Exptl. Zool.* **105**, 329.
Scheidegger, J. J., Martin, E., and Riotton, G. (1956). *J. Suisse Med.* **86**, 224.
Schinckel, P. G., and Ferguson, K. A. (1953). *Australian J. Biol. Sci.* **6**, 533.
Schjeide, O. A. (1956). *Growth* **20**, 195.
Schjeide, O. A., and Ragan, N. (1957). *J. Biol. Chem.* **227**, 1035.
Schmitt, F. O., Gross, J., and Highberger, J. H. (1953). *Proc. Natl. Acad. Sci. U. S.* **39**, 459.
Schroeder, W. A., and Matsuda, G. (1958). *J. Am. Chem. Soc.* **80**, 1521.
Schroeder, W. A., Shelton, J. R., Shelton, J. B., and Cormick, J. (1962). *Proc. Natl. Acad. Sci. U. S.* **48**, 284.
Schultze, H. E. (1959). *Clin. Chim. Acta* **4**, 609.
Sen, N. N., Das, K. C., and Aikat, B. K. (1960). *Nature* **186**, 977.

Sherman, H. W. (1919). *J. Infect. Diseases* **25**, 256.

Shmerling, Z. G., and Uspenskaya, V. D. (1955). *Biochemistry (USSR)* (Engl. Transl.) **20**, 31.

Silverstein, A. M., Uhr, J. W., Kraner, K. L., and Lukes, R. J. (1963). *J. Exptl. Med.* **117**, 799.

Simonsen, M. (1955). *Nature* **175**, 763.

Simonsen, M. (1956). *Acta Pathol. Microbiol. Scand.* **39**, 21.

Simonsen, M. (1957). *Acta Pathol. Microbiol. Scand.* **40**, 480.

Singer, K., Angelopoulus, B., and Ramot, B. (1955). *Blood* **10**, 987.

Siskind, G. W. (1962). *Federation Proc.* **21**, 34.

Slater, R. J. (1954). *Pediatrics* **13**, 308.

Smith, E. L., and Holm, A. (1948). *J. Biol. Chem.* **175**, 349.

Smith, R. T. (1960a). *Ciba Found. Symp. Cellular Aspects Immunity 1960* pp. 348-372. Little, Brown, Boston, Massachusetts.

Smith, R. T. (1960b). *Pediat. Clin. N. Am.* **7**, 269.

Smith, R. T. (1961). *Advan. Immunol.* **1**, 67.

Smith, R. T., and Bridges, R. A. (1956). *Transplant. Bull.* **3**, 145.

Smithies, O. (1955). *Biochem. J.* **61**, 629.

Smithies, O. (1959). *Advan. Protein Chem.* **14**, 65.

Smithies, O., and Walker, N. F. (1956). *Nature* **178**, 694.

Smits, G. (1957). *Biochim. Biophys. Acta* **25**, 542.

Sohar, E., Bossak, E. T., Wang, C.-I., and Aldersberg, D. (1956). *Science* **123**, 461.

Solomon, J. B. (1961). *J. Embryol. Exptl. Morphol.* **9**, 335.

Solomon, J. B. (1963a). *Nature* **198**, 1171.

Solomon, J. B. (1963b). *Transplantation* **1**, 327.

Solomon, J. B., and Tucker, D. F. (1963a). *Immunology* **6**, 592.

Solomon, J. B., and Tucker, D. F. (1963b). *J. Embryol. Exptl. Morphol.* **11**, 179.

Springer, G. F., Horton, R. E., and Forbes, M. (1959). *J. Exptl. Med.* **110**, 221.

Staub, H., and Boguth, W. (1956). *Zentr. Veterinaermed.* **3**, 653.

Stein, W. H., Kunkel, H. G., Cole, R. D., Spackman, D. H., and Moore, S. (1957). *Biochim. Biophys. Acta* **24**, 640.

Steinmuller, D. (1961). *J. Exptl. Zool.* **147**, 233.

Sternberg, J., and Dagenais-Perusse, P. (1956). *Can. Med. Assoc. J.* **74**, 49.

Sternlieb, I., and Scheinberg, I. H. (1961). *Ann. N.Y. Acad. Sci.* **94**, 71.

Šterzl, J. (1959). *Nature* **183**, 547.

Šterzl, J. (1962). "Advances in Biological Science," p. 149. Publ. House Czech. Acad., Prague.

Šterzl, J. (1963). *J. Hyg. Epidemiol. Microbiol. Immunol. (Prague)* **7**, 301.

Šterzl, J., and Trnka, Z. (1957). *Nature* **179**, 918.

Šterzl, J., Kostka, M., Říha, I., and Mandel, L. (1960). *Folia Microbiol. (Prague)* **5**, 29.

Šterzl, J., Franěk, F., Říha, I., Kostka, J., and Lanc, A. (1961). *In* "Symposium on Plasma Proteins and Gastrointestinal Tract in Health and Disease" (M. Schwartz and P. Vesin, eds.), pp. 199-213. Munksgaard, Copenhagen.

Stockell, A., Perutz, M. F., Muirhead, H., and Glauser, S. C. (1961). *J. Mol. Biol.* **3**, 112.

Stormont, C. (1949). *Proc. Natl. Acad. Sci. U. S.* **35**, 232.

Stratton, F. (1943). *Nature* **152**, 449.

Talmage, D. W. (1957). *J. Cellular Comp. Physiol.* **50**, 229.

Tempelis, C. H., Wolfe, H. R., and Mueller, A. P. (1958). *Brit. J. Exptl. Pathol.* **39**, 328.

Ten Cate, G., and van Doorenmaalen, W. J. (1950). *Proc. Acad. Sci. Amsterdam* **53**, 894.

Terasaki, P. I. (1959). *J. Embryol. Exptl. Morphol.* **7**, 409.

Terres, G., and Hughes, W. L. (1959). *J. Immunol.* **83**, 459.

Thorbecke, G. J. (1960). *J. Exptl. Med.* **112**, 279.

Thorbecke, G. J., and Keuning, F. J. (1956). *J. Infect. Diseases* **98**, 157.

Thorbecke, G. J., Gordon, H. A., Wostmann, B., Wagner, M., and Reyniers, J. A. (1957). *J. Infect. Diseases* **101**, 237.

Thorbecke, G. J., Siskind, G. W., and Goldberger, N. (1961). *J. Immunol.* **87**, 147.

Timmer, R., van der Helm, H. J., and Huisman, T. H. J. (1957). *Nature* **180**, 239.

Tiselius, A., and Kabat, E. A. (1939). *J. Exptl. Med.* **69**, 119.

Traub, B. (1943). *J. Pathol. Bacteriol.* **55**, 447.

Triplett, E. L., and Cushing, J. E. (1958). *Am. Naturalist* **92**, 287.

Turk, J. L., and Humphrey, J. H. (1961). *Immunology* **4**, 301.

Tuttle, A. H. (1955). *Science* **121**, 701.

Tyan, M. L., and Cole, L. J. (1962). *Transplant. Bull.* **30**, 136.

Tyler, A. (1946). *Growth* **10**, Suppl. 6, 7.

Tyler, A. (1957). *In* "The Beginning of Embryonic Development" (A. Tyler, R. C. von Borstel, and C. B. Metz, eds.), pp. 341-382. Am. Assoc. Advan. Sci., Washington, D. C.

Uhr, J. W. (1960). *Nature* **187**, 957.

Uhr, J. W., Dancis, J., and Newman, C. G. (1960). *Nature* **187**, 1130.

Uhr, J. W., Dancis, J., Franklin, E. C., Finkelstein, M. S., and Lewis, E. W. (1962a). *J. Clin. Invest.* **41**, 1509.

Uhr, J. W., Finkelstein, M. S., and Baumann, J. B. (1962b). *J. Exptl. Med.* **115**, 655.

Vahlquist, B., Westberg, V., and Delas Heras, M. (1953). *Acta Soc. Med. Upsalien.* **58**, 281.

van Alten, P. J. (1959). *J. Embryol. Exptl. Morphol.* **7**, 476.

van der Helm, H. J., Visser, H. K. A., van Vliet, G., and Huisman, T. H. J. (1958). *Clin. Chim. Acta* **3**, 114.

van der Helm, H. J., and Huisman, T. H. J. (1958). *Science* **127**, 762.

van Doorenmaalen, W. J. (1958). *Acta Morphol. Neerl.-Scand.* **2**, 1.

Vanstone, W. E., Maw, W. A., and Common, R. H. (1955). *Can. J. Biochem. Physiol.* **33**, 891.

Visser, H. K., Huisman, T. H., and Woldring, M. G. (1957). *Blood* **12**, 1004.

Vitt, V. O., Rozhansky, M. O., and Kovalschuk, I. S. (1959). *Dokl. Mosk. Sel' skokhoz. Akad.* **49**, 147.

Wagner, M. (1955). *Bull. N.Y. Acad. Med.* **31**, 236.

Wagner, M. (1959). *Ann. N.Y. Acad. Sci.* **78**, 261.

Wald, G., and Riggs, A. (1951). *J. Gen. Physiol.* **35**, 45.

Walker, J. (1954). *Cold Spring Harbor Symp. Quant. Biol.* **19**, 141.

Walker, J., and Turnbull, E. P. N. (1955). *Arch. Disease Childhood* **30**, 111.

Wehmeyer, P. (1954). *Acta Pathol. Microbiol. Scand.* **35**, 54.

Weinberg, M., and Guelin, A. (1936). *Compt. Rend. Soc. Biol.* **122**, 1229.

Weiss, D. W. (1958). *J. Exptl. Med.* **108**, 83.

Weller, E. M., and Schechtman, A. M. (1962). *Develop. Biol.* **4**, 517.

Westendorp Boerma, F., Huisman, T. H. J., and Mandema, E. (1960). *Clin. Chim. Acta* **5**, 564.

White, J. C., and Beaven, G. H. (1959). *Brit. Med. Bull.* **15**, 33.

Wiener, A. S. (1951a). *J. Immunol.* **66**, 287.

Wiener, A. S. (1951b). *J. Exptl. Med.* **94**, 213.

Wilt, F. H. (1962). *Proc. Natl. Acad. Sci. U. S.* **48**, 1582.

Wolfe, H. R., and Dilkes, E. (1948). *J. Immunol.* **58**, 245.

Wolfe, H. R., Mueller, A., Neess, J., and Tempelis, C. (1957a). *J. Immunol.* **79**, 142.

Wolfe, H. R., Tempelis, C., Mueller, A., and Reibel, S. (1957b). *J. Immunol.* **79**, 147.

Woodruff, M. F., and Simpson, L. O. (1955). *Brit. J. Exptl. Pathol.* **36**, 494.

Woods, A. C., and Burky, E. L. (1927). *J. Am. Med. Assoc.* **89**, 102.

Wostmann, B. S. (1959). *Ann. N. Y. Acad. Sci.* **78**, 254.

Wostmann, B. S. (1961). *Ann. N. Y. Acad. Sci.* **94**, 272.

Wunderly, C. (1960). *In* "Analytical Methods of Protein Chemistry" (P. Alexander and R. J. Block, eds.), Vol. 2, pp. 232-243. Pergamon, New York.

Wyman, J. (1948). *Advan. Protein Chem.* **4**, 407.

Wyttenbach, C. R. (1960). *Develop. Biol.* **2**, 173.

Yčas, M. K. (1949). *J. Immunol.* **61**, 327.

Yesair, D. W., Goldstein, J., and Daniel, L. J. (1959). *Arch. Biochem. Biophys.* **84**, 316.

Yoshino, M. (1960a). *Ann. Paediat. Japon.* **6**, 74.

Yoshino, M. (1960b). *Ann. Paediat. Japon.* **6**, 86.

Chapter 8

BIOCHEMICAL MECHANISM OF INFORMATION TRANSFER[1]

Matthys Staehelin

Research Laboratories
Pharmaceutical Department
CIBA Limited
Basel, Switzerland

---

[1] This chapter is based on an introductory course in molecular biology which was given by the author at the University of Basel. For further reading on this topic the following books are recommended: Anfinsen, C. B., "The Molecular Basis of Evolution," Wiley, New York, 1959; Brachet, J., "The Biological Role of Ribonucleic Acids," Elsevier, Amsterdam, 1960; Hayes, W., "The Genetics of Bacteria and Their Viruses," Blackwell, Oxford, 1964; Perutz, M. F., "Proteins and Nucleic Acids," Elsevier, Amsterdam, 1962; and the chapters by A. Lwoff (p. 187), A. Garen and L. M. Kozloff (p. 203), G. S. Stent (p. 237) *in* "The Viruses" (F. M. Burnet and W. M. Stanley, eds.), Vol. II, Academic Press, New York, 1959.

I. Substances Involved in Genetic Information Transfer

A. *DNA and the Mechanism of Reduplication*[2]

Deoxyribonucleic acid (DNA) was discovered in 1868 by the Swiss physiologist Friedrich Miescher. Miescher (1897) tried to identify the chemical constituents of cell nuclei, and it is interesting that he was able to isolate nuclei in very pure form from salmon sperm by means of a simple trick. Upon mixing the sperm fluid with an excess of distilled water plasmolysis occurred, the tails disintegrated, and the only organized structures remaining were the nuclei. These consisted almost entirely of nucleic acid and protamine. Although the chemical structure of DNA was not known at that time, since neither the sugar moiety nor all the bases had yet been discovered, Miescher himself recognized its genetic nature by virtue of its unique presence in cell nuclei. By careful elementary analyses, Miescher arrived at the following formula for DNA: $C_{40}H_{54}N_{14}O_{17} \cdot 2P_2O_5$. This is, in principle, the formula of a tetranucleotide, and it is interesting that Miescher who did not know the chemical constituents of DNA, nevertheless, recognized that it consisted of four phosphorus-containing building blocks. The actual formula of a tetranucleotide residue containing the four bases would be: $C_{39}H_{53}N_{15}O_{18} \cdot 2P_2O_5$. Salmon sperm DNA, however, is of the AT type, i.e., it contains more adenine and thymine than guanine and cytosine, so that the carbon content of the total DNA is higher and the nitrogen content lower. This is in agreement with Miescher's formula and sheds some light on the degree of care with which he carried out his analyses. It is sometimes forgotten that Miescher not only discovered nucleic acids but that he also recognized the chemical basis of heredity. The only difficulty he encountered was reconciling the great variety of genetic information with such a simple molecule. He overcame it by assuming that all forty carbon atoms were asymmetric. In 1892 he wrote: "For me the key to sexuality lies in stereochemistry."

The first experimental demonstration of the genetic role of DNA, however, was the discovery of the transforming principle by Avery *et al.* in 1944. But it was only the ingenious conception of the structure of DNA by Watson and Crick (1953) that allowed the imagination of a possible chemical basis of heredity. The proposed structure of DNA as a double-stranded helix supported the experimental data of Chargaff

---

[2] Key to abbreviations used in this chapter: Deoxyribonucleic acid, DNA; ribonucleic acid, RNA; soluble RNA, sRNA; adenosine triphosphate, ATP; deoxycytidine monophosphate, dCMP; deoxycytidine triphosphate, dCTP. Polynucleotides containing only certain bases, e.g., polyuridylic acid, Poly-U, etc. Nucleotide sequences, e.g., cytidylcytidyladenosine, CpCpA; adrenocorticotropic hormone, ACTH.

(1950) and Chargaff *et al.* (1950) about the base composition as well as the X-ray diffraction data by Wilkins *et al.* (1953) and has since been found to agree with all new experimental findings.

Although, in this form, the structure of DNA has become classic organic chemistry, one question was not settled until recently, i.e., the direction of the two strands. The backbone of DNA is not symmetrical because the phosphate is linked to the C-3 atom of one ribose and to the C-5 atom of the other. Since the DNA chain is synthesized by adding new 5'-nucleotides to the free OH group on C-3, one usually depicts the polynucleotide chain as running in the direction of the C-3 phosphate link to the C-5 bond of the next nucleotide. The question arises now, whether the complementary strand runs in the same or the opposite direction. The nearest neighbor analysis of Josse *et al.* (1961) has clearly given the answer; the two strands run in opposite directions. This appears to be not only of theoretical interest, but seems to be a very important aspect in the reduplication and enzymatic synthesis of DNA. An enzyme building up a new nucleic acid strand would only be capable of copying the two nucleic acid strands from opposite ends of the DNA molecule.

The length of these double-stranded helical molecules is extremely long. The entire DNA of a bacteriophage consisting of 4×10^5 nucleotide pairs (Stent and Fuerst, 1955) appears to be a single molecule. The same seems to be true for the DNA of *Escherichia coli* consisting of 100×10^5 nucleotide pairs (Fuerst and Stent, 1956; Jacob and Wollman, 1959). Such strands can be made visible in the electron microscope. The elegant autoradiographic studies of Cairns (1963) have actually brought visible evidence that bacterial DNA is a circular molecule for which there is also genetic evidence (Jacob and Wollman, 1961).

One finding, which is characteristic of DNA, is the ratio of the bases. Adenine is always present in amounts equal to thymine, and guanine in amounts equal to cytosine or any of its derivatives. Thus, the only variable in the over-all base composition of DNA is the ratio $(A + T)/(G + C)$. This ratio varies over a range of 0.5–2 and has even been found to reach extreme values in some crab DNA's which consist almost entirely of adenine and thymine (Sueoka and Cheng, 1962).

Although the double-stranded helix is the typical structure of DNA, it should be noted that there are a few exceptions to this structure. The best known is the DNA of phage φX-174. As Sinsheimer (1959) has shown, the DNA of this phage consists of a single strand with a chain length of about 6000 nucleotides, quite unlike any other DNA which occurs in bacteria or higher organisms.

The concept of the DNA molecule as a compound composed of two complementary strands suggests at once a possible mechanism for its reduplication, i.e., the separation of the two strands followed by the new synthesis of a complementary strand for each of the two single strands. Such a mechanism is shown schematically in Fig. 1. Kornberg and his associates (Lehmann *et al.*, 1958) have actually found an enzyme which

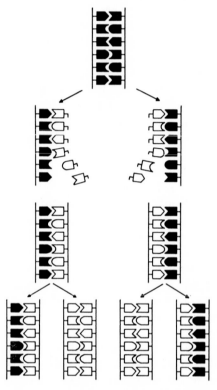

Fɪɢ. 1. Schematic representation of the mechanism of the reduplication process of DNA. *Top row:* Maternal double-stranded DNA. *Second row:* Separation of the two strands and attachment of complementary nucleotides. *Third row:* DNA of first generation. Each molecule consists of one maternal and one newly formed strand. *Fourth row:* DNA of second generation. The original DNA strands remain intact and are only transferred to half the progeny, the other half being all newly synthesized DNA.

is capable of synthesizing new DNA provided there is a piece of single-stranded DNA present to which it can attach the complementary strand. This enzyme uses 5'-nucleoside triphosphates as precursors and links the new nucleotide to the terminal free OH-group on C-3 of the pre-existing chain. The enzyme is inactive in the absence of primer DNA and does not work beyond the state of the recompleted double strand. Although this enzyme could explain the duplication mechanism depicted in Fig. 1, its existence by itself does not prove it.

It was proved beyond doubt, however, by following the fate of DNA during reduplication. Meselson and Stahl (1958) have succeeded in labeling almost the complete DNA of bacteria with heavy nitrogen and separating this heavy DNA from normal light DNA by high speed centrifugation in a density gradient. Such heavy bacteria were then placed in a medium containing only light nitrogen and allowed to multiply for one or two generations. After one generation, the DNA had changed from the heavy form to an intermediate form between the heavy and the light one. After two generations, the DNA was equally divided between the intermediate and the light form. This is exactly the result to be expected in a mechanism of reduplication in which the two maternal strands separate and each of them builds up a new complementary strand (Fig. 1).

That two complete, new DNA strands are formed which correspond in every respect to the parental DNA, has also been shown by Rudner and Chargaff (1962). By permitting bacteria to multiply in bromouracil which can replace thymine, it was possible to separate the parental and the newly formed nucleotide sequences in partial hydrolyzates. By this method it could be shown that the relative amounts of the newly synthesized sequences, i.e., those containing bromouracil, correspond exactly to amounts of thymine containing sequences in the parental DNA. Furthermore, no mixed sequences were ever encountered. All these experiments strongly point toward a so-called "semiconservative" mechanism of reduplication, in which one strand is inherited unchanged into the daughter cell, whereas the other is built up *de novo*.

If we now turn to higher organisms, the situation becomes increasingly complicated. In the nuclei of cells, i.e., in the chromosomes, the DNA is always associated with basic proteins, i.e., histones and protamines, and is present in an extremely organized form. We have as yet only a scanty knowledge of the molecular structure of chromosomes, but it appears very interesting that there are indications of a semiconservative reduplication of the DNA of the entire chromosome (Taylor, 1957). Labeling the chromosomes of the root cells of *Vicia faba* with tritium-labeled thymidine, Taylor *et al.* (1951) have been able to follow the fate of the chromosomal DNA during reduplication. In order to observe the chromosomes, the tissues were incubated with labeled thymidine sufficiently long to label all DNA. Then they were transferred to a solution containing unlabeled thymidine, and finally further cell division was blocked with colchicine. Colchicine inhibits the separation of the two daughter chromosomes in the late anaphase. Therefore, we can easily recognize the pairs of daughter chromosomes. As far as radio-activity is concerned, in a semiconservative reduplication we would expect, in principle, the same event as was shown in Fig. 1. As can be seen in Fig. 2, this is actually the case. After one division of labeled cells in an unlabeled medium, all chromosomes are equally labeled.

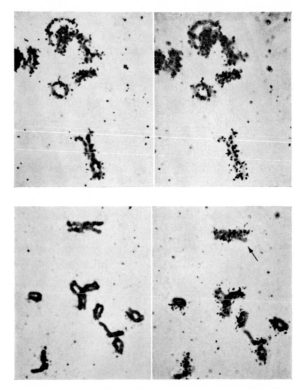

FIG. 2. Autoradiograms (right) and microscopic pictures (left) of chromosomes of *Vicia faba* after one (upper row) and two (lower row) divisions. The amount of grains (caused by the blackening of the photographic emulsion) represents by radiation the amount of H[3]-thymidine present in the DNA of the chromosomes. From Taylor *et al.* (1951). The lower right-hand autoradiogram shows that only one of the two chromosomes is labeled after two generations (cf. Fig. 1). The arrow points to a chromosome where a cross-over has occurred.

This indicates that they consist of one labeled and one unlabeled strand of DNA. After a second division, the label is confined to only one of two chromosomes of a pair showing that the entire maternal labeled DNA has been transferred to one chromosome; the other chromosome is built up entirely of newly synthesized unlabeled DNA. Although the outcome of this experiment is very similar to the results of Meselson and Stahl's experiments, it does not only demonstrate the semiconservative mechanism of reduplication in chromosomal DNA, but, in addition, it indicates that the entire DNA of one chromosome behaves as if it consisted of a physical unit of reduplication running through the whole length of the chromosome. We cannot, however, state at present whether this is actually a physical continuity of the deoxyribose phosphate backbone or whether various shorter DNA pieces are linked together by material other than DNA. Furthermore, it still seems to be a matter of controversy whether this physical unit of DNA corresponds to either a chromatid or a half-chromatid (La Cour and Pelc, 1958, 1959; Lima-de-Faria, 1962).

B. Ribonucleic Acid

1. PHYSICOCHEMISTRY

In principle, RNA has a primary structure similar to DNA. It differs from DNA in the following respects: (a) Instead of thymine, it contains uracil as a major pyrimidine base; (b) the sugar is ribose instead of deoxyribose; and (c) the base ratio shows much more variation because often the relative amounts of adenine and uracil and of guanine and cytosine are not equal, but vary considerably.

This indicates a much lesser degree of base-pairing, and it has actually been shown that RNA contains many reactive bases, whereas the reactivity of the bases in DNA is lost because of their involvement in interbase hydrogen bonds (Staehelin, 1958, 1959).

In contrast to DNA which has a more or less defined structure and occurs in the nucleus, there are a number of quite different RNA's which occur partly in the nucleus and partly in the cytoplasm.

The major portion of cellular RNA occurs in the ribosomes, the ribonucleoprotein particles of the endoplasmic reticulum. The ribosomal RNA has a rather high molecular weight. The two components have sedimentation constants which in E. coli ribosomal RNA correspond to 16 and 23 S, and in rat liver ribosomal RNA correspond to 18 and 28 S. These sedimentation constants indicate molecular weights of roughly 0.5 and 1 million, respectively (Kurland, 1960; Aronson and McCarthy, 1961). The base ratio of ribosomal RNA varies from species to species.

In the soluble cytoplasm, in contrast, there is a quite different RNA which amounts to about 15–20 % of the total cellular RNA. This so-called sRNA is about 100 times smaller than ribosomal RNA; its molecular weight of about 25,000 corresponds to a chain length of nearly 80 nucleotides. Its base ratio is of the DNA type, i.e., adenine equals uracil and guanine equals cytosine. Its chemical structure seems to be very similar in all living cells. In contrast to ribosomal RNA, it consists not only of the four major nucleotides, but, in addition, contains 5-ribosyluracil and a large number of methylated derivatives of the normal bases (Dunn, 1959). From X-ray diffraction studies, Spencer et al. (1962) have concluded that its structure consists of a chain which is folded in itself in such manner that the two halves together form a double-stranded helix, although this is not supported by more recent evidence (see Addendum, page 480).

This sRNA is capable of binding amino acids chemically to its terminal nucleotide, thus forming an amino acyl-RNA. We know further that (a) for each amino acid there is one or more specific sRNA (Zachau et al., 1961); (b) although physicochemically very similar, all these sRNA's differ in their chemical composition (Holley and Merrill, 1959; Staehelin et al., 1963); (c) all sRNA's carry the terminal sequence Cp-CpA, i.e., an adenosine followed by two cytidylic (Cp) residues. It is through this terminal adenosine (A) that the amino acid is bound (Preiss et al., 1961).

In recent years a third type of RNA has been described whose unique feature is a base composition very similar to DNA (thymine in the DNA corresponding to uracil in RNA) (Gros et al., 1961; Brenner et al., 1961). In bacteria this nucleic acid was first found in phage-infected bacteria in which the base composition corresponded to the phage DNA (Volkin and Astrachan, 1956). By the formation of DNA–RNA hybrids, it could be shown that this RNA actually has a base sequence complementary to the one of DNA (Nomura et al., 1960). This RNA has varyingly been called messenger RNA, informational RNA, template RNA, DNA-like RNA, and pulse-labeled RNA. The latter designation refers to its extremely rapid turnover in bacteria (Hayashi and Spiegelman, 1961; McCarthy and Britten, 1962; Takai et al., 1962).

The formation of a DNA-like RNA seems to be fairly well established in noninfected bacteria as well. This DNA-like RNA has a very rapid turnover in bacteria, but it seems likely that its turnover can be considerably slower in higher organisms. The synthesis of this RNA represents a mechanism by which the information contained in the base sequence in DNA can be transferred to the cytoplasm. Such a function was implied in such names as "messenger RNA" or "informational RNA" which have been given to this DNA-like RNA.

A similar RNA fraction has also been found in yeast (Yčas and Vincent, 1960) and mammalian cells (Cheng, 1961; Hiatt, 1962; Marks et al., 1962; Scherrer and Darnell, 1962; Sibatani et al., 1962). An enzyme, RNA polymerase, which is capable of synthesizing RNA in the presence of a double-stranded DNA using nucleotide triphosphates as primers, has been found in many tissues (Weiss and Gladstone, 1959; Weiss, 1960).

2. RIBOSOMES

The histochemical work of Brachet and Caspersson has clearly demonstrated that the RNA content of a cell is proportional to its capacity to synthesize proteins (cf. Brachet, 1960; Caspersson, 1950). Thus, cells of the pancreas that produce large amounts of enzymes, liver cells that produce fibrinogen and albumin, and cells of the reticuloendothelial system that produce globulins were found to be extremely rich in ribonucleic acids. This has led to the belief that RNA is involved in protein synthesis.

As mentioned previously, the major part of the cellular ribonucleic acid is found in the ribosomes. Ribosomes occur freely in bacteria, but in the cells of higher organisms they are often bound to the lipoprotein membrane of the endoplasmic reticulum. It is now generally admitted that in undifferentiated (Slautterback and Fawcett, 1959), rapidly growing cells and tumor cells (Kuff and Zeigel, 1960), the ratio between free and membrane-bounded ribosomes is greater than in fully differentiated mature cells. Especially in the case of differentiated cells which are engaged in the synthesis of export proteins (Figs. 3A–D), like many secreting cells, the membrane system of the endoplasmic reticulum is often organized with a high degree of order, and the ratio between free and membrane-bounded ribosomes is small.

When a cell carrying an endoplasmic reticulum is homogenized, the endoplasmic reticulum is destroyed, and only little vesicles carrying the ribosomes remain. These remnants of the membrane form a cell fraction, the so-called microsomes, which can be sedimented only by high-speed centrifugation. Earlier studies had shown that radioactive amino acids injected into animals are fixed first in the proteins of these microsomes. The studies of Littlefield *et al.* (1955) and of Simkin and Work (1957) revealed that it was actually the ribosomes within the microsomal fraction that were labeled.

For active incorporation of radioactive amino acids into proteins, the ribosomes require a number of cofactors, such as adenosine triphosphate, Mg^{++} plus guanosine triphosphate as well as sRNA and a number of enzymes. These latter components are all present in the precipitate which is formed upon acidification to pH 5 of a cell supernatant and are therefore called pH-5 enzymes. These pH-5 enzymes containing the sRNA are responsible for the first reactions in amino acid incorporation (Hoagland, 1960): (*a*) reaction of the amino acid with ATP and an amino-

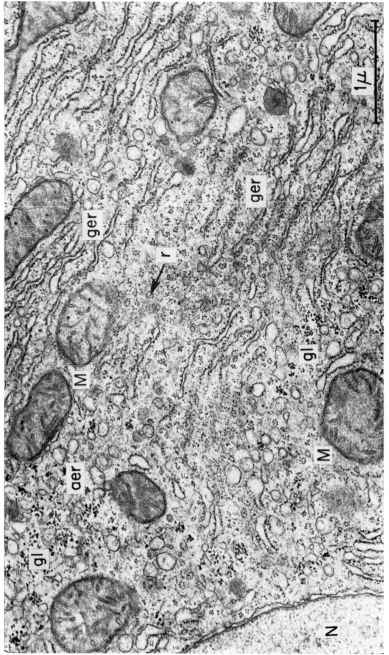

Fig. 3A. Ribosomes. Part of a mouse liver cell showing the nucleus (N), mitochondria (M), and particulate glycogen (gl) with closely associated agranular profiles (aer) of the endoplasmic reticulum. The granular (ger) part of the endoplasmic reticulum is arranged in parallel rows of elongated tubules or cisternae, the surface of which are studded with ribosomes (membrane-bounded ribosomes). Note the frequent occurrence of clusters or spirals (polysomes?) of free ribosomes (r with arrow). Osmium tetroxide fixation, Durcupan-Araldite embedding and lead hydroxide staining. Courtesy of Dr. W. Stäubli.

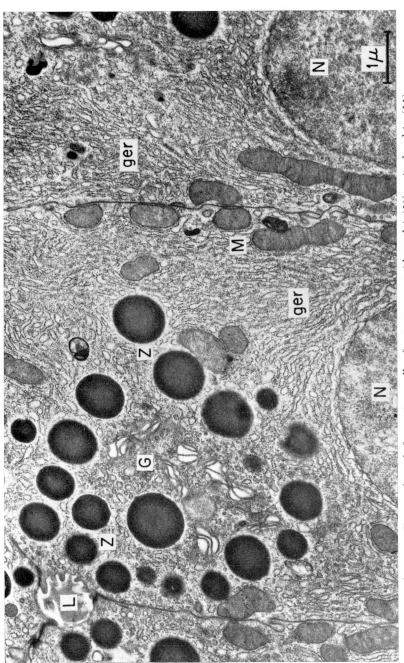

FIG. 3B. Ribosomes. Section through four acinar cells of rat pancreas with nuclei (N), mitochondria (M), zymogen granules (Z), Golgi apparatus (G), and a regular organized granular endoplasmic reticulum (ger) or ergastoplasm. This cytological situation is typical for cells which produce high amounts of proteins for extracellular purposes. The zymogen granules containing the products (digestive enzymes) of the synthetic activity of the endoplasmic reticulum discharge into the acinar lumen (L). Osmium tetroxide fixation, Durcupan-Araldite embedding, and lead hydroxide staining. Courtesy of Dr. W. Stäubli.

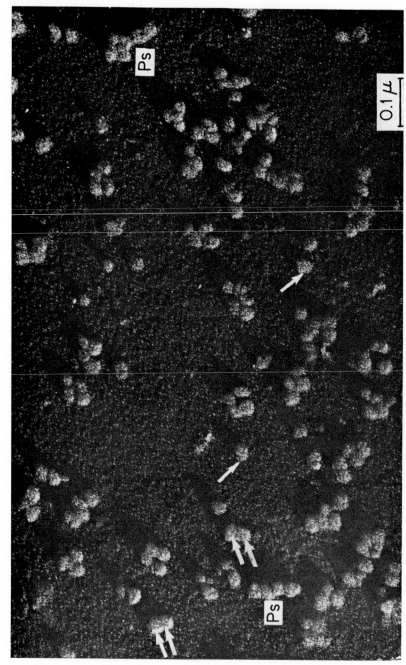

Fig. 3C. Ribosomes. Isolated rat liver ribosomes as they appeared after shadow-casting with carbon-platinum. Two monomeric (73 S) particles (single arrows) are associated to form the dimeric (110 S) particles (double arrows). The polysomes (PS) are higher oligomeres of the monomeric (73 S) particle with sedimentation coefficients of 140 S (tetramer), etc. Courtesy of Dr. W. Stäubli.

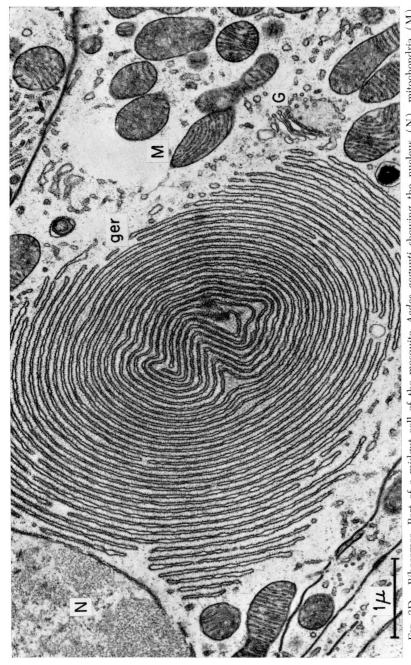

FIG. 3D. Ribosomes. Part of a midgut cell of the mosquito *Aedes aegypti* showing the nucleus (N), mitochondria (M), the Golgi complex (G) and a fingerprint-like arrangement of the granular endoplasmic reticulum (ger). Those whorls are called ergastoplasmic "Nebenkerne," and they point to a special function in the process of protein secretion. Osmium tetroxide fixation, Araldite embedding, and lead hydroxide staining. Courtesy of Dr. W. Stäubli.

activating enzyme under the formation of an amino acid adenylate which probably remains linked to the enzyme; (b) transfer of the amino acid from the adenylate-enzyme complex to the corresponding sRNA. Although physicochemically sRNA appears as a homogeneous material, it is very heterogeneous because it consists of a large number of individual and chemically different compounds. For each amino acid there exists one or more sRNA's which all differ from one another by their base composition and sequence (Staehelin et al., 1963; Holley et al., 1961). Accordingly, there is a different enzyme for the incorporation of each amino acid into sRNA (Lagerkvist and Berg, 1962). The only common feature of all sRNA molecules is their amino acid acceptor ends. They all show the terminal sequence CpCpA, i.e., two cytidylic acid residues followed by an adenosine. The amino acid is attached to one of the free hydroxyls of this terminal adenosine. Up to this point, the amino acid activation occurs in the soluble pH-5 enzymes. From the sRNA the amino acids are then transferred to the ribosomes by one or more enzymes (Nathans and Lipmann, 1961; Grossi and Moldave, 1960). On the ribosomes themselves the amino acids are incorporated through peptide linkages into proteins in a manner completely unknown at present. For the release of the proteins from the ribosomes, special enzymes seem to be necessary (Allen, 1963). The formation of the polypeptide chain appears to be stepwise, beginning at the amino end. The specificity for the synthesis of a particular protein seems to lie in the messenger, since ribosomes from reticulocytes were found to synthesize hemoglobin irrespective of whether the pH-5 enzymes came from reticulocytes, yeast, or E. coli (Lipmann et al., 1959). This would suggest that sRNA and amino acid-activating enzymes are common in nature and may represent universal cofactors.

Ribosomes which have sedimentation constants of 70–80 S are themselves built of subunits (Roberts et al., 1963). In E. coli these are described as having 30 and 50 S, respectively, and in mammalian tissues they are somewhat larger. Recently, it has been found that the monomers of 70–80 S are less active in incorporating amino acids into proteins and that more active components are aggregates consisting of five or more ribosomal monomers (Roberts et al., 1963; Warner et al., 1962, 1963; Gierer, 1963; Wettstein et al., 1963). These so-called "polysomes" can be obtained by centrifugation through density gradients and have been shown to be much more active than the monomers or smaller subunits. Two observations seem to indicate that, in addition to ribosomal RNA, the messenger RNA is involved in these polysomes: (a) Upon treatment with pancreatic RNase (ribonuclease) there is a disaggregation into monomers, and (b) such aggregates are not only encountered naturally but can be formed artificially by mixing synthetic polyribonucleotides with monomeric ribosomes (Barondes and Nirenberg, 1962).

C. Proteins, the End Products of Gene Action

Enzyme deficiencies have long been recognized as being of a genetic nature. Garrod (1923) called them "inborn errors of metabolism." In human pathology we find such examples as alkaptonuria, phenylketonuria, thalassemia (lack of glucose-6-phosphate dehydrogenase), etc. Enzyme deficiencies became accessible with *Neurospora crassa* as an experimental tool. This mold can grow on a synthetic medium, and Beadle and Tatum

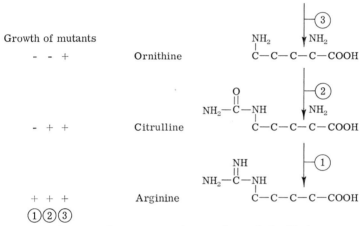

Fig. 4. Mechanisms of arginine synthesis and metabolic blocks in *Neurospora* mutants. The growth requirements of the three mutants is shown on the left, the respective metabolic blocks on the right.

and their co-workers observed that many mutants could be found which differed from the wild strain by their nutritional requirements. Furthermore, these nutritional requirements could be traced to enzyme deficiencies. The location of these metabolic blocks could be found by the exact determination of the nutritional requirement along a metabolic chain. As an example, let us take some so-called arginineless mutants of *Neurospora crassa* (Srb and Horowitz, 1944). These mutants, in contrast to the wild strain, do not grow on a medium containing only the minimal ingredients but require, in addition, the presence of arginine in the medium. The wild strain synthesizes arginine from ornithine by the chain of reactions shown in Fig. 4. In some of the mutants, precursors of arginine are capable of supporting the growth of the mold as well as arginine, whereas they cannot be used by other mutants. A biochemical analysis of the enzymatic activities of the mutants has shown that the enzymatic block always precedes the first metabolite that can support growth. Thus, in Fig. 4, the enzyme that converts citrulline into arginine is lacking in mutant 1, which grows on arginine only. In mutant 2, which grows on arginine as well as on citrulline, the enzyme that converts ornithine to citrulline is not present, and in the third mutant the enzymatic block is in the ornithine formation. Observations of this kind led Beadle and Tatum to the conclusion that each gene determines the formation of one enzyme, generally referred to as "one gene–one enzyme theory."

The question arises as to what happens in all those cases where in a particular mutant some enzyme activity is lacking. Is the enzyme not formed at all, or is it formed in some nonfunctional state? Many observations point toward the latter possibility as a rule. Levinthal (1959) has studied a mutant of *E. coli* which had no phosphatase activity. He found that in the extracts from these mutants, although no enzyme activity could be detected, there was a protein which in all physicochemical respects resembled phosphatase. This points toward the formation of a structurally altered protein, instead of the normal phosphatase. Another case in which a structurally altered protein is formed is the tyrosinase mutant discovered by Horowitz and Fling (1956). This mutant is characterized by the presence of a tyrosinase which is heat-labile, in contrast to the normally heat-stable tyrosinase of the wild strain. Thus, the enzyme of the mutant is fully active at low temperature and indistinguishable from the enzyme of the wild strain. Only at higher temperatures did the differences become apparent, again an indication that the mutation had led to a structurally different enzyme.

The best studied example of how such a structural change in a protein can be envisioned is found in human pathology. Sickle cell anemia is a genetically determined disease. Its molecular basis is an altered hemoglobin molecule. The change in the molecule consists in the replacement of one amino acid by another, i.e., in the replacement of glutamic acid by valine (Ingram, 1957, 1959). In many other cases amino acid replacements have been found as the result of mutations, e.g., in the protein of viruses; and it is generally accepted today that the primary consequences of a mutation is the alteration of the amino acid composition of a protein.

The structure of a representative protein, i.e., myoglobin, is shown in Fig. 5. Enzymes, in general, can be envisioned as polypeptide chains folded in a similar manner. Somewhere on the surface is located the site to which the substrate is bound. This receptor site could be represented in Fig. 5 by one of the grooves between the folded peptide strands. The result of the replacement of one amino acid by another does not always have the same consequences, depending on where the replacement occurs in the molecule. If the change occurs right at the receptor site, loss of activity will usually result. If the change occurs at a distant site, the activity might not be affected at all. If the change occurs at a place which is of special importance for the structural configuration of the molecule, e.g., one of the bends, the result might be a change in physico-chemical properties, such as the above mentioned thermolability, etc.

Fig. 5. Tertiary structure of a protein. Model of myoglobin. From Kendrew *et al.* (1961); courtesy of Dr. F. M. Perutz.

The result of an amino acid-replacement does not always have to be a negative one. Resistance against some antibiotic agent is often acquired through mutation in bacteria. Although we do not know the exact mechanism of such a process, we can well imagine how it could possibly be achieved. *Sulfonamide resistance* may be taken as an example. Sulfonamides interfere with the incorporation of *p*-aminobenzoic acid into folic acid (Wacker *et al.*, 1957). The structure of the metabolite and its anti-metabolite are shown in Fig. 6. The two duck-like structures differ from each other by the width of the neck—the sulfonamide having two crops and two beaks, whereas *p*-aminobenzoic acid has only one. Somewhere on the surface of the enzyme is the receptor site for *p*-aminobenzoic acid. A mutation in which one of the amino acids at this site is replaced by a larger one might result in a narrowing of the groove, thus leaving access only to the *p*-aminobenzoic acid molecule and not to the larger antimetabolite. Thus, the change of an amino acid might not result in

Fig. 6. Structure of *p*-aminobenzoic acid (right) and its antimetabolite, sulfanilamide (left).

the loss of activity, but rather in the increase in its specificity necessary for the survival of its kind under adverse conditions.

II. Biochemical Events in Gene Action

The biochemical events that occur when a gene exerts its action are very difficult to study in a multicellular organism. They can be studied in unicellular organisms under certain conditions, i.e., when the gene begins to act in all cells at once, for instance, upon induction. But the best object for study are bacteria, where new genes can be introduced in the form of bacteriophages that then begin to act (cf. Stent, 1959).

It is very important to realize that bacteriophage is not an organism. It does not grow; it does not multiply by binary fission; and it has no metabolism (Lwoff, 1959). A mature phage particle is, in principle, nothing but an inert complex nucleoprotein whose nucleic acid has potential genetic activity. This structure can attach itself to a susceptible bacterium. The enzymes of the phage tail dig a hole in the bacterial wall through which the genetic material of the bacteriophage is passed into the bacterium. Inside the infected bacterium either of two events can happen: (1) The genetic phage material enters the vegetative stage, i.e., it causes the formation of new nucleic acids and many new proteins, including all the structural elements of bacteriophage, or (2) it is converted to prophage. In this case the genetic material, after entering the cell, becomes integrated into the genetic material of the host. It rests there in a latent stage, but it is always inherited by the progeny like a host gene. Upon induction with X-ray, UV light, or some chemical agent, or sometimes even spontaneously, phage is produced, i.e., the prophage has been transformed into a vegetative phage.

All the genetic information on how new phage is formed lies in the DNA, since it is the only component to enter the cell. After the time of the absorption, no infectious virus particle is present in the medium until the first bacteria have undergone lysis, which requires, according to the conditions, anywhere from 20 minutes to an hour. This time covers one life cycle of a bacteriophage.

What happens in the bacterium during that time? The moment when the infected bacterium bursts and releases the new phage into the medium, i.e., the lysis at the end of the latent period does not coincide with the time when the new phage is formed, since infective particles have previously accumulated inside the infected cell. In the first half of the latent period, no infectious particles can be found inside the cell, but in the second half there is a linear increase in the number of infectious phage particles in each bacterium up to the time when lysis occurs. This process should not be confused with the actual synthesis of phage material, because it represents instead a maturation process in which the individual phage components are built up together to form a complete virus particle.

Synthesis of phage material proceeds in the first part of the latent period in which no infectious particles can yet be found. This part is called the eclipse and can be divided into various sections. The last part of the latent period can be characterized by the presence of phage-specific material. Serologically, these can be recognized by the presence of phage-specific antigens. Morphologically, empty phage heads and tails can be seen, and the presence of phage DNA can be determined by the presence of 5-hydroxymethylcytosine in the DNA, a base which replaces cytosine in the DNA of the T–even coliphages. Apparently, during this phase of phage development all the constituents are formed independently.

A still earlier phase is characterized by the appearance of a number of enzymes necessary for the formation of the various phage components. Of these enzymes only a few should be mentioned as examples, namely, those involved in the incorporation of 5-hydroxymethylcytosine into DNA. One enzyme is dCTPase. Since dCTP is the normal precursor of DNA, it is apparently the role of this enzyme to remove dCTP from the nucleotide pool. The hydromethyl group is introduced into dCMP on the nucleoside monophosphate stage by an enzyme, dCMP-

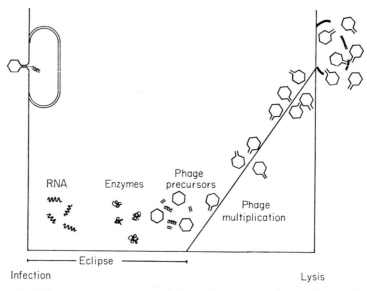

RNA   Enzymes   Phage precursors   Phage multiplication

Eclipse

Infection   Lysis

Fig. 7. Schematic representation of the various steps in phage infection. Sequential synthesis of RNA, new enzymes, phage precursors. Following maturation multiplication of phage is recognizable inside the cell followed by lysis of the cell.

hydroxymethylase. The resulting hydroxymethyl-dCMP is converted to the triphosphate through another enzyme (Zimmerman and Kornberg, 1961). All these enzymes, together with many others, are formed specifically under the genetic influence of phage DNA and prior to the appearance of any new phage component in the infected cell. Because of the necessity of the formation of these enzymes, inhibition of protein synthesis right at the onset of the virus infection not only inhibits the synthesis of phage protein but also of phage DNA.

Right after phage infection most of the endogenous protein and nucleic acid synthesis stops. A slight synthesis of RNA, which is recognizable by the incorporation of P^{32} into RNA, continues. The peculiarity of this RNA synthesized after phage infection lies in the fact that it appears to be an accurate replica of phage DNA, i.e., it contains the same base sequence as phage DNA in which uracil replaces the thymine of DNA. This is indicated (*a*) by the fact that it has the same base composition as phage DNA, in contrast to any other bacterial RNA (Volkin and Astrachan, 1956), and (*b*) by the discovery that hybrids can be formed between phage DNA and this particular RNA (Hall and Spiegelman, 1961).

The life cycle of a bacteriophage which represents an example of the expression of a gene is thus characterized by the following chain of events (Fig. 7): (1) synthesis of an RNA complementary to the DNA of the gene; (2) synthesis of a number of proteins necessary for the formation of structures which are formed under the influence of the gene; (3) formation of these structures by the newly formed enzymes; and (4) assembly of these structures to an organized morphological entity.

III. Molecular Basis of Mutation

A. *The Fine Structure of a Gene, the rII Region*

The series of processes just mentioned does not involve the expression of a single gene but of a very large number of genes. It is interesting that genetically a phage can be treated as a chromosome. The phage shows the same three characteristic features: self-duplication, mutation, and recombination. Mutation is the feature without which a gene could never be recognized. Only by the fact that something is altered in a mutant can we realize the existence of a gene. In bacteriophage we can distinguish various groups of mutants. There are mutants which result in a different appearance of the plaques which form in a layer of bacteria after infection. Another type of mutants is recognized by its inability to multiply in certain strains of bacteria, although in susceptible bacteria the appearance might be identical. These are the so-called host-range mutants. The other two features, self-duplication and recombination, are closely linked.

Determination of the frequency with which crossing-over occurs has only made the location of genes possible. In mammalian cells crossing-over between two different chromosomes occurs during the first meiosis. A very similar process occurs in infected bacteria, when the bacterium is simultaneously infected with two phages. The genetic material of these two phages can undergo the same crossing-over as chromosomes.

The result is a phage with a genome, part of which stems from one and part from the other infecting phage. From the frequency of the recombination between two markers in the two different phages, calculations can be made on the distance of these markers on the genome. Link-

age maps of various phages have thus been prepared. Among the T2 and
T4 phages which cause a different appearance are the so-called *r* phages
("*r*" for rapidly lysing). They are easily recognized by their larger and
sharp-edged plaques. The *r*-type phages can arise from changes in different genetic areas. One gene has been studied quite extensively, the
so-called *rII* region. The *r* mutants arise spontaneously with a frequency
of about 1 in 10,000, and more than half of them are *rII* mutants. Mutants
deficient in this gene show one characteristic behavior. They multiply on
the usual host *E. coli* B, but they are unable to grow in another strain of
E. coli K-12 (λ). Thus, Benzer (1961) has been able to isolate literally
thousands of *rII* mutants and, by recombination among them (i.e., by
simultaneous infection with two mutants), has tried to get some insight
into the structure of this *rII* region. Technically, there is the great advantage that recombinants of the wild type are very easily picked out, because only they can grow on *E. coli* K-12 (λ).

Benzer's (1962) results can be summarized in the following way: In
order to grow on *E. coli* K-12 (λ), recombination of the two phage genomes is not necessarily a prerequisite. The *rII* region, i.e., the "gene" in
the classic sense, falls into two segments (Fig. 8). If the mutations involve different segments in the two mutants, growth in *E. coli* K-12 (λ)
will take place, although neither of them could grow alone (Fig. 8b).
Apparently, the reason is that of each segment one is present intact in
the infected cell. If the two mutations happen to be within the same segment, the situation is different (Fig. 8c). In this case the affected segment is not intact in either phage. If the location of the defect within this
segment is different in the two mutants, recombination can take place
(Fig. 8d). This results in a wild type phage and a double mutant. Because the two segments are intact in the wild type, growth will take
place. Thus, if two mutants lie within the same segment, growth can only
occur after recombination, and the frequency of this recombination can
be used as a measure for the distance between the loci of the two mutations.

The situation has been compared with the isomerism in stereochemistry, *cis* indicating in the same direction, in this case on the same chromosome (Fig. 8d), *trans* indicating the opposite, i.e., on two different
chromosomes (Benzer, 1957) (Fig. 8c). These segments have therefore
been called "cistrons." The original meaning of the cistron was that of
the segment of a genome which had to be intact, so that after infection
with two mutants affecting the same cistron, growth could only occur
after the two mutant loci had been transferred into the *cis* position, thus
producing one intact cistron. The term cistron has now a more general

meaning indicating the unit of function in any genetic apparatus and thus represents the part of DNA coding for one polypeptide chain.

Benzer's task of locating mutants was greatly facilitated by the finding of mutants in which a larger or smaller part of the genome was lost. With the aid of mutants having such deletions which could be used as markers, it was possible to limit the location of an unknown mutation to a small part of the genome. By an immense and extremely careful work

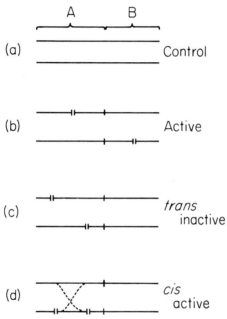

Fig. 8. *Cis-trans* arrangement of mutations. (a) Heterozygote with two intact genomes. (b) Heterozygote with two mutations located in different cistrons A and B. (c) Heterozygote with two mutations located in the same cistron A. (d) Result of cross-over having taken place in (c).

it was possible to locate more than a thousand mutants which had arisen spontaneously through some chemical treatment or irradiation. It was found that within one cistron about three hundred different loci could be recognized where mutations would arise. Interestingly, the number of mutations was not divided evenly over all these locations, but there were some "hot-spots" where mutations arose much more easily than at other places (Benzer, 1961).

Now when we raise the question, "What is a gene?" we can state that it is neither the unit of function nor the unit of mutation that it used to be. The *rII* "gene" consists of two cistrons which are the functional units.

In a given cistron, several hundred differently located mutations can be recognized. But this notion brings us much nearer to the physical size of a gene. The *rII* region occupies about 1 % of the phage genome. On the other hand, 1 % of the total phage DNA amounts to something of the order of one thousand nucleotide pairs. If this amount of DNA can still be divided into hundreds of loci of mutations, we come to the conclusion that mutations can lie as close to one another as one or two nucleotides and can, in fact, involve transformations of single nucleotides. In most cases, transformation of a single nucleotide is probably the chemical basis of a mutation.

B. *Tobacco Mosaic Virus, a Model for Chemically Induced Mutations*

Although the structure of the *rII* region has been elucidated more clearly than the structure of any other gene, there is one drawback. We do not know anything about the product of this gene. We can recognize its activity by the growth of the phage in *E. coli* K-12 (λ), but we have no idea what protein, what enzyme is responsible for this biological effect. Quite the opposite is true for the tobacco mosaic virus (TMV). Although the genetics of this virus are far from being understood, the virus protein is known even to the last amino acid sequence. This has made it possible to gain more insight into the protein changes upon mutation.

TMV contains ribonucleic acid which corresponds to only 5 % of the total virus mass. That it carries the genetic information and is also responsible for the infectivity, is apparent from the three following observations:

1. Gierer and Schramm (1956), as well as Fraenkel-Conrat (1956), discovered that isolated nucleic acid alone, free from its protein coat, is also infective.

2. The isolated nucleic acid can be reconstituted again with virus protein to intact virus rods (Fraenkel-Conrat and Williams, 1955). Reconstitution with proteins from different strains can also be achieved. In all these reconstitution experiments it has been found that the progeny always is of the strain from which the nucleic acid is derived (Fraenkel-Conrat and Singer, 1957). The nature of the protein coat in the reconstituted infecting virus has no influence on the nature of the progeny virus.

3. In order to inactivate a virus, it is necessary to alter the nucleic acid (Staehelin, 1960). Chemical virus inactivators all affect the nucleic acid which is very sensitive. Reaction of only a few bases with formaldehyde (Staehelin, 1958, 1959) or their deamination with hydroxylamine (Schuster and Schramm, 1958) leads to inactivation. Chemical modifica-

tion of the protein, in contrast, appears to be of minor importance for virus infectivity.

The fact that ribonucleic acid could be isolated, treated chemically, and its genetic property studied at the same time by its infecting property, has opened a wide new field of research. The knowledge of the exact chemical structure of the TMV protein has also contributed greatly to the interest in the genetic property of TMV-RNA, since one of its genetic expressions is the structure of the virus protein. Therefore, it is of great interest to see what effects chemical modification of TMV-RNA might have on its infectivity as well as on the nature of the progeny.

Reaction of the nucleic acid with most chemical agents leads to inactivation (Staehelin, 1960). The most interesting reaction, however, is the deamination by nitrous acid. Gierer and Mundry (1958) found that the more the inactivation proceeds, the more of the survivors turn out to be mutants. In addition to being an inactivating agent, nitrous acid is therefore also a mutagenic agent.

Nitrous acid causes three different deaminations in a nucleic acid (Vielmetter and Schuster, 1960):

$$adenosine \rightarrow hypoxanthine$$
$$guanosine \rightarrow xanthine$$
$$cytosine \;\; \rightarrow uracil$$

At first glance, the last reaction appears to be the most interesting, because it is the transformation of one natural base into another. But the reaction of adenosine to hypoxanthine is of interest also, because it was found with synthetic polymers that hypoxanthine can form a base pair with cytosine, as guanine does. Hypoxanthine would therefore be expected to be copied as cytosine first and then as guanine. Upon reaction of a virus nucleic acid with nitrous acid, two transformations could therefore occur in the progeny: cytosine to uracil, adenine to guanine. Wittmann (1962), as well as Tsugita and Fraenkel-Conrat (1962), have analyzed the structure of the virus protein in the mutants obtained by treatment with nitrous acid and have found changes in the amino acid composition. The results of the analysis of more than 117 chemically induced TMV mutants by Wittmann (1962) can be summarized in the following way:

1. In twenty-nine mutants one amino acid was replaced, and in six mutants two amino acids were replaced. Changes in the amino acid composition of the virus protein were only present in about one-sixth of all mutants indicating that, in addition to the gene for the virus protein, there are other genes which influence the appearance of the lesions as well.

2. Only a very limited number of amino acid replacements have been observed, but these have occurred repeatedly. It is especially this latter point which seems to indicate clearly that there is a very close relation between the base sequence in genetically active nucleic acid and the amino acid composition of the protein built under the influence of this gene.

IV. The Genetic Code

A. *The Messenger Concept*

It is well established that the genetic information lies in the DNA of the nucleus and that protein synthesis occurs to a great part in the cytoplasm. The mystery that remains to be solved is how the genetic information is transferred to the cytoplasm. One possible mechanism has been encountered in bacteriophage infection. After the phage DNA has entered the cell, the first event prior to the synthesis of new proteins is the synthesis of a phage DNA-like RNA.

The concept that this DNA-like RNA has the function of a messenger carrying the genetic information from DNA to the protein-synthesizing ribosomes was originally proposed to explain the rapid onset of protein synthesis following induction of some specific enzyme. Ribosomal RNA has a very slow turnover, and it seemed unlikely, therefore, that the synthesis of a new protein should require the synthesis of new ribosomes. Yet, somehow the genetic information of how to make a new protein should be transmitted to the ribosomes. The fact that upon infection with a bacteriophage the infected cell very rapidly synthesizes a ribonucleic acid with a base composition similar to that of phage DNA has suggested the intermediary role of a ribonucleic acid as a messenger carrying the message of the structure of a specific protein to the ribosomes. These unspecific structures which are capable of synthesizing any sort of protein would then, in turn, use this messenger ribonucleic acid as a template for the formation of the proper protein. Such a mechanism is shown schematically in Fig. 9. The lower part shows the formation of the amino acyl sRNA, the upper part shows the formation of a DNA-like RNA and its conjugation with ribosomes. The middle part represents the still highly hypothetical mechanism by which the part of the sRNA opposite to the amino acid-carrying end finds the counterpart of the messenger RNA with which it can combine by hydrogen bonding, thus bringing its amino acid into the proper position relative to the other amino acids. After accomplishing this, the peptide bond can be formed, and upon completion of the entire peptide chain the new protein can be released.

The messenger concept has gained strong support from the discovery of Nirenberg and Matthaei (1961) that the ribosomal amino acid-incorporating system of *E. coli* could be stimulated by the addition of various polynucleotides. Addition of tobacco mosaic virus RNA has led to the synthesis of proteins somewhat related to tobacco mosaic virus protein (Tsugita *et al.*, 1961). The addition of enzymatically synthesized unnatural polynucleotides, such as polyuridylic acid, has specifically stimulated the incorporation of individual amino acids—in the latter case, phenylalanine. This finding has since been amply confirmed and was found in mammalian systems also (Maxwell, 1962).

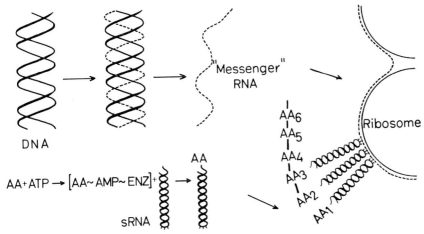

FIG. 9. Mechanism of protein synthesis. Amino acids (AA) are depicted as reacting with ATP and activating enzyme to give a complex of aminoacyladenylate (AA $\sim$ AMP) and enzyme. From this the amino acid is transferred to the transfer ribonucleic acid (sRNA). Individual transfer ribonucleic acid molecules are bound by ribosomes containing a messenger ribonucleic acid thus linking the various amino acids (AA$_1$, AA$_2$, etc.) in the genetically determined sequence.

Still another indication for the existence of a "messenger" is the discovery almost simultaneously in many laboratories that individual ribosomes show only a fraction of the activity found in ribosomal aggregates. Such ribosomal aggregates have been found in various cells including reticulocytes and liver cells (Warner *et al.*, 1962, 1963; Gierer, 1963; Wettstein *et al.*, 1963). They have been demonstrated in electron micrographs after gentle disruption of reticulocytes, but their existence is also apparent in the density centrifugation of cell homogenates in sucrose gradients. In connection with the messenger hypothesis, various facts observed in density gradient centrifugation appear to be of special importance: (*a*) Added polyuridylic acid quickly becomes connected not with individual ribosomes but with ribosomal aggregates (Barondes and Nirenberg, 1962); (b) the peak of the incorporating activity is found at the same place where the polyuridylic acid is found (Barondes and Nirenberg, 1962); (c) although heavier aggregates are more active in amino acid incorporation, the incorporation of phenylalanine can be stimulated much less by the addition of polyuridylic acid than in single or low aggregate ribosomes (Gierer, 1963); (d) the aggregate structure of ribosomes can be disrupted by ribonuclease, thus releasing single-unit ribosomes (Wettstein et al., 1963). All these findings are in accord with the concept of an RNA "messenger," and, in addition, indicate that the messenger may also cause some structural alterations. An RNA exhibiting the properties of messenger RNA has also been found in mammalian cells (Cheng, 1961; Sibatani et al., 1962; Hiatt, 1962; Marks et al., 1962; Scherrer and Darnell, 1962), where its location in the nucleus is especially noteworthy (Barondes et al., 1962).

Although everything thus far seems to point toward a simple transport of information by means of a messenger RNA, there is still some uncertainty as to the nature of this transport. The subcellular structure of the various cells studied shows great variations. E. coli has no clearly separated nucleus and no endoplasmic reticulum. Diffusion of the messenger can easily be envisioned here. Reticulocytes contain a nucleus but very few membranes. Transport of the messenger must involve passage through the nuclear membrane but can then proceed to the free-floating ribosomes. Addition of bacterial RNA to chick fibroblasts has been found to stimulate the synthesis of a protein immunologically related to the bacterial protein (Amos and Kearns, 1962), and the addition of liver RNA to ascites tumor cells was claimed to stimulate the synthesis of albumin (Niu et al., 1962). In highly organized cells, such as liver cells with a complicated system of endoplasmic HeLa cells, there is the additional complication that, at present, no transport from nuclear RNA to the cytoplasm seems to be established (Harris, 1963). RNA which stimulates the incorporation of amino acids is located mainly in the nucleus (Barondes et al., 1962). On the other hand, the existence of nuclear ribosomes and the rapid turnover of nucleolar RNA could indicate that in mammalian cells we are faced with a situation that might be quite different from that in bacteria. In addition, a factor very active in stimulating amino acid incorporation in a mammalian cell-free system is not a nucleic acid but a nucleoprotein (Hoagland and Askonas, 1963).

B. Experimental Approaches to the Code

The mechanism of protein synthesis as it is depicted in Fig. 9 involves various steps, namely, the sending of a message, the translation of this message into another language, and the putting of this message in the final print. The pulse-labeled RNA might be the messenger or rather the message itself. This message is still written in the language of base sequences of nucleic acids. The sRNA provides a possible mechanism for the translation of the nucleic acid message into proteins, if we make the following assumptions—for some there appears to be good experimental evidence:

1. There is a different sRNA for every amino acid (Zachau *et al.*, 1961; Holley and Merrill, 1959; Staehelin *et al.*, 1963).

2. There is a specific enzyme for the incorporation of each amino acid in its appropriate sRNA (Bergmann *et al.*, 1961).

3. Some base sequence in the messenger RNA can arrange one particular sRNA, so that all sRNA's line up consecutively and put their amino acids into the right position (see Addendum).

The sRNA's would thus represent a very simple device for the translation of the code. Each of them possesses a particular structure with which it combines specifically with only one code sign. In addition, each of them is so different that the amino acid incorporation enzymes can specifically select the proper sRNA. Therefore, each sRNA has two specific sites, one for the base sequence in the messenger RNA and one for its proper amino acid-activating enzyme.

The interesting question can be asked: "What would happen if for some reason the wrong amino acid is linked to an sRNA?" If a mechanism similar to the one just mentioned were at work, it would be expected that it should be incorporated at the wrong place.

Chapeville *et al.* (1962) have incorporated cysteine enzymatically into the corresponding cysteine-sRNA. This was then reduced with Raney nickel which caused the transformation of cysteine into alanine. Thus, an alanine was linked to a cysteine-sRNA. The incorporation of this alanine into proteins, however, was not stimulated in the ribosomal system by the polynucleotide stimulating alanine incorporation (Poly-CUG), but by the polynucleotide which specifically stimulates the incorporation of cysteine (Poly-UG). If this hybrid sRNA was added to the hemoglobin-synthesizing system, it was also found that alanine replaces cysteine in the hemoglobin polypeptide chain (von Ehrenstein *et al.*, 1963). It appears, therefore, that the ribosomal system can only recognize an amino acid by its corresponding sRNA to which it was previously linked by the cytoplasmic amino acid-incorporating enzyme. The problem of the genetic code thus seems to center around the question, "What structures in the ribonucleic acid determine the position of each amino acid?" Since nucleic acids are perfectly regular structures, the only variable is the sequence of the bases. But there are only four bases in nucleic acids compared to the twenty odd amino acids in the proteins. Therefore, more than one base must form the code sign for every amino acid, and the smallest number of bases which would allow twenty different possibilities would be three. The likeliness of such a *triplet code* is further strengthened by the very elaborate experimental demonstration of multiple mutants by Crick *et al.* (1961). Proflavine causes the formation of mutants which can arbitrarily be called + and —, because recombination of two mutants with different prefixes might under certain conditions result in the production of apparently wild type phage, whereas this will never be the case by recombination with two phages with the same prefix. But, interestingly, recombination of three phages having either all the + or the — prefixes can result in the production of active phage. Crick has made the assumption that the mutations are caused by the addition or deletion of one base or more. If three bases together form a code sign, insertion or deletion of one base would completely disturb the reading of the message, because the grouping of bases into groups of three would be shifted by one or two bases. From the point of insertion or deletion onward the grouping into three bases would involve bases from different code signs. Combining three such additions or deletions, however, would finally restore the order again so that the rest of the cistron could be read and translated properly. The results of the experiments with these proflavine mutants have led to the following conclusions (Crick, 1963): (1) The reading of the message starts at one particular end of the cistron, (2) the code sign for each amino acid involves three bases or a multiple thereof, (3) the message can only be read in fractions of this size from the beginning.

The first conclusion is of particular interest because Dintzis (1961) has found that the synthesis of the hemoglobin chain starts at the N-terminal end (Rychlik and Sorm, 1962). Apparently, there is collinearity between the base sequence in nucleic acid and the amino acid sequence in the protein. Two fruitful approaches have been explored in order to get insight into the actual triplet sequences of the individual code signs.

The discovery that enzymatically synthesized polynucleotides can stimulate the amino acid incorporation in the ribosomal system has opened a wide field of experimentation (Nirenberg and Matthaei, 1961; Nirenberg *et al.*, 1962; Matthaei *et al.*, 1962; Basilio *et al.*, 1962; Lengyel *et al.*, 1961, 1962; Speyer *et al.*, 1962a, b). After the original discovery that in the presence of polyuridylic acid the incorporation of phenylalanine is stimulated up to a thousandfold, various mixed polynucleotides were examined for their capacity to stimulate the incorporation of one amino acid or another. The results of these experiments have led first to the establishment of a code in which all triplets of bases contained at least one uracil, those for serine and leucine two, and that for phenylalanine three. In comparison with the stimulation of phenylalanine-incorporation by polyuridylic acid, and the effect of Poly-UC in serine- and leucine-incorporation, the stimulation of the incorporation of other amino acids was quite low. It appears that the secondary structure of the polynucleotide is of great importance because polyuridylic acid, after attachment to the complementary polyadenylic acid, is no longer active. Polyuridylic acid has a unique property in that it is incapable of forming a secondary structure, in contrast to Poly-A, for instance. Thus, it seems not unlikely that a triplet such as AAC might be more active in stimulating the incorporation of an amino acid when present in a polynucleotide containing a large amount of uracil than in polynucleotide consisting only of adenine and cytosine. Although in the latter the particular sequence might occur more frequently, the bases might be more often blocked by secondary structure. The results with synthetic polynucleotides make it difficult to understand the conclusion about the code drawn from genetic experiments. It would seem that polypeptides could only be formed under the influence of synthetic polynucleotides, if the two following assumptions are made: (1) a piece of RNA, uncoiled, long enough to code TCA-precipitable material, is present in all synthetic polynucleotides or can be formed upon fixation to the ribosomes, and (2) all possible triplets have some coding function, because otherwise too many unnatural triplets would be present in synthetic random polynucleotides which would interrupt the further elongation of the peptide chain.

Another approach to the cracking of the code is the chemical analysis of the protein in mutants of tobacco mosaic virus. Assuming that in a mutant only one base of a triplet is transformed, conclusions might be drawn from the amino acid changes to the triplet codes, i.e., the code signs of the two amino acids involved may not differ by more than one base. In the nitrite mutants the genetic base changes are only from cytosine to uracil and from adenine to guanine. It is therefore not surprising that only a limited number of amino acid changes have been observed. The analysis of naturally occurring mutants might reveal additional relationships between amino acid transformation and base exchanges in the triplets. The advantage of this method is that once a few sequences are established, it will be easy to draw conclusions about the sequence of the bases in all the other triplets. On the other hand, this method is hampered by the fact (now very probable) that more than one triplet can code for one amino acid. This is indicated by the following findings: (1) the incorporation of certain amino acids can be stimulated by more than one polynucleotide (Gardner et al., 1962; Wahba et al., 1963), (2) sometimes two sRNA's can be separated on methylated albumin columns which accept both the same amino acids (Sueoka and Yamane, 1962),

(3) using the two leucine sRNA's thus separated, Weisblum *et al.* (1962) have found that the incorporation of leucine into proteins is stimulated with Poly-UC in one case and with Poly-UG in the other. A physical basis for the possibility of two code signs was thus established.

From the incorporation data obtained with synthetic polynucleotides as well as from the amino acid replacement obtained by mutation, it would seem that the various codes for the same amino acid would be very closely related, i.e., differing only by one base in the triplet (Wahba *et al.*, 1963; Jukes, 1963). It would also seem premature to present any definite base triplet–amino acid code here, but it might be established by the time this article is published (see Addendum).

One intriguing feature about the code concerns the unusual bases which occur in sRNA. Apart from 5-ribosyluridine, they are all methyl-ated derivatives of the normal bases (Dunn, 1959). Apparently, they are methylated only after their incorporation into the nucleic acid (Fleissner and Borek, 1962). This methylation does not, however, occur in a random fashion. These methylated bases are clustered in some regions of the polynucleotide chain (Staehelin, 1962; Ingram and Pierce, 1962), and they occur in fixed sequences. Data obtained by analysis of the products of stepwise digestion (Nihei and Cantoni, 1962) seem to indicate that they are located generally in the center of the molecule. In the structure of sRNA that is suggested from the X-ray data (Spencer *et al.*, 1962), i.e., a double-stranded helix which is formed by the same strand first moving in one direction and then turning back, there is a loop in the molecule in which the bases are not linked through interbase hydrogen bonding. In the scheme in Fig. 9 it is assumed that this is the region of the sRNA through which this nucleic acid could be hydrogen bonded to the mRNA, although it must be admitted that there is no evidence for this as-sumption. It is tempting to speculate that this is actually the place where the methylated bases, in which the hydrogen-bonding capacity is impaired, are located either surrounding or representing a part of the coding region.

V. Regulation of Gene Action

If all genes in an organism would express themselves constantly, life would hardly be possible. A unicellular organism, for instance, would not be able to adapt to any change in its surroundings. It would constantly waste most of its energy for the production of metabolites which are not even indispensable under the particular conditions of its present growth, and under favorable conditions for nutrition it would quickly consume its supplies. Therefore, normally only a small part of the genetic potential is used and it appears that repression of gene activity is a prerequisite for adaptation and that it is almost as important as the presence of the gene itself. It is interesting that in addition to mutants which are deficient in a structural gene, another kind of mutant has also been found, the so-called constitutive mutant. These mutants produce all the proteins the wild type is capable of producing, but they have lost the ability for quantitative regulation.

In microorganisms the synthesis of many enzymes is regulated by the presence of some small molecular substances. In many cases, these are the end products of the enzyme itself. In the absence of orthophosphate some forms of E. coli form large amounts of phosphatase even amounting to 6 % of their total protein (Torriani, 1960; Horiuchi et al., 1959). Only a fraction of this amount of enzyme is formed in the presence of phosphate. The enzymes involved in the synthesis of amino acids, such as arginine, histidine, and tryptophan are controlled by these very same amino acids. In the presence of sufficient quantities of these amino acids the enzymes are no longer formed.

One especially interesting feature of the latter systems is the fact that the synthesis of more than one enzyme is controlled by the same metabolite, i.e., of all those enzymes involved in a certain chain of reactions.

In the enzymes just mentioned, control is exerted through *repression* by the *end products*. On the other hand, it is also possible that the biosynthesis of an enzyme is controlled by its substrate, i.e., it is only formed in the presence of the substrate. This process is called *induction*. It is the case, for instance, in the β-galactosidase of E. *coli*. But it should be mentioned forthwith that the induction is not directly related to the enzyme action, since substances very closely related to the substrate have been shown to be inducers but not substrates.

This so-called *gal* region has been studied in particular detail (Jacob and Monod, 1961). It comprises three enzymes: β-galactosidase, β-galactoside acetylase, and β-galactoside permease. The latter two activities are possibly due to the same enzyme. The very elegant recombination analyses of Jacob and Monod (1961) have shown the observed mutants to fall into three different regions: (a) two cistrons SG_1 and SG_2, representing the structural genes for β-galactosidase and permease activity. (b) A gene G_R which is the locus of constitutive mutants and which can be located at quite a distance from the structural gene, (c) a gene O which lies at one end of the structural genes. Mutants in this region are also constitutive but in a different way than in (b). In diploid cells G_R is dominant, i.e., as long as it is present, the enzymes are under metabolic control. The O region, in contrast, behaves differently. It is dominant for the adjacent region of the structural genes. If O is mutated, the metabolic control of the adjacent structural genes is lost, whether in a diploid cell some O^+ of the wild type is present or not.

All these observations have led Jacob and Monod (1961) to the following conclusions (see Fig. 10):

Structural genes (such as those for β-galactosidase or permease) are dependent for their activity, i.e., the sending off of a messenger from an adjacent operator gene. This operator gene is normally blocked by a "re-

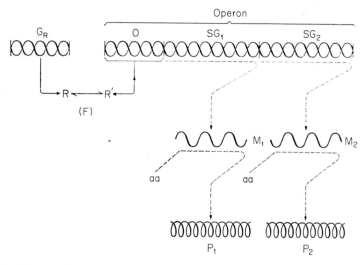

Fig. 10. Regulation of gene expression by induction and repression. From Monod *et al.* (1963). P_1 and P_2 represent two proteins synthesized from amino acids (aa) by means of messenger ribonucleic acids (M_1 and M_2). SG_1 and SG_2 are the corresponding structural genes which are located adjacent to the operator gene. The latter is under the control of a repressor gene (G_R) by means of a repressor substance (R) which can be activated or inactivated by various small molecular factors (F) such as inducers and metabolic end products.

pressor" produced by the regulator gene. Physiologically, this repressor can be blocked by low molecular substances in the case of substrate induction or, in some cases, it may also need small molecular substances for full activity as in the case of end-product repression. Constitutive mutations can occur by either of two mechanisms: by mutations in the regulator genes, in which case the repressor will be formed, or by mutations in the operator genes in which cases the repressor can no longer exert its action, resulting in the uninhibited activity of the structural genes adjacent to it. One of the most burning problems which remains to be solved is the nature of the repressor.

What mainly distinguishes an animal from a microorganism is the fact that the original animal cells divide into cells which differentiate in various directions. This differentiation is also under genetic control.

One of the most interesting questions is whether the same mechanism of gene action which has been found in bacteria operates also in mammalian cells. Inducible enzymes have been described in mammalian organs, such as tryptophan pyrrolase, and tyrosine transaminase in rat liver (cf. Huebner, 1962). Tryptophan pyrrolase activity of liver extracts is increased after prior treatment of the animals with tryptophan, i.e., the substrate, or with cortisone or any treatment of stress which results in an output of ACTH and thus in a stimulation of the adrenal (Knox, 1951). Tryptophan pyrrolase is, however, a rather complicated enzyme, having a porphyrin coenzyme upon whose concentration much of its activity depends (Tanuka and Knox, 1958; Greengard and Feigelson, 1961). Since actinomycin has a different effect on the action of cortisone and tryptophan (Greengard and Acs, 1962), respectively, the question of the inducibility of this enzyme remains obscure at present.

Another question in this connection concerns the mechanism of action of hormones which stimulate the growth of some organ or another. It could be imagined that these hormones act by regulating messenger RNA synthesis. There are several indications that at least one of them, growth hormone, in fact does act in such a way (Korner, 1962):

1. Growth hormone causes stimulation of amino acid incorporation into proteins (Korner, 1960).

2. Growth hormone acts on isolated organs or, in other words, it acts directly on the cell and not by means of regulating the blood supply of nutrients, etc. (Kostyo and Knobil, 1959).

3. Growth hormone stimulates the uptake of P^{32} into nucleic acids (Talwar et al., 1962).

4. After treatment with growth hormone more RNA is found which shows biological activity in stimulating amino acid-incorporation in a cell-free system (Talwar and Gros, 1963).

5. Ribosomes from hypophysectomized animals are more active when these animals have been treated with growth hormone (Korner, 1961, Kataja and Staehelin, 1962).

6. Ribosomes of hypophysectomized animals are deficient in polysomes as compared with normal animals. Upon addition of polyuridylic acid the activity can be increased similarly to that of control animals (Braunwalder and Staehelin, 1963).

All these observations are compatible with the concept that growth hormone stimulates the release of a messenger RNA and thus acts as an inducer.

With androgens a similar stimulation of RNA synthesis has been observed (Kassenaar *et al.*, 1962). ACTH has been reported to stimulate amino acid incorporation into adrenal (Bransome and Reddy, 1963). Thyroxine also was found to stimulate the incorporation of C^{14}-valine from valine-sRNA to protein in liver microsomes (Sokoloff *et al.*, 1962). Insulin which has a pronounced effect on the metabolism of adipose tissue was also reported to stimulate the amino acid and RNA metabolism of this tissue (Carruthers and Winograd, 1962). Insulin was also found to stimulate the incorporation of precursors into RNA (Wool, 1960) and effect a net synthesis of RNA in muscle (Wool, 1963), while it also stimulates amino acid incorporation into liver protein (Penhos and Krahl, 1962). It seems not improbable that a rather similar mechanism controls the genetic activity, or rather the expression of inherent genetic information, in animals as well as in microorganisms. What is obscure at present is why only some cells respond to the specific genetic stimulation and what inhibits the expression of the same genes in other cells. This is what is called development.

REFERENCES

Allen, J. M. (1963). *Biochem. Biophys. Res. Commun.* **11**, 201.

Amos, H., and Kearns, K. E. (1962). *Nature* **195**, 806.

Aronson, A. I., and McCarthy, B. J. (1961). *Biophys. J.* **1**, 215.

Avery, O. T., McLeod, C. M., and McCarthy, M. (1944). *J. Exptl. Med.* **79**, 137.

Barondes, S. H., and Nirenberg, M. W. (1962). *Science* **138**, 813.

Barondes, S. H., Dingmann, C. W., and Sporn, M. B. (1962). *Nature* **196**, 145.

Basilio, C., Wahba, A. J., Lengyel, P., Speyer, J. F., and Ochoa, S. (1962). *Proc. Natl. Acad. Sci. U. S.* **48**, 631.

Benzer, S. (1957). *In* "The Chemical Basis of Heredity" (W. D. McElroy and B. Glass, eds.), p. 70. Johns Hopkins Press, Baltimore, Maryland.

Benzer, S. (1961). *Proc. Natl. Acad. Sci. U. S.* **47**, 403.

Benzer, S. (1962). *Sci. Am.* **206**, 70.

Bergmann, F. H., Berg, P., and Dieckmann, M. (1961). *J. Biol. Chem.* **236**, 1735.

Brachet, J. (1960). "The Biological Role of Ribonucleic Acid." Elsevier, Amsterdam.

Bransome, E. O., and Reddy, W. (1963). *Arch. Biochem. Biophys.* **101**, 21.

Braunwalder, A., and Staehelin, M. (1963). Unpublished experiments.

Brenner, S., Jacob, F., and Meselson, M. (1961). *Nature* **190**, 576.

Cairns, J. (1963). *J. Mol. Biol.* **16**, 208.

Carruthers, B. M., and Winograd, A. I. (1962). *Am. J. Physiol.* **202**, 605.

Caspersson, T. (1950). "Cell Growth and Cell Function." Norton, New York.

Chapeville, F., Lipmann, F., Ehrenstein, G. von, Weisblum, B., Ray, W. J., and Benzer, S. (1962). *Proc. Natl. Acad. Sci. U. S.* **48**, 1086.

Chargaff, E. (1950). *Experientia* **6**, 201.

Chargaff, E., Zamenhof, S., Brawerman, G., and Kerin, L. (1950). *J. Am. Chem. Soc.* **72**, 3825.

Cheng, P.-Y. (1961). *Biochim. Biophys. Acta* **53**, 232.

Crick, F. H. C. (1963). *Science* **139**, 461.
Crick, F. H. C., Barnett, L., Brenner, S., and Watts-Tobin, R. J. (1961). *Nature* **192**, 1227.
Dintzis, H. M. (1961). *Proc. Natl. Acad. Sci. U. S.* **47**, 247.
Dunn, D. B. (1959). *Biochim. Biophys. Acta* **34**, 286.
Ehrenstein, G. von, Weisblum, B., and Benzer, S. (1963). *Proc. Natl. Acad. Sci. U. S.* **49**, 669.
Fleissner, E., and Borek, E. (1962). *Proc. Natl. Acad. Sci. U. S.* **48**, 1199.
Fraenkel-Conrat, H. (1956). *Am. J. Chem. Soc.* **78**, 882.
Fraenkel-Conrat, H., and Singer, B. (1957). *Biochim. Biophys. Acta* **24**, 540.
Fraenkel-Conrat, H., and Williams, R. C. (1955). *Proc. Natl. Acad. Sci. U. S.* **41**, 690.
Fuerst, C. R., and Stent, G. S. (1956). *J. Gen. Physiol.* **40**, 73.
Gardner, R. S., Wahba, A. J., Basilio, C., Miller, R. S., Lengyel, P., and Speyer, J. F. (1962). *Proc. Natl. Acad. Sci. U. S.* **48**, 2087.
Garrod, A. E. (1923). "Inborn Errors of Metabolism." Oxford Univ. Press, London and New York.
Gierer, A. (1963). *J. Mol. Biol.* **6**, 148.
Gierer, A., and Mundry, K. W. (1958). *Nature* **182**, 1457.
Gierer, A., and Schramm, G. (1956). *Nature* **177**, 702.
Greengard, O., and Acs, G. (1962). *Biochim. Biophys. Acta* **61**, 652.
Greengard, O., and Feigelson, P. (1961). *J. Biol. Chem.* **236**, 158.
Gros, F., Hiatt, H., Gilbert, W., Kurland, C. G., Risebrough, R. W., and Watson, J. D. (1961). *Nature* **190**, 581.
Grossi, L. G., and Moldave, K. (1960). *J. Biol. Chem.* **235**, 2370.
Hall, B. D., and Spiegelman, S. (1961). *Proc. Natl. Acad. Sci. U. S.* **47**, 137.
Harris, H. (1963). *Nature* **198**, 181.
Hayashi, M., and Spiegelman, S. (1961). *Proc. Natl. Acad. Sci. U. S.* **47**, 1564.
Hiatt, H. H. (1962). *J. Mol. Biol.* **5**, 217.
Hoagland, M. B. (1960). *In* "The Nucleic Acids" (E. Chargaff and J. N. Davidson, eds.), Vol. 3, p. 349. Academic Press, New York.
Hoagland, M. B., and Askonas, B. A. (1963). *Proc. Natl. Acad. Sci. U. S.* **49**, 130.
Holley, R. W., and Merrill, S. H. (1959). *J. Am. Chem. Soc.* **81**, 753.
Holley, R. W., Apgar, J., Merrill, S., and Zubkoff, P. L. (1961). *J. Am. Chem. Soc.* **83**, 4861.
Horiuchi, T., Horiuchi, S., and Mizuno, D. (1959). *Nature* **183**, 1529.
Horowitz, N. H., and Fling, M. (1956). *In* "Enzymes: Units of Biological Structure and Function" (O. H. Gaebler, ed.), p. 139. Academic Press, New York.
Huebner, H. (1962). *Deut. Med. Wochschr.* **87**, 438.
Ingram, V. M. (1957). *Nature* **180**, 326.
Ingram, V. M. (1959). *Biochim. Biophys. Acta* **36**, 402.
Ingram, V. M., and Pierce, J. G. (1962). *Biochemistry* **1**, 580.
Jacob, F., and Monod, J. (1961). *J. Mol. Biol.* **3**, 318.
Jacob, F., and Wollman, E. L. (1959). *In* "Recent Progress in Microbiology," 7th Intern. Congr. Microbiol., 1958 p. 15. Almquist & Wiksell, Uppsala.
Jacob, F., and Wollman, E. L. (1961). "Sexuality and Genetics of Bacteria." Academic Press, New York.
Josse, J., Kaiser, A. O., and Kornberg, A. (1961). *J. Biol. Chem.* **236**, 864.

Jukes, T. H. (1963). *Biochem. Biophys. Res. Commun.* **10**, 155.

Kassenaar, A. A. H., Querido, A., and Hauk, A. (1962). *In* "Protein Metabolism" (F. Gross, ed.), p. 222. Springer, Berlin.

Kataja, E., and Staehelin, M. (1962). *Helv. Physiol. Acta* **20**, C64.

Kendrew, J. C., Watson, H. C., Strandberg, B. E., Dickersen, R. E., Phillips, D. C., and Shore, V. C. (1961). *Nature* **190**, 666.

Knox, W. E. (1951). *Brit. J. Exptl. Pathol.* **32**, 462.

Korner, A. (1960). *Biochem. J.* **74**, 462.

Korner, A. (1961). *Biochem. J.* **81**, 292.

Korner, A. (1962). *In* "Protein Metabolism" (F. Gross, ed.), p. 8. Springer, Berlin.

Kostyo, J. L., and Knobil, E. (1959). *Endocrinology* **65**, 525.

Kuff, E. L., and Zeigel, R. F. (1960). *J. Biophys. Biochem. Cytol.* **7**, 465.

Kurland, C. G. (1960). *J. Mol. Biol.* **2**, 83.

La Cour, L. F., and Pelc, S. R. (1958). *Nature* **182**, 506.

La Cour, L. F., and Pelc, S. R. (1959). *Nature* **183**, 1455.

Lagerkvist, U., and Berg, P. (1962). *J. Mol. Biol.* **5**, 159.

Lehmann, I. R., Bessman, M. J., Simms, E. S., and Kornberg, A. (1958). *J. Biol. Chem.* **233**, 163.

Lengyel, P., Speyer, J. F., and Ochoa, S. (1961). *Proc. Natl. Acad. Sci. U. S.* **47**, 1936.

Lengyel, P., Speyer, J. F., Basilio, C., and Ochoa, S. (1962). *Proc. Natl. Acad. Sci. U.S.* **48**, 282.

Levinthal, C. (1959). *Brookhaven Symp. Biol.* **12**, 76.

Lima-de-Faria, A. (1962). *Progr. Biophys. Biophys. Chem.* **12**, 482.

Lipmann, F., Hülsmann, W. C., Hartmann, G., Boman, H. G., and Acs, G. (1959). *J. Cellular Comp. Physiol.* **54**, 75.

Littlefield, J. W., Keller, E. B., Gross, J., and Zamecnik, P. C. (1955). *J. Biol. Chem.* **217**, 111.

Lwoff, A. (1959). *In* "The Viruses" (F. M. Burnet and W. M. Stanley, eds.), Vol. 2, p. 187. Academic Press, New York.

McCarthy, J., and Britten, R. J. (1962). *Biophys. J.* **35**, 49, 57, 83.

Marks, P. A., Wilson, C., Kruh, J., and Gros, F. (1962). *Biochem. Biophys. Res. Commun.* **8**, 9.

Matthaei, J. H., Jones, O. W., Martin, R. G., and Nirenberg, M. W. (1962). *Proc. Natl. Acad. Sci. U. S.* **48**, 666.

Maxwell, E. S. (1962). *Proc. Natl. Acad. Sci. U. S.* **48**, 1639.

Meselson, M., and Stahl, F. W. (1958). *Proc. Natl. Acad. Sci. U. S.* **44**, 671.

Miescher, F. (1897). "Die histochemischen und physiologischen Arbeiten" (collected and edited by his friends), 2 vols. Vogel, Leipzig.

Monod, J. Changeux, J.-P., and Jacob, F. (1963). *J. Mol. Biol.* **6**, 306.

Nathans, O., and Lipmann, F. (1961). *Proc. Natl. Acad. Sci. U. S.* **47**, 497.

Nihei, T., and Cantoni, G. L. (1962). *Biochim. Biophys. Acta* **61**, 463.

Nirenberg, M. W., and Matthaei, J. H. (1961). *Proc. Natl. Acad. Sci. U. S.* **47**, 1588.

Nirenberg, M. W., Matthaei, J. H., and Jones, O. W. (1962). *Proc. Natl. Acad. Sci. U. S.* **48**, 104.

Niu, M. C., Cordova, L. C., Niu, L. C., and Radbill, C. L. (1962). *Proc. Natl. Acad. Sci. U. S.* **48**, 1964.

Nomura, M., Hall, B. D., and Spiegelman, S. (1960). *J. Mol. Biol.* **2**, 306.

Penhos, J. C., and Krahl, M. E. (1962). *Am. J. Physiol.* **202**, 349.

Preiss, J., Dieckmann, M., and Berg, P. (1961). *J. Biol. Chem.* **236**, 1748.

Roberts, R. B., Britton, R. J., and McCarthy, B. J. (1963). *In* "Molecular Genetics" (J. H. Taylor, ed.), Part 1, p. 291. Academic Press, New York.

Rudner, R., and Chargaff, E. (1962). *Biochim. Biophys. Acta* **55**, 997.

Rychlik, I., and Sorm, F. (1962). *Collection Czech. Chem. Commun.* **27**, 2433.

Scherrer, K., and Darnell, J. E. (1962). *Biochem. Biophys. Res. Commun.* **7**, 486.

Schuster, H., and Schramm, G. (1958). *Z. Naturforsch.* **13b**, 697.

Sibatani, A. S., de Kloet, S., Allfrey, V., and Mirsky, A. (1962). *Proc. Natl. Acad. Sci. U. S.* **48**, 471.

Simkin, J. L., and Work, T. S. (1957). *Biochem. J.* **65**, 307.

Sinsheimer, R. L. (1959). *J. Mol. Biol.* **1**, 43.

Slautterback, D. B., and Fawcett, D. W. (1959). *J. Biophys. Biochem. Cytol.* **5**, 441.

Sokoloff, L., Kaufmann, S., and Gelboin, H. V. (1962). *Biochim. Biophys. Acta* **52**, 410.

Spencer, M., Fuller, W., Wilkins, M. H. F., and Brown, G. L. (1962). *Nature* **194**, 1014.

Speyer, J. F., Lengyel, P., Basilio, C., and Ochoa, S. (1962a). *Proc. Natl. Acad. Sci. U. S.* **48**, 63.

Speyer, J. F., Lengyel, P., Basilio, C., and Ochoa, S. (1962b). *Proc. Natl. Acad. Sci. U. S.* **48**, 441.

Srb, A. M., and Horowitz, N. H. (1944). *J. Biol. Chem.* **154**, 129.

Staehelin, M. (1958). *Biochim. Biophys. Acta* **29**, 410.

Staehelin, M. (1959). *Experientia* **15**, 413.

Staehelin, M. (1960). *Experientia* **16**, 473.

Staehelin, M. (1962). *Colloq. Intern. Centre Natl. Rech. Sci. (Paris)* **106**, 249.

Staehelin, M., Schweiger, M., and Zachau, H.-G. (1963). *Biochim. Biophys. Acta* **68**, 129.

Stent, G. S. (1959). *In* "The Viruses" (F. M. Burnet and W. M. Stanley, eds.), Vol. 2, p. 237. Academic Press, New York.

Stent, G. S., and Fuerst, C. R. (1955). *J. Gen. Physiol.* **38**, 441.

Sueoka, N., and Cheng, T.-Y. (1962). *J. Mol. Biol.* **4**, 161.

Sueoka, N., and Yamane, T. (1962). *Proc. Natl. Acad. Sci. U. S.* **48**, 1454.

Takai, M., Kondo, N., and Osawa, S. (1962). *Biochim. Biophys. Acta* **55**, 416.

Talwar, G. P., and Gros, F. (1963). Personal communication.

Talwar, G. P., Panda, N. C., Savin, G. S., and Tolani, A. J. (1962). *Biochem. J.* **82**, 173.

Tanuka, T., and Knox, W. E. (1958). *J. Biol. Chem.* **234**, 1162.

Taylor, J. H. (1957). *Am. Naturalist* **91**, 209.

Taylor, J. H., Woods, P. S., and Hughes, W. T. (1951). *Proc. Natl. Acad. Sci. U. S.* **43**, 122.

Torriani, A. (1960). *Biochim. Biophys. Acta* **38**, 460.

Tsugita, A., and Fraenkel-Conrat, H. (1962). *J. Mol. Biol.* **4**, 73.

Tsugita, A., Fraenkel-Conrat, H., Nirenberg, M. W., and Matthaei, J. H. (1961). *Proc. Natl. Acad. Sci. U. S.* **47**, 846.

Vielmetter, W., and Schuster, H. (1960). *Z. Naturforsch.* **15b**, 304.

Volkin, E., and Astrachan, L. (1956). *Virology* **2**, 149.

Wacker, A., Trebst, A., and Simon, H. (1957). *Z. Naturforsch.* **12b**, 315.

Wahba, A. J., Gardner, R. S., Basilio, C., Miller, R. S., Speyer, J. F., and Lengyel, P. (1963). *Proc. Natl. Acad. Sci. U. S.* **49**, 116.

Warner, J. R., Rich, A., and Hall, C. E. (1962). *Science* **138**, 1399.

Warner, J. R., Knopf, P. M., and Rich, A. (1963). *Proc. Natl. Acad. Sci. U.S.* **49**, 122.

Watson, J. D., and Crick, F. H. C. (1953). *Nature* **171**, 737.

Weisblum, B., Benzer, S., and Holley, R. W. (1962). *Proc. Natl. Acad. Sci. U. S.* **48**, 1449.

Weiss, S. B. (1960). *Proc. Natl. Acad. Sci. U. S.* **46**, 1020.

Weiss, S. B., and Gladstone, L. (1959). *J. Am. Chem. Soc.* **81**, 4118.

Wettstein, A., Staehelin, T., and Noll, H. (1963). *Nature* **197**, 430.

Wilkins, M. F. H., Stokes, A. R., and Wilson, H. R. (1953). *Nature* **171**, 740.

Wittmann, H. G. (1962). *Z. Vererbungslehre* **93**, 491.

Wool, I. G. (1960). *Am. J. Physiol.* **199**, 719.

Wool, I. G. (1963). *Biochim. Biophys. Acta* **68**, 28.

Yĉas, M., and Vincent, W. S. (1960). *Proc. Natl. Acad. Sci. U. S.* **46**, 804.

Zachau, H. G., Tada, M., Lawson, W. B., and Schweiger, M. (1961). *Biochim. Biophys. Acta* **53**, 221.

Zimmermann, S. B., and Kornberg, A. (1961). *J. Biol. Chem.* **236**, 1480.

Addendum

Since the manuscript was submitted great progress has been made in various fields pertinent to the mechanism of information transfer. Only a few important findings should be added to the preceding discussion.

Nature of the Genetic Code

Leder and Nirenberg (1964) have made the discovery that in the absence of activating enzymes and protein synthesis ribosomes and sRNAs do interact in the presence of synthetic messenger polynucleotides. Since a trinucleotide is sufficient to cause the binding of a specific sRNA the trinucleotide nature of the code seems to be clearly established. The availability of trinucleotides with defined sequences has made it possible, furthermore, to elucidate the sequence of certain coding triplets (Leder and Nirenberg, 1964). Thus it was found, for instance, that among the three amino acids coded for by (A_2C) the following assignments can be made: asparagine, AAC; threonine, ACA; glutamine, CAA (Nirenberg et al., 1965).

It seems to be established that amino acids can be coded for by more than one triplet, i.e., that there is a degeneracy of the code. This is particularly evident from the isolation of a number of different sRNA's capable of accepting the same amino acids which can be separated by countercurrent distribution (Weisblum et al., 1965; Goldstein et al.,

1964) and which show different coding properties. Thus, the existence of leucine sRNA's with the coding properties for UC and for UG has been well established. Earlier attempts to demonstrate that the leucine from these different sRNA's was incorporated into specific positions of a defined protein synthesized *in vitro*, such as the hemoglobin or MS II phage protein, failed at first; this does not seem surprising now since Yamane and Sueoka (1963) showed that leucine-activating enzymes can perform an AMP-dependent transacylation from one leucine RNA to another. The problem was further studied by Weisblum *et al.* (1965) who found that the leucine from the RNA with the coding properties of UG was only incorporated into one single peptide in the hemoglobin chain.

The Ribosome-Messenger sRNA Complex

More insight has also been gained into the mechanism of the growth of the peptide chain on bacterial ribosomes. Gilbert (1963a) has demonstrated that the polyphenylalanine synthesized in the presence of polyuridic acid remains attached to the sRNA which is linked to the ribosome. Thus it seems that the nascent protein remains linked to the ribosome by the sRNA of the last amino acid which has been incorporated. The linking of this sRNA-polyphenylalanine has been shown to involve the 50 S subunit of the ribosome (Gilbert, 1963b). The removal by dialysis is reversible at higher Mg^{++} concentration (Schlesinger and Gros, 1963). A similar mechanism seems to operate in mammalian ribosomes (Wettstein and Noll, 1965).

The messenger RNA appears to attach itself to the 30 S subunit as judged from the specific attachment of polyuridylic acid to this subunit (Okamoto and Takanami, 1963). This attachment seems to involve a large number of nucleotides (approximately twenty-five), since this number of nucleotides of the messenger are rendered ribonuclease resistant by the binding to the ribosomes (Takanami and Zubay, 1964).

Transfer RNA

Recently, the first complete structure of one sRNA was reported (Holley *et al.*, 1965). This structure shows that no double-stranded complementarity of the two halves of the polynucleotide chain is possible. This is in accord with recent findings by Spencer and Poole (1965) who found that degradation products of ribosomal RNA showed regular helical regions, whereas sRNA did not. The minor bases, furthermore, are scattered over a wide range of the molecule although some clustering occurs in certain regions, one of which is probably the anticodon capable of binding to the messenger. Another region shows a specific sequence of five nucleotides which is probably of particular significance since it seems to be common to all sRNA molecules (Zamir *et al.*, 1965). It does not seem improbable that this common sequence is involved in the binding of sRNA to ribosomes.

How the messenger produced on the DNA triplet reaches the ribosomes upon which the proteins are synthesized still remains a puzzle. As more and more evidence accumulates, however, it appears that membranes are involved in this process in bacteria (Hendler *et al.*, 1964; Spiegelman, 1959) and in mammalian cells (Penman *et al.*, 1964; Howell *et al.*, 1964).

ADDENDUM REFERENCES

Gilbert, W. (1963a). *J. Mol. Biol.* **6**, 374.

Gilbert, W. (1963b). *J. Mol. Biol.* **6**, 389.

Goldstein, J., Bennet, T. P., and Craig, L. C. (1964). *Proc. Natl. Acad. Sci. U. S.* **51**, 119.

Hendler, R. W., Banfield, W. G., Tani, J., and Kuff, E. L. (1964). *Biochim. Biophys. Acta* **80**, 307.

Holley, R. W., Apgar, J., Everett, G. A., Madison, J. T., Marquesee, M., Merrill, S. H., Penswick, J. R., and Zamir, A. (1965). *Science* **147**, 1462.

Howell, R. R., Loeb, J. N., and Tomkins, G. M. (1964). *Proc. Natl. Acad. Sci. U. S.* **52**, 1241.

Leder, P., and Nirenberg, M. W. (1964). *Proc. Natl. Acad. Sci. U. S.* **52**, 1521.

Nirenberg, M. W., Leder, P., Bernfield, M., Brimacombe, R., Trupin, J., Rottman, F., and O'Neal, C. (1965). *Proc. Natl. Acad. Sci. U. S.* in press.

Okamoto, T., and Takanami, M. (1963). *Biochim. Biophys. Acta* **68**, 325.

Penman, S., Becker, Y., and Darnell, J. E. (1964). *J. Mol. Biol.* **8**, 541.

Schlesinger, O., and Gros, F. (1963). *J. Mol. Biol.* **7**, 350.

Spencer, M., and Poole, F. (1965). *J. Mol. Biol.* **11**, 314.

Spiegelman, S. (1959). "Recent Progress in Microbiology," Ahlquist & Wiksell, Stockholm, p. 81.

Takanami, M., and Zubay, G. (1964). *Proc. Natl. Acad. Sci. U. S.* **51**, 834.

Weisblum, B., Gonano, F., v. Ehrenstein, G., and Benzer, S. (1965). *Proc. Natl. Acad. Sci. U. S.* **53**, 328.

Wettstein, F. O., and Noll, H. (1965). *J. Mol. Biol.* **11**, 35.

Yamane, T., and Sueoka, N. (1963). *Proc. Natl. Acad. Sci. U. S.* **50**, 1093.

Zamir, A., Holley, R. W., and Marquesee, M. (1965). *J. Biol. Chem.* **240**, 1267.

Chapter 9

INFORMATIONAL MOLECULES
AND EMBRYONIC DEVELOPMENT

PHILIP GRANT

National Science Foundation
Washington, D. C.

I. Introduction

For a number of years the concepts of the information theory have contributed a useful framework upon which to construct explanations and models of biological phenomena. The brilliant successes in genetics in the last decade have established the view that complex biological macromolecules are indeed capable of storing and transmitting genetic and developmental information.

Elsasser (1958), reviewing the age-old problem of preformation versus epigenesis in terms of information theory and modern biology asserts that the informational content of the adult is far greater than could be stored in the primary sequence of macromolecular subunits contained in a fertilized egg. Adopting the epigenetic viewpoint, he affirms the presence in the fertilized egg of only a small portion of the total informational content of the organism, either in the form of coded macromolecules or, for that matter, any other configurational patterns and he stresses the acquisition of additional information, presumably from the environment, throughout the course of development. Raven (1961), on the other hand, argues that the informational content of the egg is greater than that contained in the genome and underlines the cytoplasm and cortex as major vehicles of developmental information. Moreover, he stresses that a major difference between the informational content of the adult and the egg resides in the degree of redundancy of information rather than in the specific informational content, which he contends, is equivalent. Raven defends the view of the preformationists and affirms that epigenetics elicits no change in specific information— rather the environment provides substrate and energy essential to the multiplication of information.

These traditional views have been brought into sharp contrast within the sophisticated framework of our modern concepts of gene replication, transcription, and translation at the molecular level. The current thinking concerning the mechanism and control of protein synthesis has been carefully reviewed in Chapter 8 and the question at issue for the developmental biologist is: To what extent can we apply the molecular models of gene action as derived from microbial systems to the multicellular aggregates that form the basis of morphogenesis at higher levels of organization?

The exciting developments in the genetics of phage and E. coli now provide the tools which may facilitate analyses of important questions relating to gene action during development. Furthermore, it seems imminently possible that experiments may be designed bridging the gap between different levels of organization, between the macromolecular and cell organelle, between the organelle and the cell. Grobstein (1962) has illuminated this key problem of embryogenesis, emphasizing the necessity of relating the events at one level of organization with those that occur at the next level. The challenging models that are derived from the microbial field suggest useful working hypotheses explaining the origin of specific proteins associated with cytodifferentiation. (Jacob and Monod, 1961, 1963). They may also offer some insight into the morphogenetic behavior of cell populations.

Can we assume, for example, that relatively homogeneous cell populations, given certain properties with respect to surface structure and enzymatic constitution, organize into a predictable tissue pattern? The formation of tissue fabrics from homogeneous and heterogeneous cell populations may be due to random interactions of cells whose surfaces are characterized by specified molecular patterns (Steinberg, 1964). Cell-specific, lipid-protein membrane systems on the surfaces of cells may define unique arrays of cell behavior, influence intercellular reactions, and ultimately determine the final architecture of multicellular aggregates. On the other hand, specificity of aggregation and adhesion may involve the production of specific mucoprotein matrices (Moscona, 1962) which temper the associative behavior of cells and specify the final tissue fabric achieved. Whether one accepts the Steinberg view or that proposed by Moscona, the population behavior of cells is determined by the properties of macromolecules at the surface (or adjacent to the surface), which in response to the external environment, may induce predictable behavioral patterns of cells leading ultimately to the formation of tissues. Eventually, then, one can assume that the kinetics of cell population interactions may be attributable to the species of macromolecules at the surface, and these, in turn, are regulated by the controlled expression of specific gene constellations. The problems of embryogenesis, however, extend beyond mechanisms of "transcription" and "translation" essential in cytodifferentiation. They require an understanding of the regulatory devices which successfully channel all levels of this process into integrative behavior between different cell populations resulting in meaningful cell and tissue fabrics with higher levels of organized activity.

Since the basic hypothesis applicable to our analysis of developmental phenomena is the controlled synthesis of macromolecules, it is essential to derive some understanding of the kinds of informational macromolecules that exist in the mature egg, their organization within the egg, the means of their expression, and their subsequent fate. Formulated into a series of questions, the problems of embryogenesis as they relate to the nature of information-bearing molecules, may be simply stated as follows: What kinds of informational macromolecules are contained within the egg? How are they organized into functional structures? How were they introduced into the egg? What kind of developmental information do they contain? When and how is the information read during the course of development? What factors control the reading of this information and at what levels is this control expressed? What new information is produced during development and how is it produced? These represent only a few of the many questions formulated within the context of the fashionable concepts of "information flow" in biological systems which one may ask of developmental systems. They direct our attention to those classes of macromolecules known to participate in the information transfer process, i.e., deoxyribonucleic acid (DNA), ribonucleic acid (RNA), and protein. An attempt will be made to analyze what is currently known about the developmental behavior of these macromolecules during embryogenesis as it relates to various morphogenetic activities. This will permit an evaluation of the relevance of microbial models to multicellular systems.

II. The Egg as a Developmental System

Arbitrarily, we separate a dynamic biological process, such as development, into well-defined segments or "time slices" to facilitate our analyses of those complex systems, since it is simpler to study the behavior of relatively homogeneous cell populations. Unfortunately, it is virtually impossible with embryonic systems to achieve the homogeneity and synchrony that one obtains in microbial populations. Each phase of embryogenesis, however, may be characterized as containing relatively homogeneous cell populations exhibiting more or less specific developmental phenomena. Oogenesis is characterized by a rapid and intense synthesis of specific yolk proteins; at fertilization, synchronous populations may be obtained undergoing activation and the initiation of first cleavage, while during cleavage the majority of cells undergo DNA replication, mitosis, and cell division. In later development, cell heterogeneity becomes more pronounced, yet it is still possible to isolate cell populations exhibiting specific patterns of cytodifferentiation. Each phase reveals a fundamental principle of development, having general significance and applicability to cell behavior in other systems. It becomes possible to single out these developmental phenomena and focus our attention on them in the light of our understanding of the macromolecular events of gene replication and transcription. All we can hope to accomplish at this point is a formulation of questions to be asked of developing systems within working hypotheses, accessible to fruitful investigation.

A. *The Origin of Primordial Germ Cells*

All too frequently, we forget the fertilized egg has had a long developmental history, which in itself, is responsible for its unusual morphogenetic properties. The egg arises from oocytes whose origin is the primordial germ cell. Either as a result of an early interaction with a specialized region of the egg cytoplasm, or as a result of some intrinsic modification, nuclei destined for germ cells undergo some primary differentiation distinct from somatic nuclei. Such "chosen" cells eventually migrate into the presumptive gonad region where they remain relatively quiescent, in some cases for years, until induced to a new behavioral pattern by some exogenous stimuli.

Some indication of the nature of the process may be obtained by referring briefly to the events of chromosomal diminution in *Ascaris* (Boveri, 1887) and chromosomal elimination in the insects *Sciara* and *Miaster* (Metz, 1938). In these cases the complete (or supernumerary) genome is retained by the germ cells, whereas the somatic cells exhibit profound chromosomal losses during early cleavages. In *Miaster*, for example, 36 of the 48 chromosomes found in the zygote are eliminated from the somatic nuclei in the female, while the full complement is retained in the germ line. The role of nucleocytoplasmic interactions in the determination of this nuclear behavior has been explored in a number of studies and all are in agreement that some cytoplasmic factor is responsible for eliciting specific chromatin activity (Boveri, 1910; King and Beams, 1938; Geigy, 1931). The molecular basis of this interaction and the mechanism of its regulation of DNA replication and the continuity of chromosome structure is completely unknown. Yet, this represents one of many instances of "information flow" in a direction opposite to that normally assumed to operate within cells. It is a control system that one would not expect to find in microbial systems, although in the ciliated protozoa, similar nucleocytoplasmic regulatory mechanisms operate to specify macro- and micronuclear behavior (Nanney, 1958).

In all instances of chromosome diminution, loss of chromosomal DNA occurs, and one wonders whether it involves elimination of a portion of the real genome in cells in which it occurs or a loss of genetically "inactive" DNA (heterochromatin?). Does the presence of extra DNA determine the fate of the germ cell? What is the mechanism of this determination? What is the fate of the DNA discharged into the cytoplasm during the process of elimination?

For a varying period of time, the primordial germ cells in the ovary are inactive until appropriate physiological stimuli initiate new patterns of activity. At some phase, a critical step in the history of the oocyte is initiated; namely, its differentiation. In insects (particularly dipterans) secondary oogonia embark on a series of ordered, limited divisions and in cases involving supernumerary chromosomes these divisions may be differential, only one of the daughter cells receiving the extra chromatin (Beermann, 1956). In the classical case of *Dytiscus*, differentiation between oocyte and nurse cells is also determined by a differential division, the oocyte ultimately receiving additional chromatin in the form of a ring of Feulgen-positive material around the metaphase plate during division. This extra chromatin is incorporated into the nucleus of the future oocyte.

Beermann (1956) suggests that the ability of the oocyte to enter meiosis may depend on this material. In most organisms, the major growth period of the oocyte during oogenesis occurs while the oocyte nucleus remains in a state of suspended meiosis, usually in the pachytene of the first meiotic prophase. Does this extra DNA within the germ line contain controlling elements, functioning to modify the physical behavior of the oocyte chromosomes, insuring the events leading to the all important stages of oocyte growth? The extra chromatin eliminated from the somatic line and retained in the germ line is generally considered to be heterochromatin. Schultz (1956) has presented evidence that heterochromatic regions may affect genetic loci via their influence on nucleic acid syntheses.

However, the mechanisms of heterochromatin function are quite obscure. Presumably, its presence modifies coiling of the DNA chain. This should influence gene replication as well as gene transcription since a condensation of a DNA coil may physically prevent its function as a template.

It seems possible, therefore, that retention of extra chromatin in germ lines is related to the control of DNA syntheses essential to the initiation and regulation of the complex events of meiosis, the fundamental distinguishing feature of the presumptive gamete. Maturation during oogenesis, involving the syntheses of yolk and the establishment of the morphogenetic potential of the egg proceeds during the suspended prophase of meiosis. This condition undoubtedly contributes to the elaborate structural modifications that occur in chromosomes (the lampbrush found in many elasmobranchs, teleosts, amphibians and sauropsida). These, in turn must be responsible for the intense nuclear activity characteristic of oogenesis, as evidenced by a remarkable increase in nuclear size, and the formation of numerous nucleoli. Extensive evidence of nucleolar metabolic activity (its close proximity to the chromosomes, the accumulation of RNA within nucleoli, extrusion of nucleoli from the nucleus) supports the view that the major direction of information flow during this period is from nucleus to oocyte cytoplasm.

B. *The Vegetative Phases of Oogenesis*

The details of this critical phase of development have been carefully presented by Williams in Chapter 1 of this volume. Only a few comments relating to the direction of information flow, its storage, and its subsequent expression during morphogenesis are necessary.

The oocyte nucleus is not alone in transmitting "informationally important macromolecules" to the cytoplasm of the maturing oocyte. The accessory, follicle, and nurse cells, also display a heightened metabolic activity, particularly of their nuclei. The oocyte, therefore, is the recipient of developmental information from a number of different nuclei, including its own. Moreover, in many systems, the contribution from the accessory cells may be the predominant source of informational macromolecules. The nurse cells in insects with their elaborately branched polyploid or polytene nuclei play a dominant role in maturation, contributing significantly to the accumulation of nutrients within the oocyte. Besides the synthesis of a wide variety of nutritive substances, accessory cell nuclei are also responsible for the synthesis and transmission of a spectrum of polynucleotides and nucleoproteins stored for subsequent use during development as sites for the syntheses of developmentally significant enzymes and structural proteins.

Do all the genes contribute to the oocyte cytoplasm during maturation or are only a small portion expressed? If only a small proportion of the genome is expressed during oogenesis, which genes are expressed? Those involved in oogenesis only? Those involved in fertilization and cleavage? Is it possible to determine the character of the messenger RNA population produced during oogenesis? If all genes are functioning can we assume a differential lability of different gene messengers?

Besides the production of numerous macromolecules, many of which bear developmental information, the subsequent translation of that information during development is conditioned by the elaborate structural relations that are formed during the maturation of the egg. Yet, when we analyze this process, the morphogenetic potential of the egg exhibits some restriction. Its elaborate cytoplasmic organization seems limited only to the production of a population of cells, a blastula elaborated through rapid cell division.

Several instances of cleavage without nuclei have been reported (Harvey, 1936; Briggs et al., 1951) resulting in blastulae without functional chromatin, incapable of further development. Subsequent morphogenetic events are dependent upon the presence of functional nuclei. The organization of the egg at the time of fertilization may be conceived as specifically designed to replicate nuclei during early cleavage, to reproduce developmental information, and to supply each daughter cell with an equivalent genome. Numerous studies with metabolic inhibitors demonstrate that cleavage is generally quite insensitive to a variety of chemical and physical agents. Observations of such relative cleavage insensitivity, of maternal effects, and of the insignificance of nuclei in segmentation agree with the hypothesis that egg organization, differentiated during oogenesis, is initially equipped to elaborate a multicellular system, itself capable of morphogenesis. One may say that cleavage is preformed, whereas morphogenesis is epigenetic.

C. *Egg Activation and Cleavage*

The activation of the egg following the attachment and penetration of sperm is the stimulus to the "reading" of the stored developmental information. Impressive structural and metabolic alterations occur at the moment of activation initiating the expression of the morphogenetic potential. Is the genome activated at this time? How? If not, how are the subsequent events of cleavage controlled? What factors regulate DNA replication and how do they relate to the initial events of activation? What is the developmental significance of sperm-egg interactions at fertilization and what influence do these have on the replication and transcription of DNA?

Early cleavage is synchronous and is primarily committed to DNA replication, mitosis, and cell division. As cleavage progresses, synchrony is lost and is followed by the appearance of a mitotic gradient (Agrell, 1964). The degree of synchrony may vary from species to species, usually ending early in so-called mosaic eggs (in some cases after the third division cycle), whereas in other embryos (insects) it may continue until the eighth to ninth mitotic cycle. Agrell (1963) observed that during the beginning of the ninth cleavage cycle in the *Calliphora* embryos, while all nuclei pass from interphase to metaphase in synchrony, anaphase takes the form of a mitotic gradient, appearing first at the anterior, or micropyle pole of the egg, spreading gradually over the egg. Subsequent cycles exhibit a progressive anterior-posterior mitotic gradient. During the tenth cycle, the pole cell (presumptive germ cell line) buds off and adopts a mitotic rhythm of its own.

The morphogenetic importance of gradients of mitosis must not be underestimated. It represents the first evidence of any morphogenetic heterogeneity of cell populations during early development. In some instances it may be associated with a gradient in blastomere size. In many mollusk and annelid eggs, the first division is responsible for an initial "differentiation" of two blastomeres of unequal size, AB and CD. This size difference persists during subsequent synchronous divisions, but very soon, the derivatives of the CD blastomere establish a separate, irregular mitotic rhythm. Derivatives of these blastomeres later assume a dominant role during larval morphogenesis. Spratt (1963) has focused particular attention on the morphogenetic role of mitotic gradients in the early chick blastoderm. He has suggested that form changes, regulatory ability, and the apparent migratory activities of the endodermal layers of the blastoderm may be attributed to the existence of a "growth center" of high mitotic activity, and "cell pressure" produced by mitosis is implicated in establishing the axial organization of the early chick embryo.

Agrell (1963) suggests that the graded time sequence of interphases in relation to mitosis must evoke a corresponding graded differentiation. This may be more evident in echinoderm development where micromeres established in the fourth cycle depart from the mitotic activity of most blastomeres and establish a pattern unique to themselves. In contrast to the other cells, the micromeres exhibit a division delay and their descendants are first to exhibit any significant change in behavior as they migrate out into the blastocoel cavity as primary mesenchyme. The precocity of this behavior may be related to the earlier onset of prolonged interphases in this cell population.

Profound modifications of cell surfaces, critical to their subsequent behavior during migration, specific adhesion, and aggregation may also be intimately related to the division cycle and its regulation.

Trinkaus (1963) has observed that isolated blastula cells from a *Fundulus* blastula exhibit little adhesive properties in culture, remaining spheroidal without flattening against a glass surface. Early gastrula cells, under similar conditions, exhibit flattening very early in culture and adhere to the glass substratum. The number of flattened cells increases gradually *in vitro* presumably at the same rate at which it occurs *in vivo*. This behavioral change is inversely related to the mitotic activity, since blastula cells are mitotically more active than the cells of the gastrula. Regrettably, no data are available comparing different regions of the embryo with respect to this property, since it would be of interest to compare the mitotically more active with less active regions at the same stage.

The mitotic events of cleavage generate a blastula with unusual morphogenetic potential. Heterogeneous cell populations are established exhibiting quantitative differences with respect to the original constituents of the egg. For some constituents (yolk), a distinct gradient exists related to the original polarity of the egg. Gradients with respect to other constituents (nucleic acids) as well as cell organelles (mitochondria) also appear. Because of this cellular heterogeneity, there are early physiological heterogeneities. Mitotic activity, cell adhesivity, and cell migration exhibit gradients over the surface of the blastula. This implies the existence of micropopulations of relative homogeneity distributed in a gradient fashion over the blastula. Each micropopulation, a physiological entity unto itself, interacts with other micropopulations at indistinct marginal regions where the properties of one gradually merge with those of the other. Gradients of pH, oxygen, and CO_2 reinforce cell population heterogeneity. Nevertheless, in spite of extensive physiological heterogeneity at the blastula stage, the developmental potential of nuclei of individual blastomeres is largely equivalent. Briggs and King (1952) have demonstrated that blastula nuclei of *Rana pipiens* are totipotent, capable of initiating normal development when transferred into activated, enucleated eggs.

It is known that early regionalizations are evident in cleavage stages of most embryos. In the amphibian egg, the classic experiments with the gray crescent region in the newly fertilized egg (Spemann, 1938), more recently confirmed by the original cortex transplantation experiments of Curtis (1960), have demonstrated that a developmentally significant regionalization exists in the fertilized egg, presumably within the cortex. It is of interest that the nature of this cortical field changes with cleavage so that by the 8-cell stage the potency of the gray crescent region has changed (Curtis, 1962). Similarly, in the eggs of echinoderms, some degree of differentiation already exists in the fertilized egg, since it can be shown that animal halves develop differently from vegetal halves when isolated at the zygote stage. One can agree with Raven (1961) that regionalization results from a cortical differentiation pre-existing in the egg. The extreme case, of course, is the high degree of precocious differentiation exhibited by eggs characterized by so-called determinate cleavage in which the pattern of cleavage seems to be related to the highly coordinated segregation of specified cytoplasmic and cortical "information" spatially organized within the fertilized egg. It is, of course, interesting to speculate as to the nature and organization of this information at the molecular level. Does it represent a specified distribution of "programmed" ribosomes?

The events of cleavage are independent of nuclear control since a normally functioning genome is not essential. Yet nuclear behavior and interactions with cytoplasm, cortex, and yolk during this period must have profound effects on later development.

What activates DNA replication and cell division at fertilization? What is the mechanism responsible for early cleavage synchrony? How is the mitotic gradient established? What is the basis for the decline in mitotic activity in the blastula? Is there a relationship between the number of rounds of DNA replication and the transcription of DNA later in development? The factors controlling DNA replication are intimately related to the first events of morphogenesis and require more attention than is now being given to them. A recent review by Dettlaff (1964) attempts to analyze some of these questions.

D. *Cell Division and Cell Differentiation*

The literature is full of references to the apparent incompatibility between cell division and cell differentiation. In all instances of embryogenesis, in situations of vegetative or regenerative growth, the initial phases are characterized by a period of rapid cell division creating a population of morphogenetically active cells. Subsequently, these cell populations pursue a developmental course leading ultimately to cytodifferentiation. During the morphogenetically active phase the frequency of mitosis in the cell population decreases markedly leaving only a small population of dividing cells contrasted with an enormous population of differentiating, mitotically inactive cells. In tissue cultures the situation is reversed, since culture conditions either select cells that still retain the ability to divide or transform differentiated cells into a mitotically active condition, rapidly eliminating vestiges of their differentiated state. In either case it is rare to find a cell simultaneously undergoing cytodifferentiation and cell division.

This phenomenon has recently been the object of intense analysis by Holtzer and his group (Holtzer *et al.*, 1960; Stockdale *et al.*, 1963) who have studied the relationship between cell division and differentiation in embryonic cartilage. It has been observed that rapidly dividing chondrocytes lose the potentialities for synthesizing specific molecules, such as chondroitin sulfate, essential to the differentiation of cartilage. It would appear from these studies that stimulation of cell division in the artificial environment of *in vitro* culture leads to morphological and biochemical simplification. This has been the general result of establishing a variety of differentiated cells in culture.

It has been recognized, however, that many cell lines in culture no longer exhibit a normal karyotype. Levan and Biesele (1958) studying primary cultures of trypsinized chick embryo cells clearly demonstrated the early appearance of karyotypic abnormalities that accumulate through several transfer generations. The evidence that embryonic tissues when placed in culture do exhibit, even in the first generation, a high frequency of abnormal mitoses—a frequency which increases greatly after trypsin treatment—may explain the observed failure of differentiation after several generations as monolayers. As the cell line is subcultured, active selection of cells which survive and proliferate under the *in vitro* culture conditions is the rule (Hsu and Moorehead, 1957). In all instances observed, the karyotype is generally abnormal and one must expect fundamental changes in the physiology of cells and in their morphogenetic capacity. Human cell lines and neoplasms in culture exhibit the same tendency toward a heteroploid condition as the best adapted for rapid growth *in vitro*. It should be noted that not all cells in culture, or rapidly dividing cell populations like neoplasms, necessarily exhibit abnormal karyotypes.

The persistence of the differentiated state in adrenal cell culture has been reported (Buonassisi *et al.*, 1962; Sato and Buonassisi, 1964). Several recent studies of muscle cell differentiation in colonies derived from single cell platings (Konigsberg, 1963) have indicated that cells morphologically identifiable as myoblasts are capable of division and ultimate differentiation into myotubes with typical muscle cell myofibrils and cross striations. The culture of myoblasts in a monolayer situation from groups of small cells (and single cell clones) results in muscle differentiation usually between days 7 and 10. Konigsberg suggests that failure of many cell populations to retain the differentiated state in culture may be attributed to changes occurring in cells including loss of ability to aggregate and loss of specific antigens prior to any significant proliferation.

In Konigsberg's analysis of the formation of differentiated myotubes from single cell clones, the rates of cell division and the total number of divisions do not affect the capacity of these cells to differentiate. In the conditions employed (conditioned media) cells arising late in culture presumably after passing through 20–26 divisions could differentiate as well as cells having undergone only 4–8 divisions early in the culture. It seems as if there is a population of rapidly dividing cells (a clone of stem cells) continuing to produce differentiating myoblasts. As soon as the cells become included in the myotube, they cease to divide and differentiate the characteristic muscle morphology. The proliferating myoblasts are morphologically different from intermixed fibroblast-like cells and retain this difference during the course of proliferation.

The conditions of culture employed by Konigsberg (the conditioned medium) are different from those used by Holtzer, whose major purpose in inducing monolayer growth is to force rapid proliferation and cell migration. This behavior may induce leaching and dilution of essential nutrients, growth factors, and morphogenetic materials. Modifications experienced by cells under these conditions may be irreversible (karyotypic?) and may also reflect the loss of ability to aggregate, a primary requirement for tissue differentiation (Moscona, 1962).

It is evident that cell behavior in culture is governed by the culture situation. The capacity of cells to proliferate or to differentiate may be related to the nature and concentration of specific nutrients in a medium rather than any profound alteration in the genome or in its underlying control patterns. To what extent do nutritional factors function as casual agents or modifying agents in differentiation?

It has been shown that the spreading of cells on a substratum and the physical nature of the substratum have profound effects on the behavior of cells and their ultimate differentiation (Weiss, 1962). Form and shape changes, adhesiveness, and cell-to-cell contacts are intimately dependent upon the chemical composition of the medium, its ionic content, pH, and presence or absence of specific proteins. The presence of horse serum in the medium induces (or promotes) the spreading and adhesive tendencies of monkey kidney cells. In a medium free of serum, these cells become spherical, detach, and exhibit an entirely different pattern of behavior. Ambrose (1964) observed that the ability of lymph node cultures to exhibit a second antibody response in culture is related to the hydrocortisone concentration in serum. Moreover, it was also found that the presence of serum reduced the effective period when such cells continue to maintain the "differentiated state" as exhibited by antibody production. Ambrose explains the serum effect by citing its promotion of cell migration, an activity that precludes tissue differentiation. Local variations in oxygen and CO_2 concentrations produce profound changes in cell shape and surface activity (Weiss, 1962), and similar alterations in cell behavior are induced by contact with other cells. The behavior of cells is specific to cell type. Chick embryo liver, kidney, and retinal cells differ from monkey kidney cells in their greater adhesiveness to glass in the absence of horse serum. Flattened, spread, migrating cells expose a far greater surface to the environment than compact, spherical cells. Altered cell morphology must "condition" the surrounding medium in different ways and influence either the differentiated or proliferative potentialities of cell populations.

Proliferation of cells is dependent upon the complex of organic constituents of the surrounding medium. Some cell lines in culture display specific requirements for nutrients—in some cases a requirement for only one or two amino acids. Eagle and Piez (1962) have shown that the requirements in dispersed cell cultures will vary widely according to the population density. A wide variety of substances synthesized by cells are incorporated into the medium and become essential for growth. Cells will not grow unless a critical mass of cells is achieved, capable, presumably, of sustaining a concentration of unique growth nutrients. The magnitude of critical mass undoubtedly varies with cell

type and with the specific metabolite in question. At low population
densities, specific metabolites are probably lost to the medium at a rate
in excess of the biosynthetic capacity of the cells.

Is there a direct correlation between the general morphology of cells
in culture and their functional behavior? Does the spread, attached,
monolayer organization favor cell division in distinction to the compact
"package" state which favors differentiation? Moscona (1962) has shown
that the longer cells remain in monolayer culture, the greater is their
inability to aggregate into compact tissue masses. The size of the aggregates diminish with time, and this is usually accompanied by a loss in
ability to differentiate. Similarly, in those tissue interaction systems
studied by Grobstein (1964) and his colleagues (Wessells, 1964a,b; Rutter et al., 1964) an essential condition fostering pancreatic differentiation
is a prior "packaging" of the epithelial cells into compact masses, possibly
under the influence of inducing mesenchyme. Do cells exhibiting a maximum exposure of surface to the medium and facilitating a maximum
exchange of materials develop into replicating populations rather than
one equipped for differentiation? Conversely, do cells having limited
capability of free exchange with the environment tend toward differentiation? The Stanford group has observed that maximum mitotic activity
(and DNA synthesis as measured by thymidine incorporation) is found
in the peripheral layer of cells in a compact mass of differentiating pancreatic epithelium. There is a distinct peripherocentral gradient of
maturation, with maximum attainment of the differentiated state (as
measured by the appearance of zymogen granules and the synthesis of
amylase) achieved in the center of the tissue mass. Differentiation of
pancreatic epithelium is dependent upon exposure to mesenchyme (any
mesenchyme functions in this system) and this mesenchyme can now
be replaced by extracts of chick embryos (Grobstein, 1964; Wessells,
1964c). By varying the concentration of embryo juice, pancreatic epithelium can grow and differentiate in the absence of mesenchyme, although the amount of zymogen granule differentiation is not as great
as that obtained in a mesenchyme "induced" control. The basis of differentiation may therefore be nutritional with cells depending upon
extrinsic nutritional cues to initiate the pattern of differentiation.

Systems like the pancreas inductive system described above have
attained a level of control and understanding which may now facilitate
analyses of questions about regulation at the molecular level. The investigations of Wessells (1964b) are directed toward an understanding
of the relationship between DNA replication and transcription during
cytodifferentiation. The complex phenomenon of inductive tissue interactions may now be resolved into its components. Neighboring cells

extrude nutrients which influence cell shape, migration, adhesiveness, aggregation, proliferation, and cytodifferentiation. Each of these properties represents an essential component of the stepwise maturation of a differentiating cell population. At the molecular level, each of these phenomena must be translated into biochemical or enzymatic terms and ultimately transposed to the level of the genome. Understanding of developmental phenomena will be achieved when we can answer such questions as: "Can a strand of DNA replicate and transcribe simultaneously?" or, "Does DNA require a determined number of rounds of replication before it can begin transcribing in embryonic systems?" Systems have already been devised to permit answers to these and many other questions in embryonic as well as in microbial cell populations. In the sections that follow an effort will be made to evaluate some of the vast amount of data relating to informational macromolecules and their role in embryogenesis. If it succeeds in illuminating a few of the exciting new areas of investigation, and provides a limited scan of the promising future potentialities, this modest goal will have been achieved.

III. The Developmental Behavior of DNA

A. *Oogenesis*

Williams (Chapter 1 of this volume) has already reviewed considerable literature directed toward the question of the formation and metabolism of DNA during egg maturation. In this section some phenomena concerning the patterns of DNA synthesis and their control as they relate to the storage and organization of informational macromolecules in the egg will be briefly examined. An attempt will be made to evaluate these phenomena within the context of the questions posed previously (page 489). It will be impossible to include an exhaustive review of these problems and we must limit ourselves to a few issues which are critical to morphogenesis and differentiation.

1. CYTOPLASMIC DNA

The process of egg formation in animals exhibits a common feature—the inclusion of additional nuclear material in the cytoplasm of the developing oocyte. There is, unfortunately, little information about the nature of these materials; however, a good deal of the cytoplasmic influence over the behavior of nuclei and of the cell during embryogenesis may be attributed to the existence within the cytoplasm of macromolecules which regulate information transfer between nucleus and cytoplasm.

Morphogenesis as exhibited in the protozoa is strongly influenced by the cytoplasm; in some cases, specific regions of the cytoplasm are involved in determining the morphogenetic role of the nucleus (Weisz, 1954), and in other instances the specificity of surface proteins (antigenicity) is mediated largely by cytoplasmic factors (Nanney, 1958). Are such epigenetic phenomena related to the existence in the cytoplasm of copies of DNA found in the nucleus? During each conjugation cycle, elements of the genome (macronucleus) are emptied into the cytoplasm prior to genetic transfer and these may continue to function in genetic control.

DNA in the cytoplasm of ameba is indicated by cytoplasmic incorporation of tritium-labeled thymidine (Plaut and Sagan, 1958; Rabinovitch and Plaut, 1962a,b). A discrete particle, 0.3–0.5 μ in diameter (containing RNA also), seems to be the site of DNA (Rabinovitch and Plaut, 1962b). It is capable of self-duplication and its replication is unrelated to the presence of a nucleus. Although the evidence does not eliminate the possibility of the existence of intracellular parasites, it is suggestive of extranuclear DNA which may have an essential function in the physiology of these cells.

In fern embryos (Bell, 1960; Bell and Muhlethaler, 1962) DNA in the cytoplasm has been reported, its role presumably being associated with the formation of plastids. Plastids appear to arise from nuclear membranes that peel off into the cytoplasm. Plastid DNA has been confirmed in a number of studies (Gibor and Izawa, 1963; Gibor and Granick, 1964; Ris and Plaut, 1962; Sager and Ramanis, 1963; Sager and Ishida, 1963) and has been implicated as contributing to a cytoplasmic inheritance in algae. The nature of chloroplast DNA has been determined by Sager and Ishida (1963) and shown to be different from nuclear DNA in base composition and density.

Although it is generally assumed that plant cytoplasmic DNA is related to the ontogeny and specificity of plastids, the presence in plant tissues of two kinds of metabolically different functional DNA's has been reported in root tips and embryo tissue with respect to the incorporation and retention of a P^{32} label (Sampson et al., 1963). One fraction (high molecular weight) retains the label and could be considered the more stable component. The other fraction (low molecular weight) exhibits a greater turnover, losing the label shortly after its incorporation. The base ratios of these two DNA's were also shown to be distinctive. It is noteworthy that the labile DNA is found only in tissues which are undergoing some sort of differentiation.

The existence of heterogeneous DNA is not a new observation since Bendich et al. (1953) reported on the heterogeneity of DNA in animal tissues. Heterogeneity of DNA with respect to density and base composition has also been observed in a number of other tissues, employing the more sophisticated techniques current today (Cheng and Sueoka, 1963).

Cytoplasmic DNA is more generally distributed than the observations above suggest. Chèvremont, and his associates in a series of publications (Chèvremont et al., 1959, 1961; Chèvremont, 1963) have observed DNA under special conditions in the cytoplasm of fibroblasts in tissue culture, using Feulgen staining and tritium-labeled thymidine autoradiography. They report that DNA is associated with the mitochondria, exhibits a dynamic flux during the cell cycle, and is presumably related to mitosis. These observations were made on cells treated by DNase (neutral or acid) and/or heating and cooling, agents undoubtedly deranging the normal metabolism of DNA and producing an accumulation of DNA in the cytoplasm. Thymidine incorporation does occur in the cytoplasm and is eliminated by treatment with DNase. It appears that cytoplasmic DNA is not derived from the nucleus during the treatment.

Egg formation in animals is also characterized by an unusual behavior of DNA. Cells destined to become mature eggs are characterized by the early possession of special or additional chromatin material (chromosome diminution, chromosome bodies, supernumeraries, etc.). Painter (1959) has suggested that the retention of chromosomal material by presumptive germ cells is related to the establishment of a store of cytoplasmic nucleic acids in the mature egg. In addition, maturing eggs accumulate large amounts of DNA or DNA-like material in their cytoplasm, either as a result of the activity of the oocyte nucleus or more usually as a result of the incorporation of nuclear material from accessory cell nuclei and nurse cells. In sponges and coelenterates, for example, oocyte volume increases by the direct fusion of neighboring cells with the oocyte cytoplasm. The nuclei usually "disappear" in the cytoplasm, their components presumably enzymatically transformed into low molecular weight precursors. The disappearance of stainability once the nucleus enters the cytoplasm is assumed to represent degradation of chromatin into smaller components. Stainability is, however, no satisfactory criterion for the presence of DNA since dilution by large volumes of cytoplasm and changes in physical state (hydration) are sufficient to prevent staining even in the nucleus. Consequently, loss of stainability of nuclear fragments in the cytoplasm cannot be assumed to reflect a loss of the macromolecular structure of DNA. The fact that under certain situations DNA can be demonstrated in the cytoplasm by Feulgen staining as well as by thymidine incorporation (Chèvremont et al., 1961) indicates that polynucleotide DNA can persist in the cytoplasm of animal cells.

   a. Analytical Procedures. The accumulation of large amounts of DNA in the cytoplasm of eggs of many animal species and the relative ease of detection of DNA by analytical and microbiological assay suggests an important role of DNA in the development of these eggs. It is essential, however, to assess the reliability of the methods for demonstrating this DNA in eggs and embryos and to ascertain, where possible, the nature of this material. Reviews of the early literature in this field are to be found in Brachet (1950, 1954) and Løvtrup (1959). Early analyses of DNA in unfertilized eggs of sea urchins were somewhat contradictory. While Brachet (1933) was reporting relatively small amounts of DNA in these eggs, a few like Blanchard (1935) and Schmidt (1934) were reporting DNA in appreciable amounts. Schmidt relied on the Feulgen reaction, and his observations pointed to the presence of DNA in the cytoplasm. This was immediately criticized because of the nonspecificity of the Feulgen reaction in lipid-rich eggs. The plasmal reaction was generally assumed to be responsible for cytoplasmic Feulgen staining [and is still a criticism of similar reports of Feulgen-positive egg cytoplasm (Grosch, 1958)] and at a time when DNA was being relegated to the nucleus and RNA to the cytoplasm, the weight of opinion quickly banished the heretical thought from the discussions current at the time. Blanchard's observations, however, were based on chemical analyses of kilogram quantities of unfertilized eggs. He reported measurable amounts of DNA, contesting Brachet's hypothesis concerning the synthesis of DNA from RNA during development. These data, however, were also unreliable since contamination from ovarian tissue was a strong possibility. Obviously, the resolution of these contradictory observations had to await further refinements in analytical and cytochemical techniques.

   When the tempo of nucleic acid investigations increased, newer procedures were applied to developing systems. This occurred when the relationship of DNA to the gene was being developed, when the constancy hypothesis was elaborated, and the relation between DNA content and chromosome number was being firmly established. Schmidt *et al.* (1948) reported the synthesis of DNA during development in *Arbacia*, based on their technique of isolation of phosphorus compounds. The amount of DNA per egg as calculated by Mazia (1949) was approximately thirty times that contributed by the sperm. Later, Vendrely and Vendrely (1949) found in *Arbacia* and *Paracentrotus* that the egg contained an amount of DNA almost 290 times that of the sperm. Elson *et al.* (1954) employing a modified Schmidt-Tann-hauser procedure for isolation and assaying DNA either microbiologically or colorimetrically by the Dische reaction reported that the egg contained 5–28 times more DNA than the sperm. Later criticisms of the Schmidt-Tannhauser technique, particularly with respect to specificity and contamination by other phosphate compounds, placed these results in doubt (Drasher, 1953).

The development of the microbiological assay technique by Hoff-Jørgensen (1951) for the determination of DNA and its application to eggs and embryos (Hoff-Jørgensen and Zeuthen, 1951; Hoff-Jørgensen, 1954) did much to stimulate interest in this problem. At the same time Sze (1953) reported an amount of DNA in the *Rana pipiens* egg 95,000 times that found in the sperm, using a modification of the Schmidt-Tannhauser technique. Different values were reported by Brachet (1954) for some European frog species, using other extraction and assay procedures. Agrell and Persson (1956) also reported values for echinoderm eggs that were in excess of those published by Hoff-Jørgensen (1954), while Marshak and Marshak (1953, 1954, 1955a,b) presented evidence questioning the existence of DNA in *Arbacia* eggs, even within the nuclei. These latter authors claimed that all of the so-called cytoplasmic DNA could be attributed to contaminating follicle cells and polar bodies adhering to the egg.

Baltus and Brachet (1962) have reported amounts of DNA in frog eggs using a fluorimetric ultramicrochemical method which gave values and patterns of synthesis identical to those obtained with the microbiological assay. It seems that as the analytical methods are refined, the amounts of DNA observed in eggs are much less than those previously reported. However, disagreement continues since Haggis (1964a) using the fluorimetric assay has reported that the *Rana pipiens* egg contains approximately 0.2 μg DNA, and can be as much as 0.5 μg depending on assay. Haggis criticizes the microbiological assay procedure since it depends upon hydrolysis of the insoluble polynucleotides into assayable nucleotides by DNase. A number of investigators have reported difficulties in obtaining complete hydrolysis of the DNA under the conditions employed (Grant, 1958a; Løvtrup and Roos, 1957). At best, Grant reported 80% hydrolysis. Interfering substances are known to effect the microbiological assay (Løvtrup and Roos, 1957) and careful evaluation of the conditions of assay to insure optimal amounts of all growth factors is essential.

For those using the microbiological assay, differences have been reported as a result of variations in the method of DNA extraction. A prior cold acid treatment of the egg or embryo homogenate to extract soluble nucleosides and/or nucleotides usually yields values for DNA half those obtained without preliminary extraction of acid-soluble nucleotides (Grant, 1958a; Kuriki and Okazaki, 1959; Sugino, 1957; Sugino et al., 1960). The Japanese investigators were able to demonstrate the existence of deoxyribosidic-choline complexes in the acid-soluble extract only after digestion of the extract with snake venom. These observations indicate that prior determinations of DNA by the methods of Hoff-Jørgensen (Hoff-Jørgensen, 1954; Gregg and Løvtrup, 1955) were made on mixtures of acid-soluble and acid-insoluble deoxynucleotide-containing compounds.

Dawid (1963), in his efforts to extract and characterize cytoplasmic DNA from *Rana pipiens* eggs, observed an association of DNA with protein in a relatively firm complex which influenced the solubility of DNA. It is possible, therefore, that reported variations in the amount of DNA may simply be a measure of the relative extractability of DNA under different extraction procedures (Løvtrup and Roos, 1961).

Indicative of the difficulties associated with the measurement of DNA in eggs are the observations of Durand (1961) on *Gryllus* ovaries. Using four different methods, four different results have been obtained as shown in the following tabulation.

Assay	µg DNA per egg	Diploid equivalents
Phosphorus	1.00	100,000
Deoxyribose	0.083	7,400
Bound thymine	0.013	1,200
Bound adenine	0.004	440

Durand interprets these results by suggesting that there is a wide spectrum of substances behaving like DNA in the egg. One substance behaves like a true DNA and other components exhibit a high thymine to adenine ratio suggesting cytoplasmic compounds rich in thymine nucleotides.

Complexing of DNA with other substances undoubtedly determines the ease with which it can be extracted and characterized. A change in the physical state of DNA during the course of development may also influence its complexing behavior. Agrell and Bergqvist (1962), using cytochemical microspectrophotometric techniques, studied the hydrolysis behavior of nuclear DNA in early and late embryos of the frog and observed that Feulgen stainability varied with time of hydrolysis. In adult nuclei, only one peak of maximum stainability was observed, whereas in undifferentiated cells two and three peaks were observed diminishing to one peak as development proceeded. Multiple peaks suggest different complexes of DNA and it appears that more labile DNA complexes characterize rapidly proliferating nuclei.

Many factors influence the analytical determination of the amounts of DNA in eggs and embryos. A few may be listed as follows: (1) The presence of nucleotide complexes that behave like DNA, (2) variable extractability of DNA as a result of changes in its physical structure, (3) contamination of assay procedures by extraneous, similarly reacting substances, (4) application of different extraction methods, and (5) bacterial contamination, a factor particularly true in the eggs of *Xenopus* (Brown, 1964).

b. Chemical Nature of Cytoplasmic DNA. Initially, the character and behavior of egg cytoplasmic DNA was evaluated by its behavior during extraction. The material is acid insoluble, alcohol-ether insoluble, soluble in hot trichloroacetic acid (TCA) or PCA and is hydrolyzed by DNase. It seems to behave like standard polynucleotide DNA. Isolation of this material has been more difficult and only recently have several attempts at isolation been successful, providing some indication of its nature.

Bieber *et al.* (1959), employing a technique developed by Bendich to extract different kinds of DNA, reported the presence of two DNA species in frog eggs. The bulk of the DNA (85%) was found in the alcohol-soluble fraction, suggesting that cytoplasmic DNA is predominantly low molecular weight or possibly denatured during extraction. Haggis (1964b) has attempted to isolate and characterize cytoplasmic DNA using the density-gradient procedure. DNA extracted from embryos beyond the gastrula stage has the same buoyant density as frog liver DNA.

Recently Dawid (1964) has been able to isolate a DNA from frog eggs (*R. pipiens* and *Xenopus*) which he assumes to be "cytoplasmic" DNA. The procedure involved a series of phenol extractions during which several acid-insoluble, deoxyribose-rich fractions were eliminated because they failed to exhibit the behavior of high molecular weight DNA. Dawid succeeded in isolating a relatively uncontaminated, high molecular weight DNA which exhibits properties almost identical to frog liver DNA. Its sedimentation behavior is similar, although base ratios differ. In several preliminary strand hybridization experiments, he observed that egg cytoplasmic DNA is not competitive with either liver DNA or tadpole DNA, suggesting that it differs significantly from nuclear DNA. Dawid intimates that this DNA may be mitochondrial and the amount per egg (2 mμg per egg) and its properties would tend to support this hypothesis. No conclusive evidence, however, has been obtained other than the fact that it sediments with the mitochondrial fraction. More will be said about this later.

Dawid admits that some of the acid-insoluble, deoxyribose-containing material eliminated during extraction may have some importance in the egg. He has not attempted to identify the material and it is possible that prior reports of large amounts of cytoplasmic DNA in amphibian eggs may, in fact, represent these unknown deoxyribosidic compounds.

The association of cytoplasmic DNA with protein correlates well with suggestions that cytoplasmic DNA is associated with or located in the yolk platelet (Baltus and Brachet, 1962). Ohno et al. (1964) report no Feulgen stainability in yolk platelets of Triturus and Wallace (1964) has reported negligible amounts of DNA in isolated yolk platelets from Rana pipiens. The evidence is clearly not convincing that DNA is included in the yolk platelet, since yolk may become contaminated as it is isolated. The ease with which DNA complexes with proteins during isolation suggests that adsorption may explain earlier observations of DNA in yolk.

Evidence of base composition of egg cytoplasmic DNA in different species is rather meager. Durand (1961) compared the base composition of ovarian and testicular DNA in the cricket, Gryllus. Testicular DNA exhibits a classic A-T composition, whereas ovarian DNA was found to be anomalous with a high A/T molar ratio of 0.57, like single-stranded DNA. Since ovarian DNA is contaminated by follicle cell nuclei, one cannot equate this DNA with ovarian cytoplasmic DNA. By means of an isotope dilution technique for thymine and adenine, however, the peculiar A/T ratio was again evident in eggs and embryos. The DNA appears to revert to the classic A/T type found in testis in those embryonic regions characterized by mitotic activity and morphogenetic movements.

Some of the variations observed in eggs of the same species may be due to seasonal factors. Bieber et al. (1959) demonstrated a reduction in nucleotides extracted by hot TCA from oocytes obtained in February when compared with oocytes in May. Starvation during storage results in a diminution of egg constituents, particularly acid-soluble components. Consequently, control of the nutritional and seasonal state of the animal is essential in any analysis of egg constituents. This is particularly essential for insects which undergo a rapid oogenesis cycle, since slight variations in the nutritional state of the female may be reflected in variations in the macromolecular constituents in the egg.

c. Origin of Cytoplasmic DNA. The evidence available from insect oogenesis suggests that follicle and nurse cells synthesize DNA, which is later transferred to the oocyte cytoplasm. Durand (1961), using autoradiography, reported that DNA is synthesized in the nuclei of cricket follicle cells giving an intense Feulgen reaction. A part of this DNA enters follicle cell cytoplasm and is ultimately transferred to oocyte cytoplasm. Nigon and Nonnenmacher (1961), studying the incorporation of tritium-labeled thymidine into larval ovaries in *Drosophila*, observed no passage of label from follicle cells to the oocyte. Rather, incorporation was observed in the nuclei and cytoplasm of nurse cells and, as the larva matured, an increasing incorporation was observed in the cytoplasm. Subsequently, a channel of labeled cytoplasm proceeds from the nurse cell to the oocyte. The material in the cytoplasm is largely DNase sensitive; however, some label is also eliminated after RNase treatment. Surprisingly, however, in a more recent study attempting to repeat these earlier observations, Nigon and Gillot (1964) report that cytoplasmic labeling is not DNase or RNase sensitive; moreover, the primary labeling is in the nucleus. It was demonstrated that different thymidine preparations were responsible for different incorporation patterns and one is left, therefore, with the impression that at least for *Drosophila* (and no doubt in other cases) the situation is quite unresolved.

In the amphibian the situation is also not clear. Efforts to label cytoplasmic DNA of amphibian oocytes have not been successful (B. C. Moore, 1963). This is understandable in view of the long 3-year period for egg maturation required of oocytes in some amphibians. Injection of isotope into females prior to ovulation could not be expected to label cytoplasmic DNA, since it is probably not synthesized in large, mature oocytes. Once formed, it may be quite stable with synthesis occurring only at a brief period early in the lengthy maturation cycle. This would explain the relatively insignificant amounts of labeled precursor (P^{32}, glycine, thymidine, uridine, etc.) incorporated into the DNA of the mature egg (Grant, 1958b; Ficq, 1961a). Ficq (1961a) using radioactive thymidine reported labeling of DNA in follicle cells without any labeling of the oocyte cytoplasm. Any cytoplasmic labeling is eliminated by extraction with cold perchloric acid. Dawid (1963) attempted to label DNA of oocytes with thymidine in *Rana pipiens* by injecting the female and inducing ovulation 2–4 months later. He also induced ovulation in *Xenopus* females injected with labeled thymidine and induced ovulation 3 months later. In both cases only 2% of the radioactivity of the eggs resided in phenol-extracted DNA (approximately 1 cpm per egg). Here again, failure to label the DNA may reflect only the failure to introduce label at the time when DNA is being synthesized.

The elaborate synthetic behavior of the lampbrush chromosomes in amphibian oocytes (Gall and Callan, 1962) identifies these structures as possible sites of DNA synthesis. Autoradiographic studies with tritium-labeled thymidine, however, have revealed no incorporation of label in the chromosomes or in the cytoplasm (Ficq, 1961a; Izawa et al., 1963a).

The sources of cytoplasmic DNA in eggs may vary for each pattern of oogenesis. Reports of excessive amounts of DNA in isolated germinal vesicles of Rana pipiens oocytes (Finamore et al., 1960) might be interpreted as illustrating a site of cytoplasmic DNA synthesis. However, contamination by oocyte cytoplasm during isolation has not been completely eliminated. Without more direct evidence it is unlikely that the germinal vesicle is the site of an elaborate synthesis of cytoplasmic DNA.

A more likely source of cytoplasmic DNA are the extruded nucleoli. Replication of oocyte nuclear DNA occurs in the early premeiotic phase and ceases during subsequent phases of oogenesis. In this arrested meiotic state the germinal vesicle appears as the chromosomes are transformed into a diffuse, extended, and in many instances, Feulgen-negative structure. Subsequent nuclear growth results in the appearance of a single large nucleolus or a large number of small nucleoli. In some forms an intimate relation exists between the chromatin and the nucleolus. Nucleoli are formed by the activity of heterochromatic parts of the chromosomes, the nucleolar organizers. At the end of the premeiotic phases, when the chromosomes become dispersed into granules, some nucleoli are seen to be associated with Feulgen-positive granules [in Daphnia and Cyclops (Fautrez and Fautrez-Firlefyn, 1951)] or the nucleolus may be surrounded by a ring of Feulgen-positive granules, the nucleolus-associated chromatin [Artemia (Fautrez-Firlefyn, 1950); Oncopeltus (Bonhag, 1955); mouse (Alfert, 1950)]. In still other cases, Feulgen-positive granules are included in the substance of the nucleolus [Phascolosoma (Gonse, 1953)] or the total mass of the chromosomes may be included in the cortical substance of the nucleolus [Acanthoscelides (Mulnard, 1954)]. The role of the nucleolus-associated chromatin is unknown, but it has been implicated in the synthesis of nucleolar RNA. The fate of these Feulgen-positive materials is also unknown; however, they are presumed to follow the nucleoli, as they are extruded into the cytoplasm during vitellogenesis. Nucleolar extrusion during oogenesis is so widely distributed throughout the animal kingdom that one can assume it is a constant and general feature of animal oogenesis.

In some forms (Hemiptera), DNA of the oocyte cytoplasm may be traced to the fusion of nurse cell nuclei (Schrader and Leuchtenberger, 1952; Bonhag, 1955). In this instance, nurse cells and developing oocytes are connected by a cytoplasmic trophic core in the central part of the nutrient egg chamber. Occasionally, nuclei pass from apical and peripheral regions into the trophic core, where they may coalesce into giant nuclei and finally disintegrate. During the process of nuclear fusion, the amount of DNA per nucleus increases in multiples of the diploid amount and may reach a value as high as seventeen times the diploid amount. These nuclei then lose their Feulgen-positive material in the form of extruded droplets, presumably into the cytoplasm of the oocyte.

2. CONTROL OF DNA REPLICATION DURING OOGENESIS

Very little data are available on the metabolism of oocytes and accessory cells during the course of oogenesis. Recently, investigations of this question have relied heavily on autoradiographic studies which have yielded the bulk of our information on the dynamic activities operating during this process. There have been surprisingly few enzymatic studies on this difficult material, which explains a serious lack in our information about possible control mechanisms. Whatever fragmentary information is available focuses on the primary role of genetic regulation.

Too little is known about the factors which control DNA replication in cells; most of our understanding of this process has come from studies of synchronously dividing microbial populations and these have provided useful models with some applicability to multicellular systems. Lark (1963) has reviewed the question recently and has pointed to several different levels of control either operating independently or jointly during the cell cycle in bacteria. Control of DNA replication may be (1) a function of the concentration of DNA precursors and enzymes contributing to their synthesis and turnover; (2) related to the concentration of enzymes essential in the replication process (DNA phosphorylase); (3) linked to over-all protein and RNA synthetic activity of the cell; and finally, (4) a function of the physical state of the DNA template involved in its own synthesis.

Nothing is known about these mechanisms during oogenesis. The developing oocyte seems to be an ideal system to study control mechanisms of DNA synthesis since it represents a system in which the commitment of cytoplasmic protein synthesis is at a maximum while the replication of DNA is completely inhibited. In most situations, particularly in bacteria, the control of DNA replication is evaluated in rapidly dividing cells; it would be of interest to investigate regulation in cells that have completed DNA replication and are unable for long periods of time to continue with DNA synthesis. Since little evidence is available, it is impossible to resolve the specific mechanism or mechanisms involved in the inhibition of DNA synthesis in the oocyte during oogenesis.

Nurse cells predominate in insects and the characteristic feature is a large nucleus which, in many species, undergoes endopolyploidy, or polyteny, producing large amounts of DNA. In other species (Hemiptera) fusion may occur yielding polyploid nuclei. The factors responsible for the initiation and control of polyploidization are unknown. However, the unique feature in these cells as contrasted with other somatic cells is a release of this replicated DNA into the cytoplasm and subsequent transfer into oocyte cytoplasm. Although it has been demonstrated that insect hormones may control the process of oogenesis (as is presumably the case in vertebrates), the mechanisms of action are completely unknown. It is possible in view of the recent observations concerning the direct effect of hormones on the puffing behavior of dipteran chromosomes (Clever and Karlson, 1960; Clever, 1961) that a hormone functions directly at the chromosomal site, inducing either a physical change in the DNA molecule to initiate the replication process and/or alter the physical arrangement of enzyme, template, and substrate so as to initiate the process of replication. Ecdysone has been implicated as a hormone that presumably shows some relation to cell division. Over-all DNA replication in most tissues seems to follow the ebb and flow of ecdysone titers throughout the pupation and diapausing cycle. Moreover, the initiation of cell division and DNA syntheses in the hypodermis of diapausing *Cecropia* and *Rhodnius* seems to respond to ecdysone treatment (Bowers and Williams, 1964; Wigglesworth, 1963). It is also noteworthy that meiotic divisions in spermatogonia respond to situations characterized by high titers of ecdysone [during the pupal molt, after beginning of adult development, and after large injuries (Bowers and Williams, 1964)]. The exact mechanism of action of this hormone on DNA replication is unknown, although Kroeger (1963) has observed that the ecdysone effect on chromosome puffing may be imitated with zinc ions or wounding and suggests the influence of ecdysone is not directly at the chromosomal site but must be mediated through the nuclear sap. Kroeger (1960) also observed the induction of puffing pattern in salivary gland nuclei when these were placed into the egg cytoplasm of *Drosophila*, an effect which seems to be restricted only to the egg cytoplasm of certain ages. Obviously, there are numerous situations which can trigger the puffing behavior of chromosomes. It should be noted, however, that the puffing pattern of chromosomes is largely a reflection of RNA and protein synthesis rather than DNA replication.

B. Replication of DNA during Development

1. The Initiation of DNA Synthesis at Fertilization

The mature egg arises as a result of the differentiation of an oogonial cell through elaborate nuclear and cytoplasmic syntheses in concert with the synthetic activities of accessory cells. Intense cytoplasmic syntheses in the oocyte and the accumulation of large amounts of preformed proteins and lipids from exogenous sources contribute to this cytoplasmic differentiation at a time when the oocyte nucleus assumes a morphology conducive for the transcription of information from DNA molecules. The active RNA synthesis of lampbrush chromosomes is a vivid example of the extent of the commitment of the DNA to transcription activities (Gall, 1963). This results in a complete cessation or inhibition of DNA replication that undoubtedly persists until the egg is activated. Sometime after the completion of vitellogenesis, the germinal vesicle breaks down spilling its contents into the cytoplasm and this is usually followed by completion of meiotic divisions. The time at which this occurs varies with each species and may be dependent upon sperm activation. Irrespective of the time at which activation occurs in relation to the stage of maturation, the ultimate result is similar, i.e., the initiation of DNA replication. The initiation of this process is dependent on the state of the egg cytoplasm rather than on any factor introduced by the sperm, because artificial activation and development is possible in most eggs. The egg seems primed to initiate rounds of DNA replication but is somehow inhibited and can be readily released from this inhibition by chemical and physical changes occurring in the cytoplasm. There is considerable evidence which suggests that the "state" of the cytoplasm determines the onset of DNA replication in many different cell types, such as the slime mold *Physarum polycephalum* where nuclei undergo simultaneous division, presumably under the influence of the cytoplasm (Nygaard *et al.*, 1960).

Activation transforms the egg into an actively replicating system. The activation of the egg by a sperm cell may be considered as analogous to phage infection of *E. coli*—in both cases a cell is injected with DNA followed immediately by DNA replication. In the microbial situation, infection occurs at a time in the life cycle of the bacterium when DNA synthesis is "shut off." Viral DNA presumably turns on DNA replication by an immediate transcription of messenger RNA's which rapidly function in the synthesis of several key enzymes required in the specific synthesis of phage DNA (Cohen, 1960). Some of these enzymes are thymidylate synthetase and a deoxycytidylate hydroxymethylase which are essential for phage DNA synthesis. In the egg, however, the sperm nucleus apparently contributes nothing since the egg may be induced to cleave and initiate mitosis without sperm activation. It is possible that the enzymes (DNA phosphorylase, thymidylate kinase, etc.) essential for DNA replication are "masked" or inhibited and are released upon activation.

The germinal vesicle plays an important role in this entire activation process as demonstrated by several classic merogony experiments on marine eggs. Delage (1899) observed that activation of enucleated star-fish eggs was not possible prior to germinal vesicle breakdown. Costello (1940) observed that activation of the enucleated *Nereis* egg prior to germinal vesicle breakdown was also not possible. If the *Nereis* egg was separated, however, into nucleated and enucleated halves after the breakdown of the germinal vesicle, the enucleated half could be induced to cleave after insemination. In the case of *Nereis*, the sperm aster failed to form suggesting that germinal vesicle material is essential for cytaster formation.

Germinal vesicle contents have only been analyzed cytochemically, except for the few chemical analyses that have been completed with respect to the incorporation of isotopes (Finamore *et al.*, 1960). Cyto-chemical analyses of many different oocytes have revealed that the germinal vesicle is rich in proteins, unusually rich in SH compounds (Brachet, 1939) and ribonucleic acid (Finamore *et al.*, 1960). The high protein content coupled with SH compounds suggests that the material of the germinal vesicle may have some role in establishing the spindle during the first cleavages. The germinal vesicle may also contain RNA molecules which enter the cytoplasm after germinal vesicle breakdown and proceed to activate or prime sites of enzyme synthesis essential for DNA replication. Activation of DNA synthesis would require the as-sembly of DNA primer and enzymes into a functional unit for synthesis. Huff (1962) has injected germinal vesicle contents from mature *Rana pipiens* oocytes into the blastocoel cavity of blastulae and observed rather specific effects on neurulation. The neural tubes fail to close leading to a *spina bifida* condition. The effect is rather species-specific, since injection of *R. catesbiana* germinal vesicles into *R. pipiens* blastulae did not exhibit the same effect. The factors responsible for such effects are unknown and could be completely unrelated to those responsible for cleavage initiation.

Evidence for migration of protein from the nucleus to the cytoplasm and back again during the mitotic cycle has been obtained from the nuclear transplantation experiments on *Amoeba* (Goldstein, 1963). This has been confirmed and amplified by Byers *et al.* (1963) and by Prescott and Bender (1963). They have demonstrated the existence of nuclear specific proteins that shuttle between nucleus and cytoplasm during mitosis, returning to the nucleus at the end of mitosis. The proteins exhibit a slow turnover and are clearly not irreversibly associated with the chromosomes. Their role is certainly not clear although participation in the regulation of RNA or DNA synthesis in the nucleus has been suggested. The proteins persist during interphase and enter the cytoplasm presumably in prophase or when the nuclear membrane breaks down. Byers *et al.* (1963) have some evidence that the proteins are synthesized in the cytoplasm; moreover, transplantation experiments (transplantation of an amino acid-labeled nucleus into an unlabeled host cell) have revealed the existence of two kinds of proteins, one which migrates rapidly between nucleus and cytoplasm and another which moves more slowly. Both these proteins are relatively stable since they remain in the nuclei after four divisions. During mitosis these proteins are distributed throughout the cytoplasm and exhibit no concentration over the spindle.

The generality of the phenomenon described above is of course unknown. However, germinal vesicle breakdown at the termination of oogenesis illustrates most dramatically a transfer of large amounts of protein to the cytoplasm prior to the completion of maturation divisions. The behavior of egg and sperm nuclei during fertilization focuses on the reverse process, i.e., the transfer of protein materials from cytoplasm to pronuclei prior to amphimixis and first cleavage. No evidence is available to support the hypothesis that specific proteins are involved in the shuttling between germinal vesicle cytoplasm and these pronuclei; however, the observations in *Amoeba* certainly suggest, as a working hypothesis, that these proteins are essential for controlling the synthesis of DNA at the chromosomal site.

During pronucleus formation chromosomes undergo noticeable morphological transformations. From the contracted, minute meiotic chromosomes of the female nucleus, a rapid despiralization and hydration of chromosome structure produces a diffuse staining pattern. Similarly, the compact nucleus of the sperm hydrates, and the chromatin despiralizes. Transitions of protein from protamine to histone also occur at this stage (Bloch and Hew, 1960). Protamines are lost from the nucleus leaving only some weakly basic protein which is replaced later by a more typical histone complement at gastrulation. Such alterations in the structure of chromosomal DNA at fertilization may be responsible for activating the primer function of DNA initiating replication.

The complicated interactions of nuclei and egg cytoplasm during activation, pronucleus formation, and amphimixis must function normally to insure the initiation of cleavage and the replication of chromosomes. It is becoming evident that the interactions between sperm nucleus and egg surface or cortex are essential for subsequent developmental events. For example (Hiramoto, 1962), has observed that injection of sperm into sea urchin eggs is not sufficient to initiate cleavage. Apparently, the sperm must attach normally and penetrate before the egg is appropriately activated. In a series of experiments comparing androgenetic haploids with haploids produced by nuclear transplantation as they respond to the effect of nitrogen mustard on nucleocytoplasmic interactions, Grant and Stott (1962) have demonstrated that critical sperm-egg surface interactions must occur to determine cleavage initiation. Cleavage may occur normally even in the presence of X-irradiated or UV-irradiated sperm in amphibians (Rugh and Exner, 1940) indicating that the cleavage initiation properties of the sperm are separable from its contribution of nuclear material. The observations of Harvey (1936) concerning cleavage without nuclei certainly suggest that this separation is possible. Frog eggs treated with nitrogen mustard produce partially cleaved blastulae, containing large masses of Feulgen-stained material (Grant, 1965). These are regions of intense DNA synthesis without accompanying cleavage illustrating the separation of the two processes. Similarly, mercaptoethanol may inhibit centriole duplication accompanied by a blockage of cleavage without influencing the synthesis of DNA in sea urchin embryos (Bucher and Mazia, 1960).

It appears that some modification of the sperm takes place as it interacts with either the surface or the cortex of the egg. This "primes" the sperm's capacity to initiate cleavage and DNA synthesis.

The nature of this regulation is unknown, yet it must involve some profound interaction between the replicating mechanism at the site of the DNA macromolecules and some factors in the cytoplasm. Regulation may relate to the absence of or inhibition of enzymes required for DNA synthesis such as DNA phosphorylase or perhaps enzymes essential in the synthesis of precursors, such as the nucleoside triphosphates.

Hinegardner and Mazia (1962), Mazia (1963), and Mazia and Hinegardner (1963) have examined the DNA phosphorylase activity of sea urchin embryos during development. The enzyme seems to be associated almost exclusively with nuclei and apparently with chromosomes, since a direct correlation between chromosome number and enzyme activity is observed. Activity per nucleus is greatest in the earliest cleavage stages, suggesting a correlation between the level of polymerase activity and the rate of cell division. Extrapolating to the fertilized egg stage, one could assume that activity is at a maximum at that time. It is uncertain, however, whether the enzyme is already present in the mature egg in a nonfunctional state or whether it is brought in by the sperm cell at insemination. Mazia suggests that the priming activity of DNA may be controlled by an enzyme, possibly DNase, since DNase was observed to increase the priming activity of a preparation of nuclei from sea urchin embryos. He speculates that some degree of scission of the DNA molecule is necessary before it can function effectively as a primer. DNase may serve this purpose, since it appears to associate with the nucleus during development (Mazia, 1949). The fertilized egg of *Arbacia* contains equal amounts of DNase in nucleated and enucleated halves. During the course of development, although the total activity per embryo does not change, the activity in the sedimentable fraction (presumably containing nuclei as well as the particulate components of the cytoplasm) exhibited an increase in activity. When these determinations were done, assay procedures for DNase were less well developed. DNase's are now known to exist with widely different pH optima (an acid and alkaline DNase) requiring different ionic environments for optimal activity. In the light of more recent studies the activity observed in the sea urchin embryo may be less than that reported by Mazia. It is interesting to note that Coleman (1962), studying these enzymes in *Rana pipiens* development, finds no detectable DNase I activity during development until stage 23 (posthatching), whereas low levels of DNase II activity are found in early development, increasing rapidly after stage 18 (tailbud). Although it is present in early development, its role in the frog embryo is completely unknown.

What regulatory role, if any, is played by cytoplasmic DNA during activation? Since the DNA may be localized in three different sites, each characterized by different activity, several alternative roles may be involved. DNA may be localized in the mitochondria or in nucleolar granules (nucleolar extrusion) or may be relatively "free" in the cytoplasm. Does it simply remain inactive or is it capable of functioning as a site of RNA synthesis in mitochondria? Does it replicate within the cytoplasm in small amounts, incapable of detection by autoradiography? In a recent study by Mezger-Freed (1963) synthesis of DNA (as measured by microbiological assay) has been observed in the activated, nonnucleated eggs of *Rana pipiens*, which suggests a possible template role for cytoplasmic DNA after fertilization. In this case, it is possible the so-called synthesis of DNA observed was, in fact, deoxyribonucleotide synthesis, since no effort was made to separate acid-insoluble from soluble nucleotides.

2. DNA REPLICATION DURING EARLY CLEAVAGE SYNCHRONY

In a recent review Dettlaff (1964) emphasized the important relationships between cleavage and the relative duration of developmental periods with later embryonic differentiation. At the molecular level these relationships must be translated into the patterns of control of DNA replication during cleavage and its influence on the transcription of DNA during the course of differentiation. Most eggs exhibit a relatively early synchrony period of cell division followed by an asynchronous period, usually around the mid to late blastula period (Dettlaff, 1964). What is the nature of DNA replication during the synchronous phase and what factors are responsible for modifying this pattern in certain populations of cells?

The earliest cleavages after activation are generally synchronous (Agrell, 1964), the extent of synchrony varying with species. In most eggs, however, synchrony persists for only a few divisions, to be followed shortly by the establishment of mitotic gradients. The early synchrony of cleavage has been investigated by Zeuthen (1953) who has correlated cyclical respiratory changes with mitotic phases during cleavage. There seems to be some relationship between respiratory metabolism and DNA replication in cleaving eggs (Comita and Whiteley, 1953), since reduction in DNA synthesis is accompanied by a reduction in oxygen consumption. Similar correlations have been observed by Brachet (1954) in frog eggs, although it is certainly not clear whether this implies a causal relationship. Synchronized microbial cultures have been produced by a variety of procedures, the most successful being temperature shifts. Respiratory rhythms in such cultures are correlated with the synthesis of DNA, since oxygen consumption is constant during the predivision period and increases during DNA synthesis. These observations suggest that synchrony may be a function of the availability of energy from respiratory metabolism, an interpretation offered by those stressing the importance of an energy reservoir for mitosis (Swann, 1953; Bullough, 1952). This hypothesis, based on the observations of mitotic inhibition by respiratory inhibitors suggests that energy reserves are stored before mitosis and this energy reservoir, once established, is available for utilization during mitosis independent of continuous oxidative phosphorylation. Synthesis of DNA and subsequent events of mitosis consequently depend upon a pre-existing energy reserve and appropriate coupling to synthetic pathways. Cyclic synthesis and cell division synchrony is a reflection of the cyclic formation and utilization of such energy reserves. Recent studies by Epel (1963), however, have shown that the original experiments of Swann upon which these views were based failed to evaluate photorecovery effects of green light used after treatment of sea urchin eggs with carbon monoxide. Epel finds that green light partially relieves the inhibition produced by carbon monoxide and cells which would not complete mitosis after exposure to carbon monoxide in prophase in darkness will complete mitosis if observed in green light. Epel has re-examined the mitotic requirements for adenosine triphosphate (ATP) and has observed that CO inhibition of sea urchin eggs in the dark results in a 50% reduction of ATP, whereas in green light only 25% of the ATP is eliminated which explains the ability of cells under the latter situation to complete mitosis. In complete anoxia, the ATP level decreases to about 30% of normal, sufficient to inhibit mitosis. The longer it takes to reach this level, the further the progress of the cell in mitosis before it is arrested. A clear dependence of cleavage on oxidative phosphorylation exists in the sea urchin egg. It is unlikely that the synchrony observed in early cleavage is dependent upon fluctuations in the production of ATP since the levels of ATP are probably in equilibrium, reflecting a balance between its production and utilization. No significant change in ATP levels has been observed during mitosis in sea urchin embryos.

The frog egg, however, is quite different. It cleaves synchronously during the first few divisions (five divisions) in the absence of oxygen or when exposed to respiratory inhibitors. One could not expect synchrony here to depend upon the existence of fluctuating energy stores. Other cyclic factors must be operating in this case.

The division cycle in cells is arbitrarily separated into different phases during their life. The birth of a cell at mitosis is followed by a period in which no synthesis of DNA occurs—the G1. The synthetic phase, S, follows when DNA is replicated and this period precedes an interval of relative maturity prior to mitosis known as G2. The duration of these periods varies from system to system, although different cells within the same system will exhibit remarkably similar patterns. The demonstration of these periods in the life cycle of the cell has been made possible with tritiated thymidine autoradiography based on the time course of appearance of labeled metaphase plates at intervals after the injection of the labeled precursor.

Microspectrophotometric investigations of cleaving echinoderm eggs have shown that syntheses of DNA may occur very early in the interphase or even during telophase (McMaster, 1955; Lison and Pasteels, 1951). Early cleavages are rapid for most eggs. In the frog egg (*Rana pipiens*) the generation time may be 1 hour for the first five cleavages. In *Xenopus* the rate is more rapid, the generation time as low as $\frac{1}{2}$ hour in some cleavages. In *Triturus pyrrhogaster* the time between cleavages may be as great as 3 to 4 hours in the early divisions. The situation in marine embryos is more impressive. Generation time may be as low as 20 minutes or less. Of course, these rates vary with temperature, but it is obvious that these eggs are capable of very rapid divisions with a limited amount of time involved in either the G1 or G2 phases of the cycle. Hinegardner et al. (1965) have shown this to be true for the first few cleavages of the sea urchin embryo which exhibit no G1 phase, while G2 is approximately 20 minutes with a brief S period of 13 minutes. The mitotic time of 50 minutes literally dominates the entire cell cycle. As cleavage progresses, less and less of the cell cycle is devoted to DNA synthesis and more time is proportionably spent in G1 and G2 phases.

Synchrony in the cleaving egg may be related to the fact that the G1 and G2 periods, most prone to variation, are relatively unimportant during this time. In mammalian cells the S period is relatively constant, representing a constant proportion of the cell cycle. If we assume that the replication of a DNA strand is polarized and occurring at one point in the chromosome at any given time (Cairns, 1963) and if the S period dominates the life cycle, one could expect that all cells would be in relatively the same stage of chromosomal duplication, all other factors such as enzyme level being equal.

Synchrony in cleaving eggs may also be attributed to variations in precursor levels. Grant (1958a), in a study later confirmed by Kuriki and Okazaki (1959), observed that early cleavage in amphibian eggs is characterized by the existence of a large store of deoxyribonucleotide precursors, some synthesized during the first 12 hours of segmentation. The sea urchin egg was also found to contain large amounts of acid-soluble deoxyribosidic compounds (Sugino et al., 1960). Synchronized mitosis also occurs in developing microspores in the anthers of Lilium longiflorum and Trillium erectum, and is correlated with fluctuations in acid-soluble deoxyribonucleosides (Foster and Stern, 1959; Stern, 1960). Stern (1961) later showed a periodic induction of DNase activity in relation to the mitotic cycle, while Hotta and Stern (1963a,b) have also shown that a phosphorylating enzyme, thymidine kinase, appears shortly after the precursors reach their peak, suggesting enzyme synthesis under the influence of exogenous nucleosides. The regulation of mitosis in these cells is viewed as indicative of a sequential induction of key enzymes required for the synthesis of chromosome constituents (Stern and Hotta, 1963) and probably is an expression of sequential activation of genes.

Information about such sequential changes in eggs is woefully lacking; consequently, we are unable to extrapolate from the microspore. Nevertheless, it is likely that very similar mechanisms operate in the egg. A review of the data on patterns of DNA synthesis during development, enzyme fluctuations during this period, and variations in deoxyribonucleotide precursors should provide some insight into the factors regulating synchrony and mitosis in cleaving eggs.

3. PATTERNS OF DNA SYNTHESIS DURING DEVELOPMENT

The phenomenon of DNA synthesis during embryonic development has been reviewed a number of times (Brachet, 1950, 1954; Løvtrup, 1955; Durand, 1961). The issue is discussed at length in Brachet's book (1950) where embryonic systems are classified in terms of "partial" or "total" patterns of DNA synthesis during development. Several recent observations of the existence of cytoplasmic DNA have renewed interest in this recurrent question concerning patterns of synthesis as they may emerge during embryonic development.

The cytological evidence during cleavage underscores a rapid replication of chromatin and nuclear material. Feulgen stainability of nuclei becomes more intense with advancing development, explained in part by a decrease in nuclear size. Several different explanations have been cited as the source of nuclear DNA during cleavage and early development.

1. Nuclear DNA is derived from small molecular weight precursors stored in egg cytoplasm—a *de novo* synthesis. This was the view presented originally, although in modified form by Loeb (1913) who maintained that the necessary phosphate was derived from a hydrolysis of phospholipids, whereas the purine and pyrimidines were synthesized *de novo*. This has been called "total" synthesis by Brachet (1950).

2. This view was opposed by Godlewski (1918) who, discussing only the origin of nuclear substances and not referring specifically to DNA, suggested that during oogenesis and also after germinal vesicle breakdown, nuclear substances accumulate in the cytoplasm. These are reincorporated later into the nuclei during cleavage. The presence of cytoplasmic DNA in a large number of eggs and its behavior during development certainly agrees with this hypothesis. This has been characterized by Brachet as a "partial" synthesis. There are no data eliminating the possibility of cytoplasmic DNA being utilized as large polynucleotide fragments for nuclear DNA, similar to the incorporation of provirus into the DNA of the bacterial chromosome or similar to the incorporation of the transforming DNA in the bacterial transformation phenomenon.

3. Brachet (1950) suggested the existence of another pathway, namely, the conversion of cytoplasmic RNA into nuclear DNA. This too is a "partial" synthesis and was originally based on data correlating a reduction in RNA with an increase in DNA in sea urchin embryos. The analytical methods were later shown to be unreliable, and in sub-

sequent experiments by Schmidt *et al.* (1948) and Villee *et al.* (1949) in sea urchin embryos the time course of P^{32} incorporation into DNA was greater than incorporation into RNA, eliminating RNA as a possible precursor for DNA. For a while, Brachet's hypothesis lacked much support until biochemical evidence was presented (Rose and Schweigert, 1953; Reichard, 1958, 1959) illustrating the utilization of ribonucleotides for DNA synthesis in chick embryos as well as mammalian tissues. Although the direct precursor role of RNA in the synthesis of DNA is not accepted, its role as a source of ribonucleotide precursors subsequently converted to DNA precursors certainly merits full consideration.

4. Several pathways may be functioning simultaneously during early cleavage. Turnover studies (Grant, 1958b, 1960; Cohen, 1954; Flickinger, 1954; Bieliavsky and Tencer, 1960) have revealed that small molecular precursors like glycine, thymidine, uridine, etc., are incorporated into DNA during early cleavage. In addition, turnover of ribonucleotides during early cleavage may also be contributing to the synthesis of DNA during cleavage.

a. De novo Synthesis. The contributions of Kornberg and his colleagues have established a fundamental understanding of some molecular mechanisms involved in DNA biosynthesis. The systems studied illustrate the *de novo* mechanism—synthesis from small molecular weight precursors in the presence of a DNA primer.

The components of this system are as follows: a DNA primer, DNA phosphorylase, deoxynucleoside triphosphates of all four nucleosides, and magnesium ions. Are all these components present initially in the unfertilized egg or do they appear at the time of fertilization? What evidence is there that *de novo* synthesis occurs during early cleavage?

i. Determinations of DNA per embryo. In several embryonic systems, estimations of DNA per embryo have revealed a net synthesis of DNA even during the early cleavage stages. Grant (1958a), using the microbiological assay on an acid-insoluble fraction of *Rana pipiens* eggs, observed a net synthesis during cleavage, from the fertilized egg through an early blastula (12 hours at 15°C). At a higher temperature this synthesis was even more apparent. Kuriki and Okazaki (1959) confirmed this in *Bufo vulgaris formosus* and *Triturus pyrrhogaster*. Solomon (1957a), analyzing DNA in isolated chick embryo explants, also demonstrated a net synthesis. The stages employed were later than cleavage; however, they did demonstrate net synthesis during stages which were shown not to exhibit net synthesis when assayed by other means (Hoff-Jørgensen, 1954). Sugino *et al.* (1960), using a microbiological assay, followed DNA synthesis in sea urchin embryos (*Hemicentrotus*) and observed a net synthesis of DNA throughout cleavage, even in the first few divisions. Using a different technique Chen *et al.* (1961) also observed an early net synthesis in sea urchin embryos. Brachet (1954) and later Baltus and Brachet (1962) reported a net synthesis in the frog embryo, *Rana temporaria*, and the salamander, using two different methods of assay. Although the absolute amounts per fertilized egg differed, the later study employing a sensitive fluorometric assay revealed amounts of DNA comparable to the values obtained by microbiological assay. Earlier, Kutsky (1950), studying phosphate metabolism, and Sze (1953) observed a net synthesis of DNA during early cleavage in *Rana pipiens*; however, the amounts observed (approximately 1 µg per egg) and the relatively insensitive methods employed made these values suspect. Finally, in insect embryos increases in the amounts of DNA per embryo were also observed during early cleavage stages (Durand, 1958; Nigon and Daille, 1958).

The absolute increase in DNA during the first few cleavages did not correspond with the increase in cell number (Grant, 1958a) in *Rana pipiens*. The rate of cell number increase is more rapid than the rate of DNA increase until an early blastula, when the rates of increase are comparable. From Grant's data (1958a) it can be shown that during early cleavage the absolute amount of DNA per embryo is in excess of the amount of DNA in nuclei, assuming a tetraploid value in all cases. At the 500-cell stage an excess of 0.022 µg exists, an amount comparable to that found originally in the fertilized egg. Development from the early blastula to a late blastula results in a rapid increase in the number of cells, and at the latter stage, DNA per embryo corresponds to the amount of DNA per total nuclei, assuming a tetraploid amount of DNA. This disagrees with Sze's data (1953) which showed that correspondence of DNA per embryo and DNA per total nuclei occurred much later in development at stage 17. He interpreted this as an exhaustion of cytoplasmic DNA at that stage. His observations of total DNA synthesized per embryo in early cleavage stages is in excess of the calculated nuclear DNA suggesting the synthesis of DNA in the cytoplasm. Since his data were obtained by the less sensitive Schmidt-Tannhauser technique, the large DNA values observed are difficult to reconcile with other presumably more sensitive analyses.

Recently, Mezger-Freed (1963) has reported the synthesis of DNA in activated, enucleated *Rana pipiens* eggs, confirming Sze's hypothesis that cytoplasm can indeed synthesize DNA. The assay employed by Mezger-Freed, however, does not distinguish acid-soluble deoxynucleotides from acid-insoluble DNA. Since there is a detectable synthesis of deoxynucleotides (Grant, 1958a), it is possible that she was measuring synthesis of deoxynucleotides released only by the combined treatment by DNase and snake venom phosphatase. In fact, Sugino *et al.* (1960) have shown that some acid-soluble deoxynucleotides are bound in sea urchin embryos and readily released if hydrolyzed with snake venom phosphatase.

The data of Kuriki and Okazaki (1959) also demonstrate DNA synthesis per embryo in excess of the DNA calculated per nucleus in early cleavage stages, prior to an early blastula. Up to the 32-cell stage, approximately forty times more DNA is synthesized than is actually required in the nuclei of *Bufo vulgaris formosus* (Kuriki and Okazaki, 1959). It is not possible to calculate the data for later stages; however, these observations, using the more sensitive microbiological assay, confirm Sze's observations and support the view that DNA may be synthesized in the cytoplasm in early stages. It is evident that further investigations are required to resolve this problem of the cytoplasmic synthesis of DNA. It would be useful to use the enucleation procedure employed by Mezger-Freed with a careful fractionation procedure to separate acid-soluble deoxynucleotides.

Contrary to the reports of constancy of DNA per embryo until the blastula stage (Hoff-Jørgensen, 1954; Gregg and Løvtrup, 1955) a net synthesis of DNA occurs in the amphibian egg, correlated with increase in cell number, supporting the existence of a *de novo* mechanism for DNA synthesis during cleavage.

ii. De novo synthesis as demonstrated by isotope incorporation studies. A number of different incorporation studies on a variety of embryos have demonstrated that small molecular weight precursors are utilized for the synthesis of DNA during early cleavage and in later development. The early studies involving the sea urchin embryo (Schmidt *et al.*, 1948; Villee *et al.*, 1949) showed that radioactive phosphate could be taken up from the medium and incorporated into DNA of developing embryos. In the frog embryo, injected phosphate is utilized by the early cleaving egg for the synthesis of DNA (Kutsky, 1950; Grant, 1958b). Similarly, CO_2 (Flickinger, 1954; Cohen, 1954) as well as glycine can be utilized by these embryos for DNA synthesis (Grant, 1958). The sea urchin embryo also has been shown to utilize other exogenous small molecular weight precursors for DNA synthesis early in development (Abrams, 1951; Hultin, 1957a,b; Markman, 1960). Thus, the metabolic pathways known to be involved in the synthesis of purines and pyrimidines from smaller precursor molecules are certainly present in these early embryos. Studies of formate incorporation in the chick embryo also support the view that these *de novo* pathways for DNA synthesis are present (Marrian *et al.*, 1956).

With the more modern techniques of autoradiography using tritium-labeled precursors, it has been possible to refine the sensitivity of the method of analysis and explore synthesis patterns *in situ*. A series of such studies in the sea urchin in a number of laboratories (Ficq *et al*, 1963; Ficq and Brachet, 1963; Simmel and Karnofsky, 1961; Nemer, 1962a) have confirmed earlier observations that segmentation stages may be characterized as exclusively devoted to DNA synthesis, chromosome replication, and cell division. Using tritium-labeled thymidine, uridine, and cytidine, they have found that the nuclei of early blastomeres are most heavily labeled with all precursors and that a bulk of the label is associated with DNA during segmentation, whereas in later stages, more of the nuclear RNA becomes labeled.

Similar results have been obtained in amphibians (Bieliavsky and Tencer, 1960; Tencer, 1961b) with tritiated uridine. An initial, exclusive incorporation into nuclei of the morula and blastula could be shown, by DNase digestion, to be DNA. In the gastrula nuclear incorporation continues as well as cytoplasmic incorporation. Some of the nuclear activity can be shown to be attributable to DNA. Unfortunately, in these studies the embryos were dissociated into cell suspensions within their vitelline membranes prior to incubation by placing them in a calcium-free medium. Major modifications of cell surface and cell-cell contacts undoubtedly resulted, modifying permeability and possibly influencing the pattern of DNA incorporation. B. C. Moore (1963) in a later study injected tritium-labeled thymidine into *Rana pipiens* eggs and observed an early incorporation into cleavage nuclei.

Cleaving mammalian eggs have also been shown to incorporate exogenous pyrimidine precursors *in vitro* into nuclear DNA (Mintz, 1962, 1964) and mollusk as well as insect eggs are equally capable of pyrimidine utilization for DNA synthesis during cleavage (Collier, 1963; Nigon and Gillot, 1964).

More recent fractionation studies on sea urchin and amphibian embryos have confirmed the autoradiographic results in the demonstration of incorporation of pyrimidine precursors into DNA extracted from cleaving eggs and fractionated by sucrose density-gradient centrifugation (Brown and Littna, 1964a; Wilt, 1964). A large proportion of the activity is associated with DNA peaks in early stages.

At some stage in development the synthesis of DNA must follow a *de novo* pattern typical of adult cells. However, some questions have arisen concerning the time at which this occurs. The evidence cited above suggests that for most embryos the *de novo* pathway is active after fertilization and is probably responsible for the intense nuclear synthesis observed. It is important to confirm the existence of all components of the *de novo* system in the embryo and to determine their changing patterns during the course of development.

iii. The presence of deoxynucleotide precursors. Previous mention has been made of the existence of deoxynucleotide precursors in eggs and embryos of several different species. In amphibian eggs, sea urchin eggs, *Drosophila*, cricket, chick, and mollusk eggs, a pool of acid-soluble deoxynucleotide precursors have been demonstrated in the unfertilized egg as well as in later developmental stages (Grant, 1958a; Kuriki and Okazaki, 1959; Sugino *et al.*, 1960; Travaglini *et al.*, 1957; Durand, 1961; Emanuelsson, 1961; Collier, 1961). In several instances these substances have been characterized by column chromatography and have been shown to be a mixture of mono-, di-, and trideoxynucleotides with a small proportion of nucleosides, usually less than 10% (Kuriki and Okazaki, 1959). The pattern of nucleotides and nucleosides in the acid-soluble pool of developing eggs is found in other rapidly dividing tissues, such as lily microspores, regenerating liver, and tumors (Schneider, 1955; Schneider and Brownell, 1957; Foster and Stern, 1959).

The deoxynucleotide precursors exhibit a developmental pattern suggesting involvement in nuclear DNA synthesis during development (Grant, 1958a). In the amphibian, an early synthesis of deoxynucleotides during the first 12 hours of development doubles the initial amount. These are rapidly utilized to the end of blastulation as cell number rapidly increases. A constant low level of these precursors characterizes development from gastrulation to hatching, undoubtedly reflecting the marked reduction in mitotic activity that occurs at the time of gastrulation. The sea urchin embryo is similar (Sugino *et al.*, 1960) and in the insect embryo, although no prior synthesis occurs, the high deoxyribonucleoside levels decrease as cleavage continues (Schultz, 1956).

The situation in the sea urchin embryo is complicated by the presence of "masked" deoxynucleotides during cleavage; it is necessary to treat the acid-soluble extract with snake venom phosphatase to release maximum deoxynucleotide activity for microbiological assay (Sugino *et al.*,

1960). These "masked" deoxynucleotides are found in high concentrations in the fertilized egg and during cleavage. At the blastula stage the level of these precursors falls to approximately one-quarter the original amount, when the rate of cell division has decreased significantly. The pattern in these eggs is fundamentally similar to the amphibian embryo—high levels of precursor when mitotic activity is at a maximum. Masked deoxynucleotides have also been found in amphibian eggs by Kuriki and Okazaki (1959) and exhibit a peak of activity early in cleavage followed by a reduction to one-half the amount in subsequent development. Moreover, this amount remains constant, as in *Rana pipiens*, at least until after hatching. The nature of one of these masked deoxynucleotides has been determined and found to be deoxycytidine diphosphocholine (Sugino, 1957). Finamore and Warner (1963) isolated a diguanosine tetraphosphate from brine shrimp eggs.

iv. Ribonucleotide precursors of DNA. Large amounts of acid-soluble ribonucleotides have been demonstrated in a number of different eggs and embryos. Mono-, di-, and triphosphates of purine and pyrimidine nucleosides are found in a number of different eggs and embryos: sea urchin, amphibian, chick, insect, and mollusk (Hultin, 1957b; Finamore and Crouse, 1958; Nilsson, 1959, 1961; Berg and Kato, 1959; Emanuelsson, 1961). Generally, adenosine derivatives predominate, as one would expect in view of their role in respiratory metabolism. In some eggs, such as in the chick, the accessory white and yolk contain large amounts of nucleotides as well as nucleic acids (Emanuelsson, 1961). It is curious that uridine nucleotides represent more than 60% of the total nucleotide pool in the egg white. The manner of their utilization is still not clear; however, reduction in the amount of this material during development has been observed and one assumes that it is employed in nucleic acid synthesis in the embryo. In the sea urchin (Hultin, 1957b) the trinucleotides of adenosine and uridine predominate in the early stages and then decrease during development, whereas mononucleotides remain constant.

Ribonucleotide utilization for DNA synthesis has been demonstrated in a number of tissues. Rose and Schweigert (1953) have shown the incorporation of ribonucleotides into the DNA of mammalian tissue. Some mechanism for the reduction of the sugar moiety to deoxyribose must therefore exist. It was later confirmed in a series of experiments in the chick embryo by Reichard (1958, 1959, 1961; Reichard *et al.*, 1961) and the enzymes involved in these conversions have been shown to exist in different embryonic tissues.

The synthesis of thymidylic acid has been shown to occur through deoxyuridylic acid via a methylation; moreover, the conversion of uridine diphosphate to deoxyuridine diphosphate has also been observed (Bertani *et al.*, 1961) illustrating a pathway for thymidylate biosynthesis from uridylic acid.

To what extent are ribonucleotides utilized for the synthesis of DNA? It has been shown that during early development in the amphibian and the sea urchin there is no net synthesis of total RNA per embryo (Steinert, 1951; Kutsky, 1950; Chen, 1960; Grant, 1960; Scarano and Kalckar, 1953). Similar observations have been made in the embryo of *Ilyanassa* (Collier, 1961) and the early chick embryo (Novikoff and Potter, 1948; Solomon, 1957b). Isotope incorporation studies with glycine and phosphate have shown that RNA turnover is extremely high during these early stages in the amphibian embryo (Grant, 1958b). Moreover, the acid-soluble component of these embryos, particularly in early stages, is generally actively turning over. This large pool of ribonucleotides that can be utilized is probably available for nucleic acid synthesis and, since early development is largely concerned with DNA synthesis, one would expect a major utilization of these precursor pools for DNA synthesis. Utilization of exogenous ribonucleosides for DNA synthesis has been demonstrated in a number of different embryos, confirming the suggestion outlined above.

The high turnover of RNA with no net synthesis during cleavage, the utilization of ribonucleosides and nucleotides for the synthesis of DNA, and the greater incorporation of isotopes into DNA during this period all point to a pattern of metabolism during early development fully committed to mitosis and cell division.

v. Coenzymes involved in DNA biosynthesis. The folic acid coenzymes, tetrahydrofolic acid (THFA) and hydroxymethyltetrahydrofolic acid (HMTHFA), are known to be involved in methylation reactions, one-carbon transfer reactions essential in the synthesis of purines and pyrimidines, particularly thymidine (Huennekens *et al.*, 1958). In fact, the methylation of deoxyuridylic acid to thymidylic acid requires HMTHFA which supplies the methyl group. This pathway represents an important biosynthetic mechanism for thymidylate synthesis dependent upon the availability of THFA whose synthesis is linked to respiratory metabolism via TPN-TPNH equilibria.

Grant (1960), studying the effects of folic acid analogs on development in the frog embryo, demonstrated the relative sensitivity of gastrulation and neurulation to amethopterin contrasted with the absence of an effect on cleavage. The inhibition is reversed by *citrovorum*, and partially reversible by thymidine, suggesting that the sensitive reaction sequence is the synthesis of thymidylate via the deoxyuridylate pathway, a THFA-dependent reaction. How then can one explain the insensitivity of cleavage to the analog? Does it imply that different mechanisms of DNA synthesis are involved? Several factors unique to the cleavage period undoubtedly contribute to its relative insensitivity. An intense synthesis of deoxyribonucleotides during early cleavage provides a large precursor pool which, in addition to cytoplasmic DNA, could provide all the essential thymidine for DNA. Total folic acid activity as measured by bioassay was found to be highest during cleavage, providing sufficient folic acid coenzyme (THFA?) to insure thymidylate biosynthesis from deoxyuridine compounds in the precursor pool (Grant, 1960).

Sensitivity at the gastrula stage reflects a dependence upon a continuing production of folic acid coenzymes via an amethopterin-sensitive pathway, the conversion of folic acid to tetrahydrofolic acid. During this period precursor levels are minimal, cytoplasmic DNA is exhausted, and cell division is diminished to a much reduced level characteristic of later development (Sze, 1953). A major shift in metabolism occurs at this critical developmental stage, since a marked net synthesis of RNA is initiated as evidenced by intense incorporation of precursors into RNA. Equilibrium between various folic acid coenzymes could serve as a control mechanism switching development from a major commitment to mitosis and cell division (with a requirement for a major source of thymidylate) to metabolism associated with differentiation (RNA synthesis, with a limited requirement for thymidylate) (Grant, 1960). The coenzyme hydroxymethyltetrahydrofolic acid is involved in thymidylate biosynthesis, whereas the derivative formyl tetrahydrofolic acid is involved in purine biosynthesis, and the relative amounts of these two components may serve to regulate the extent of thymidylate biosynthesis. Friedkin (1959) has stressed the key role played by thymidylate in the control of DNA synthesis and it is possible that such relatively simple "mass action" devices may serve as one of several morphogenetic regulatory mechanisms.

Conversion of ribonucleotides to deoxyribonucleotides has been suggested as regulating the competition between DNA replication and protein synthesis in phage infection in *E. coli* (Cohen *et al.*, 1961). The hypothesis states that RNA synthesized immediately after phage infection is initially involved in synthesis of enzymes like thymidylate synthetase, deoxycytidylate deaminase, and deoxycytidylate hydroxymethylase. These enzymes are essential for phage DNA synthesis and the termination of their synthesis is accompanied by hydrolysis of RNA into ribonucleotides, followed by rapid conversion to deoxyribonucleotides to function as precursors for DNA synthesis. This hypothesis suggests that RNA molecules (presumably messenger RNA) may have a dual function, i.e., they may serve in protein synthesis and may also be degraded to form a pool of nucleotide precursors for DNA synthesis. In phage-infected *E. coli* the transformations are compressed into a short time interval so that it is possible to follow metabolic exchanges. In the cleaving egg the situation is extended in time and is complicated by the presence of large nucleotide pools established in the egg during oogenesis. However, the rapid incorporation of labeled glycine into RNA early in cleavage, the absence of net RNA synthesis, and the rapid depletion of label from RNA at a time when DNA labeling is increasing suggests a high turnover of RNA and provides some indirect evidence for the existence of the mechanism suggested by Cohen, namely, the utilization of RNA as a precursor of DNA, at a time when DNA synthesis is the predominant metabolic pathway.

Control of DNA synthesis via folic acid coenzymes may be a function of respiratory metabolism, since coenzyme equilibria depend upon the ratio of TPN to TPNH. Some correlation exists between a break in the respiratory curve at gastrulation in amphibian embryos with a reduction in cell division, DNA synthesis, and the initiation of net RNA synthesis (Løvtrup, 1955). Enzymes directly involved in the TPN–TPNH hydrogen transport system are synthesized at gastrulation (Wallace, 1961). Insufficient data are available, however, on levels of TPN and TPNH in embryos to evaluate their role as controlling metabolites. These have been implicated in the lethal hybrid syndrome in amphibia (Brachet *et al.*, 1962) and may be correlated with the observed derangement of nucleic acid metabolism in these embryos.

A key control reaction may reside in the biosynthesis of thymidylate, as suggested by Friedkin (1959). The essential reaction may be the conversion of deoxyuridylate to thymidylate. The rapid utilization of tritium-labeled uridine for DNA synthesis in cleavage stages of the amphibian embryo (Bieliavsky and Tencer, 1961) and the sea urchin embryo (Ficq *et al.*, 1963) suggests that this reaction may function optimally in these embryos. Obviously, the conversion of uridylate to deoxyuridylate must occur rapidly to account for its immediate utilization for DNA synthesis. The enzyme involved, "thymidylate synthetase," is presumably present in these embryos and it would be of considerable interest to follow its developmental pattern during embryogenesis.

vi. Enzymes involved in DNA synthesis and its regulation. Previous mention has been made of the observations of Mazia and Hinegardner (1963) concerning the activity and distribution of DNA phosphorylase in the sea urchin embryo. The enzyme is localized in the egg nucleus and its activity correlates well with cell division manifesting high activity in early stages when the mitotic rate is a maximum. A correspondence between chromosome number and polymerase activity denotes physical association of the enzyme with the chromosomes. Mazia admits that the data simply mean that a doubling of DNA per nucleus results in a doubling of enzyme activity. It is reasonable to assume that the enzyme should be bound to the template or primer DNA to facilitate DNA replication. Mazia (1963) also suggests that control of DNA synthesis may be associated with intermittent binding of the polymerase to the primer during the life cycle of the cell. In rapidly dividing cells, like sea urchin blastomeres, the enzyme and primer may be intimately associated for extended periods during early cleavage. This would be true if cells exhibit a compressed division cycle without a G1 phase as is evidenced by the cleaving blastomere. As development proceeds, more and more cells enter a G1 phase. Nuclei are found to have approximately one-quarter the enzyme activity, when the cell division rate has fallen to approximately one-sixtieth of its rate at the 16-cell stage (Mazia, 1963).

Conceivably, intrinsic control of DNA replication may demand the attachment of enzyme to the chromosome. The number of enzyme molecules associated with chromosomes may be finite, high at fertilization, and segregating with each division, each daughter nucleus getting about one-half the original amount. As cleavage continues, this dilution of enzyme per nucleus continues until the enzyme concentration is sufficiently low or virtually depleted in some cells as to make DNA replication impossible. If sufficient enzyme molecules are combined with primer, the limiting factors controlling DNA synthesis may be the availability of precursors or the physical state of the primer.

Determinations of enzyme activity per nucleus provide only an average value for a heterogeneous population of cells. After gastrulation, at least in the amphibian, the mitotically active population represents less than 7% of the total cell population (Bragg, 1938). Only actively dividing cells may contain enzyme, whereas most cells undergoing differentiation may lack activity entirely. This heterogeneity complicates efforts to resolve regulating mechanisms in operation at different developmental stages.

The enzyme deoxyribonuclease has been examined in embryos of the sea urchin, the frog, and the salamander (Mazia, 1949; Blumenthal, 1957; Finamore, 1955; Coleman, 1962). Recent interest in this enzyme as a regulator of DNA synthesis derives from the fact that the primer activity of DNA in a cell-free system may be increased by prior treatment with DNase (Bollum, 1963a). Although denatured or native DNA may have its priming activity increased by treatment with DNase, it is clear that DNase is not required for polymerase action. It appears, however, that DNA must be converted into a primer state for maximum activity in the phosphorylase reaction and the implication is that in situ, under physiological conditions, DNA is transformed into a primer prior to DNA synthesis. Bollum (1963b) recently made several attempts to detect "primer" DNA in intact cells without too much success. There are reports of unusual forms of DNA as determined by density and solubility, suggesting that during the normal replication cycle several different cryptic states of DNA must be present. The possibility that DNase may have a physiological role in the priming of native DNA has been suggested (Bollum, 1963b) although with some well-advised caution. Chèvremont et al. (1959, 1961) demonstrated a distinct cytoplasmic synthesis of DNA (associated with the mitochondria) after treatment of fibroblasts with (acid) DNase, a procedure which may transform mitochondrial DNA into primer DNA, activating it sufficiently for some DNA synthesis. Admittedly, the conditions of treatment are long (1 to 2 days of DNase treatment, under conditions which undoubtedly result in severe cell damage, including death) and of doubtful physiological significance.

Several DNase assays have been completed on Rana pipiens embryos, leading to conflicting results (Finamore, 1955; Blumenthal, 1957; Coleman, 1962). Finamore observed a fluctuating pattern for alkaline DNase, although his determinations were made at suboptimal pH and not properly controlled for homogenate autolysis. Blumenthal was unable to detect DNase I (alkaline) in eggs, embryos, larvae, or even adults; however, the conditions of assay were suboptimal with the possibility of enzyme inactivation owing to high ionic strength. She did find acid DNase in adult frogs, but was unable to detect any in embryos or larvae. Coleman, in a careful study of both DNase I and II, found detectable activity in embryos, larvae, and adults. Alkaline DNase exhibited no activity until after hatching and increased rapidly during the larval period. Coleman assigned this enzyme to gut and pancreas differentiation. Acid DNase exhibited low levels of activity in the fertilized egg, decreased slightly at gastrulation, then increased gradually at neurulation, and continued this rapid increase late into larval life. The early portion of the curve resembles the curve for DNA synthesis, following the pattern of increase in nuclei. Although Coleman stresses the role of the enzyme in cell degradation processes, based on its association with lysosomes in mammalian tissues, its developmental pattern suggests a possible role in the synthesis of DNA during development.

If the enzyme is associated with nuclei and is involved in activating the primer state of the DNA template, we would expect to find enzyme activity to correspond with the increase in nuclei. Obviously, the increase in activity observed may not represent net enzyme synthesis; rather it could reflect a change in the state of the enzyme facilitating its extractability. Since the data are inadequate to resolve this difficulty, further speculation at this time is certainly premature.

vii. Enzymes in deoxynucleotide synthesis. Recent experiments in cell-free systems demonstrate that deoxyribosyl compounds may be derived from reduction of ribosyl components. (See review by Bessman, 1963.) Tracer experiments with ribosyl derivatives have shown a significant utilization of these compounds for the synthesis of DNA. Much of this work has been carried out with the chick embryo (Reichard, 1958, 1959, 1960) in cell-free extracts showing that conversion to the deoxyribosyl derivative occurs at the diphosphate level for purines as well as pyrimidines. The studies of Reichard involved embryos of late development (5–9 days) undergoing histogenesis and organogenesis. Mitotic activity in these embryos is relatively low compared to early developmental stages. Although these later stages contain enzyme systems for the synthesis of deoxyribonucleotides from ribonucleotides, no data are available for their presence earlier in development.

It had been mentioned previously that a possible limiting reaction in the synthesis of DNA is the synthesis of thymidylate. Recently, a series of investigations have provided information about several pathways for the synthesis of thymidylate, some of which are shown to be present in different embryos. Friedkin and Kornberg (1957) have demonstrated thymidylate synthesis in *E. coli* via the transfer of an active one-carbon fragment to deoxyuridylate, the carbon donor being tetrahydrofolic acid. The enzyme involved has been called thymidylate synthetase (Flaks and Cohen, 1957) and it was shown to increase sevenfold in T2-infected *E. coli*. The enzyme is present in late chick embryos (Friedkin and Roberts, 1956), although it has not been assayed in earlier stages or in other embryos.

A different pathway for thymidine biosynthesis, which may play an important role in control of DNA synthesis during development has also been postulated. The enzyme deoxycytidylic deaminase converts deoxy-cytidylate to deoxyuridylate and was originally described in sea urchin embryos (Scarano, 1958; Scarano and Maggio, 1959), rat embryo liver (G. F. Maley and F. Maley, 1959; Scarano et al., 1959), regenerating liver (F. Maley and G. F. Maley, 1960), chick embryo (Scarano et al., 1959; G. F. Maley and F. Maley, 1959; Roth and Buccino, 1963), as well as tumors (G. F. Maley and F. Maley, 1959; Roth et al., 1963b). The enzyme seems to be associated with proliferating tissues, exhibiting a marked increase in regenerating liver, for example. Although high activities were found in the unfertilized eggs of Sphaerechinus granularis, very low activities (about ten times less) were found in the unfertilized eggs of Paracentrotus lividus (Scarano and Maggio, 1959).

In the Sphaerechinus embryo, activity is at a maximum during cleavage, relatively constant to the 64-cell stage and declines gradually during development from the blastula until the lowest activities were observed in the pluteus, a reduction of approximately 75% of the original activity. It was shown that inhibitors are not present in the later stages and the authors concluded the conversion to deoxyuridine 5'-monophosphate (dUMP) from deoxycytidine 5'-monophosphate (dCMP) may represent a control mechanism for DNA synthesis, since it effectively reduces the amount of dCMP precursor. The high activities early in development are assumed to be correlated with the high precursor levels during those stages. High activities were also observed early in the chick embryo and were shown to decrease with development (Scarano et al., 1960; Roth and Buccino, 1963). Roth and Buccino's data indicate that specific activity is highest at day 3 and decreases slowly to day 15. However, absolute amounts of enzyme per embryo increased. Activity per embryo doubles each day from 4–8 days. From 8–11 days, an increase of 50% a day is observed. Thus enzyme synthesis is proceeding rapidly. Mention is made of the possibility of activities being low in the first few days of incubation reaching a maximum on day 3.

The situation in the amphibian embryo is quite different. Specific activity is low in the fertilized egg and increases during cleavage until it attains more than twice the activity in the neurula stage, at which time it remains relatively constant until after hatching when it rises rapidly (De Petrocellis et al., 1965). Ploidy has no effect on enzymatic activity indicating that the enzyme is not associated with chromosomes, nor does it depend upon the sperm contribution since gynogenetic haploids exhibit identical activity as normal diploids. Moreover, treatment of the egg with nitrogen mustard before fertilization has no effect on enzyme activity, illustrating the relative independence of enzyme activity from a normally functioning genome.

The enzyme in the amphibian embryo reaches its high levels of activity at a time when the synthesis of thymidine is limiting at the neurula stage (Grant, 1960). During cleavage the egg contains a reserve of nucleotides that decreases when mitotic activity decreases during neurulation, and the embryo is quite sensitive to thymidine analogs. Tencer (1961a) has observed that the blastula stage is sensitive to 5-fluorodeoxyuridine (FUDR) without effecting cleavage and this could be partially reversed by thymidine. It was found that FUDR inhibited uridine-H^3 incorporation into DNA without effecting incorporation of thymidine. These experiments are complicated by permeability problems since the surface coat represents a formidable barrier. The pattern in the sand dollar egg (Karnovsky and Basch, 1960) suggests that a similar mechanism is operating. Sensitivity to the analog FUDR is maximum at the blastula stage, 8 hours after fertilization. Cleavage is completely insensitive even at very high doses. Inhibition at the blastula stage may be protected by prior treatment with thymidine and, if low doses of the inhibitor are used, with deoxyuridine. The effect is reversed if treated blastulae are exposed to thymidine within 6 hours after exposure to the analog. Later stages of development beyond the blastula are not as sensitive as the blastula stage. In these instances, however, it is possible that insensitivity is related to a decreased permeability to the analog. Nemer (1962a) has reported similar effects of FUDR on the sea urchin embryo, although at the higher concentrations employed, development was inhibited at the 8-blastomere stage. Thymidine reverses this effect also, at least permitting development to the blastula stage.

In the sea urchin embryo, as in the frog embryo, the rate of cell division diminishes (Mazia, 1963) at the late blastula or early gastrula stage, and presumably at this stage, thymidine availability becomes limiting for future development. Prior to the gastrula, sufficient precursors are present to facilitate thymidine biosynthesis. Since the analog inhibits the synthesis of thymidine from deoxyuridylate, one may assume that this reaction is limiting at a stage when precursors are exhausted. In the sea urchin, this period is also associated with a low level of deoxycytidylic deaminase, the enzyme responsible for the conversion of deoxycytidylate to deoxyuridylate. It is not possible to determine to what extent this latter reaction is necessary for the synthesis of thymidine. Sugino et al. (1960) characterized one of the acid-soluble deoxynucleotide derivatives in sea urchin embryos as deoxy-diphospho-choline. This component is at least in sufficiently large amounts during early development to facilitate its isolation and characterization. If the sea urchin egg contains a bulk of its precursors stored as deoxycytidylate compounds, then one could expect their conversion to deoxyuridylate prior to thymidine synthesis. This could explain, in part, the high levels of the enzyme at the early cleavage stages in the sea urchin embryo and its later decline as the need for thymidine diminishes.

Enzyme activity in regenerating liver (F. Maley and G. F. Maley, 1960) rises after partial hepatectomy, reaches a peak at 48 hours, then falls to the normal low levels characteristic of intact liver. Such sudden shifts in activity are correlated with variations in mitotic activity and DNA synthesis. This correlation is not always evident in embryos since the amphibian embryo differs significantly from the sea urchin, the chick, or the rat embryo. Activity increases with development in the amphibian embryo, whereas activity decreases during later development in other embryos when mitotic activity is low. However, Roth (1963) in evaluating the role of the enzyme in tumors and other proliferating tissue demonstrated that all tumors do not exhibit high levels of activity and that enzyme patterns are not necessarily correlated with high proliferative rates. Tumors are unusual since they may exhibit deletions of key enzymes. For example, Kit *et al.* (1963) have shown that a tumor line is deficient in thymidylate synthetase, yet it continues to incorporate thymidine into DNA and grow rapidly. This implies that different deoxynucleotide pathways may exist in different tumors. One must, therefore, assume that different embryonic systems similarly may exhibit different patterns of deoxynucleotide metabolism, synthesizing DNA by several alternate *de novo* pathways.

The enzyme has been extracted and relatively purified from sea urchin eggs (Scarano *et al.*, 1960) and more recently from chick embryos (G. F. Maley and F. Maley, 1964). The activity of the enzyme is effectively stabilized when it is extracted in the presence of the substrate (Scarano, 1961). Activity may be inhibited, however, by various ribonucleotides and deoxyribonucleotides as shown by Maley and Maley (1959). The most effective inhibitors are dUMP and thymidine monophosphate (TMP), both products of the reaction, suggesting that some sort of feedback inhibition may be involved in the control of the activity of the enzyme. Similarly, F. Maley and G. F. Maley (1964) have suggested that the appearance of the enzymes involved in nucleotide metabolism in regenerating liver suggests a sequential induction. Deoxycytidylate deaminase appears within 8 hours after partial hepatectomy, whereas thymidylate synthetase appears closer to the 18-hour period. Since it has been found that TMP may induce or activate thymidylate kinase (Hiatt and Bojarski, 1960), the Maleys suggest that the product of the deamination reaction, dUMP, may serve to induce or activate the formation of thymidylate synthetase, which in turn could effect the formation of thymidylate kinase through its product TMP. However, Hiatt and Bojarski (1960) explain the apparent induction of thymidylate as thymidine stabilization of the enzyme during extraction.

Such control of enzyme levels in the embryo is certainly plausible in view of the large nucleotide stores that exist early in development. G. F. Maley and F. Maley (1960) have reported the inhibition of deoxyribonucleic acid snythesis in the chick embryo by deoxyadenosine. Incorporation of cytidine-2-C^{14} and uridine-2-C^{14} into DNA cytosine and thymine are both inhibited by deoxyadenosine. The effect could not be attributed to any dilution of pyrimidine pools. The Maleys explain this phenomenon as an inhibition of deoxycytidylate deaminase by any excess dAMP synthesized, assuming the bulk of thymidine for DNA is derived via the dCMP to dUMP to TMP conversion. The dilution data implicate cytidine as a major source of DNA thymine in these chick embryo homogenates. Cytidine is a more effective precursor of DNA pyrimidines than uridine, an observation made by others in different systems. In embryos the major component of the acid-soluble fraction seems to be deoxycytidine or cytidine nucleotides [(Kuriki and Okazaki, 1959)—in the frog embryo and (Sugino et al., 1960)—in the sea urchin embryo].

Inhibition of chick embryo growth has been obtained by exposure of explants to deoxyguanosine monophosphate (dGMP) (Roth et al., 1963a). There is a correlation between doses which inhibit growth and those which inhibit deoxycytidylic deaminase. The effect could be alleviated by treatment with deoxycytidine derivatives. The inhibition of embryonic growth by dGMP is related to its inhibition of the enzyme in situ. Although the data are suggestive of a relationship, inhibition of growth by dGMP may involve a number of unrelated reactions in situ, some of which may be as important for normal growth as is the deaminase. It is interesting, however, that dAMP has no effect on growth, yet it is known to inhibit the enzyme.

At this stage of our knowledge about the interconversions of nucleotides, it is difficult to resolve even one of the many control reactions which undoubtedly regulate biosynthetic pathways leading to the synthesis of DNA. For example, Maley and Maley (1963a,b) have recently demonstrated phosphotransferase activity in chick embryo minces, capable of transferring phosphate from pyrimidine deoxyribonucleotides to other deoxyribonucleosides. In fact, the in vitro syntheses promoted by this reaction are more active than synthesis of deoxynucleotides promoted by ATP kinases. In addition, pool sizes of cytidine deoxynucleosides may be regulated by levels of thymidine—a thymidine-sparing effect having been observed which, by virtue of conversion to thymidine triphosphate (TTP), an inhibitor of deoxycytidylate deaminase, diverts deoxycytidylate to the cytosine of DNA rather than the thymine moiety.

Other enzymes are necessary to provide the triphosphates of purine and pyrimidine nucleosides. These enzymes, deoxynucleotide kinases, phosphorylate mononucleotides to the diphosphate in conjunction with ATP. Similarly, diphosphate nucleotides must be further phosphorylated to the triphosphate level. Deoxynucleoside diphosphate kinases have been postulated to exist in crude extracts of E. coli, regenerating liver, and ascites tumors, because phosphorylation of the monophosphates have usually resulted in the formation of triphosphates in these systems. Unfortunately, these enzymes have not been studied carefully in embryonic tissues, but one may assume, in view of the numerous incorporation studies showing the utilization of nucleosides (uridine, cytidine, thymidine, etc.) for DNA synthesis in embryonic tissues, that the necessary kinases are present even in the earlier stages of development.

b. Partial Synthesis—The Role of Cytoplasmic DNA during Development. Most investigators analyzing DNA synthesis during embryogenesis have generally assumed that excess DNA found in the egg and during early cleavage serves primarily as a precursor store for the synthesis of nuclear DNA. The sensitive microbiological assay procedure demonstrates a constant amount of DNA per amphibian embryo during early cleavage (Hoff-Jørgensen, 1954; Gregg and Løvtrup, 1955). It was noted previously, however, that these studies failed to distinguish acid-soluble from the acid-insoluble components (Grant, 1958a; Kuriki and Okazaki, 1959). The large amount of the former substances undoubtedly conceal the small net acid-insoluble synthesis, when both are analyzed simultaneously. Grant (1958a) calculated that the bulk of the nuclear DNA formed during cleavage in the amphibian embryo prior to the late blastula could come from the newly synthesized deoxyribonucleotides. The remainder could come from the cytoplasmic DNA; however, there is no direct evidence of cytoplasmic DNA utilization for nuclear DNA synthesis. Its precursor role rests primarily on calculations of cytoplasmic DNA per embryo approximately equivalent to 1000–3000 diploid nuclei, a cell number usually found in an early blastula. In addition, the amount of DNA per blastula corresponds to the number of nuclei present, suggesting exhaustion of cytoplasmic DNA at this stage. This kind of evidence has led to the general acceptance of a precursor role for cytoplasmic DNA. Unfortunately, it has been difficult to carry out direct labeling experiments to determine how cytoplasmic DNA is utilized. It should be possible to inject some labeled DNA (preferably some extracted from embryos) into fertilized eggs and determine by autoradiography whether there is any specific incorporation into the nuclei during development. One would have to deal with highly labeled material since the dilution may be very great. This experiment would at least indicate whether such an incorporation is possible.

Besides the precursor role outlined above, other explanations for excess DNA in eggs and embryos have been offered. Some have claimed that:

(1) Excess DNA has no developmental significance, representing contamination, principally from polar bodies, follicle cells, and accessory cells. This view has been propounded by Marshak and Marshak for the sea urchin egg (1955a,b), but may not be applicable to the insect or amphibian egg.

(2) Cytoplasmic DNA may be ascribed to cytoplasmic structures like mitochondria and remnants of extruded nucleoli with nucleolar associated chromatin (Dawid, 1964). Such chromatin may represent duplicated loci for ribosomal RNA synthesis during oogenesis, a mechanism designed to facilitate the intense protein synthesis characteristic of that period (Brown, 1964). Since its primary role is restricted to oogenesis, the material remaining at fertilization may be utilized as a source of deoxyribonucleotide precursors during development.

(3) Cytoplasmic DNA is developmentally significant although primarily as a precursor for nuclear DNA. This view was suggested initially by J. A. Moore (1960, 1963) as a result of interspecific nuclear transplantation experiments (Moore, 1958a,b).

Moore found that *Rana pipiens* haploid nuclei, after replication to the blastula stage in foreign *Rana sylvatica* cytoplasm, are unable to sustain normal development when transplanted to *R. pipiens* cytoplasm. This was later confirmed by Hennen (1961) for diploid nuclear transfers. Moore postulated that exposure of replicating chromosomes to foreign cytoplasmic DNA is responsible for nuclear modification produced by the incorporation of cytoplasmic DNA into nuclear DNA as genetically significant polynucleotide fragments. Hennen found all cases of abnormal development associated with aberrant karyotypes. It appears that replication in foreign cytoplasm is responsible for inducing chromosome lesions leading to aneuploidy.

As mentioned previously, Dawid (1964) has succeeded in extracting high molecular weight DNA from unfertilized eggs of *R. pipiens* and *Xenopus* having identical properties with liver DNA of the same species. Egg DNA has the same density in cesium chloride gradients, similar UV spectra, and a melting profile identical to liver DNA indicating that it is double stranded. In the analytical ultracentrifuge, egg and liver DNA have the same densities yielding a GC content of approximately 42%. It is interesting that in *Xenopus,* egg DNA differs slightly from tadpole DNA in cesium chloride, with a 2% GC difference in over-all base composition.

In a few preliminary hybridization experiments, using the agar gel procedure, Dawid has shown that *Xenopus* egg DNA does not compete with *Xenopus* erythrocyte DNA indicating, at least tentatively, that there is no sequence homology between egg DNA and somatic cell DNA. Diphenylamine-reacting material was found to sediment largely in the mitochondrial fraction; moreover, the reacting material in the pellet is of the same order of magnitude as the total egg-reacting material. Since some material is also found in the yolk fraction, it is admittedly difficult to conclude unequivocally that the DNA is definitely associated with mitochondria.

The amount of this material per egg was found to be far less than all previous measurements of cytoplasmic DNA in amphibian eggs. In *R. pipiens,* 1.4 mµg per egg and in *Xenopus* 2.1 mµg per egg were found, representing 100–300 times the normal diploid amount per egg. This is approximately one-tenth the lowest amount reported for *R. pipiens* (Grant, 1958a). During isolation Dawid noted a large amount of diphenylamine-reacting material that is alcohol soluble and acid precipitable but of low molecular weight. This material is approximately 8.2 mµg per egg and was not characterized. Obviously, this latter material would be detected by microbiological assay or direct analytical assay of diphenylamine-reacting material as DNA in analyses of total DNA per embryo and may explain the high DNA values previously published. The diphenylamine reaction with this material is different from normal DNA, suggesting a difficultly extracted contaminant.

Dawid postulates that the high molecular weight DNA extracted and characterized above is associated with mitochondria. This is consistent with other observations of plastid DNA, where DNA is double stranded, high molecular weight, but with a base composition differing from nuclear DNA. In view of the small amount found, it is unlikely that it serves significantly as a precursor for nuclear DNA during development. In a few preliminary experiments involving the incorporation of P^{32} into cleaving eggs, the labeled material followed the DNA peak in sucrose density gradients suggesting that *de novo* synthesis is active immediately at fertilization. Moreover, the amount of newly synthesized DNA during the first few cleavages is insufficient to detect. DNA per embryo does not exhibit any new increase until a large number of cells are produced at the blastula.

Other diphenylamine-reacting acid-insoluble precursors are different from high molecular weight DNA. These may be oligonucleotides having some unknown developmental role. Dawid does not eliminate the possibility that some nuclear DNA may be formed during cleavage via partial pathways; however, he states there is no satisfactory evidence to support Moore's hypothesis for the utilization of "blocks" of cytoplasmic DNA for the synthesis of nuclear DNA.

These new data are extremely important to our understanding of the role of the excess DNA found in eggs and early embryos. They tend to support the second of the three alternatives mentioned previously, namely, DNA is associated with cell organelles (plastids, etc.) found in large numbers in the unusually large cell, the mature oocyte. It may function initially during the intense synthetic phase of oogenesis and is rapidly segregated with the organelles into individual blastomeres during cleavage. However, other diphenylamine-reacting materials found in much larger amounts in the egg may contribute significantly to the formation of nuclear DNA during early and possibly later development.

A further investigation of the Moore hypothesis concerning the developmental significance of cytoplasmic DNA was initiated by Grant (1961). Nitrogen mustard was employed (Grant, 1961; Grant and Stott, 1962) as a probe to interfere with nucleocytoplasmic interactions during amphibian development. Brief exposure of eggs to a solution of nitrogen mustard is sufficient to modify development. At the concentrations employed ($2.5 \times 10^{-6} M$) cleavage is unaffected, whereas development is inhibited at the beginning of gastrulation, very similar to the hybrid arrests studied by Moore. By appropriate manipulation of conditions of treatment combined with nuclear transplantation, it is possible to prepare different nucleocytoplasmic combinations and analyze the developmental effects. In diploid combinations (Grant, 1961) treatment of egg cytoplasm followed by enucleation and transplantation of a normal blastula nucleus results in a blastula-gastrula inhibition. The lesion is definitely nuclear since a second-generation nuclear transfer to normal egg cytoplasm from a treated blastula generally leads to an identical developmental syndrome. This suggests that some cytoplasmic, alkylated derivative has interacted with the nuclei to induce nuclear lesions, restricting their capacity to initiate and sustain normal development when returned to normal cytoplasm. Continued passage of such nuclei through a series of different transplant generations results in a significant improvement of the developmental capacity of these nuclei. Employing a dose of nitrogen mustard which inhibits normal gastrulation, it is possible in the third and fourth transfer generations to double the number of completely normal gastrulae, in spite of the fact that control transfers reveal a gradual decline in developmental capacity with each additional transplant generation.

In later studies with haploid transfers (Grant and Stott, 1962) the interaction between treated cytoplasm and normal haploid nuclei was found to produce chromosomal abnormalities. Aneuploidy, chromosomal fragmentation, anaphase bridges, and ring chromosomes represented a few of the major chromosomal disturbances. Serial transfers of such nuclei into normal cytoplasm did not result in recovery, which agrees with Moore's observations of failure of haploid *pipiens* nuclei to recover after exposure to foreign cytoplasm for one generation. Hennen (1961) observed chromosomal abnormalities after exposure of *pipiens* diploid nuclei to *sylvatica cytoplasm.*

These observations suggest that repair of nitrogen mustard-induced chromosomal damage is possible in normal cytoplasm, at least for the diploid nucleus. Such recovery would be more evident in the diploid since few homozygous lesions would be produced, assuming random production. In the haploid every nitrogen mustard-induced lesion is undoubtedly expressed. Fischberg *et al.* (1958), studying interspecific transfers between *Rana temporaria* and *Xenopus*, observed that diploid *temporaria* nuclei transferred to *Xenopus* and allowed to duplicate generally formed an arrested blastula. Subsequent transfer of such nuclei to *temporaria* cytoplasm, however, resulted in partial recovery to the gastrula. Moore (1960) reported no recovery of haploid *pipiens* nuclei even after five serial transfers in their own cytoplasm.

In vivo and *in vitro* studies of nitrogen mustard reactions indicate that it combines most rapidly with nucleic acids and their derivatives. DNA is apparently more sensitive than RNA. Bodenstein and Kondritzer (1948) have shown that DNA synthesis is generally inhibited in amphibian embryos, whereas RNA synthesis continues unaffected. Alkylation of cellular constituents by nitrogen mustard is extremely rapid. Consequently, lesions induced in nuclei interacting with alkylated egg cytoplasm are undoubtedly mediated through cytoplasmic substances normally participating in nucleocytoplasmic exchanges during cleavage. Such substances may be deoxynucleotide or polynucleotide precursors. Mustard also reacts with ribonucleotides, RNA, and may modify proteins, although at the concentrations employed, it is unlikely that protein alkylation is particularly important. An alkylated derivative incorporated into a DNA strand introduces appropriate disturbances which can initiate chromosomal breaks and other aberrations. "Sticky" chromosomes are produced which lead to anaphase bridges, fragmentation, ring chromosomes, and aneuploidy.

Restoration of abnormal nuclei by serial transplantation in normal cytoplasm is probably brought about by a similar mechanism. Normal egg cytoplasm contains a spectrum of DNA precursors which may replace the alkylated derivatives during the course of chromosomal replication, "repairing" damaged regions. This should result in a blastula consisting of a greater proportion of nuclei with normal chromosomal complements. Obviously, only small chromosomal lesions could be repaired by this mechanism. The chances of choosing one such nucleus in the transfer procedure is increased and one should find occasional evidence of recovery. Abnormal chromosome strands may be repaired by replacement with normal nucleotide sequences.

The key issue is whether these represent polynucleotide replacement as suggested by Moore or typical trinucleotide precursor replacement. The frequency of chromosomal abnormalities increases with cell division after direct nitrogen mustard treatment of blastulae (Grant and Stott, 1962). Direct exposure of sperm nuclei prior to insemination or direct treatment of blastulae prior to their use in nuclear transplantation induce abnormal development characterized by nuclei with abnormal karyotypes. These directly induced nuclear lesions differ from those produced by transfer of normal nuclei to nitrogen mustard-treated cytoplasm. The former nuclei do not recover even after serial transplantation in normal cytoplasm, suggesting that the mechanisms for lesion production by direct alkylation may be qualitatively different from those produced indirectly via the cytoplasm. No significant modification of several physiochemical properties of DNA extracted from mouse fibroblasts treated in culture with $10^{-6} M$ nitrogen mustard have been demonstrated (Brewer and Aronow, 1963). Extracted DNA treated *in vitro*, however, with higher concentrations of mustard exhibited profound changes in these properties. Apparently cross-linking of DNA is not a result of *in vivo* alkylation and is not responsible for growth inhibition. Rutman *et al.* (1961), studying the effect of nitrogen mustard on Ehrlich ascites tumor cells, observed no direct quantitative relation between cytotoxic effects and the degree of alkylation of DNA. They concluded that cytotoxicity is a function of the kind rather than of the extent of intra- or intermolecular cross-linking of DNA. They did imply, however, that mixed cross-linking between protein and nucleic acid is a significant feature of the *in vivo* process. Direct treatment of amphibian nuclei may result in modifications of protein-DNA relations in the chromosome leading to "weak spots" which initiate breaks. The indirect, cytoplasmically mediated effect, although also responsible for chromosomal abnormalities (though fewer in number), may result from actual replacement by alkylated purine and pyrimidine bases in the DNA strand. Recovery in this instance is possible because random substitutions are repaired during replication in normal cytoplasm by direct replacement of alkylated regions with normal precursors. The data do not permit a distinction between the kinds or size of precursors involved, however.

Several mechanisms have been postulated for the induction of mutations by alkylating agents (Freese, 1963). Alkylation of the phosphate moieties of the DNA chain is different from alkylation of the bases. Alkylation of the former could lead to chain breaks as a result of hydrolysis of the triester linkage. This, ultimately, would be expressed as large scale chromosomal abnormalities and aneuploidy. Most evidence favors the view that the phosphate group in nucleoproteins (sperm heads) is the most sensitive site of alkylation (Alexander and Stacey, 1958). The lesions induced by "alkylated cytoplasm" may involve a replacement of normal bases by alkylated derivatives which would either inhibit DNA replication or cause base-pairing mistakes during DNA duplication. Thus, repair by replacement of alkylated bases with normal precursors could occur more readily than refusion of broken chains.

We are left then with the question of the role of cytoplasmic DNA still unresolved, although in a much better state than it was a year ago. The so-called cytoplasmic DNA is probably a mixture of diphenylamine-containing substances, some of which include high molecular weight DNA associated with cell organelles, possibly mitochondria. This complex mixture of deoxyribonucleotides, oligonucleotides, and other nucleotide complexes are found in the unfertilized egg as well as during early development in the eggs of echinoderms, amphibians, and insects. The evidence from all sources is certainly not conclusive with respect to the precursor role played by these derivatives. It is clear, however, that synthesis of nuclear DNA during the first few cleavages until the early blastula is not easily detected by the methods available, particularly in a background of numerous deoxyribonucleotide derivatives having solubility properties similar to DNA. Presumably, a bulk of these deoxyribonucleotide precursors are available for incorporation into nuclear DNA. This leaves a large fraction of relatively unknown polydeoxyribonucleotides, with an undefined function.

It is unnecessary to invoke several different pathways of DNA synthesis during development. One *de novo* pathway, similar to that found in actively proliferating tissues of the adult, does exist in the egg and embryo. The specific details relating to precursor levels, enzyme pathways, and coenzymes may differ for different embryonic systems, but the utilization of small molecules for purine and pyrimidine biosynthesis, their subsequent conversion into phosphorylated deoxynucleosides by the appropriate enzyme systems, and their eventual polymerization in the presence of DNA primer and DNA polyphosphorylase undoubtedly occur in all embryos after fertilization. The pattern of DNA increase per embryo can be explained almost exclusively on this basis, since it follows the mitotic and cell division patterns. Control of DNA synthesis and mitotic activity undoubtedly rests on mechanisms which regulate enzyme synthesis, precursor levels, and physical state of the DNA primer. The over-all *de novo* pathway as a mechanism of DNA synthesis may not change during development. Specific enzyme systems and precursors and their respective control mechanisms may be altered at different stages of development and in different tissues as differentiation occurs. Just as different hepatomas will exhibit different deoxyribonucleotide interconversion pathways, cytodifferentiation may elicit a profound modification in the regulation of DNA synthesis in different cell populations. Some cell populations exhibit irreversible changes in the DNA synthetic machinery, preventing further replication, as may be the case in nerve cells. Other cells may display a temporary cessation of DNA synthesis, such as the liver cell, still responsive to extrinsic signals switching the enzymatic machinery toward DNA synthesis. A few cell populations may retain controls characteristic of the embryonic cell, permitting a period of synthesis and mitotic activity to be followed by a specific maturation and differentiation, as exists in hematopoietic tissue. Finally, cell populations may arise exhibiting no apparent control over the mitotic process and DNA synthesis. Such neoplastic cell populations are unresponsive to extrinsic growth-regulating mechanisms. Obviously, the ultimate fate of a cell population is determined by the nature of the mechanisms differentiated to control DNA replication and mitotic activity.

c. *Constancy of Nuclear DNA during Embryonic Development.* Shortly after the development of the constancy hypothesis (Boivin *et al.,* 1948), some exceptions to this hypothesis were presented (Lison and Pasteels, 1951) suggesting that significant variations to constancy were associated with embryonic tissues. The observations of Lison and Pasteels were not confirmed by other investigators; in fact, the observed variations from constancy could be explained by difficulties with the instrumentation and techniques employed (Alfert and Swift, 1953). However, the problems raised are of sufficient interest to warrant an evaluation of the hypothesis as it applies to embryogenesis.

Moore (1952, 1957) reported large variations in the amount of DNA per nucleus in embryonic cells of *Rana pipiens*, in the diploid and haploid state and in androgenetic hybrids. She found good correlation between ploidy and DNA content; however, the range of values beyond the experimental error of the technique was quite large, usually 15%. Moore claimed that values of DNA between diploid and tetraploid cannot be attributed to intermediate stages of synthesis, since there is no correlation with mitotic index. However, Walker (1954) points out that variations in mitotic index may be due to one or both of two factors, i.e., changes in the proportion of nonproliferating cells and changes in the synthesis of DNA during the interphase. The more recent findings with tritiated thymidine concerning the G1, S, and G2 phases during the cell cycle certainly justify Walker's emphasis on using caution in interpreting mitotic index data as a measure of variations in the interphase patterns of DNA synthesis. Moore stresses the wide variation in DNA values; in fact, in diploid embryonic tissues haploid amounts of DNA were observed in several nuclei, whereas only a few tetraploid values were found. One would expect a greater frequency of tetraploid, or near tetraploid values, in rapidly dividing cells; yet, for the diploid series this is relatively rare. The haploid series consistently fell within the haploid to diploid range and could readily be explained as different stages in the synthesis of DNA.

The range of values (in forebrain, for example) is less in 11-day embryos than in 7-day embryos, and Moore attributes this difference to differentiation. However, her data for the 7-day embryo may reflect different rates of DNA synthesis, since almost two distinct classes are shown. The 11-day forebrain probably contains fewer dividing cells; consequently, most nuclei are diploid.

Moore suggests that differentiation may involve a selective synthesis of DNA at different loci in different tissues which accounts for the wide range of DNA values in nuclei of differentiating tissue. Adult tissue, having completed differentiation, has settled down to a constant, narrow DNA range because few loci are actively synthesizing DNA. This interesting hypothesis has not received much attention, particularly after several questions of technique were pointed out.

In a later study on the sea urchin, McMaster (1955) has shown that variation in DNA values in early cleavage and larval cells could be explained by differential rates of DNA synthesis. Her data were significantly different from those reported by Lison and Pasteels (1951) on *Paracentrotus*, where large variations in DNA were observed, including values of DNA less than the diploid and greater than the tetraploid values. Lison and Pasteels interpreted their data on the basis of some morphogenetic role, possibly associated with differentiation. McMaster, however, was able to show little deviation from the constancy hypothesis in *Arbacia* embryos. During early cleavage, McMaster also observed a wide range of values which she interprets as variability in the measuring technique having no biological significance. The mean amount in larval tissue was less than that found in cleavage (0.53 as compared to 1.05) and this can be ascribed to the diploid and tetraploid values, respectively.

In later stages many nuclei contained intermediate values, with few at the 4N level. McMaster explained this absence of 4N nuclei in larval tissue by assuming that the cell immediately enters prophase as soon as the 4N condition is achieved. This would mean an extremely short G2 phase. These data may also be interpreted as evidence of DNA synthesis at different loci during differentiation of larval tissues. Localized DNA synthesis may connote replication of controlling elements of the genome (heterochromatin?) rather than structural genes.

There are some data which support the hypothesis of partial duplication of DNA. Recent observations of Plaut and Howard (1963; Plaut, 1965) on incorporation of tritium-labeled thymidine into Drosophila salivary chromosomes in vitro illustrate that specific labeling of different loci does, in fact, occur and that with increasing exposure to the label, more band regions incorporate label until finally the entire chromosome may be labeled. Unequal labeling of chromosomes has also been observed by Hsu (1964) in mammalian chromosomes. In fact, the phenomenon of delayed duplication usually associated with the more compact, heterochromatic regions of the chromosome has been observed in a number of systems and may have general significance, particularly as it is related to the phenomenon of differentiation (Lima de Faria, 1959; Taylor, 1960; Grumbach et al., 1963).

A more impressive demonstration of unequal replication of DNA has been observed in some puff regions of dipteran salivary chromosomes. Tritium-labeled thymidine incorporation studies have been completed on both Drosophila and Chironomous salivary chromosomes, both in vivo and in vitro, and in general it has been shown that labeling of both bands and puffs occurs differentially (Ficq et al., 1958; Keyl and Pelling, 1963; Rudkin and Schultz, 1961). Unequal labeling may reflect differential rates of polytenization at different loci along the chromosome, an asynchronous synthesis of DNA. It is interesting that here too heterochromatic regions are generally late labeling (Keyl and Pelling, 1963). Differential labeling is also observed in euchromatic and heterochromatic regions of interphase nuclei of lymphocytes (Frenster et al., 1963). Chromatin, morphologically distinguishable as euchromatin incorporates more thymidine precursor than the heterochromatic regions after incubation in vivo. Can such asynchronous DNA replication, particularly in nuclei rich in heterochromatic regions, explain the high frequency of intermediary DNA values, particularly in embryonic nuclei. This focuses attention on the interesting hypothesis posed by Schultz (1952, 1956) relating heterochromatization with cytodifferentiation.

He has shown that the expression of certain genes in Drosophila is influenced by their proximity to heterochromatic regions of the chromosome. The variegation phenomenon in Drosophila has been well documented and related position effects have been carefully explored by McClintock (1956) in maize, which agree with the hypothesis that heterochromatin may function as a controlling element, influencing gene expression, possibly through some control of the biosynthesis of nucleic acid (Schultz, 1956). Evidence of late labeling of these compact regions of the chromosome, correlated with their absence of genetic expression [the X chromosome in human tissue (Grumbach *et al.*, 1963)] encourages the speculation that the limiting factor in the cell division cycle may very well be the replication of these highly condensed, relatively inactive heterochromatic regions.

How can control of this replication express itself morphogenetically and what is the nature of its influence on cytodifferentiation? The variegation patterns observed by Schultz could be modified by analogs of folic acid known to interfere with DNA synthesis. These effects are reversible by thymidine, demonstrating that the bristle pattern expression may be influenced by interfering with DNA replication. Schultz postulates that differentiation is accompanied by an "inactivation" of gene loci by heterochromatization. This process occurs gradually during development and its immediate expression might be a delay in DNA replication, accompanied by a restriction in developmental potentiality.

The experiments of nuclear transplantation have clearly demonstrated an increasing restriction in the capacity of nuclei to initiate and sustain normal development as nuclei from older, more differentiated tissue are transferred to enucleated, activated eggs (see review by Gurdon, 1963). Careful chromosome analyses by Briggs *et al.* (1961) have shown that two classes of abnormalities are produced as a result of such studies —abnormalities with visibly normal chromosomal complements and those with abnormal chromosome sets. Interest, of course, focuses on those nuclei with a normally appearing genome, yet exhibiting a loss of capacity for normal development. Conceivably, these nuclei may have had nonvisible chromosomal aberrations (minute deletions, breaks, etc.) or may have experienced some fundamental irreversible alteration possibly associated with differentiation. Some instances of abnormal chromosomal constitutions may result from damage induced during the transplantation procedure. This seems unlikely for most cases since small cells (primordial germ cells) when transferred yield 40% normal development (Smith, 1964), whereas larger, less fragile endodermal cells from similar stages exhibited a severe restriction of development. Evidently, chromosomal damage may not be induced solely as a result of manipulation during transfer, but may have some fundamental explanation, possibly associated with differentiation. Briggs *et al.* (1964) and King (1964) have interpreted the high frequency of chromosomal damage as attributable to an increased heterochromatization associated with differentiation. Late replication of heterochromatic regions places them out of phase with the replicative mechanisms built into the egg cytoplasm. On transfer these late replicating regions, probably unsynchronized with the rapid mitotic "clock" of early cleavage, could lead to chromosomal breaks and adhesions which are ultimately expressed as anaphase bridges, minutes, and aneuploidy.

If this situation does exist, failure to demonstrate specific developmental defects correlated with specific donor nuclei is understandable. If any specific genetic modifications occurred in nuclei during differentiation these could not be revealed against the heterogeneous background of developmental abnormalities derived from such abnormal karyotypes.

Such an interpretation of differentiation provides an explanation for the dichotomy between cell division and differentiation, since heterochromatic regions, inactive genetically, may effectively limit DNA replication, permitting the expression of other loci. Control may depend specifically upon the physical state of the DNA molecule. In its contracted form, DNA cannot function as a primer; moreover, it is possible that a contracted DNA strand may influence transcription of neighboring loci.

These admitted speculations emphasize the significance of reported deviation from the constancy hypothesis in embryonic and larval tissue. They also stress the observed heterogeneity sometimes observed in cytophotometric studies of adult nuclei and attribute biological significance to these variations rather than ascribing them entirely to experimental error or to variations in replication rate of DNA in different nuclei. The weight of evidence is clearly against the developmental significance of such variations; however, as our techniques become more sophisticated and our resolving power increases, we are beginning to realize that variations in the rate of DNA replication within a single genome do exist which may have profound effects on the expression of that genome. A hypothesis for heterochromatin and its role in differentiation has been proposed. It merits serious consideration and justifies a major experimental effort.

IV. The Developmental Behavior of RNA

The exciting developments in molecular genetics and biochemistry have introduced a new language for old concepts in development. We now refer to such terms as "informational macromolecules," "readout," "transcription," "translation," "programming," and "feedback control."

Yet we fail to emphasize that no essentially new concepts have resulted; rather we employ a new vocabulary, operationally fashionable (because our techniques are new and more sophisticated) still committed to the old question of control of gene action during development. Although we are somewhat familiar with the molecular species that are involved in gene expression, we are still very ignorant of the intrinsic and extrinsic factors regulating their interactions during cell life cycles. We have only some useful models and hypotheses permitting a wide spectrum of experimentation at different levels of organization.

The models developed in microbial systems for control of gene action have been proposed for differentiating systems (Jacob and Monod, 1963). We now have techniques which permit the design of critical experiments to answer questions relating genetic transcription with development and differentiation. Some of these questions are as follows: (1) Is the genome transcribed during oogenesis? If so, how much? (2) Does the unfertilized egg contain preformed genetic messages which can be translated into protein before fertilization? (3) What changes occur in the message fraction subsequent to fertilization? During cleavage? Later development? (4) What proportion of the genome is read out during various developmental stages? (5) How is the production of and use of message fractions controlled? (6) Do different tissue types produce different message fractions? (7) Is commitment to the production of a specific message fraction in a differentiated cell irreversible or can the same cell transcribe more than one major message fraction during the course of its life history? (8) Wherein lies control of gene expression—at the transcription level or at the level of translation into protein? Does the level of control vary significantly during the course of development?

Answers to a number of these questions are currently being sought in many laboratories. For some questions the techniques are still too primitive to provide unequivocal answers. For others, however, the techniques are highly sophisticated and, appropriately applied, are bound to produce critical information.

A. *Transcription of the Genome during Oogenesis*

Williams (Chapter 1 of this volume) has reviewed the pertinent literature on the RNA constitution of developing oocytes, pointing out that all major species of RNA are found in the oocyte during oogenesis. On the basis of autoradiographic evidence, Ficq (1961a) has suggested that three species are present in the amphibian oocyte—high molecular weight nuclear RNA, metabolically active and associated with the DNA; a high molecular weight cytoplasmic RNA, metabolically inactive, possibly ribosomal RNA and, finally, an active soluble RNA fraction found in the cytoplasm and to a lesser degree in the nucleus. This latter fraction characterized as transfer RNA has also been localized in the nucleus and cytoplasm of *Asterias* oocytes (Ficq, 1962). To what extent are these RNA components involved in the intense protein synthesis and yolk formation characteristic of the oocyte and to what extent are they utilized ultimately in development? Is it possible to distinguish protein-synthesizing systems which function only during oogenesis from those elaborated in the egg as part of its "morphogenetic equipment" for use during development?

The growth of the oocyte may be arbitrarily divided into separate phases, each displaying a distinct nucleocytoplasmic pattern of behavior. The earliest generative phase is characterized by a nucleus which undergoes preliminary prophase events characteristic of meiotic chromosomes. While arrested during prophase the nucleus assumes the morphology of an interphase nucleus, whereas the cytoplasm exhibits little or no growth. During the vegetative stage, the bivalents unwind and develop the lampbrush condition in many instances, whereas the nucleus becomes a typical germinal vesicle, accompanied either by increase in nucleolar size or increase in nucleolar number. It is during this latter phase that cytoplasmic growth occurs. This phase may be divided into two distinct subphases—cytoplasmic growth phase characterized by increase in cytoplasmic volume without yolk synthesis signifying an increase in the number of cytoplasmic inclusions (mitochondria, Golgi bodies, lipochondria, yolk nuclei, ribosomes) and a yolk synthesis phase. The former process is usually accompanied by an increase in cytoplasmic basophilia, in many instances concentrated about yolk nuclei. The structure of these yolk nuclei has been studied by electron microscopy in a number of laboratories (Rebhun, 1956; Afzelius, 1957) and found to consist of annulate lamellae, rich in ribosomal-like granules. Yolk nuclei are dispersed later during the vitellogenesis phase, a period of intense yolk synthesis and storage.

Little information is available on the nature and behavior of the RNA species characteristic of the very early generative or cytoplasmic growth phases of oogenesis. Much work has been done on growing oocytes, well into the vitellogenesis phase. Following incorporation of RNA and DNA precursors (uridine-H³, thymidine-H³, and cytidine-H³) into the growing ovary of the cricket, Favard-Sereno and Durand (1963) observed a rapid incorporation into the nuclei of follicle cells during the early to middle stages of the cytoplasmic growth phase. Longer incubations resulted in labeling of the cytoplasmic RNA. During rapid cytoplasmic growth, the oocyte germinal vesicle RNA exhibits initial incorporation after 5- to 15-minutes incubation, diminishing slightly when the follicle cells become active. After 40-minutes incubation, activity is associated with chromatin masses. Finally, at the beginning of vitellogenesis, brief exposure reveals activity at the chromosomes of the follicle cells followed by nucleolar labeling which ultimately progresses into the cytoplasm. Ficq (1961b) has followed the incorporation of RNA precursors into nuclei and cytoplasm of young oocytes in amphibia and has found after various periods of incubation that germinal vesicles and nucleoli are more heavily labeled than the cytoplasm. The youngest oocytes exhibit most intense nuclear labeling which progressively diminishes as development proceeds. Nucleoli of larger oocytes are generally heavily labeled. Some label could be removed with cold ethanol (solube RNA?), whereas the remainder in the nucleus and cytoplasm was extractable by RNase, presumably ribosomal RNA. Although these data demonstrate that RNA's having different properties exist in the oocytes, it would be desirable to have analytical data on populations of young oocytes prior to vitellogenesis. The direction of "information transfer" in these systems seems to be chromosome → nucleoplasm → nucleolus → cytoplasm in follicle cells and in the oocyte. Geuskens (1963) has observed a different incorporation pattern in the *Asterias* oocyte with the precursors adenosine-H^3 and cytidine-H^3. In this instance, the activity accumulated in oocyte nucleoli at the same time that it diminished in the nucleoplasm and cytoplasm. It would appear that the nucleoplasm is a precursor of nucleolar RNA without migration of label from the nucleolus to the cytoplasm. Since no controls involving RNase digestion were employed, it is not certain that one is dealing exclusively with RNA in this case. It was also noted that incorporation patterns exhibited a seasonal variation.

Edström *et al.* (1961) have characterized the relative amounts and base ratios of RNA extracted from nuclei, nucleoplasm, and cytoplasm in starfish oocytes of various sizes. The smallest oocytes (it was not clear whether these are previtellogenesis oocytes; they are referred to as "growing oocytes") contain approximately one-third of total RNA as nucleoplasm RNA (with base ratio similar to DNA), the remainder largely in the cytoplasm, with 5% in the nucleoli. As oogenesis proceeds, the proportion of nucleoplasm RNA varies considerably with cell size, but as the bulk of cytoplasmic RNA is synthesized, a smaller proportion of total RNA is nucleoplasm RNA. The nucleolar and cytoplasmic RNA have very similar base ratios, generally characteristic of ribosomal RNA with a high G-C content. These data certainly suggest a nuclear synthesis of ribosomal RNA which accumulates in the cytoplasm of the maturing oocyte.

During vitellogenesis, the major growth activity of the oocyte is expressed. Reserve materials of the egg are synthesized and the organization of the egg is established. The synthesis of all species of RNA during this phase is particularly intense, occurring at a number of different sites in the oocyte. Lampbrush chromosomes are most active during this phase in the synthesis of RNA (Callan, 1962; Gall, 1963; Gall and Callan, 1962; Izawa *et al.*, 1963a). Gall and Callan (1962) have recently reviewed the more pertinent data on uridine-H^3 incorporation into the loops of these chromosomes in an effort to understand the asymmetrical structure of the loops, as this structure is related to the synthesis of ribonucleoproteins. Initial labeling of the loops predominates at the thinner end, while over a period of 10 days the labeling pattern progresses over the length of the loop until it reaches the thicker end. This asymmetrical, sequential pattern of labeling is not generally found on all loops exhibiting incorporation, and all loops do not synthesize at the same rate. Labeling with phenylalanine is qualitatively quite different since the entire loop is labeled after 1 day. One interpretation states that the matrix material of the loop moves like a conveyer belt, synthesizing protein and RNA (Gall, 1963). Newly synthesized RNA and protein accumulate on the moving thread making earlier synthesizing regions thicker than those initiating synthesis later. The implications of this "conveyer belt" hypothesis are rather interesting, since it suggests that the entire genome is capable of being read during the course of oogenesis. Although there are approximately 10,000 loops, one cannot assume that a good proportion of the genome is being read at any one time. Gall has calculated that at any instant only 2–3% of the genome is in the form of loops. If the entire chromosome is moving, then every genetic locus has an opportunity of being associated with a loop, and presumably each may transcribe. Protein is also synthesized on the loops and Gall mentions a sluffing of protein material from the loops, presumably into the nucleoplasm, perhaps ultimately into the nucleoli or cytoplasm. The nature and function of this protein are unknown.

Base composition of chromosomal RNA has been determined (Edström and Gall, 1963) to be largely identical to the base composition of DNA from salamander erythrocytes and different from nucleolar and cytoplasmic RNA. Compared to the studies on salivary chromosomes in *Chironomous* (Edström and Beermann, 1962), these data suggest that the full genome is, in fact, being expressed since salivary chromosomes are characterized by RNA heterogeneity between parts of the same chromosome, particularly in a comparison of three puff regions on chromosome IV. The base composition of the three regions differ from one another and from the composition of the RNA from chromosome I. None of these ratios is similar to the base composition of *Chironomous* DNA, indicating that at least for individual loci, RNA base composition differs from that of the total average DNA extracted from all loci. The fact that amphibian oocyte DNA base composition is similar (although not exactly) to that of chromosomal RNA (and not nucleolar and cytoplasmic RNA) suggests that the entire genome is transcribed in the oocyte compared to the reading of only a small proportion of the genome in a somatic cell.

Such speculations are complicated by serious lacunae in our knowledge of the behavior of RNA after its synthesis. Relative degrees of stability of different RNA species can seriously confuse data bearing on the proportion of the genome transcribed at any stage in the life history of a cell. RNA degradation may occur shortly after its utilization in the production of specific proteins during some phase of yolk synthesis. At present there is no way of resolving this question.

An active RNA metabolism is revealed in the unusual behavior of nucleoli prior to and during vitellogenesis. Raven (1961) has reviewed the cytological literature illustrating the frequent observations of multiple nucleoli, changes in nucleolar morphology, and finally, extrusion of nucleoli and emission of nucleolar contents into the cytoplasm. Kessel and Beams (1963) have demonstrated by electron microscopy the extrusion of nucleoli in the oocyte of *Thyone* and the bulk of classic light microscope studies leave no question that the phenomenon is important during oogenesis. Such nucleolar materials may be utilized only during yolk synthesis or they may represent storage in the cytoplasm of morphogenetic materials for use in embryogenesis.

An accumulating body of evidence implicates the nucleolus as either the site of synthesis and storage or assembly of ribosomes (Sirlin, 1963). Comparisons of base ratios of nucleolar and cytoplasmic ribosomal RNA (Edström and Gall, 1963; Edström and Beermann, 1962) have shown similarities, although Vincent and Baltus (1960) have reported no similarity between base ratios in mature starfish oocytes. Edström *et al.* (1961) have observed similarity of base ratios early in development, but as the oocyte matures, the compositions diverge. It is possible that nucleolar organizers in chromosomes of many cells, including oocytes, represent ribosomal RNA loci. Support for this hypothesis is obtained from the studies of Brown and Gurdon (1964) on the anucleolate mutant of *Xenopus.* This mutant, described by Elsdale *et al.* (1958), is characterized by possessing one rather than two nucleoli in its cells. A genetic analysis has revealed that the mutation behaves like a simple Mendelian recessive and the homozygous condition results in the complete absence of nucleoli, a lethal condition after hatching of the embryo. Chromosomes of wild type have a pair of homologous chromosomes with a secondary constriction on each (nucleolar organizer), whereas the heterozygote (producing only one nucleolus) has only one of the homologs with this constriction and the homozygous mutant has none (Kahn, 1962). Brown and Gurdon found that anucleolate mutants produced a relatively small amount of RNA during development (less than half that of the controls) and an equally reduced amount of ribosomal RNA. A sucrose density-gradient analysis of the ribosomal species, using radioactive carbon dioxide, revealed that no synthesis of 18 and 28 S ribosomal RNA occurred in the mutant. The mutants do synthesize about the same amount of 4 S or transfer RNA and it is interesting that the mutants contain an amount of RNA equivalent to the amount contained in the egg before fertilization or the amount synthesized during oogenesis. Since the oocyte is heterozygous, normal amounts of ribosomal RNA are synthesized during oogenesis. Synthesis of ribosomal RNA is correlated with the appearance of nucleoli at gastrulation; moreover, the heterozygote with one nucleolus produces amounts of ribosomal RNA equivalent to the wild type with two nucleoli.

Wallace (1962), although observing that the total RNA extracted from post-tailbud mutants is less than controls, demonstrated that individual tissues exhibited profound differences. Whereas notochord and somite cells showed similar cytoplasmic pyronine affinity in anucleolate and normal embryos, all other tissues in the mutant showed a decreased pyronine affinity following retardation of development. This was further extended by Esper and Barr (1964), employing quantitative cytophotometry of azure B dye binding, who found cytoplasmic RNA concentration in spinal cord and pharyngeal epithelium of the mutant to be less than the control. These latter authors also observed nucleolar "blobs" appearing in the anucleolate mutant; in some cases a single large mass was observed, presumably resulting from a fusion of smaller nucleolar masses.

It is unlikely that the sole function of the nucleolus during oogenesis is the synthesis and storage of ribosomal RNA or ribosomes. Conceivably, other kinds of RNA may be synthesized, assembled, or stored in the nucleolus. Vincent (1957) has reported the presence of two kinds of nucleolar RNA in starfish oocyte nucleoli, a rapidly labeled component exhibiting some of the properties of transfer RNA and a more slowly labeling, relatively high molecular weight RNA.

Nucleoli from amphibian oocytes have also been implicated in protein synthesis (Brandt and Finamore, 1963). Their isolated nucleolar preparations, admittedly of questionable purity, exhibited amino acid activating ability (threefold increase as measured by the pyrophosphate-exchange reaction) and also an appreciable amino acid-incorporating ability. The in vitro system is resistant to the action of RNase and the crude preparations employed raise some serious questions about the reality of the phenomenon. However, incorporation of amino acids into nucleoli of oocytes has been observed by autoradiography (Ficq, 1964) which suggest some protein synthesis (or storage) within nucleoli. The nature of these proteins, their relation to ribosomal proteins, and their role during oogenesis are completely unknown. Vincent (1964) recently reported that isolated starfish nucleoli may substitute for ribosomes in an *in vitro* amino acid incorporation system. C^{14}-Phenylalanine is incorporated into TCA-precipitable protein after *in vitro* incubation with nucleoli obtained from starfish oocytes and this incorporation is stimulated after the addition of polyuridylic acid.

In order to distinguish the relative contribution of nucleoli to oogenesis and embryogenesis, it would be helpful to compare oocytes which passively receive ooplasmic constituents from neighboring nurse and follicle cells with those actively involved in yolk synthesis. In several insect eggs, electron microscope studies have shown relatively few organelle systems (rough-surfaced endoplasmic reticulum) which one generally associates with active syntheses (Anderson (1964)—for the cockroach; Roth and Porter (1964)—for the mosquito). In the latter study, yolk formation and accumulation is associated with extensive pinocytosis at the oocyte membrane. Yolk proteins are formed in the midgut and transported via the circulation to the oocyte through the follicle cells. On the other hand, Beams and Kessel (1963) observed an elaborate rough-surfaced endoplasmic reticulum in crayfish oocytes anastomosing extensively with smooth-surfaced lamellae apparently involved in the synthesis of yolk.

In the cockroach ovary (Anderson, 1964) there are fairly well-defined morphological regions permitting accurate staging of oogenesis and separation of the cytoplasmic growth phase from vitellogenesis. Nucleolar extrusion apparently occurs in two phases, each characterized by morphologically distinct products extruded during vitellogenesis. Anderson has shown that oocytes do not have a typical fine structural organization associated with actively synthesizing cells. Yolk or yolk precursors are introduced from accessory cells through the follicle cells by pinocytosis. One can assume, therefore, that nucleolar extrusion products are not necessarily required for yolk synthesis, but may represent ribosomes to be used later in embryogenesis.

Brown and Littna (1964a) have shown that isotope incorporation into immature *Xenopus* oocytes is usually found in two ribosomal peaks, 18 S and 28 S. These immature oocytes are permitted to mature, induced to ovulate 5 months later, fertilized, and allowed to develop. Embryos are collected at different stages, fractionated for ribosomal RNA, and radioactivity is still present in these two ribosomal components, illustrating their long stability. It also illustrates ribosomal synthesis during oogenesis for use during morphogenesis. The immature oocyte is a site of active ribosomal synthesis, considerably more so than the mature oocyte and the developing embryo.

A major function of nuclear and nucleolar activity during amphibian vitellogenesis is the production of ribosomal RNA. An accumulation of soluble or transfer RNA as well as ribosomal RNA also seems to occur (Ficq, 1961a,b). Much attention also focuses on the question of template or messenger RNA synthesis during oogenesis and its importance during development. What proportion is utilized for protein synthesis in the oocyte and what proportion of messenger RNA is sufficiently stable to be utilized later during embryogenesis?

Brown and Littna (1964a) indicate that at least in immature oocytes (those large oocytes remaining in the ovary after the induction of ovulation) rapidly labeled RNA could not be considered messenger RNA. The label accumulated readily in the 28 and 18 S ribosomal RNA. The mature egg exhibits no ribosomal RNA labeling. During the course of oogenesis, RNA related to DNA is certainly produced. The studies on the lampbrush chromosomes (Edström and Gall, 1963), on the composition of nucleoplasm RNA from starfish oocytes (Edström et al., 1961), and on rapid labeling of chromosomal RNA in cricket oocytes and in follicle cells (Favard-Sereno and Durand, 1963) cite only a few of the many instances of rapid nuclear RNA labeling during oogenesis. Ficq (1964) has observed that nuclear incorporation of uridine in *Xenopus* oocytes increases with maturation and has found this to be particularly sensitive to actinomycin treatment. There are no data as to the stability of this RNA, nor do we know anything about its properties. It is certainly impossible to conclude that rapidly labeled RNA with a DNA-like base composition represents messenger RNA, even if sensitivity to actinomycin is exhibited. Actinomycin sensitivity inhibits the synthesis of ribosomal RNA and, in part, transfer RNA, both presumably transcribed at specific DNA loci and both representing the bulk of RNA produced (Franklin, 1963). All RNA synthesis is probably directed by a DNA template. Some evidence of participation in specific protein synthesis must be obtained before designation as messenger RNA is justified. Further discussion of this question is reserved for a subsequent section.

Are the ribosomes produced in the mature oocyte active? Burr and Finamore (1963), using a crude high-speed supernatant preparation from ovarian tissue of *Rana pipiens*, demonstrated an *in vitro* incorporation of amino acids into TCA-precipitable material. The incorporation displayed a peculiar magnesium sensitivity, was independent of exogenous energy sources, and could be eliminated only partially by treatment with RNase. Some stimulation is achieved by adding DNA; however, it was surprising that the system was stable to heat denaturation and exhibited a curious resistance to p-chloromercurobenzoate. Admittedly, the system is too crude to provide any significant information (it contains immature oocytes as well as follicle tissue), but does suggest, at least, that there may be some ribosomes present capable of functioning in protein synthesis, possibly derived from young oocytes or from follicle cells.

The protein synthesis ability of oocytes is still an open issue. Most incorporation and autoradiographic studies have employed systems characterized by oocytes surrounded by accessory cells. It is impossible to distinguish between intrinsic capabilities of the oocytes as contrasted with protein transport from follicle cell. Obviously, the latter has been shown to occur. Good data are needed on relatively free oocytes to ascertain their synthesizing capacity (Brown, 1964).

B. *Transcription of the Genome during Development—The Synthesis of RNA during Embryogenesis*

Earlier studies on RNA synthesis during development were concerned primarily with bulk RNA extracted by a variety of procedures and assayed usually by means of phosphorus content, ribose content, or UV absorption. In most instances the preparations were relatively crude and contaminated by unknown phosphorus and sugar compounds. Most of the evidence indicates that no net RNA synthesis occurs in embryos during the early stages of embryonic development in many different species. The time at which a net synthesis of RNA is measurable will vary with the organism. In general, however, cleavage and blastulation do not exhibit any net synthesis of RNA, whereas in some amphibia (Chen, 1960, 1961) measurable synthesis of total RNA has been reported during gastrulation and neurulation. In other species of amphibia, net synthesis occurs much later in development, usually late in neurulation or around hatching (Kutsky, 1950; Brown and Caston, 1962a; Brown and Littna, 1964b). In invertebrate eggs, a similar phenomenon is found, net RNA synthesis in *Ilyanassa* begins after gastrulation when the organ systems are developing (Collier, 1961). In the sea urchin, however, there is some difference in the results reported. Schmidt *et al.* (1948) and Chen *et al.* (1961) (recently confirmed by Tocco *et al.*, 1963) reported no significant change in the RNA per embryo until the pluteus stage. Elson *et al.* (1954), however, have reported significant variations of

RNA content during sea urchin development. An appreciable decrease occurs shortly after fertilization, followed by a rise and leveling off during blastulation and an additional slight increase before gastrulation, the amount remaining constant until the pluteus. The changes observed by Elson, *et al.* are extremely small (0.001 gm RNA per embryo) and their significance is in doubt.

Whole-embryo analyses of bulk RNA barely scratch the surface of our understanding of RNA metabolism during embryogenesis. Fractionation of RNA into several characteristic, easily identifiable species is now possible. It is difficult, however, to avoid the complications of whole-embryo analyses in view of their small size and all determinations, even of fractionated RNA components, must be tempered by the realization that one is almost always dealing with extremely heterogeneous cell and tissue populations during embryogenesis.

A turnover of different RNA components correlated with region-specific patterns of protein synthesis is expected. Net synthesis of ribosomal RNA accompanying protein synthesis in one region may be balanced by a region having completed its differentiation and exhibiting little RNA synthesis. For example, Denis (1964b) has reported differential precursor incorporation into nuclear nucleic acid in different tissues at different developmental stages. This problem must be simplified by taking well-defined stages characterized by relatively homogeneous cell populations. Unfertilized and fertilized eggs may be compared with respect to their RNA populations since these are relatively homogeneous. Similarly, cleavage may also be analyzed with some reasonable assurance that one is dealing with actively dividing cells. At blastula and gastrula stages, however, physiological heterogeneity is evident and functional regionalization is initiated. During histogenesis most cells are not dividing, but are committed to patterns of differentiation, involving specific protein syntheses. Analyses of such whole embryos lead to an average pattern of RNA metabolism. Extracting RNA from late embryos is equivalent to fractionation of a whole animal, comparing its RNA-sucrose density profiles with those obtained from a younger stage. Such studies are quite difficult to interpret in terms of specific morphogenetic events occurring at a particular stage.

In order to facilitate review of the transcription of DNA during development, data for different groups will be treated separately. Although many embryos exhibit some basic similarities in the metabolism of RNA, the differences are of sufficient importance to merit individual consideration.

C. Amphibian Development

1. RIBOSOME SYNTHESIS

Ribosome synthesis was initially observed in late embryos of *Rana pipiens* by Brown and Caston (1962a). The situation in *Rana pipiens* is somewhat complicated by the fact that ribosomes become adsorbed to the pellet fraction during homogenization. Correction for this adsorption by isotopic dilution demonstrates that small amounts of ribosomes are present during development until after hatching, when pronounced ribosomal RNA synthesis is observed. The bulk of the RNA is found in the low-speed pellet (yolk-nuclear fraction) and this exhibits a rapid increase throughout development, at least until a stage-25 larva. Brown and Caston (1962b) have also demonstrated a high molecular weight RNA component (16 S) in unfertilized eggs (presumably ribosomal RNA because of its similarity in base ratio to adult ribosomes) and this persisted throughout development. New synthesis of this RNA does not begin until a stage-16 neurula and is most evident at stage-18 tailbud and thereafter. This RNA totals 1 μg per embryo in the late blastula and increases to 4 μg per embryo in a hatched tadpole. Ribosomes are synthesized with the production of a heavy RNA component which begins to be synthesized in the neurula while the fully formed ribosome appears later.

Brown and Littna (1964a) have shown that immature oocytes in *Xenopus* are actively synthesizing excessively large amounts of ribosomal RNA as contrasted with the mature egg which, prior to ovulation, synthesizes only a small amount of heterogeneous RNA. The oocyte also synthesizes a relatively small amount of soluble RNA with a characteristic base composition. Ribosomes synthesized during oogenesis are conserved in later development and can be found as radioactive ribosomal RNA (28 and 18 S) 8 months after incorporation during oogenesis. This remarkable stability of the ribosomal RNA in the amphibian embryo implies that once organized, the ribosome does not turn over appreciably.

Brown and Littna (1964b) also demonstrated that new ribosomes in *Xenopus* embryos are synthesized late in development, the initial synthesis observed during gastrulation and neurulation. Shortly thereafter a rapid synthesis of new ribosomes is manifested and these must coexist with old ribosomes previously synthesized in oogenesis. The bulk of RNA in the mature oocyte (and unfertilized egg) is ribosomal RNA (approximately 95%), whereas the remainder is soluble RNA. As development proceeds, early cleavage is characterized by a synthesis of soluble RNA, yet the amount synthesized is too small to be detected as a net increase in total RNA, because of the large proportion of "old" ribosomal RNA present. Although radioactive labeling experiments reveal specific synthesis of RNA, these are far too small to influence the total RNA per embryo. In later swimming stages, most of the RNA is ribosomal, whereas approximately 15–20% may be soluble RNA. It is only in these later stages, when synthesis of new ribosomes becomes important, that total net RNA synthesis is demonstrable.

DeCroly *et al.* (1964), following P^{32} incorporation in *Xenopus*, observed some RNA synthesis after fertilization and during cleavage; however, a considerable increase in RNA incorporation occurred after gastrulation. In pulse experiments at different stages of development, no significant difference in total RNA base composition in 4-cell to medullary plate stages (stage 16) was observed. Since the predominate RNA component is ribosomal RNA, this is not too surprising. The authors claim, however, that most of the RNA incorporation represented nuclear RNA, particularly in the early stages, and it is suggested that this ribosomal-like RNA may be a precursor for cytoplasmic ribosomes. These results are difficult to interpret, since the uptake of P^{32} from the medium by *Xenopus* eggs or early cleaving stages is generally quite poor because of their relative impermeability. The marked increase observed during gastrulation and neurulation may simply indicate that more uptake occurred through the blastopore and the inner surfaces of cells lining the presumptive archenteron.

The developmental pattern of 28 and 18S ribosomal RNA's expresses an intimate relationship between their syntheses during all phases of development. It can be calculated that the relative amounts of each fraction synthesized is the same for every stage. Brown and Littna have presented evidence that a heavy RNA fraction is present even in fertilized eggs. This heavy fraction is synthesized very rapidly without accumulating at any stage during development. Although 28 S ribosomal RNA accumulates from gastrula to tailbud stages, there is no increase in heavy RNA. This RNA has a base composition intermediate between the high G-C content of ribosomal RNA and the high A-U content expected of DNA-like RNA. Moreover, this base composition does not change significantly with development, whereas the base composition of the 18 and 28 S shifts from an intermediate type at the gastrula stage to a typical high G-C of ribosomal RNA prior to hatching. In a comparison of rapid labeling of RNA in a normal and anucleolate mutant of *Xenopus* (Brown and Gurdon, 1964), heavy RNA is rapidly labeled in two peaks in the normal and in only one peak in the mutant. The authors suggest that heavy RNA is a precursor for 28 and 18 S ribosomal RNA in agreement with the observations of Scherrer and Darnell (1962) on a similar heavy RNA precursor for ribosomal RNA in HeLa cells. Additional confirmation for a heavy RNA rapidly labeled precursor for ribosomal RNA is obtained in the data of Rake and Graham (1964) for L cells, where the kinetic data support a clear precursor role for the 50 and 40 S nuclear RNA.

Autoradiographic studies with RNA precursors (Bieliavsky and Tencer, 1960; Ficq, 1964) illustrate that initial labeling during cleavage is primarily in the nucleus and is largely associated with DNA and nuclear RNA. Later in development at the gastrula and neurula stages, nuclei continue to be rapidly labeled while cytoplasmic RNA synthesis commences. Embryonic RNA activity appears first in nuclei and is followed later by nucleolar and cytoplasmic labeling. These data are in excellent agreement with the analytical data characterizing early cleavage as committed primarily to DNA synthesis, synthesis of a heavy nuclear RNA fraction with a DNA-like base composition, and soluble or 4 S RNA. If large, heavy nuclear RNA is cleaved to serve as precursor for ribosomal RNA, then one should expect cleavage products to include small species of RNA not utilizable for ribosomal RNA but possibly useful as precursors of 4 S RNA and for DNA (Roberts et al., 1963). Degradation of heavy RNA may explain the rapid synthesis of 4 S RNA during early development (Brown and Littna, 1964b) and may also contribute nucleotides for the synthesis of DNA, a major activity of cleavage.

Finamore and Volkin (1958, 1961) have evidence for the existence of two species of RNA in ovarian eggs of *Rana pipiens* differing with respect to solubility in 0.5 M perchloric acid. The acid-soluble RNA, with a high G-C content may represent 40–60% of the total RNA. More recently, Finamore (1964) has followed these two RNA fractions during development of the amphibian embryo and has found that the acid-soluble RNA is composed largely of oligonucleotides. During cleavage there is a constant level of incorporation of P^{32} (introduced in the oocyte prior to ovulation) into the acid-soluble RNA, greater than that found in the acid-insoluble RNA. From gastrulation to hatching the P^{32} incorporation is very rapid in the acid-soluble fraction and it is only after hatching that incorporation occurs significantly in the acid-insoluble RNA. This latter incorporation seems to be correlated with a decline in activity in the acid-soluble RNA, although there is no good evidence that there is any precursor relation between the two. These data correlate well with the observations of an early rapid synthesis of 4 S RNA through blastulation, as contrasted with a synthesis of ribosomal RNA in later development (Brown and Caston, 1962a; Brown and Littna,

1964b), and also suggest that acid-soluble RNA may represent a degraded heavy RNA component.

2. Messenger RNA

Information about the relative contribution of so-called messenger RNA to the early phases of development in the amphibian has been derived from a study of the effect of such substances as actinomycin D known to interfere with DNA-dependent RNA synthesis. One should note that all transcription of the DNA is not completely inhibited by actinomycin, nor is there any selectivity of action since ribosomal and soluble RNA transcription are also effected by the inhibitor. There has been an unfortunate tendency to equate all actinomycin-sensitive RNA synthesis as messenger RNA in spite of the fact that ribosomal precursor RNA is known also to be transcribed on a DNA template. Moreover, it has not been conclusively demonstrated that actinomycin has the same specificity in all tissues to which it has been applied. Harel et al. (1964) indicated that synthesis of sRNA and ribosomal RNA was inhibited completely, whereas another fraction (8–10 S) with DNA-like base composition was inhibited only 50–70% in rat tissues. In each case, it is essential where employing actinomycin that: (1) the tissue is shown to be permeable to actinomycin; (2) RNA synthesis is inhibited without effecting either DNA or protein synthesis; (3) it has no other side effects; and (4) the inhibition is complete with respect to RNA synthesis. Unfortunately, in many situations of its employ, few efforts have been made to satisfy these conditions (Flickinger, 1963; Klein and Pierro, 1963; Moscona and Moscona, 1964; Wallace and Elsdale, 1963; Brachet et al., 1964).

In a series of studies on the amphibian embryo by Brachet and his group (Brachet and Denis, 1963; Denis, 1963, 1964a,b,c; Brachet et al., 1964) the effect of actinomycin on development and nucleic acid metabolism was studied. No effect on cleavage was obtained even after injection of 0.2 µg per egg. Development stopped at the blastula stage with cytological effects of severe chromosomal damage, aneuploidy, and anaphase bridges, which probably explains the failure of these embryos to develop further. Similar results are obtained after brief exposure to low doses of nitrogen mustard (Grant, 1961). Chromosome replication is possible, but occurs abnormally. Exposure of blastulae and early gastrulae to actinomycin (continuous immersion) results in delayed and abnormal gastrulation, neurulation, and depending on concentration, leads to microcephaly and severe dorsoventral and cephalocaudal abnormalities. In these cases, mitoses are present and apparently normal.

No analysis was made of differences in mitotic activity, although it appears that regions with high mitotic activity are most severely inhibited, an effect incidentally also produced by folic acid analogs (Grant, 1960). These same regions are undergoing differentiation and it is possible that the morphogenetic effects may result, as Brachet suggests, from inhibition of DNA-like RNA synthesis.

The studies of Denis (1964b) have indicated that actinomycin does inhibit incorporation of H^3-uridine into nuclear nucleic acids in early development. The amount of inhibition is lowest during the early stages and increases in later development, when ribosomal RNA synthesis is at a maximum. However, incorporation of uridine into DNA also is inhibited by actinomycin. The relative incorporation into RNA and DNA (as determined after enzyme digestion) into individual nuclei usually reveals only one nucleic acid exhibiting incorporation. Consequently, observed inhibition of incorporation by actinomycin applies to DNA-labeled as well as RNA-labeled nuclei. The morphological effects in this study [and in the analysis of actinomycin effects on primary induction in sandwich experiments (Denis, 1964a)] may also be interpreted as an inhibition of mitotic activity. The evidence for greater sensitivity of RNA synthesis to the antibiotic is primarily a decrease in basophilia at low doses without serious influence on mitotic activity. Induction experiments (Denis, 1964a) also show many cases of neural inhibition accompanied by a reduction in cell mass, as well as cell disaggregation, without affecting DNA or RNA; thus, in all these experiments it is certainly not evident that actinomycin is functioning in the specific manner generally assumed.

Brachet (1963) interprets the biochemical transformations at gastrulation in the amphibian embryo as an activation of genes and messenger RNA synthesis, according to the regulator gene repressor hypothesis of Jacob and Monod. The appearance of nucleoli, the beginning of ribosomal RNA synthesis, the incorporation of uridine into nuclear RNA, and the sensitivity of gastrulation and neurulation to actinomycin tend to support this hypothesis. He postulates that newly formed messenger RNA is essential to ribosome activation, facilitating organization into functional polysome aggregates capable of protein synthesis. Certainly the evidence of ribosomal RNA synthesis after gastrulation is in agreement with the view that functional new ribosomes are created in later development. The unfertilized egg does contain ribosomes and the protein synthesis observed during cleavage (Brachet et al., 1964) presumably occurs on these ribosomes after activation. The results of Brown and Littna (1964b) show a small amount of DNA-like RNA synthesized in the mature oocyte after hormone stimulation and this material is found associated with ribosomes throughout early cleavage. Its sedimentation pattern is between 8 and 16 S, similar to the density of messenger RNA. This material is newly synthesized during gastrulation, and in subsequent development becomes associated with old ribosomes and new ribosomes as they are synthesized. These latter populations of ribosomes probably participate in the synthesis of tissue-specific proteins characteristic of cytodifferentiation.

It appears that during oogenesis the genome of the amphibian is transcribed for two functions—the syntheses of protein-forming systems (PFS) required during oogenesis and the storage of developmentally significant protein-forming systems to be used later. There is still some question as to how much protein synthesis is performed by the amphibian oocyte. Electron microscopy (EM) studies of oogenesis have failed to demonstrate an elaborate endoplasmic reticulum structure (Lanzavecchia, 1961; Ward, 1962; Kessel, 1963; Karasaki, 1963a). Only populations of free ribosomes are present. Although the EM studies demonstrate yolk formation within the oocyte by several different mechanisms, it is not possible to distinguish between the assembly of or the crystallization of yolk platelets from proteins transferred to the oocyte by accessory cells from intrinsic *de novo* synthesis via peptide assembly of amino acids.

The activation of the amphibian egg at fertilization initiates the patterns of DNA replication, spindle formation, and energy cycling associated with mitosis and cell division. These events are possible in the absence of a nucleus, as well as under anaerobiosis and in the presence of actinomycin, nucleic acid analogs, and nitrogen mustard. This suggests that functional protein-forming systems and an energy source sufficient to carry the egg through cleavage are preformed in the egg. Presumably most protein synthesis occurring during this phase is specifically associated with cell division, since no net synthesis of protein is evident during most of development (Brown and Caston, 1962a).

Development of the blastula is dependent upon reading of the genome. During early cleavage, no significant reading occurs since little nuclear RNA labeling is evident; however, in the blastula stage (at least in *Xenopus*) there is a significant increase in the newly labeled, labile heterogeneous RNA (Brown and Littna, 1964b) suggesting nuclear RNA synthesis. Some of this material has a sedimentation pattern between 8 and 16 S and has a DNA-like base composition. It may be degraded messenger RNA heralding the initiation of the morphogenetically significant transcription of the genome, since nucleoli appear at gastrulation and ribosomal RNA synthesis begins at this time when cell division diminishes. RNA metabolism is intensified as the genome

is transcribed for two purposes—the production of new ribosomes and
the transcription of structural genes essential for morphogenesis. Cell
surface changes also occur at this time, critical to cell sorting-out and
cell aggregation behavior. It is interesting that Wallace and Elsdale
(1963) have shown that aggregation of amphibian blastula cells is possible even in the presence of actinomycin, whereas fragments at the
neurula stage begin to disaggregate in the presence of equivalent doses
of actinomycin. Can one conclude that materials essential for continued
reaggregation of older cells are dependent upon DNA-dependent RNA
synthesis? These experiments were done at low doses (2 μg per milliliter)
presumably ineffective in inhibiting mitosis. Conceivably, initial transcription of the genome during gastrulation includes activation of loci
responsible for the synthesis of cell-surface specific proteins, critical in
cell morphogenesis. Moscona and Moscona (1963) have shown actinomycin sensitivity of adhesive and aggregation properties of chick embryo
tissue. These same tissues exhibited a more profound sensitivity to
puromycin implicating some form of protein synthesis (surface proteins?) as essential to the aggregation phenomenon. The specificity of
these effects, however, was not completely demonstrated and it is con-
ceivable that general inhibition of protein synthesis is bound to have
a major impact on various aspects of cell behavior, including adhesiveness.

After gastrulation, ribosomal RNA synthesis dominates RNA metabolism in the embryo. This represents the only stable form, since other
species probably turnover or are degraded. Nuclear RNA labeling becomes more apparent, since fewer nuclei are committed to DNA replication. Later populations of embryonic cells are highly heterogeneous
and include mitotically active cells as well as cells initiating tissue-specific
and organ-specific protein syntheses. Differential sensitivity of organ
formation to actinomycin (Flickinger, 1963) is interpreted as a sequential activation of DNA-dependent RNA synthesis associated in time with
the morphogenesis of specific organ regions. The data do not justify
this conclusion in view of the absence of any evidence of effects on
RNA synthesis, DNA replication, and cell division. The tissues most
sensitive to actinomycin are the brain and the anterior portion of the
spinal cord, regions which are mitotically active. These regions are also
quite sensitive to a number of different agents, including mitotic inhibitors. The notochord, pronephric region, and endodermal derivatives
found to be less sensitive to actinomycin are also regions which are
relatively insensitive to other agents, like folic acid analogs (Grant,
1960).

Maximum synthesis of ribosomal RNA seems to occur well after
several major histogenic events have occurred in embryogenesis (stage

18 in *Rana pipiens*—Brown and Caston, 1962a; late neurula in *Xenopus*—Brown and Littna, 1964b). As development proceeds, a heterogeneity with respect to populations of ribosomes undoubtedly occurs. Some cells will contain exclusively old ribosomes (late differentiating regions?), whereas actively differentiating regions, like the brain and spinal cord, may be the site of new ribosomal synthesis. Moreover, the pattern of ribosomal synthesis is such (Roberts *et al.*, 1963) that RNA components of the ribosomes may be synthesized before the protein components, with assembly into functional ribosomal units taking place at later developmental stages. In a developmental system, assembly of functional ribosomes may have an ontogeny of its own within cells undergoing differentiation. Thus, old ribosomes may be used as sites for the synthesis of new ribosomal proteins.

The ribosomes, having formed, may differ with respect to their function. Function may depend upon a number of factors including association with messenger RNA, an essential requirement for their subsequent organization into polysomes (Rich *et al.*, 1963). The stability of messenger RNA also influences the functional activity of the polysome, and a review of some recent evidence for the existence of stable messenger RNA and its effect on polysome organization during differentiation will be deferred to a later section.

D. *Genome Transcription in Other Vertebrate Embryos*

The telolecithal eggs of fish and birds establishes a qualitatively different situation with respect to the embryo and its reserve of nutrients during embryogenesis. The large yolk stores are physically separated from the embryo, the cells generally completely lacking in yolk reserves except for those endodermal cells closely applied to the yolk. In these embryos, there is no partitioning of yolk material (and all other nutrient reserves) accompanying cleavage; rather the embryonic region simply draws from the yolk its required materials through the yolk sac membranes. In addition to lipids and proteins, a reserve of nucleic acid precursors is also found in the yolk region and is utilized by the embyro during its development. In the chick egg (Hoff-Jørgensen, 1954) the total DNA of the embryo plus yolk did not change until day 3 of development. Solomon (1957a,b), separating yolk from the embryo, observed that nucleic acid increased in the embryo and correlated with the increase in cell number. Presumably, this increase occurred at the expense of precursors (including nonnuclear DNA?) in the yolk. He was, however, also able to demonstrate (Solomon, 1957c) that the increase in both DNA and RNA could take place in explanted embryos on glucose (in some instances the synthesis of nucleic acid was 100% of that found in ova in equivalent stages) which suggests that yolk is not essential for nucleic acid synthesis in the early stages of incubation. Solomon raises the possibility that nucleic acid reserves in the yolk and white of the chick egg may be used much later in development, rather than in the early stages when DNA synthesis is at a maximum.

Similar observations have been made in studies on the groundling *Nisournus fossilis* that indicate no change in total nuclei acid of the embryo plus yolk during the first 18 hours of development until the late gastrula stage (Aytkhozhin *et al.*, 1964). Analyses of the embryo separated from the yolk, however, revealed that DNA per embryo increased linearly from fertilization to the end of gastrulation, whereas RNA increased most rapidly during cleavage and blastulation attaining a maximum in mid-blastula where it remained constant through gastrulation. Obviously, these changes in the embryo are obscured by the large amount of both nucleic acids in the yolk.

Data on the pattern of early RNA synthesis in the chick embryo are not readily available. Most studies begin on day 2 of incubation after cleavage and the morphogenetic events of gastrulation and neurulation have occurred. The embryo is quite heterogeneous at this stage and includes mitotically active centers along with regions undergoing morphogenesis and differentiation. Bulk changes in RNA during later development have little significance in the complicated events of morphogenesis and differentiation.

Some attempt to resolve this problem in the chick embryo was initiated in the analysis of ribosomal RNA during development (Lerner *et al.*, 1963). Ribosomal RNA synthesis occurs from the primitive streak through the first 7 days of development, both 28 and 16 S peaks observed. Similar base compositions between 3-day and 7-day ribosomal RNA preparation were also observed. As in the amphibian, rapid labeling of a heavy RNA component (40 S) occurs, suggesting the presence of a heavy ribosomal RNA precursor. These analyses of older embryos are difficult to interpret, since a complicated mixture of different tissues are included. The fish embryo has the advantage of facilitating analyses of early cleavage, blastulation and neurulation, a difficult situation in the chick.

Aytkhozhin *et al.* (1964) investigated the high rate of RNA synthesis during cleavage in the groundling, following incorporation of adenine-C^{14} into RNA fractions. An attempt was made to determine whether the embryo is synthesizing ribosomal RNA early in development from precursors in the yolk or whether there is a redistribution of RNA from yolk to embryo to account for the early rapid increase of RNA. The isotope data revealed that embryos between late blastula and gastrula exhibited no incorporation into ribosomal RNA; all the activity entered the soluble and heterogeneous RNA (so-called messenger RNA). Ribosomes from late gastrula embryos exposed to the precursor for 3 hours evidence no ribosomal RNA synthesis. During the period of rapid RNA synthesis in cleavage, the label (adenine-C^{14} and uridine-H^{3}) is incorporated into the soluble fraction without any synthesis of ribosomal RNA. This pattern parallels that observed in amphibian and echinoderm embryos. New ribosomal synthesis occurs late in development, whereas early development is made possible via ribosomes synthesized during oogenesis. In the fish egg, these ribosomes are present in the yolk and are transferred to the embryo during cleavage, as preformed ribosomes (Aytkhozhin et al., 1964).

The ribosomal content per cell should, therefore, decrease rapidly during early development until the gastrula stage when a synthesis of new ribosomes occurs. Gastrula embryos (Belitsina et al., 1964) exhibit a proportionally intense incorporation of a mixture of labeled precursors (adenine-C^{14}, uridine-C^{14}, and guanine-C^{14}) into soluble RNA and a high molecular weight, heterogeneous RNA which is not ribosomal RNA or ribosomal RNA precursor. This heavy peak of radioactivity is not observed in cytoplasmic extracts, suggesting a nuclear origin. A fraction of radioactivity did remain in cytoplasmic extracts in the region of ribosomal RNA which may be a small amount of newly synthesized RNA (the authors, however, discount this possibility since they find no newly formed ribosomal RNA when ribosomes are extracted). Heterogeneous RNA in cytoplasmic extracts may represent messenger RNA.

As in echinoderms, the bulk of amino acid incorporation into these cytoplasmic extracts is found in the heavy ribosomal fractions as well as the standard 80 S ribosomal component. In vitro incorporation of amino acids in embryo extracts also exhibits significant incorporation into a polysome fraction. A large proportion of the nucleic acid precursors is also incorporated into heavy polysomal fractions, indicating that most of the newly formed RNA is associated with these heavier components, a property characteristic of messenger RNA.

Fundamentally, the situation in the fish egg with respect to the pattern of ribosomal synthesis is not significantly different from amphibians. Early development is possible with preformed ribosomes. These may be held as a reserve in the large yolk mass of telolecithal eggs and transferred to the embryo as development proceeds. As cell number increases, a reduction in the number of ribosomes per cell is the result. At some stage in development, this obviously limits the continued existence of the cell and new ribosome synthesis is initiated. This occurs when a majority of new proteins are being synthesized accompanying cytodifferentiation. These latter phases are characterized by the production of polysomal aggregates in the chick embryo involving a shift in the profile from smaller to larger polysomes (Scott and Bell, 1964). Presumably, this shift represents a change in the size of messenger RNA being produced at a particular time. This transition may occur over a very short period during the differentiation of a tissue, and significantly, may occur prior to any visible evidence of differentiation. This latter phenomenon has been reported for the feather (Bell and Thathachari, 1963; Bell, 1964; Humphreys *et al.*, 1964). In this latter system, synthesis of keratins in the down feather occurs between 13 and 17 days of incubation. Apparently, this process involves a two-step maturation. Prior to 13 days, a polysome aggregate of four ribosomes is produced and retained as a nonfunctional, ribonuclease-resistant aggregate. After 13 days, larger functioning aggregates of four, five, and six ribosomes are produced as a result of new messenger RNA synthesis.

It is evident that analyses of specific protein synthesis accompanying differentiation of cell populations is being most effectively studied in chick and mouse systems where it is relatively simple to isolate tissues and control their differentiation by exposure to the appropriate inducing system. The events of genetic transcription accompanying the initiation of specific protein syntheses will be most intelligently studied in these systems. An initial approach will be one of defining the molecular events and attempting to correlate these with morphogenetic events either within the cell or between cells. Such approaches are currently being undertaken in a number of systems (Grobstein, 1964; Rutter *et al.*, 1964; Scott and Bell, 1964; Wilt, 1964; Kirk and Moscona, 1963). The questions currently being asked are: What are the new proteins being synthesized? When does this occur? What species of RNA molecules are involved? Is there evidence of mRNA produced during the process of differentiation? What can we learn of its stability? How are these molecular events correlated with visible evidence of morphogenesis?

E. *Genome Transcription during Echinoderm Development*

The situation in echinoderms exhibits some similarities and several differences from that in amphibians. During oogenesis, autoradiographic studies of Ficq (1962, 1964) have shown that the oocyte is a site of RNA synthesis during different stages of maturation.

Ficq (1964) studied the effect of actinomycin and puromycin on incorporation of nucleic acid precursors and amino acids into growing oocytes of the sea urchin, *Paracentrotus*. Actinomycin inhibited cytidine incorporation into nucleoli and cytoplasm and only partially inhibited nucleoplasm activity. The failure of actinomycin to inhibit phenylalanine incorporation suggests that protein synthesis during oogenesis is not dependent upon a nuclear synthesis of RNA. This is not absolutely true since no complete inhibition of nuclear RNA incorporation was obtained. This latter RNA may be essential in a continuing synthesis of protein. The complete inhibition of nucleolar incorporation suggests inhibition of ribosomal synthesis. Virtually complete inhibition of cleavage was observed after exposure of *Xenopus* oocytes to actinomycin during oogenesis, followed by fertilization 6 weeks later. Ficq interprets these results as evidence of messenger RNA synthesis and storage during oogenesis for use in later development particularly during cleavage. The evidence could also be interpreted to mean that early development depends upon a synthesis of ribosomes since ribosomal RNA is also inhibited by actinomycin.

We have no information concerning the proportion of the genome read during oogenesis. The large amount of ribosomal RNA synthesis could be an expression of a very small proportion of the genome, possibly of the order of 0.1–0.2% as found in bacteria (Yankofsky and Spiegelman, 1962). Soluble RNA accumulation implies that another fraction of the genome is also being read. It is certainly possible that only a small proportion of this RNA is utilized during oogenesis, the bulk amassing as a morphogenetic reserve. Evidence for the presence of messenger RNA is relatively incomplete and unsatisfactory.

The mature unfertilized egg contains ribosomes with the appropriate ribosomal RNA (Nemer, 1962b; Monroy and Tyler, 1963; Wilt, 1964) and apparently some adsorbed 4 S RNA (Wilt, 1964). The sedimentation pattern of these ribosomes and their RNA components is similar to that found in fertilized eggs. These represent ribosomes synthesized during oogenesis. Yet it has been found that ribosomes of the unfertilized egg are relatively inactive in protein synthesis when compared to those from fertilized eggs (Hultin, 1961a, 1964). These early studies have been recently confirmed in a number of laboratories (Nemer, 1962b; Wilt and Hultin, 1962; Tyler, 1962, 1963) where it has been shown that addition of the synthetic polynucleotide, polyuridylic acid, to homogenates of unfertilized and fertilized sea urchin eggs, strikingly stimulates the incorporation of radioactive phenylalanine into protein. It was initially suggested that absence of protein synthesis in unfertilized eggs is due to a deficiency of endogenous messenger RNA (Nemer, 1962b; Wilt and Hultin, 1962). It was postulated that fertilization stimulates new messenger RNA synthesis which activates ribosomes. Subsequent studies have modified these initial claims since observed differences between fertilized and unfertilized eggs may be explained by existence of a stable inactive messenger RNA in the unfertilized egg unavailable for ribosomal protein synthesis. Several lines of evidence support each hypothesis and as yet there is insufficient information to distinguish between the two.

The former view, initially presented by Nemer (1962b) and Wilt and Hultin (1962), is based on the following lines of evidence.

1. Stimulation of amino acid incorporation is possible in homogenates and ribosomal preparations of unfertilized eggs by the addition of synthetic polynucleotides like polyuridylic acid. (Nemer, 1962b; Nemer and Bard, 1963; Wilt and Hutlin, 1962; Tyler, 1962, 1963.) The amount of stimulation is quite large (about a twentyfold increase) and, according to Nemer, the degree of stimulation diminishes in later developmental stages. Tyler (1963), however, provides data that illustrate levels of stimulation in later stages virtually equivalent to those found in unfertilized eggs. Intact unfertilized eggs are also more stimulated in the presence of poly U than all later stages, which are either unaffected or manifest diminished incorporation. These latter effects are difficult to interpret since they may involve permeability changes accompanying development or variations in the size of amino acid pools. That such variations do exist has been demonstrated by Kavanau (1954) and by Tyler (1964).

Several difficulties are associated with these experiments since artificial stimulation induced by poly U is possible only when large amounts are employed (almost a milligram per milliliter of poly U in the incubation mixture; far greater than that used in the *E. coli* system). The incorporation is also largely specific for phenylalanine. (Although Tyler has reported a stimulation of valine incorporation.)

2. Additional evidence for the view that messenger RNA is absent in the unfertilized egg and is synthesized immediately after fertilization comes from the sedimentation analyses of RNA in fertilized eggs and early embryos of the sea urchin after or during exposure to precursors like uridine-H^3. The experiments of Nemer (1963), Wilt (1963, 1964), and Gross *et al.* (1964) all indicate an immediate synthesis of RNA of heavy sedimentation values shortly after fertilization. Moreover, this rapidly labeled material is not synthesized when eggs are preincubated in 20 µg/ml actinomycin and then allowed to incorporate (Gross *et al.*, 1964). Pulse and chase experiments have shown (Nemer, 1963) that the initially labeled RNA is heterogeneous, most of which is 4 S or transfer RNA. Since no ribosomal RNA is synthesized, it is assumed that messenger RNA is also included in this heterogeneous material. The unfertilized egg exhibits a very similar pattern in pulse experiments (Nemer, 1963) and it is only in the chase that differences are noted. Most of the activity is incorporated in the transfer RNA fraction, the

major differences being the level of radioactivity attained which is always greater in fertilized eggs.

Unmistakably, there is a rapid synthesis of nuclear RNA shortly after fertilization and the material does have heterogeneous density. Moreover, the material is found on the ribosomes (Wilt, 1964) during these early cleavage stages in the absence of new ribosomal RNA synthesis. This would suggest that this RNA, "messenger RNA," attaches to "old" ribosomes (established during oogenesis) launching an active protein synthesis characteristic of cleavage. During early pregastrula stages this heterogeneous RNA is dominated by a 10 S component (Nemer, 1963) which broadens toward the heavy RNA region during development. Part of the heterogeneity observed could be attributed to DNA since rapid labeling of DNA with uridine and cytidine occurs in very early cleavage (Ficq et al., 1963) and undoubtedly contributes to the great DNase sensitivity in these regions.

Since all species of RNA are synthesized in the nucleus (Franklin, 1963), it is not surprising that the newly synthesized RNA would have a DNA-like base composition. Ribosomal RNA precursors, consequently, would also have this composition. One cannot, therefore, assume (Wilt, 1963) that a DNA-like base composition alone is evidence of messenger RNA.

3. Formation of polysomal aggregates after fertilization (Monroy and Tyler, 1963) may denote synthesis of messenger RNA which assembles ribosomes into functional protein-synthesizing units (Rich et al., 1963). Since some polysomal units do exist in these unfertilized eggs, however, absence of functional polysomal complexes may derive from a specific, spatial noncomplementarity. Ribosomes or messenger RNA, although present together, may be masked or inhibited (Hultin, 1961a). At fertilization, the complex may be activated possibly as a result of some enzymatic process.

The evidence in support of the existence of preformed messenger RNA in unfertilized eggs stems from several sources.

1. Cleavage in echinoderms can occur in the absence of nuclei after parthenogenetic activation (Harvey, 1936). This, of course, means that cleavage is independent of continued production of nuclear RNA. Synthesis of protein during cleavage must also be independent of nuclear RNA synthesis. This has been demonstrated by Brachet et al. (1963b) and Denny and Tyler (1964) who observed continued amino acid incorporation into protein of enucleated eggs. There is some doubt, however, whether true cleavage rather than fragmentation is manifested in parthenogenetically stimulated enucleated eggs (Costello, 1955). Cytoplasmic DNA in the egg also signifies that cleavage of merogones occurs

in the presence of DNA capable of transcribing RNA. It would be useful to determine how much RNA synthesis persists in parthenogenetic merogones. Continued synthesis of RNA would imply a "transcribing" function for cytoplasmic DNA.

2. Chemical enucleation, by eliminating all DNA-dependent synthesis, is possible with actinomycin D. In a series of studies (Gross and Cousineau, 1963a,b, 1964; Gross et al., 1964) it has been demonstrated that cleavage is possible, even in the presence of relatively high doses of actinomycin (20–120 μg/ml), although cleavage delay is apparent at higher doses. At these very high doses (115 μg/ml), amino acid incorporation into protein is unaffected; in fact, there is some evidence of stimulation (Gross et al., 1964). These same doses were shown to inhibit 95% of the incorporation of uracil into RNA after the first 4 hours. It was later shown (Gross et al., 1964) that the bulk of nonsensitive RNA incorporation is found in the 4 S transfer RNA, agreeing with other data from mammalian tissues (Franklin, 1963). Terminal incorporation at the CpCpAp end of the transfer RNA molecule takes place in the presence of actinomycin, even at high doses. The more recent experiments of Gross et al. (1964) clearly demonstrate inhibition of incorporation of uridine into heavy, heterogeneous RNA during early cleavage.

A major difficulty with such studies is that actinomycin exposure is continuous from some time prior to fertilization, throughout the period of development in question, and it is also present during precursor incorporation. The influence of actinomycin on permeability has not been determined in these systems. High doses also inhibit DNA synthesis, as measured by thymidine incorporation and induce chromosomal abnormalities (Brachet and Denis, 1963). Gross (1964) has stated that mitotic figures appear normal with lower doses and no anaphase bridges appear similar to those observed by Brachet and Denis (1963) in the amphibian. At these lower doses, DNA synthesis is normal, yet the synthesis of RNA is inhibited.

Studies with D_2O sea water (P. R. Gross et al., 1963) have provided another approach to this same problem. In the presence of D_2O, cleavage is inhibited, with the appearance of numerous cytasters in the cytoplasm. Incorporation of amino acids into proteins is activated in D_2O sea water with most activity accumulating over the cytasters (Gross and Cousineau, 1963b). Nevertheless, incorporation of RNA precursors is inhibited in the presence of D_2O and it is claimed that this is another instance of activation of protein synthesis without any concurrent RNA synthesis. This may be interpreted as evidence of active ribosomal populations, capable of protein synthesis, because of the presence of functional messenger RNA.

3. Additional evidence for the existence of template or messenger RNA comes from the experiments of Maggio *et al.* (1964), who have shown that total RNA extracted from unfertilized eggs of *Paracentrotus* will stimulate amino acid incorporation into proteins of an *in vitro* rat liver assay system consisting largely of a supernatant obtained after a 30,000 × g centrifugation of a whole homogenate. Stimulation is greater than that produced by liver ribosomal RNA and equivalent to that obtained from total RNA extracted from a mesenchyme blastula. These data suggest that an RNA present in the unfertilized egg is capable of stimulating amino acid incorporation into protein in an appropriate system. Unfertilized egg ribosomes are unable to respond to this RNA fraction from unfertilized eggs, yet ribosomes obtained from blastulae respond to unfertilized egg RNA as well as blastula RNA. Evidently, ribosomes from unfertilized eggs are unable to react functionally with any template RNA contained in the egg. This is in agreement with Hultin's original explanation that failure of ribosomes from unfertilized eggs to incorporate amino acids is due to some kind of specific masking or inadequacy of the ribosome.

4. Monroy and Tyler (1963) have interpreted the proportionately greater amount of polysomal material appearing after fertilization and cleavage as activation of a preformed messenger RNA which transforms free ribosomes into polysomal aggregates.

The nature of protein synthesis shortly after fertilization and during early cleavage is consistent with the view (Gross and Cousineau, 1963a) that preformed "blocked" messenger RNA is programmed for the synthesis of essential proteins required during early cleavage, i.e., spindle proteins, chromosomal fibers, histones, residual proteins in chromosomes, cell membrane proteins, etc. The autoradiographic experiments of Gross and Cousineau (1963b) suggest that at least some of the spindle protein is made *de novo* shortly after fertilization. This has been confirmed by Stafford and Iverson (1963) who also show that a large amount of C^{14}-leucine is incorporated into the isolated mitotic apparatus after fertilization. There is no evidence of ribosomal protein contamination of the isolated mitotic apparatus. Nevertheless, these experiments do not conclusively demonstrate synthesis of spindle proteins, since the spindle area must be contaminated with non-spindle proteins which are difficult to eliminate during isolation. Puromycin inhibits cleavage and amino acid incorporation in sea urchin embryos at the streak stage which suggests that protein synthesis is essential for cleavage (Hultin, 1961b). Although maximum inhibition is only 50%, it is possible that proteins critical for cleavage are effectively inhibited by the drug. Most of the evidence supports the hypothesis that the unfertilized egg is morphogenetically "programmed" to undergo cleavage, and in terms of the old preformationist argument, must contain the preformed synthetic machinery necessary for the synthesis of special proteins required by rapidly dividing cells. This "translation" process is functional in the absence of continuous transcription of further "instructions" from the genome.

Early synthesis of RNA immediately after fertilization seems to be a controversial question. The pulse-chase experiments of Nemer (1963) have certainly demonstrated that the unfertilized egg is capable of synthesizing new RNA with uridine as a precursor. This is in agreement with the observations of Tocco et al. (1963) for P^{32} incorporation into unfertilized eggs. Fertilization simply increases this activity without any qualitative changes, particularly in pulse experiments. On the other hand, Brachet et al. (1963a) report no phosphate incorporation into RNA nucleotides after a short 10-min pulse until the blastula stage, in spite of heavy incorporation into other components. They observe H^3-uridine incorporation into nuclei at the 4-cell stage, but not before. Obviously, the pool sizes are quite different for these two precursors. Phosphate participates in a wide variety of metabolic pathways and is more distantly removed from direct pathways of RNA synthesis than is uridine. Large variations in nucleotide pool sizes during development (Hultin, 1957b; Nilsson, 1959, 1961) will significantly influence the uptake of purine and pyrimidine precursors. Pulse experiments at different stages of development must contend with variable endogenous pools yet in many incorporation studies, little attention is directed to this important phenomenon.

Incorporation of uridine into 4 S and heavy RNA shortly after fertilization in *Arbacia* (Gross et al., 1964) certainly demonstrates uridine incorporation into RNA prior to the 4-cell stage, contrary to the observations by Brachet et al. (1963a). The latter employed autoradiographic techniques for detection and it is likely that the amounts of synthesis of stable RNA per nucleus in the early stages is too small to be detected by this procedure. It seems, therefore, that RNA synthesis is activated immediately after fertilization and increases rapidly during development. The absence of any net RNA synthesis during this early phase of development points to a significant RNA turnover. Amounts synthesized are probably too small to be detected against a background of bulk ribosomal RNA; moreover, the species synthesized (heavy, heterogeneous RNA?) may be quite labile and subject to rapid degradation.

Tocco et al. (1963) have reported an increase in nuclear RNA with development, presumably at the expense of microsomal and nonsedimentable RNA, although the relation is not too clear since all sedimentable fractions incorporate P^{32} during development. Comb and R. Brown

(1964) in an effort to evaluate the extent of RNA degradation have compared RNA in nuclear and ribosomal fractions during development. They find a decided decrease in ribosomal RNA during early cleavage and blastulation accompanied by an increase in nuclear RNA. At the mesenchyme blastula stage, a rapid synthesis of ribosomal RNA is activated which continues until the gastrula stage. Nuclear RNA exhibits a slight decline during these later stages, whereas soluble RNA remains constant throughout development. The authors conclude that degradation of ribosomal RNA contributes precursors for nuclear RNA during these stages. However, D. D. Brown (1964) observed a similar phenomenon in *Xenopus* embryos and interprets it as a shift in the location of ribosomes with development, marking a change in their binding capacity or in their relation to membrane systems such as the nuclear membrane. If ribosomes attach more readily to membrane systems at different stages they could have been centrifuged down into the 30,000 $\times$ g pellet discarded in Comb's study. One cannot conclude, therefore, that any significant degradation of ribosomal RNA does, in fact, take place during early development.

The amount of RNA synthesis as indicated by endogenous incorporation of precursors is relatively insignificant and is not detectable against the large ribosomal RNA background. Synthesis of RNA early in development, particularly during cleavage, when DNA synthesis is at a maximum poses an interesting problem. It implies that the genome may be replicating and transcribing at the same time. Several studies of nucleoside incorporation immediately after fertilization and through the first cleavages (Nemer, 1962a; Hinegardner *et al.*, 1965) have shown a distinct cyclic behavior with respect to thymidine incorporation, connoting a cyclic DNA synthesis. Nemer (1962a) observed that incorporation of cytidine into RNA during these synchronized divisions (4- to 16-cell stage) is also cyclic and occurs approximately at the same time as incorporation of cytidine into DNA. Although the resolving power of these experiments was insufficient to accurately distinguish the times of incorporation, it is possible that a portion of DNA may begin to transcribe immediately after it has replicated while another portion of the DNA molecule is still replicating. Similar observations were made in *Euplotes* (Prescott and Kimball, 1961) where RNA synthesis is absent in a band of the U-shaped macronuclear synthesizing DNA. At the molecular level, the dichotomy between cell division (DNA replication) and cell differentiation (DNA transcription) may not be profound. In a rapidly cleaving embryo, both may be operating in different portions of the genome simultaneously. Undoubtedly, the proportion of the genome transcribed is relatively small, possibly limited to the production of transfer RNA. A few structural genes responsible for several enzymes required during late cleavage or blastulation may also transcribe. Finally, relatively limited transcription of ribosomal RNA loci may occur, producing precursor molecules for later assembly into ribosomes. The predominant activity during cleavage is DNA replication, since nucleoside precursor studies have indicated that the major incorporation of ribonucleosides as well as deoxyribonucleosides is into the DNA.

Since the bulk of the RNA seems to be associated with ribosomes, the distribution of RNA in the developing embryo as revealed by basic staining should reflect the distribution of ribosomal populations in various regions of the embryo. In the case of the sea urchin, gradients of metabolism and differential sensitivity to various agents (Lallier, 1964) play an important role in embryogenesis. Evaluation of relative content of RNA in different regions on the basis of staining is difficult, since variations in the volume of cells as well as the distribution organelles will affect intracellular staining. Granules evenly dispersed throughout the cell will not stain as readily as granules accumulated in a small region. The density of stainable structures plays an important role in its distribution and it is essential to exercise caution in the interpretation of so-called gradients.

Markman (1957) has made several observations on RNA distribution in *Paracentrotus*. Ectodermal nuclei of the animal region in mesenchyme blastula and subsequent stages have a high content of RNA, whereas the vegetal cells exhibit abundant RNA in the cytoplasm. Markman has extended these studies with radioisotopes, following the pattern of incorporation of nucleic acid precursors in different embryonic regions (Markman, 1961, 1962). Limited incorporation of adenine-C^{14} in early cleavage through the 64-cell stage demonstrates little regional differentiation. At the blastula stage, a marked increase in incorporation is evident and 8 hours after fertilization, regional differences appear, with the animal pole region exhibiting strong nuclear RNA incorporation. Subsequent development of the mesenchyme blastula and gastrula elicits increased incorporation in the vegetal region, as the developing archenteron becomes the most heavily labeled region. These latter results parallel the biochemical data of an intense ribosomal synthesis later in development. Vegetal regions may be more active in ribosomal synthesis during these later stages (Markman, 1962).

Developing animal halves incorporate more than half the total C^{14}-adenine activity incorporated. The pattern for C^{14}-leucine incorporation is very similar. Metabolic gradients originate at the same time that cell division synchrony ceases and a mitotic gradient is initiated (Agrell, 1964). A strong positive correlation exists between these initial gradients and patterns of DNA replication; mitotically active regions also appear to have a higher turnover of nuclear RNA. Early cleavages exhibit a mitotic gradient with macromeres initiating mitosis prior to the meso- meres, whereas during gastrulation, another vegetal-animal gradient of mitotic activity is established which shows some correlation with the autoradiographic data.

The significance of these nucleic acid metabolic gradients in develop- ment is obscure. Interpretation will be difficult, until it is possible to iso- late smaller cell populations, relatively synchronous with respect to a specific morphogenetic activity. For example, at the blastula stage, the ectodermal cells soon develop cilia, presumably as a result of synthesis of special ciliary proteins. Obviously, their nucleic acid metabolism will be qualitatively different from cells in the interior, migrating as primary mesenchyme. Our understanding of the mechanisms of development is limited by our ability to isolate individual cell populations relatively homogeneous with respect to single patterns of morphogenetic behavior.

The presence of different cell populations within the embryo, each with different metabolic requirements implies that many new species of proteins will be synthesized. That this is the case has been suggested by some recent evidence of Gross (1964) showing that the soluble protein profile in the 2-cell stage is relatively simple with only one major peak, whereas in the blastula stage the profile is more heterogeneous. Incorporation of amino acids reflects this heterogeneity. In the presence of actinomycin D, the heterogeneity is eliminated yielding a profile identical to the earlier stages. Thus, the blastula stage seems to be in- volved in the initiation of new protein synthesis. Postgastrula protein incorporation is sensitive to actinomycin D in contrast to the situation during cleavage which is, in part, stimulated by the antibiotic. Gross implies that the former synthesis reflects unstable "messenger RNA" associated with new protein synthesis characteristic of this period, whereas the latter represents preformed "messenger RNA," stored dur- ing oogenesis.

RNA synthesis prior to gastrulation seems to be heterogeneous RNA, a large proportion of which is found after a chase in the 4 S transfer RNA (Nemer, 1963; Wilt, 1964; Gross et al., 1964). Little or no ribosomal RNA seems to accumulate. Prior to the gastrula stage, however, the bulk of the RNA synthesized is ribosomal RNA with a proportionately lower contribution by the heterogeneous RNA. It appears as if the peak of ribosomal RNA synthesis occurs at the time when feeding is initiated in the larva. In the amphibian, this also occurs since rapid increase in ribo- somal RNA occurs after hatching (Brown and Caston, 1962). Does this mean that synthesis of ribosomes in these embryos is not possible in the absence of exogenous nutrients? Has the yolk been exhausted by this stage in those cells which initiate ribosomal synthesis? Yolk utilization in the amphibian may be initiated early in blastula and gastrula stage dorsal mesoderm (Karasaki, 1963b). However, the ventral endoderm exhibits no changes in yolk throughout development until after hatching. The bulk of the yolk is found in this region and it is not surprising therefore that a correlation seems to exist between the utilization of yolk and the initiation of ribosomal synthesis. Unfortunately, little is known about the mechanism of yolk utilization.

Our understanding of echinoderm development is limited to the period from the egg to the formation of the larva. The significant events are restricted to the construction of the larva and its few organ systems. Histogenesis is largely limited to the differentiation of the ciliary system of the epidermis, the enzyme systems of the gut, and the skeletal system. There are no useful systems for the analysis of cytodifferentiation, histogenesis, and organogenesis, since most of these events occur much later in development during metamorphosis into the adult. Consequently, one can predict that the usefulness of the echinoderm system will be limited to analyses of the early events of embryogenesis—cleavage, gastrulation, and possibly some of the events associated with skeletal formation in the plutei. It will be difficult to analyze small populations of cells in the course of specific cytodifferentiation and in view of the difficulties of invertebrate tissue culture, analysis of *in vitro* systems must be relegated to the future. It is in this latter category that the vertebrate embryo achieves its major utility.

F. Conclusions

We have been concerned with biochemical parameters of nuclear activity, the population of DNA and RNA molecules, and their behavior during the course of development. The essential issue in development now focuses on the problem of control of genomic transcription, or more familiarly, "what turns genes on and off during embryogenesis?" Approaches to the question of genome transcription and its control during development have been attempted in enucleation experiments or in experiments designed to modify nuclei either through hybridization or irradiation.

Neyfakh (1960a,b; Neyfakh and Dontsova, 1962; Neyfakh and Davidov, 1964) in a series of studies has directed his attention to the question of the stage at which nuclei become functional during development. In agreement with the biochemical data revealing relatively limited RNA turnover during early cleavage, removal of the nucleus or irradiation with X-ray does not affect development to the mid-blastula stage.

The irradiation experiments of Neyfakh (1960b) in the sea urchin embryo indicate (assuming that irradiation damage is restricted to nuclei) that nuclei do not exert any control on cleavage until the mid-blastula stage. From this stage, an increased sensitivity to irradiation is evident. Another period of nuclear inactivity occurs (as measured by radiation insensitivity) from the late blastula to the mesenchyme blastula stage, since irradiation during this period results in an arrest to development at the mid-gastrula stage. After the mesenchyme blastula stage nuclei are again sensitive. These observations suggest that nuclei may exhibit waves of activity alternating with periods of inactivity. Here again, however, the embryo is being treated as a population of homogeneous cells, whereas the observed response to the X-irradiation may be a function only of a small, unusually sensitive population that may play an important role in development (primary mesenchyme cells in the early stages or the formation of cilia in the epidermis). For example, unless cilia appear at the appropriate time, subsequent development will be inhibited, since motility of the embryo facilitates efficient respiratory exchange. The fact that low levels of nuclear RNA are synthesized during cleavage would indicate that nuclear activity during cleavage may be essential for subsequent development, i.e., populations of RNA molecules produced during the cleavage stages may be essential to enzyme formation in later development. Consequently, destruction of cleavage nuclei would be expressed not as an immediate effect on cleavage (which can occur even in the absence of nuclei) but an effect on critical developmental phases dependent upon products of cleavage nuclear activity. One must conclude, therefore, that these experiments of Neyfakh tell us little about nuclear function during development. Later experiments on loach embryos in which nuclear effects on enzyme functions were examined demonstrated that the increase in respiratory activity during development is dependent on nuclei. Anuclear embryos exhibit no increase, whereas haploids exhibit a respiratory increase similar to diploids (Neyfakh, 1960b). Cathepsin activity, however, is completely independent of nuclei, since all combinations with unirradiated cytoplasm exhibit a normal increase in activity (Neyfakh and Davidov, 1964).

It cannot be generally assumed that nuclear function relates to immediate cellular activities, since activity at one stage may have profound developmental effects at later stages. The possibility of stable messenger RNA must be considered and an ontogeny of specific cell organelles must occur during development involving stepwise synthesis of different components. Nuclear RNA for ribosomal synthesis may be produced some time before the appropriate protein components have been synthesized (Roberts et al., 1963). Possible nucleic acid control mechanisms operating during cleavage in the sea urchin have recently been suggested by Scarano *et al.* (1964) in their studies on the effect of actinomycin C on dCMP aminohydrolase. In normal development, the concentration of this enzyme is high in the fertilized egg and decreases during development until very low values in the pluteus stage (Scarano and Maggio, 1959). In the presence of varying concentrations of actinomycin, the reduction in the level of the enzyme does not occur and these authors suggest that a DNA-dependent RNA synthesis is essential for the control of the normal pattern of enzyme change. It is implied that a repressor molecule which normally appears during blastulation to inhibit the synthesis of the enzyme does not appear in the presence of actinomycin.

The transcription of DNA or the synthesis and turnover of RNA during development is dependent upon a number of factors, about which there is very little information. We may enumerate some of these parameters to focus our attention on areas which require intensive investigation.

1. Primary control undoubtedly rests on intrinsic mechanisms associated with the activation and inhibition of gene loci. Since several different species of RNA are involved, different control mechanisms may be operating in regulating the transcription of these different types of RNA. In bacteria, only a small portion of the genome transcribes ribosomal and soluble RNA. Intrinsic control at the level of the DNA molecule may involve several factors, probably the most important being the structural configuration of the DNA strands. *In vitro* (and *in vivo*) actinomycin effects on DNA suggest that its mechanism of inhibition of RNA polymerase is related to modification of the spatial orientation of the DNA molecule, creating steric inhibition of enzyme function (Reich, 1964). This implies that control of RNA transcription and synthesis may hinge on the physical and spatial configurations of the DNA molecule at particular sites along the strand. Conformational changes in specific loci may, as in the case of actinomycin, relate to the frequency of particular base pairs. Actinomycin reacts with guanosine residues and one can imagine specific controlling molecules which engage portions of the genome, preventing their read-out. Such molecules may be repressors—RNA molecules transcribed at repressor sites—which because of their special configuration are capable only of altering the template orientation of a specific locus. Like actinomycin, this could serve as a steric inhibitor of RNA polymerase. Moreover, the data of Reich (1964) on actinomycin interaction with DNA has stimulated the hypothesis that the enzymes DNA polymerase and RNA polymerase view the DNA template from different aspects, the RNA polymerase occupying the minor groove of the double helix and the DNA polymerase in the major groove. If actino-

mycin occupies only the minor groove, this could explain the greater sensitivity of RNA polymerase to the antibiotic. One may speculate that intrinsic control of DNA replication and transcription at the level of the template fundamentally depends upon the production of specific molecules which combine with the major and minor grooves, respectively, modifying template structure and inhibiting a specific polymerase. Such molecules could be protein, possibly histones.

2. Intrinsic control may also depend upon the concentration of the RNA polymerase. The enzyme must establish some relation to the template during synthesis, and variations in the level of the enzyme during development in different regions of the embryo may regulate RNA synthesis.

3. Control may reside at the level of the precursor pool. Wide variations characterize the precursor pool of ribonucleotides in sea urchin development. The early stages after fertilization are rich in nucleotide triphosphates which decrease gradually during development. In the amphibian (Warner and Finamore, 1962) the concentration of free ribonucleotides increases during early cleavage with the largest gain in the adenosine polyphosphates. During gastrulation a decrease in the concentration and specific activity of all nucleoside polyphosphates occurred. Undoubtedly this nucleotide pool serves as a common pool for DNA and RNA synthesis and control may ultimately depend upon the relative rates of these two syntheses. Thus, enzymes of nucleotide metabolism, regulating the conversion of ribonucleotides into deoxyribonucleotides, may play an important role in modulating the syntheses of these nucleic acids.

The naturally occurring nucleoside compounds have been shown to influence embryogenesis in a number of ways. They may be stimulatory, accelerating neurulation in amphibia (Ambellan, 1955; Ambellan and Webster, 1962) or inhibitory as in ascidian, echinoderm, and chick development (Cusimano, 1961a,b; Stearns et al., 1962; Roth et al., 1964). These substances have also been shown to exhibit allosteric effects on enzymes involved in nucleic acid metabolism in embryos, (Scarano et al., 1963; Maley and Maley, 1963c). It is inevitable that efforts to correlate effects on the morphological level with those on the enzymatic level would be initiated (Roth et al., 1963a) with the hope of unraveling some mechanism operative during embryogenesis. The repressor control circuits suggested as models for differentiation by Jacob and Monod (1963) and their relationship to allosteric inhibition of enzymes must serve as an important working hypothesis for analyses of development. Undoubtedly, these will not represent the only regulatory mechanism for multicellular systems, since the bacterial genome on which these models are based is considerably less complicated than the chromosomes of higher organisms.

The problem of the time of gene action is also being analyzed in systems exhibiting specific protein synthesis correlated with morphological events such as lens formation, feather formation, or the differentiation of muscle or cartilage. This provides another, perhaps more profound and direct probe into the time of transcription and translation of gene loci during the course of cytodifferentiation. Such biochemical criteria provide additional aspects of the end products of differentiation, perhaps a step closer to the primary events of gene transcription than the gross morphological criteria used formerly. As in the case of morphological parameters, it is recognized that this analysis brings us no closer to the critical issue of "commitment" (or determination) of cells to a specific developmental fate. Although several systems may be controlled with respect to predictable synthesis of cell-specific proteins in clonal cell populations, our techniques are still too crude to resolve the genetic regulators that activate and inhibit structural gene arrays initiating developmental "programs."

Past investigations of sequential protein changes during development have included immunological analyses designed to detect the appearance of new, adult proteins as well as assays of various enzymes during development to correlate enzymatic activity with characteristic morphogenetic events. Such studies offer only superficial, descriptive biochemical representations of extremely complicated phenomena which are difficult to interpret. Changes in enzyme activity during embryogenesis may derive from a number of different factors, none of which are related to a change in the number of enzyme molecules. Changes in enzyme configuration, spatial association within cell organelles, or contiguity with coenzymes may contribute to profound modifications in enzymatic activity. The presence or absence of inhibitors, activators, or changes in the physiological behavior (permeability) of organelles and membrane systems to which enzymes are attached may trigger critical alterations of enzyme activity (c.f. chapter 6, this volume).

Equally difficult of interpretation are the attempts to compare antigens at different stages of development by using the assortment of agar diffusion, immunoelectrophoresis, and fluorescent antibody techniques currently available. These techniques provide information about immunological identity, but tell us little or nothing about the equivalence of the entire protein molecule. The observations of Markert and Møller (1959) that a given enzymatic activity may be associated with molecules of different electrophoretic and antigenic properties (isozymes) only emphasize the difficulties of interpreting differences either in antigenic or enzymatic behavior during development.

Our concept of the protein molecule is also undergoing a fundamental change. An enzyme was originally assumed to have sites for attachment of substrate and coenzyme and its activty was considered a function of the kinetics involving these three components. We now recognize, however, that an enzymatic protein may be one of several different polymeric combinations derived from smaller subunit polypeptide chains, each a product of a different but presumably closely linked and related gene (Yanofsky, 1963). This may result in the production of species of molecules, all with relatively identical enzymatic activities and substrate specificities but with different physicochemical properties. A protein also has structural configurations responsible for its antigenic behavior and these may be completely unrelated to the sites of catalytic activity. Alterations of secondary or tertiary structure by antigen-antibody interaction may modify enzymatic activity, completely obliterate it, or have no effect. Finally, the relation of structure to function is best illustrated by the phenomenon of allosteric control of enzymatic activity, where small molecules, usually unrelated to the substrate, are capable of inhibiting or activating enzyme function, presumably as a result of attachment to the protein at specific sites different from the enzymatic active site (Jacob and Monod, 1963).

The existence of isozymes and the possible control of protein function through an allosteric mechanism complicates the already complicated problem for the developmental biologist interested in correlating macromolecular events with morphogenetic patterns. It is not sufficient to concentrate on factors regulating gene transcription, because this is only the initial phase of an extremely complicated series of events at the molecular level. The elaboration of a polypeptide chain on a polysome is only the first step in the ontogeny and "life history" of a protein, since its synthesis is no guarantee of its ultimate function within the economy of a cell in that phase of the cell's history. The configuration assumed by the polypeptide chain, its association with similar chains to form dimers, its association with existing cell organelles, and its spatial relations and interactions with coenzymes, substrates, activators, and inhibitors, all have an intricate and profound influence on the behavior of the protein within the physiology of the cell. Morphogenetic patterns, cell interactions, and cytodifferentiation are the ultimate results of these second-step phenomena of protein function, "posttranslation" events, as important as the mechanisms of transcription and translation.

There is another facet to this problem, namely, the macromolecular events at the subcellular level responsible for the origin and development

of membrane systems, vesicles, and finally the more elaborate organization of the mitochondria, secretion granules, centrioles, cilia, flagella, etc.
These are several steps removed from the primary events of synthesis of
the respective protein components; however, their ontogenic history undoubtedly controls morphogenetic behavior at the cellular level of organization. Control mechanisms which insure correct integration of different
molecular species into highly organized, functioning entities appearing
at the appropriate period in the history of a cell are completely obscure.
Studies of the behavior of collagen have provided preliminary information on the factors which may be involved in the ordered elaboration of
protein molecules within cells. A recent review by J. Gross *et al.* (1963)
stipulated that complex highly ordered macromolecular arrays assumed
by collagen can be attributed to the aggregation of tropocollagen molecules in response to varying nonspecific environmental conditions. *In vitro*
studies have provided evidence that a predictable banding pattern of
collagen can be obtained under different ionic conditions. The protein
molecule is equipped with a wide range of intrinsic properties for elab-
orating ordered patterns as a function of its primary structure and its
response to the ionic milieu. It appears "inevitable" that a particular
structure will be achieved.

This "principle of inevitability," however, may apply only to a few
relatively simple systems—the elaboration of secondary patterns from one
homogeneous molecular species. Most biological structures are polytypic,
consisting of mixtures of different molecules, and pattern formation
demands qualitatively different controls. The genetic and electron microscopy studies of assembly of the T-even phages of *E. coli* (Epstein *et al.*,
1963) point to genetic mechanisms regulating the construction of an infectious virus particle. We have useful information about assembly of
highly complex, functional biological entities from different protein and
nucleic acid components. These studies emphasize the ordered, stepwise
assembly of head, tail, and tail filament components under the influence
of "assembly" or morphogenetic genes. Mutation may result in a failure
to join head and tail or may result in the unbalanced overproduction of
one protein or macromolecular component. Such a morphogenetic controlling factor, at the macromolecular level suggests the presence of
enzymes whose function is, perhaps, to expose or eliminate certain small
peptide groups, the active assembly sites of the protein components.
Once exposed, these subunits reorganize into ordered arrays or protein
"crystals." Genetic mapping of the phage chromosome has also disclosed
a sequential arrangement of loci suggesting the "programming" of the
phage chromosome bearing the complete information for a stepwise synthesis of primary components and their ultimate assembly into the

finished infectious phage. These exciting studies offer another level of analysis providing useful conceptual models applicable to problems of morphogenesis in multicellular systems. One may predict that future investigations in morphogenesis will center upon these fascinating problems of the ontogeny of subcellular structures within developing cells. It is likely that current studies of the origin of subcellular organization in single cells represent the initial phases of a more intensive attack on their behavior in multicellular systems. The origin of mitochondria, chloroplasts, pigment granules, centrioles, cilia, and flagella are critically important to our understanding of cellular behavior and it is assumed that the continued successes achieved in our understanding of these events in single cells (protozoa and algae) will have wide applicability to similar phenomena in more complex organizations.

REFERENCES

Abrams, R. (1951). *Exptl. Cell Res.* **2**, 235-242.
Afzelius, B. A. (1957). *Z. Zellforsch. Mikroskop. Anat.* **45**, 660-675.
Agrell, I. (1963). *Arkiv Zool.* **15**, 143-148.
Agrell, I. (1964). *In* "Synchrony in Cell Division and Growth" (E. Zeuthen, ed.), p. 39-67. Wiley (Interscience), New York.
Agrell, I., and Bergqvist, H. A. (1962). *J. Cell Biol.* **15**, 604-606.
Agrell, I., and Persson, H. (1956). *Nature* **178**, 1398-1399.
Alexander, P., and Stacey, K. A. (1958). *Ann. N. Y. Acad. Sci.* **68**, 1225.
Alfert, M. (1950). *J. Cellular Comp. Physiol.* **36**, 381.
Alfert, M., and Swift, H. (1953). *Exptl. Cell Res.* **5**, 455-560.
Ambellan, E. (1955). *Proc. Natl. Acad. Sci. U. S.* **41**, 428-432.
Ambellan, E., and Webster, G. (1962). *Develop. Biol.* **5**, 452-467.
Ambrose, C. T. (1964). *In* "Retention of Functional Differentiation in Cultured Cells" (V. Defendi, ed.), p. 7. Wistar Inst. Symp. Monograph. Wistar Press, Philadelphia.
Anderson, C. (1964). *J. Cell Biol.* **20**, 131.
Aytkhozhin, M. A., Belitsina, N. V., and Spirin, A. S. (1964). *Biokhimiya* **29**, 189.
Baltus, E., and Brachet, J. (1962). *Biochim. Biophysica Acta* **61**, 157-163.
Beams, H. W., and Kessel, R. G. (1963). *J. Cell Biol.* **18**, 621.
Beermann, W. (1956). *Cold Spring Harbor Symp. Quant. Biol.* **21**, 217-232.
Belitsina, N. V., Aytkhozhin, M. A., Gavrilova, L. P., and Spirin, A. S. (1964). *Biokhimiya* **29**, 363-374.
Bell, E. (1964). *Natl. Cancer Inst. Monograph* **13**, 1.
Bell, E., and Thathachari, Y. T. (1963). *J. Cell Biol.* **16**, 215-223.
Bell, P. R. (1960). *Proc. Roy. Soc.* **B153**, 421-432.
Bell, P. R., and Muhlethaler, K. (1962). *J. Ultrastruct. Res.* **7**, 452-466.
Bendich, A., Russell, P. J., Jr., and Brown, G. B. (1953). *J. Biol. Chem.* **203**, 305-318.
Berg, W. E., and Kato, Y. (1959). *Acta Embryol. Morphol. Exptl.* **2**, 227-233.
Bertani, L. E., Hagmark, A., and Reichard, P. (1961). *J. Biol. Chem.* **236**, 67.
Bessman, M. J. (1963). *In* "Molecular Genetics" (J. H. Taylor, ed.), pp. 1-64. Academic Press, New York.
Bieber, S., Spence, J. A., and Hitchings, G. H. (1959). *Exptl. Cell Res.* **16**, 202-214.
Bieliavsky, N., and Tencer, R. (1960). *Exptl. Cell Res.* **21**, 279-285.

Blanchard, K. C. (1935). *J. Biol. Chem.* **108**, 251.

Bloch, D. P., and Hew, H. Y. C. (1960). *J. Biophys. Biochem. Cytol.* **8**, 69-81.

Blumenthal, G. (1957). *J. Embryol. Exptl. Morphol.* **5**, 377-395.

Bodenstein, D., and Kondritzer, A. A. (1948). *Exptl. Zool.* **107**, 109-121.

Boivin, A., Vendrely, R., and Vendrely, C. (1948). *Compt. rend.* **226**, 1061.

Bollum, F. J. (1963a). *In* "Progress in Nucleic Acid Research" (J. N. Davidson and W. E. Cohn, eds.), Vol. I, pp. 1-26. Academic Press, New York.

Bollum, F. J. (1963b). *J. Cellular Comp. Physiol.* **62**, Suppl. 1, 61-71.

Bonhag, P. F. (1955). *J. Morphol.* **96**, 381.

Boveri, T. (1887). *Anat. Anz.* **2**, 688-693.

Boveri, T. (1910). *Arch. Entwicklungsmech. Organ.* **30**, 101-125.

Bowers, B., and Williams, C. (1964). *Biol. Bull.* **126**, 205-219.

Brachet, J. (1933). *Arch. Biol. (Liege)* **44**, 519.

Brachet, J. (1939). *Arch. Exptl. Zellforsch. Gewebezuecht.* **22**, 541.

Brachet, J. (1950). "Chemical Embryology." Wiley (Interscience), New York.

Brachet, J. (1954). *Arch. Biol. (Liege)* **65**, 1-72.

Brachet, J. (1963). *J. Cellular Comp. Physiol.* **60**, Suppl. 1, 1-18.

Brachet, J., and Denis, H. (1963). *Nature* **198**, 205-206.

Brachet, J., Bieliavsky, N. and Tencer, R. (1962). *Bull. Classe Sci. Acad. Roy. Belg.* **48**, 255.

Brachet, J., Decrosy, M., Ficq, A., and Quertier, J. (1963a). *Biochim. Biophys. Acta* **72**, 660.

Brachet, J., Ficq, A., and Tencer, R. (1963b). *Exptl. Cell Res.* **32**, 168-169.

Brachet, J. H., Denis, H., and de Vitry, F. (1964). *Develop. Biol.* **9**, 398-434.

Bragg, A. N. (1938). *Z. Zellforsch. Microskop. Anat.* **28**, 154-178.

Brandt, E. E., and Finamore, F. J. (1963). *Biochem. Biophys. Acta* **68**, 618-624.

Brewer, H. B., and Aronow, L. (1963). *Cancer Res.* **23**, 285-290.

Briggs, R., and King, T. (1952). *Proc. Natl. Acad. Sci. U. S.* **38**, 455-463.

Briggs, R., Green, E. V., and King, T. J. (1951). *J. Exptl. Zool.* **116**, 455-500.

Briggs, R., King, T. J., and DiBerardino, M. A. (1961). *In* "Symposium on Germ Cells and Earliest Stages of Development" (S. Ranzi, ed.), pp. 441-477. Ist. Lombardo, Fondazione A. Baselli, Milan.

Briggs, R., Signoret, J., and Humphrey, R. R. (1964). *Develop. Biol.* **10**, 233-246.

Brown, D. D., and Caston, J. D. (1962a). *Develop. Biol.* **5**, 412-434.

Brown, D. D., and Caston, J. D. (1962b). *Develop. Biol.* **5**, 435-444.

Brown, D. D., and Gurdon, J. B. (1964). *Proc. Natl. Acad. Sci. U. S.* **51**, 139-146.

Brown, D. D., and Littna, E. (1964a). *J. Mol. Biol.* **8**, 669-687.

Brown, D. D., and Littna, E. (1964b). *J. Mol. Biol.* **8**, 688-695.

Brown, D. D. (1964). Personal communication.

Bucher, N. L. R., and Mazia, D. (1960). *J. Biophys. Biochem. Cytol.* **7**, 651-655.

Bullough, W. S. (1952). *Biol. Rev. Cambridge Phil. Soc.* **27**, 133.

Buonassisi, V., Sato, G., and Cohen, A. I. (1962). *Proc. Natl. Acad. Sci. U. S.* **48**, 1148-1156.

Burr, M. J., and Finamore, F. J. (1963). *Biochim. Biophys. Acta* **68**, 608-617.

Byers, T., Platt, D., and Goldstein, L. (1963). *J. Cell Biol.* **19**, 453.

Cairns, J. (1963). *J. Mol. Biol.* **6**, 208-213.

Callan, H. G. (1962). *Intern. Rev. Cytol.* **15**, 1-34.

Chen, P. S. (1960). *Exptl. Cell Res.* **21**, 523-534.

Chen, P. S. (1961). *In* "Symposium on Germ Cells and Earliest Stages of Development" (S. Ranzi, ed.), Vol. IIE, pp. 525-536. Ist. Lombardo, Fondazione A. Baselli, Milan.

Chen, P. S., Baltzer, F., and Zeller, C. (1961). *In* "Symposium on Germ Cells and Earliest Stages of Development" (S. Ranzi, ed.), pp. 506-523. Ist. Lombardo, Fondazione A. Baselli, Milan.

Cheng, T. Y., and Sueoka, N. (1963). *Science* **141**, 1194-1196.

Chèvremont, M. (1963). *In* "Cell Growth and Cell Division," I.S.C.B. Symp. (R. J. C. Harris, ed.), Vol. 2, pp. 323-333. Academic Press, New York.

Chèvremont, M., Chèvremont-Comtiaum, S., and Baeckeland, E. (1959). *Arch. Biol.* (*Liege*) **70**, 811-849.

Chèvremont, M., Bassleer, R., and Baeckeland, E. (1961). *Arch. Biol.* (*Liege*) **72**, 511-524.

Clever, U. (1961). *Chromosoma* **12**, 607-675.

Clever, U., and Karlson, P. (1960). *Exptl. Cell Res.* **20**, 623-626.

Cohen, S. S. (1954). *J. Biol. Chem.* **211**, 337-354.

Cohen, S. S. (1960). *Cancer Res.* **20**, 698.

Cohen, S. S., Barner, H. D., and Lichtenstein, J. (1961). *J. Biol. Chem.* **236**, 1448.

Coleman, J. R. (1962). *Develop. Biol.* **5**, 232-251.

Collier, J. R. (1961). *Exptl. Cell Res.* **24**, 320-326.

Collier, J. R. (1963). *Exptl. Cell Res.* **32**, 442-447.

Comb, D. G., and Brown, R. (1964). *Exptl. Cell Res.* **34**, 360-370.

Comita, J. J., and Whiteley, A. H. (1953). *Biol. Bull.* **105**, 412.

Costello, D. P. (1940). *J. Morphol.* **66**, 99-114.

Costello, D. P. (1955). *In* "Analysis of Development" (B. H. Willier, P. A. Weiss, and V. Hamburger, eds.), pp. 213-229. Saunders, Philadelphia, Pennsylvania.

Curtis, A. S. G. (1960). *J. Embryol. Exptl. Morphol.* **8**, 163-173.

Curtis, A. S. G. (1962). *J. Embryol. Exptl. Morphol.* **10**, 231.

Cusimano, T. (1961a). *Acta Embryol. Morphol. Exptl.* **4**, 62-69.

Cusimano, T. (1961b). *Acta Embryol. Morphol. Exptl.* **4**, 305-312.

Dawid, I. (1963). *Carnegie Inst. Wash., Ann. Rept. Dept. Embryol.*, pp. 419-420.

Dawid, I. (1964). Personal communication.

De Croly, M., Cape, M., and Brachet, J. (1964). *Biochem. Biophys. Acta* **87**, 34-39.

Delage, Y. (1899). *Arch. Zool. Exptl. Gen.* [3] **7**, 383-417.

Denis, H. (1963). *Exptl. Cell Res.* **30**, 613-615.

Denis, H. (1964a). *Develop. Biol.* **9**, 435-457.

Denis, H. (1964b). *Develop. Biol.* **9**, 458-483.

Denis, H. (1964c). *Develop. Biol.* **9**, 484-504.

Denny, P. C., and Tyler, A. (1964). *Biochem. Biophys. Res. Commun.* **14**, 245-249.

DePetrocellis, B., Grant, P., and Scarano, E. (1965). *Biochim. Biophys. Acta* **95**, 209-216.

Dettlaff, T. A. (1964). *Advan. Morphogenesis* **3**, 323-362.

Drasher, M. L. (1953). *Science* **118**, 181-183.

Durand, M. C. (1958). *Exptl. Cell Res.* **29**, 246.

Durand, M. C. (1961). *Bull. Biol. France Belg.* **95**, 28-122.

Eagle, H., and Piez, K. (1962). *J. Exptl. Med.* **116**, 29.

Edström, J. E., and Beermann, W. (1962). *J. Cell Biol.* **14**, 371-380.

Edström, J. E., and Gall, J. G. (1963). *J. Cell Biol.* **19**, 279-284.

Edström, J. E., Grampp, W., and Schor, N. (1961). *J. Biophys. Biochem. Cytol.* **11**, 549-557.

Elsasser, W. M. (1958). "The Physical Foundation of Biology." Macmillan (Pergamon), New York.

Elsdale, T. R., Fischberg, M., and Smith, S. (1958). *Exptl. Cell Res.* **14**, 642.

Elson, D., Gustafson, T., and Chargaff, E. (1954). *J. Biol. Chem.* **209**, 285-294.

Emanuelsson, H. (1961). *Acta Physiol. Scand.* **53**, 46-57.

Epel, D. (1963). *J. Cell Biol.* **17**, 315-320.

Epstein, R. H., Bolle, A., Steinberg, C. M., Kellenberger, E., Boy De La Tour, E., Chevaney, R., and Edgar, R. S., Susman, M., Denhardt, G. H., and Lielausis, A. (1963). *Cold Spring Harbor Symp. Quant. Biol.* **28**, 375.

Esper, H., and Barr, H. J. (1964). *Develop. Biol.* **10**, 105-121.

Fautrez-Firlefyn, N. (1950). *Compt. Rend. Soc. Biol.* **149**, 1127-1128.

Fautrez, J., and Fautrez-Firlefyn, N. (1951). *Biol. Jaarboek Konink. Natuurw. Genoot. Dononaea Gent* **18**, 27.

Favard-Sereno, C., and Durand, M. (1963). *Develop. Biol.* **6**, 184-205.

Ficq, A. (1961a). *In* "Symposium on Germ Cells and Earliest Stages of Development" (S. Ranzi, ed.), pp. 121-140. Ist. Lombardo, Fondazione A. Baselli, Milan.

Ficq, A. (1961b). *Exptl. Cell Res.* **23**, 427-429.

Ficq, A. (1962). *Exptl. Cell Res.* **28**, 543-548.

Ficq, A. (1964). *Exptl. Cell Res.* **34**, 581-594.

Ficq, A., and Brachet, J. (1963). *Exptl. Cell Res.* **32**, 90-108.

Ficq, A., Pavan, C., and Brachet, J. (1958). *Exptl. Cell Res.* Suppl. 6, 105-114.

Ficq, A., Aiello, F., and Scarano, E. (1963). *Exptl. Cell Res.* **29**, 128-136.

Finamore, F. J. (1955). *Exptl. Cell Res.* **8**, 533-542.

Finamore, F. J. (1957). *Exptl. Cell Res.* **12**, 356-362.

Finamore, F. J. (1964). *J. Biol. Chem.* **239**, 1882.

Finamore, F. J., and Crouse, G. T. (1958). *Exptl. Cell Res.* **14**, 160-165.

Finamore, F. J., and Volkin, E. (1958). *Exptl. Cell Res.* **15**, 405-411.

Finamore, F. J., and Volkin, E. (1961). *J. Biol. Chem.* **236**, 443-447.

Finamore, F. J., and Warner, A. H. (1963). *J. Biol. Chem.* **238**, 344-348.

Finamore, F. J., Thomas, D. J., Crouse, G. T., and Lloyd, B. (1960). *Arch. Biochem. Biophys.* **88**, 10-16.

Fischberg, M., Gurdon, J. B., and Elsdale, T. R. (1958). *Exptl. Cell Res.* Suppl. 6, 161-178.

Flaks, J. G., and Cohen, S. S. (1957). *Biochim. Biophys. Acta* **25**, 667.

Flickinger, R. A. (1954). *Exptl. Cell Res.* **6**, 172-180.

Flickinger, R. (1963). *Science* **141**, 1063-1064.

Foster, T., and Stern, H. (1959). *J. Biophys. Biochem. Cytol.* **5**, 187-192.

Franklin, R. M. (1963). *Biochim. Biophys. Acta* **72**, 555-565.

Freese, E. (1963). *In* "Molecular Genetics" (J. H. Taylor, ed.), p. 207. Academic Press, New York.

Frenster, J. H., Allfrey, V. G., and Mirsky, A. E. (1963). *Proc. Natl. Acad. Sci. U. S.* **50**, 1026-1032.

Friedkin, M. (1959). *In* "Kinetics of Cellular Proliferation" (F. Stohlman, ed.), pp. 97-103. Grune and Stratton, New York.

Friedkin, M., and Kornberg, A. (1957). *In* "The Chemical Basis of Heredity" (W. D. McElroy and B. Glass, eds.), pp. 609-613. Johns Hopkins Press, Baltimore, Maryland.

Friedkin, M., and Roberts, D. (1956). *J. Biol. Chem.* **220**, 653-660.

Gall, J. G. (1963). *In* "Cytodifferentiation and Macromolecular Synthesis" (M. Locke, ed.), pp. 119-143. Academic Press, New York.

Gall, J. G., and Callan, H. G. (1962). *Proc. Natl. Acad. Sci. U. S.* **48**, 562-570.

Geigy, R. (1931). *Rev. Suisse Zool.* **38**, 187-288.

Geuskens, M. (1963). *Exptl. Cell Res.* **30**, 322-330.

Gibor, A., and Granick, S. (1964). *Science* **145**, 890.

Gibor, A., and Izawa, M. (1963). *Proc. Natl. Acad. Sci. U. S.* **50**, 1164-1169.

Godlewski, E. (1918). *Arch. Entwicklungsmech. Organ.* **49**, 499.

Goldstein, L. (1963). *In* "Cell Growth and Cell Division," I.S.C.B. Symp. (R. J. C. Harris, ed.), Vol. 2, p. 129-149. Academic Press, New York.

Gonse, P. H. (1953). *Comp. Rend.* **236**, 528.

Grant, P. (1958a). *J. Cellular Comp. Physiol.* **52**, 227-248.

Grant, P. (1958b). *J. Cellular Comp. Physiol.* **52**, 249-268.

Grant, P. (1960). *Develop. Biol.* **2**, 197-251.

Grant, P. (1961). *In* "Symposium on Germ Cells and Earliest Stages of Development" (S. Ranzi, ed.), pp. 483-502. Ist. Lombardo, Fondazione A. Baselli, Milan.

Grant, P. (1965). Unpublished material.

Grant, P., and Stott, P. (1962). *In* "Biological Interactions in Normal and Neoplastic Growth," Henry Ford Hospital Symposium (M. Brennan and W. L. Simpson, eds.), Little, Brown, Boston, Massachusetts.

Gregg, J., and Løvtrup, S. (1955). *Biol. Bull.* **108**, 29-34.

Grobstein, C. (1962). *Am. Scientist* **50**, 46-58.

Grobstein, C. (1964). *Science* **143**, 643-650.

Grosch, D. S. (1958). *Nature* **181**, 1078.

Gross, J., Lapiere, S. M., and Tanzer, M. L. (1963). *In* "Cytodifferentiation and Macromolecular Synthesis" (M. Locke, ed.), p. 175. Academic Press, New York.

Gross, P. R. (1964). Personal communication.

Gross, P. R., and Cousineau, G. H. (1963a). *Biochem. Biophys. Res. Commun.* **10**, 321-326.

Gross, P. R., and Cousineau, G. H. (1963b). *J. Cell Biol.* **19**, 260-265.

Gross, P. R., and Cousineau, G. H. (1964). *Exptl. Cell Res.* **33**, 368-395.

Gross, P. R., Spindel, W., and Cousineau, G. H. (1963). *Biochem. Biophys. Res. Commun.* **13**, 405.

Gross, P. R., Malkin, L. I., and Moyer, W. A. (1964). *Proc. Natl. Acad. Sci. U. S.* **51**, 407-413.

Grumbach, M. M., Morishima, K., and Taylor, J. H. (1963). *Proc. Natl. Acad. Sci. U.S.* **49**, 581-589.

Gurdon, J. B. (1963). *Quart. Rev. Biol.* **38**, 54-78.

Haggis, A. (1964a). *Develop. Biol.* **10**, 358-377.

Haggis, A. (1964b). Personal communication.

Harel, L., Harel, J., Baer, A., Imbenott, S., and Corpeni, N. (1964). *Biochim. Biophys. Acta* **87**, 212-218.

Harvey, E. B. (1936). *Biol. Bull.* **71**, 101-121.

Hennen, S. (1961). *Genetics* **48**, 869-870.

Hiatt, H. H., and Bojarski, T. B. (1960). *Biochem. Biophys. Res. Commun.* **2**, 35.

Hinegardner, R. T., and Mazia, D. (1962). *Science* **27**, 326.

Hinegardner, R. T., Rao, B., and Feldman, D. E. (1965). *Exptl. Cell Res.* **36**, 53-61.

Hiramoto, Y. (1962). *Exptl. Cell Res.* **27**, 416-426.

Hoff-Jørgensen, E. (1951). *Biochem. J.* **50**, 400-403.

Hoff-Jørgensen, E. (1954). *In* "Recent Developments in Cell Physiology" (J. A. Kitching, ed.), p. 79-90. Butterworth, London and Washington, D. C.

Hoff-Jørgensen, E., and Zeuthen, E. (1951). *Nature* **169**, 245.

Holtzer, H., Abbott, J., Lash, J., and Holtzer, S. (1960). *Proc. Natl. Acad. Sci. U. S.* **46**, 1533-1542.

Hotta, J., and Stern, H. (1963a). *Proc. Natl. Acad. Sci. U. S.* **49**, 648.

Hotta, Y., and Stern, H. (1963b). *Proc. Natl. Acad. Sci. U. S.* **49**, 861.

Hsu, T. C. (1964). Growth Symposium (in press).

Hsu, T. C., and Moorehead, P. S. (1957). *J. Natl. Cancer Inst.* **18**, 463-471.

Huennekens, F. M., Osborn, M. J., and Whiteley, H. R. (1958). *Science* **128**, 120-124.

Huff, R. E. (1962). *Develop. Biol.* **4**, 398-422.

Hultin, T. (1957a). *Exptl. Cell Res.* **12**, 518-525.

Hultin, T. (1957b). *Exptl. Cell Res.* **12**, 413-415.

Hultin, T. (1961a). *Exptl. Cell Res.* **25**, 405.

Hultin, T. (1961b). *Experientia* **17**, 410-411.

Hultin, T. (1964). *Develop. Biol.* **10**, 305-328.

Humphreys, T., Penman, S., and Bell, E. (1964). *Biochem. Biophys. Res. Commun.* **17**, 618.

Izawa, M., Alfrey, V. G., and Mirsky, A. E. (1963a). *Proc. Natl. Acad. Sci. U. S.* **49**, 544-551.

Izawa, M., Allfrey, V. G., and Mirsky, A. E. (1963b). *Proc. Natl. Acad. Sci. U. S.* **50**, 811.

Jacob, F., and Monod, J. (1961). *Cold Spring Harbor Symp. Quant. Biol.* **26**, 193-211.

Jacob, F., and Monod, J. (1963). *In* "Cytodifferentiation and Macromolecular Synthesis" (M. Locke, ed.), pp. 30-64. Academic Press, New York.

Kahn, J. (1962). *Quart. J. Microscop. Sci.* **103**, 407-409.

Karasaki, S. (1963a). *J. Cell Biol.* **18**, 135.

Karasaki, S. (1963b). *J. Ultrastruct. Res.* **9**, 225-247.

Karnofsky, D. A., and Basch, R. S. (1960). *J. Biophys. Biochem. Cytol.* **7**, 61-71.

Kavanau, T. L. (1954). *Exptl. Cell Res.* **7**, 530-557.

Kessel, R. (1963). *J. Cell Biol.* **19**, 391-414.

Kessel, R. G., and Beams, H. W. (1963). *Exptl. Cell Res.* **32**, 612-615.

Keyl, H. G., and Pelling, C. (1963). *Chromosoma* **14**, 347-359.

King, R. L., and Beams, H. W. (1938). *J. Exptl. Zool.* **77**, 425-443.

King, T. J. (1964). Personal communication.

Kirk, D., and Moscona, A. (1963). *Develop. Biol.* **8**, 341.

Kit, S., Dubbs, D. R., and Piekarski, L. J. (1963). *Exptl. Cell Res.* **31**, 297-312.

Klein, N. W., and Pierro, L. J. (1963). *Science* **142**, 967-969.
Konigsberg, I. R. (1963). *Science* **140**, 1273-1284.
Kroeger, H. (1960). *Chromosoma* **11**, 129-145.
Kroeger, H. (1963). *J. Cellular Comp. Physiol.* **62**, Suppl. 1, 45-59.
Kuriki, Y., and Okazaki, R. (1959). *Embryologia* (*Nagoya*) **4**, 337-348.
Kutsky, P. (1950). *J. Exptl. Zool.* **115**, 429-460.
Lallier, R. (1964). *Advan. Morphogenesis* **3**, 147-196.
Lanzavecchia, G. (1961). *In* "Symposium on Germ Cells and Earliest Stages of Development" (S. Ranzi, ed.), pp. 61-74. Ist. Lombardo, Fondazione A. Baselli, Milan.
Lark, K. G. (1963). *In* "Molecular Genetics" (J. H. Taylor, ed.), pp. 153-206. Academic Press, New York.
Lerner, A. M., Bell, E., and Darnell, J. E. (1963). *Science* **141**, 1187-1188.
Levan, A., and Biesele, J. J. (1958). *Ann. N.Y. Acad. Sci.* **71**, 1022-1053.
Lima de Faria, A. (1959). *J. Biophys. Biochem. Cytol.* **6**, 457-466.
Lison, L., and Pasteels, J. (1951). *Arch. Biol.* (*Liege*) **62**, 2-64.
Loeb, J. (1913). Chicago
Løvtrup, S. (1955). *Compt. Rend. Trav. Lab. Carlsberg* **29**, 261-314.
Løvtrup, S. (1959). *J. Exptl. Zool.* **141**, 545-570.
Løvtrup, S., and Roos, K. (1957). *Exptl. Cell Res.* Suppl. 4, 269-278.
Løvtrup, S., and Roos, K. (1961). *Biochim. Biophys. Acta* **53**, 1.
McClintock, B. (1956). *Cold Spring Harbor Symp. Quant. Biol.* **21**, 197-216.
McMaster, R. D. (1955). *J. Exptl. Zool.* **130**, 1-28.
Maggio, R., Vittorelli, A. M., Rinaldi, A. M., and Monroy, A. (1964). *Biochem. Biophys. Res. Commun.* **15**, 436-441.
Maley, F., and Maley, G. F. (1959). *J. Biol. Chem.* **234**, 2975.
Maley, F., and Maley, G. F. (1960). *J. Biol. Chem.* **235**, 2968-2970.
Maley, F., and Maley, G. F. (1964). *Natl. Cancer Inst. Monograph* **13**, 117-129.
Maley, G. F., and Maley, F. (1960). *J. Biol. Chem.* **235**, 2964-2967.
Maley, G. F., and Maley, F. (1963a). *Biochim. Biophys. Acta* **68**, 293-301.
Maley, G. F., and Maley, F. (1963b). *Arch. Biochem. Biophys.* **101**, 342-349.
Maley, G. F., and Maley, F. (1963c). *Science* **141**, 1278-1279.
Maley, G. F., and Maley, F. (1964). *J. Biol. Chem.* **239**, 1168-1176.
Malkin, L. I., Gross, P. R., and Romanoff, P. (1964). *Develop. Biol.* **10**, 378-394.
Markert, C., and Møller, R. (1959). *Proc. Natl. Acad. Sci. U.S.* **45**, 753-763.
Markman, B. (1957). *Exptl. Cell Res.* **12**, 424.
Markman, B. (1960). *Exptl. Cell Res.* **23**, 197-200.
Markman, B. (1961). *Exptl. Cell Res.* **23**, 118-129.
Markman, B. (1962). *Exptl. Cell Res.* **25**, 224-227.
Marrian, D. H., Hughes, A. F. A., and Werba, S. M. (1956). *Biochim. Biophys. Acta* **19**, 318-323.
Marshak, A., and Marshak, C. (1953). *Exptl. Cell Res.* **5**, 288-300.
Marshak, A., and Marshak, C. (1955a). *J. Biophys. Biochem. Cytol.* **1**, 167-171.
Marshak, A., and Marshak, C. (1955b). *Exptl. Cell Res.* **8**, 126-146.
Mazia, D. (1949). *Growth* **9**, 5-31.
Mazia, D. (1963). *J. Cellular Comp. Phys.* **62**, Suppl. 1, 123-140.

Mazia, D., and Hinegardner, R. T. (1963). *Proc. Natl. Acad. Sci. U. S.* **50**, 148-156.

Metz, C. W. (1938). *Am. Naturalist* **72**, 485-520.

Mezger-Freed, L. (1963). *J. Cell Biol.* **18**, 471-474.

Mintz, B. (1962). *Am. Zoologist* **2**, 432.

Mintz, B. (1964). *In* "Differentiation and Development," N. Y. Heart Assoc. Symp. Little, Brown and Co., Boston.

Monroy, A., and Maggio, R. (1964). *Advan. Morphogenesis* **3**, 95-146.

Monroy, A., and Tyler, A. (1963). *Arch. Biochem. Biophys.* **103**, 431-435.

Moore, B. C. (1952). *Chromosoma* **4**, 563-576.

Moore, B. C. (1957). *J. Morphol.* **101**, 227-274.

Moore, B. C. (1963). *Ann. Histoch.* **9**, Suppl.

Moore, J. A. (1958a). *Exptl. Cell Res.* **14**, 532-540.

Moore, J. A. (1958b). *Exptl. Cell Res.* Suppl. 6, 179-191.

Moore, J. A. (1960). *Develop. Biol.* **2**, 535-550.

Moore, J. A. (1963). *J. Cellular Comp. Physiol.* **60**, Suppl. 1, 19-33.

Moscona, A. A. (1962). *J. Cellular Comp. Physiol.* **60**, Suppl. 1, 65-80.

Moscona, M. H., and Moscona, A. A. (1963). *Science* **142**, 1070-1071.

Mulnard, J. (1954). *Arch. Biol. (Liege)* **65**, 261.

Nanney, D. L. (1958). *Proc. Natl. Acad. Sci. U. S.* **44**, 712-717.

Nemer, M. (1962a). *J. Biol. Chem.* **237**, 143-149.

Nemer, M. (1962b). *Biochem. Biophys. Res. Commun.* **8**, 511-515.

Nemer, M. (1963). *Proc. Natl. Acad. Sci. U. S.* **50**, 230-235.

Nemer, M., and Bard, S. G. (1963). *Science* **140**, 664-666.

Neyfakh, A. A. (1960a). *Biokhimiya* **25**, 658.

Neyfakh, A. A. (1960b). *Compt. Rend. Acad. Sci. URSS* **132**, 1458.

Neyfakh, A. A., and Davidov, Y. R. (1964). *Biokhimiya* **29**, 1-15.

Neyfakh, A. A., and Dontsova, G. V. (1962). *Biokhimiya* **27**, 339.

Nigon, V., and Daille, J. (1958). *Biochim. Biophys. Acta* **29**, 246-255.

Nigon, V., and Gillot, S. (1964). *Exptl. Cell Res.* **33**, 29-38.

Nigon, V., and Nonnenmacher, J. (1961). *Develop. Biol.* **3**, 210-224.

Nilsson, R. (1959). *Acta Chem. Scand.* **13**, 395-408.

Nilsson, R. (1961). *Acta Chem. Scand.* **15**, 583-591.

Novikoff, A., and Potter, V. R. (1948). *J. Biol. Chem.* **173**, 233.

Nygaard, O. F., Guttes, A., and Rusch, H. P. (1960). *Biochim. Biophys. Acta* **38**, 298-306.

Ohno, S., Karasaki, S., and Takata, K. (1964). *Exptl. Cell Res.* **33**, 310-318.

Painter, T. A. (1959). *Proc. Natl. Acad. Sci. U. S.* **45**, 897.

Plaut, W. (1964). *In* "The Role of Chromosomes in Development," 23rd. Growth Symp. (M. Locke, ed.), Academic Press, New York.

Plaut, W., and Howard, E. (1963). *J. Cell Biol.* **19**, 56A.

Plaut, W., and Sagan, L. A. (1958). *J. Biophys. Biochem. Cytol.* **4**, 843-844.

Prescott, D. M., and Bender, M. A. (1963). *J. Cellular Comp. Physiol.* **62**, Suppl. 1, 175-194.

Prescott, D. M., and Kimball, R. F. (1961). *Proc. Natl. Acad. Sci. U. S.* **47**, 686.

Rabinovitch, M., and Plaut, W. (1962a). *J. Cell Biol.* **15**, 525-534.

Rabinovitch, M., and Plaut, W. (1962b). *J. Cell Biol.* **15**, 535-540.

Rake, A. V., and Graham, A. F. (1964). *Biophys. J.* **4**, 267.

Raven, C. P. (1961). "Oogenesis." Macmillan (Pergamon), New York.

Rebhun, L. I. (1956). *J. Biophys. Biochem. Cytol.* **2**, 159-170.

Reich, E. (1964). *Science* **143**, 684-689.

Reichard, P. (1958). *Biochim. Biophys. Acta* **27**, 434.

Reichard, P. (1959). *J. Biol. Chem.* **234**, 1244-1252.

Reichard, P. (1960). *Biochim. Biophys. Acta* **41**, 368-369.

Reichard, P. (1961). *J. Biol. Chem.* **236**, 2511-2513.

Reichard, P., Canelakis, Z. N., and Canelakis, E. S. (1961). *J. Biol. Chem.* **236**, 2514-2519.

Rich, A., Warner, J. R., and Goodman, H. M. (1963). *Cold Spring Harbor Symp. Quant. Biol.* **28**, 269-285.

Ris, H., and Plaut, W. (1962). *J. Cell Biol.* **13**, 383.

Roberts, R. B., Britten, R. J., and McCarthy, B. J. (1963). *In* "Molecular Genetics" (J. H. Taylor, ed.), pp. 291-352. Academic Press, New York.

Rose, I. A., and Schweigert, B. S. (1953). *J. Biol. Chem.* **202**, 635.

Roth, J. S. (1963). *J. Theoret. Biol.* **4**, 113-123.

Roth, J. S., and Buccino, G. (1963). *Arch. Biochem. Biophys.* **101**, 516-522.

Roth, J. S., Buccino, G., and Klein, N. W. (1963a). *Science* **142**, 1473.

Roth, J. S., Shied, B., and Morris, H. P. (1963b). *Cancer Res.* **23**, 454-461.

Roth, T. F., and Porter, K. R. (1964). *J. Cell Biol.* **20**, 313-332.

Rudkin, G. T., and Schultz, J. (1961). *Genetics* **46**, 893-894.

Rugh, R., and Exner, F. (1940). *Proc. Am. Phil. Soc.* **83**, 607.

Rutman, R., Steele, W. J., and Price, C. C. (1961). *Biochem. Biophys. Res. Commun.* **4**, 278.

Rutter, W. J., Wessels, N. K., and Grobstein, C. (1964). *Natl. Cancer Inst. Monograph* **13**, 51-61.

Sager, R., and Ishida, M. R. (1963). *Proc. Natl. Acad. Sci. U. S.* **50**, 725.

Sager, R., and Ramanis, Z. (1963). *Proc. Natl. Acad. Sci. U. S.* **50**, 260-268.

Sampson, M., Katoh, A., Hotta, Y., and Stern, H. (1963). *Proc. Natl. Acad. Sci. U. S.* **50**, 459-463.

Sato, G., and Buonassisi, V. (1964). *In* "Retention of Functional Differentiation in Cultured Cells," Wistar Inst. Symp. Monograph, No. 1 (V. Defendi, ed.), pp. 27-32. Wistar Press, Philadelphia.

Scarano, E. (1958). *Biochim. Biophys. Acta* **29**, 459.

Scarano, E., and Kalckar, H. (1953). *Pubbl. Staz. Zool. Napoli* **24**, 195-215.

Scarano, E., and Maggio, R. (1959). *Exptl. Cell Res.* **18**, 333-346.

Scarano, E., Talarico, M., and Caserta, G. (1959). *Boll. Soc. Ital. Biol. Sper.* **35**, 788.

Scarano, E., Bonaduce, L., and DePetrocellis, B. (1960). *J. Biol. Chem.* **235**, 3556.

Scarano, E., Geraci, G., Polzella, A., and Campanile, E. (1963). *J. Biol. Chem.* **238**, 1556-1557.

Scarano, E., DePetrocellis, B., and Austusti-Tocco, G. (1964). *Biochim. Biophys. Acta* **87**, 176.

Scherrer, K., and Darnell, J. E. (1962). *Biochem. Biophys. Res. Commun.* **1**, 486.

Schmidt, C., Hecht, L., and Thannhauser, S. J. (1948). *J. Gen. Physiol.* **31**, 203.

Schmidt, G. Z. (1934). *Z. Physiol. Chem.* **223**, 81.

Schneider, W. C. (1955). *J. Biol. Chem.* **216**, 287-301.

Schneider, W. C., and Brownell, L. W. (1957). *J. Natl. Cancer Inst.* **18**, 579-586.

Schrader, F., and Leuchtenberger, C. (1952). *Exptl. Cell Res.* **3**, 136-146.

Schultz, J. (1952). *Exptl. Cell Res.* Suppl. 2, 17-43.

Schultz, J. (1956). *Cold Spring Harbor Symp. Quant. Biol.* **21**, 307-328.

Scott, R. B., and Bell, E. (1964). *Science* **145**, 711-713.

Simmel, E. A., and Karnofsky, D. A. (1961). *J. Biophys. Biochem. Cytol.* **10**, 59.

Sirlin, J. L. (1963). *Intern. Rev. Cytol.* **15**, 35-96.

Smith, D. (1964). Cited in Briggs *et al.* (1964).

Solomon, J. B. (1957a). *Biochim. Biophys. Acta* **23**, 24-27.

Solomon, J. B. (1957b). *Biochim. Biophys. Acta* **24**, 584-591.

Solomon, J. B. (1957c). *Biochim. Biophys. Acta* **25**, 69-73.

Spemann, H. (1938). "Embryonic Development and Induction." Yale Univ. Press, New Haven, Connecticut.

Spratt, N. T. (1963). *Develop. Biol.* **7**, 51-63.

Stafford, D. W., and Iverson, R. M. (1963). *Science* **143**, 580-581.

Stearns, L. W., Martin, W. E., Jolley, W. B., and Bamburger, J. W. (1962). *Exptl. Cell Res.* **27**, 250-259.

Steinberg, M. (1964). *In* "Cellular Membranes in Development" (M. Locke, ed.), pp. 321-366. Academic Press, New York.

Steinert, M. (1951). *Bull. Soc. Chim. Biol.* **33**, 549-554.

Stern, H. (1960). *In* "Developing Cell Systems and Their Control" (D. Rudnick, ed.), p. 135. Ronald Press, New York.

Stern, H. (1961). *J. Biophys. Biochem. Cytol.* **9**, 271.

Stern, H., and Hotta, Y. (1963). *In* "Cell Growth and Cell Division," I.S.C.B. Symp. (R. J. C. Harris, ed.), Vol. 2, p. 57-76. Academic Press, New York.

Stockdale, F. E., Abbott, J., Holtzer, S., and Holtzer, H. (1963). *Develop. Biol.* **7**, 293-302.

Sugino, Y. (1957). *J. Am. Chem. Soc.* **79**, 5074.

Sugino, Y., Sugino, N., Okazaki, R., and Okazaki, T. (1960). *Biochim. Biophys. Acta* **40**, 417-424.

Swann, M. M. (1953). *Quart. J. Microscop. Sci.* **94**, 369.

Sze, L. C. (1953). *J. Exptl. Zool.* **122**, 577-602.

Taylor, J. L. (1960). *J. Biophys. Biochem. Cytol.* **7**, 455.

Tencer, R. (1961a). *Exptl. Cell Res.* **23**, 418-419.

Tencer, R. (1961b). *Nature* **190**, 100-101.

Tocco, G., Orengo, A., and Scarano, E. (1963). *Exptl. Cell Res.* **31**, 52-60.

Travaglini, E. C., Levenbook, L., and Schultz, J. (1958). *Exptl. Cell Res.* **15**, 62-79.

Trinkaus, J. P. (1963). *Develop. Biol.* **7**, 513-532.

Tyler, A. (1962). "Proceedings of Conference on Immuno-Reproduction," pp. 13-15. Population Council, New York.

Tyler, A. (1963). *Am. Zoologist* **3**, 109-126.

Tyler, A. (1964). Personal communication.

Vendrely, C., and Vendrely, R. (1949). *Compt. Rend. Soc. Biol.* **143**, 1386.

Villee, C. A., Lowens, M., Gordon, M., Leonard, E., and Rich, A. (1949). *J. Cellular Comp. Physiol.* **23**, 93.

Vincent, W. S. (1957). *Science* **126**, 306-307.

Vincent, W. S. (1964). *Proc. 11th Intern. Congr. Genet., 1964.*

Vincent, W. S., and Baltus, E. (1960). *In* "The Cell Nucleus" (J. S. Mitchell, ed.), pp. 18-23. Butterworth, London.

Walker, P. H. B. (1954). *J. Exptl. Biol.* **31**, 8-15.

Wallace, H. (1962). *Quart. J. Microscop. Sci.* **103**, 25-35.

Wallace, H., and Elsdale, T. R. (1963). *Acta Embryol. Morphol. Exptl.* **6**, 275.

Wallace, R. D. (1961). *Develop. Biol.* **3**, 486-515.

Wallace, R. D. (1964). Personal communication.

Ward, R. T. (1962). *J. Cell Biol.* **16**, 309.

Warner, A. H., and Finamore, F. J. (1962). *Comp. Biochem. Physiol.* **5**, 233-240.

Weiss, P. (1962). *In* "Biological Interactions in Normal and Neoplastic Growth," Henry Ford Hospital Symposium (M. J. Brennan, ed.), pp. 3-20. Little, Brown, Boston, Massachusetts.

Weisz, P. B. (1954). *Quart. Rev. Biol.* **29**, 207.

Wessells, N. K. (1964a). *Develop. Biol.* **9**, 92.

Wessells, N. K. (1964b). *J. Cell Biol.* **20**, 415.

Wessells, N. K. (1964c). *Proc. Natl. Acad. Sci. U. S.* **52**, 252.

Wigglesworth, V. B. (1963). *J. Exptl. Biol.* **40**, 231-245.

Wilt, F. (1963). *Biochem. Biophys. Res. Commun.* **11**, 447-451.

Wilt, F. (1964). *Develop. Biol.* **9**, 299, 313.

Wilt, F. H., and Hultin, T. (1962). *Biochem. Biophys. Res. Commun.* **9**, 313-317.

Yankofsky, S. A., and Spiegelman, S. (1962). *Proc. Natl. Acad. Sci. U. S.* **48**, 1466-1472.

Yanofsky, C. (1963). *In* "Cytodifferentiation and Macromolecular Synthesis" (M. Locke, ed.), p. 15. Academic Press, New York.

Zeuthen, E. (1953). *Arch. Neerl. Zool. Suppl.* **10**, 31.

Author Index

Numbers in italics indicate the pages on which the complete references are listed.